About Pearson

Pearson is the world's learning company, with presence across 70 countries worldwide. Our unique insights and world-class expertise comes from a long history of working closely with renowned teachers, authors and thought leaders, as a result of which, we have emerged as the preferred choice for millions of teachers and learners across the world.

We believe learning opens up opportunities, creates fulfilling careers and hence better lives. We hence collaborate with the best of minds to deliver you class-leading products, spread across the Higher Education and Test Preparation spectrum.

Superior learning experience and improved outcomes are at the heart of everything we do. This product is the result of one such effort.

Your feedback plays a critical role in the evolution of our products and you can contact us - reachus@pearson.com. *We look forward to it.*

CLASS

10

Trishna's

PEARSON IIT FOUNDATION

Physics

Thirteenth Edition

2025

Pearson

Photo Credits

Chapter 1 Opener: Karel Miragaya / 123RF
Chapter 2 Opener: stockshoppe / Shutterstock
Chapter 3 Opener: Pop Nukoonrat / 123RF
Chapter 4 Opener: ioat / Shutterstock
Chapter 5 Opener: magnetix / Shutterstock
Chapter 6 Opener: Mike H / Shutterstock
Chapter 7 Opener: Anton Khrupin anttoniart / Shutterstock
Chapter 8 Opener: Kostenko Maxim / Shutterstock
Chapter 9 Opener: Yurchanka Siarhei / Shutterstock

ISBN 978-93-6159-259-1

First Impression

Published by Pearson India Education Services Pvt. Ltd, CIN: U72200TN2005PTC057128.

Head Office: 1st Floor, Berger Tower, Plot No. C-001A/2, Sector 16B, Noida - 201 301, Uttar Pradesh, India.
Registered Office: Featherlite, 'The Address' 5th Floor, Survey No 203/10B, 200 Ft MMRD Road, Zamin Pallavaram, Chennai – 600 044.
Website: in.pearson.com, Email: companysecretary.india@pearson.com

Compositor: Satish Kumar Shrivastava
Printer in India at: Rahul Print O Pack

Brief Contents

Contents

UNIT IV: THERMODYNAMICS

UNIT V: ELECTRICITY AND MAGNETISM

Preface

"If you have a great ambition, take as big a step as possible in the direction of fulfilling it. The step may only be a tiny one, but trust that it may be the largest one possible for now."

Mildred McAfee

The *Pearson IIT Foundation* Series has been created keeping in mind the learner's ambition to excel in a competitive examination like IIT-JEE. The series can be used in addition to the books being studied in school to attain that extra edge required to strengthen the concepts and prepare well for future endeavours.

Why Start Early with Pearson IIT Foundation

Classes VI to X are the base years of a learner's academic life. In these years learner explore their interests and determine the goals they wish to attain. *Pearson IIT Foundation* series is filled with interactive learning that not only nurtures a learner's interest in science and mathematics but also strengthens their concepts.

The series uses real-life examples and application-based problems to teach theoretical concepts. The objective of this series is to help learners cultivate an analytical mind.

Most of the lessons to be learnt are introduced to the learners in the books for class VI. As they get promoted to higher classes, new topics are added to these lessons. This additive method helps the learners' span their learning over four standards, from VI-X. Thus, learners are not overwhelmed by the introduction of completely new lessons every time they are promoted to a new class.

While their learning is being spanned across five years, so is their ability to resolve doubts for further conceptual clarity. For instance, they can use concepts learnt in class VI to solve questions in class VII. If, in case, they get stuck while answering a question, the learners can infer for themselves that they might be lacking in conceptual clarity. They can then approach their teachers, requesting them to explain the concept once again. This helps the learner to clarify their concepts while revising the lessons previously learnt.

Since classes VI-X are deemed to be a student's formative years, we, at Pearson, aim to provide a foundation level course which serves more than just a standard curriculum.

Here is how it makes a difference to a learner's overall learning...

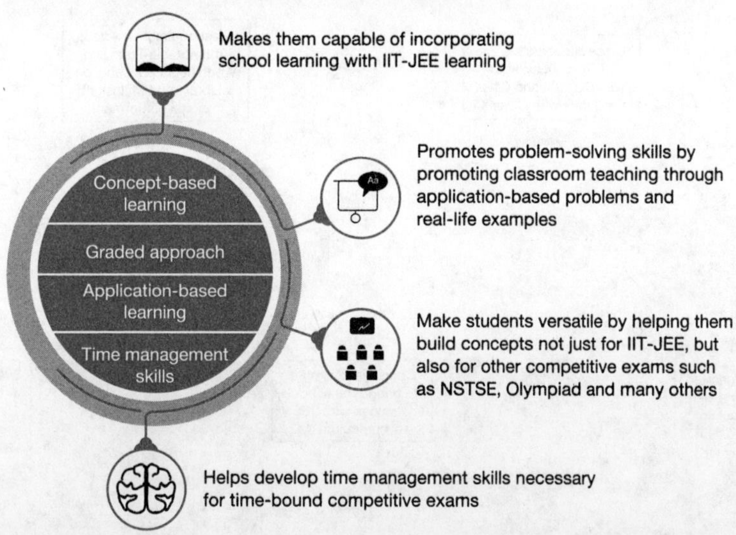

Other Uses of the Series

Instead of limiting themselves to IIT-JEE, a learner can also use this series to prepare for several other competitive examinations such as NSTSE, National and International Olympiads, NEET, BITSAT, etc. This series offers a level of concept learning that empowers learners to handle the challenging nature of questions posed in these examinations. Moreover, this will also allow the learners to have an early insight into their key strengths as well as improvement areas and help them work on themselves.

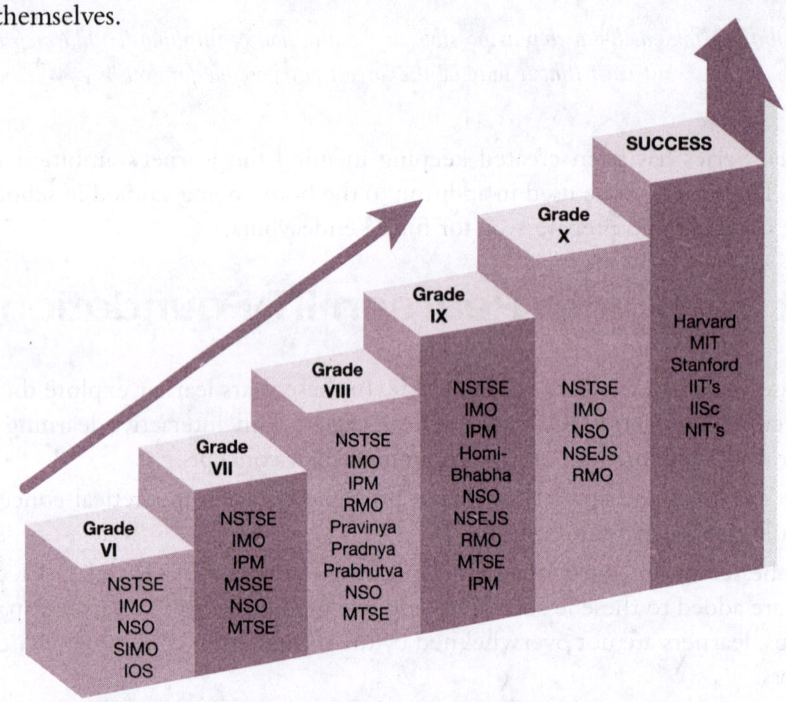

[IMO: International Mathematics Olympiad; NSO: National Science Olympiad, IOS: International Olympiad of Science, NSTSE: National Level Science Talent Search Examination, MTSE: Maharashtra Talent Search Examination, RMO: Regional Mathematical Olympiad, PPP: Pravinya Pradnya Prabhutva, NSEJS: National Standard Examination in Junior Science, IIT: Indian Institute of Technology, IISc: Indian Institute of Science, NIT: National Institute of Technology.]

Highlights of the Series

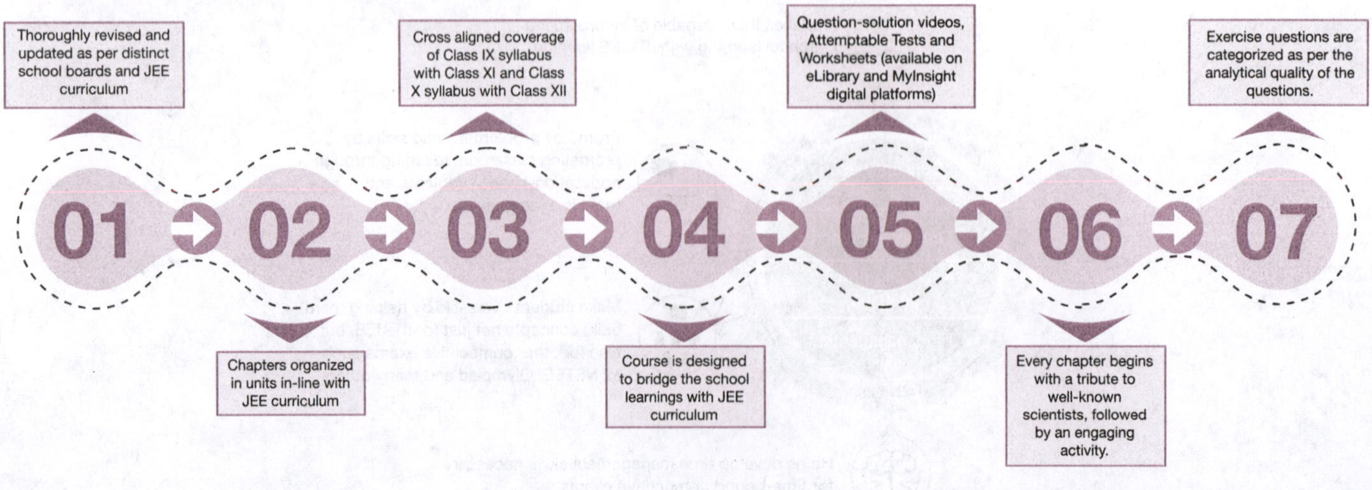

Pearson IIT Foundation series provides a perfect blend of learning through theory and practice questions with a fusion of school and JEE curriculum. It is imperative to note that this series would be as profound as you want it to be. Therefore, to get maximum benefit from this book, we recommend following the given study plan.

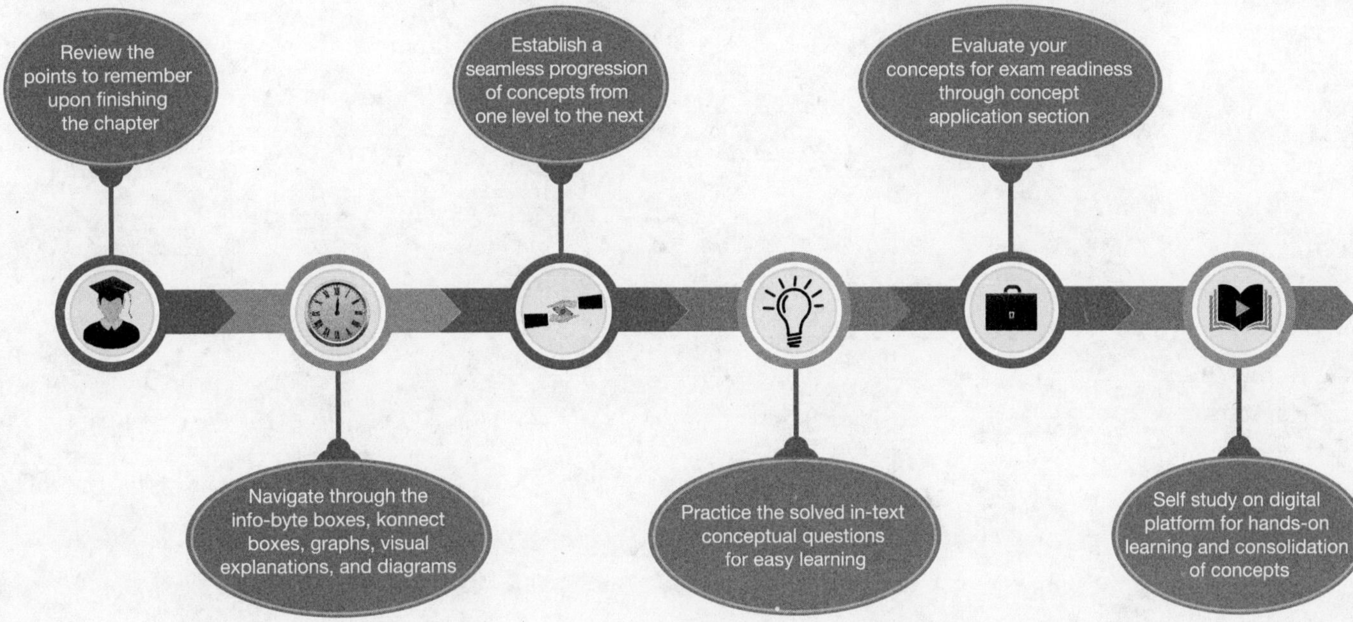

To provide a graded learning approach, the exercise part of each chapter is categorized by using four icons for question tagging. The question categorization helps the learners assess their own problem-solving and analytical skills and motivates them to improve to reach their objectives.

The following icons are used to categorize the questions with specific meanings:

Real-life Situations Questions: 

Analytical Questions: 

Conceptual Questions: 

Value-based Questions: 

With this refined and well-tuned course from Pearson, students will become more confident when they enter the competitive world for actual IIT-JEE preparation. The effort put in today will transform into a valuable asset, contributing to success in future competitive examinations.

Chapter Insights

Remember

Before beginning this chapter, you should be able to:

- Learn about the different types of wave motion and to represent simple harmonic motion graphically.

Remember section will help them to memorize and review the previous learning on a particular topic

Key points will help the students to identify the essential points in a chapter

Key Ideas

After completing this chapter, you should be able to:

- Understand the classification of waves, sound as a mechanical wave.

Scientific Crypt

A Tribute to Madame Curie (1867 - 1934)

Madame Curie born on November 7th, 1867 in Warsaw, Poland was one of the first women scientists of the 20th century. She went to Paris for higher studies. She married Pierre Currie a professor in the school of physics in 1895.

Madame Curie along with her husband studied on Radioactivity and discovered that radioactivity was not a result of chemical reaction. She discovered radium and both of them received a Nobel Prize in 1903, for the studies they had done on radium. For her work on radioactivity she was awarded the Nobel Prize for chemistry once again in 1911.

In 1910, Madame Curie competed for a membership in a science academy in France. The male society of the academy tried to stop her advancement in Science. During her research she was exposed to an incredible level of radiations and died on July 4, 1934 in France.

FUN TIME

CROSSWORD

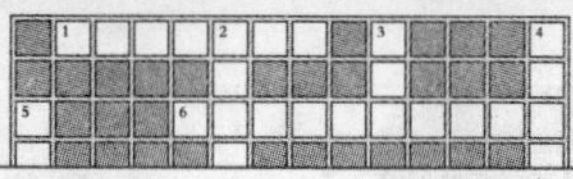

Scientific Crypt provides information about well-known scientists related to the chapter. The engaging activity is also given in the form of a crossword to keep the learners interested.

Introduction section helps to lay the foundation of the following chapter and leads the way for further learning

INTRODUCTION

Sensation of hearing through the vibrating ear drum IS caused by Sound which is a form of energy. A loud thunder or high-intensity sound produced by a low-flying jet plane results in the rattling of window panes and doors. We know that work is done at the expense of energy and the rattling of doors and windows is caused by the sound, thus, indicating that sound is a form of energy.

Music and Noise

Sound that causes a pleasing sensation to ears is called music. Sound that causes an unpleasant or irritating sensation to ears is called noise. A sound cannot be strictly classified into either music or noise, as a sound that causes a pleasing sensation to one person can cause an unpleasant sensation to another person. But based on certain characteristics, we can broadly classify any sound note into either music or noise.

Characteristics of Musical Sound

Pitch

It is a special characteristic of sound based on which we can differentiate between two sounds having equal loudness. The pitch of a given sound can be measured by its frequency.

Example: Female voices in general are high pitched compared to male voices though both the female voice and the male voice may have equal loudness.

Concepts are explained in a well-structured and lucid manner

Konnect boxes are some add-on information of related topic

Konnect

Eddy currents are used in induction cooking, where they heat up the cooking pan directly without a heating element.

Info Bytes!

LEDs use the lighting effect of electricity more efficiently than traditional incandescent bulbs.

Info bytes are interesting trivia and facts that engage young minds and keep the grey cells ticking!

EXAMPLE 6.3 The electric potentials at the two ends of a conductor are 15 *V* and 7 *V*, respectively. 16*J* of work needs to be done to move a certain amount of charge from the end at higher potential to the end at lower potential. Find the amount of charge moved.

SOLUTION

The potential difference between the two ends of the conductor (V) = 15 V – 7 V = 8V.

Work done (W) = 16 J

Charge (Q) = ?

$$\text{Potential difference} = \frac{\text{Work}}{\text{Charge}}$$

$$V = \frac{W}{Q} = \frac{16J}{8V} = 2 \text{ coulomb.}$$

Examples are given in the form of in-text exercises to reinforce the concepts learnt in a particular chapter

Illustrative examples solved in a logical and step-wise manner

POINTS TO REMEMBER

- ✔ If the frequency of the vibrations is less than 20 Hz, it is called infrasonic sound and the sound produced by bodies vibrating with a frequency greater than 20 kHz, is called ultrasonic sound.
- ✔ When a wave propagates from one place to another, the particles of the medium do not undergo any translatory motion but have only vibratory or oscillatory motion.
- ✔ Mechanical waves, also called elastic waves, require a material (an elastic) medium for their propagation
- ✔ If the direction of the vibration of the particles of the medium is perpendicular to the direction of the propagation of the wave, the wave is called transverse wave. both as the wave is propagated in a medium are called 'damped vibrations'.
- ✔ If a body is set into vibrations by the influence of another vibrating body or an external periodic force, the vibrations executed by the former are known as forced vibrations
- ✔ The elasticity factor in solids is given by Young's modulus (Y).
- ✔ The elasticity factor in liquids is taken as its bulk modulus of elasticity (K).
- ✔ The phenomenon in which when one of the two bodies having confusing natural frequencies is set into vibration, then under its influence the other body also vibrates with increased amplitude.

Points to remember summarises the concepts and topics presented in each chapter

PRACTICE QUESTIONS CLASSROOM WING

Very Short Answer Type Questions

Directions for questions 1 to 5:
True or false.

1. The length measured by a standard Vernier Calipers is more accurate compared to the length measured by a standard Screw Gauge.
2. The difference between one Main Scale Division (M.S.D.) and one Vernier Scale Division (V.S.D.) of a vernier calipers gives its Least Count (L.C.)

13. If the number of head scale divisions of screw gauge is doubled then its least count ________.
14. The least count of a screw gauge is 0.0002 mm. The tip of the screw advances 0.1 mm when the screw is rotated through 2 rotations. Then the thimble of the screw gauge contains ________ divisions.
15.

Short Answer Type Questions

25. How can wind energy be converted to ele energy?
26. Write a short note on various types of fuels (wi erence to their physical presence).
27. Give the characteristics of sources of energy.
28. Explain the production of geothermal electricity

Essay Answer Type Questions

41. Explain how various petroleum products are obtained from crude oil.
42. 'Solar energy is the chief source for all other forms of energy'. Explain.

Different typologies of questions have been included in the *Classroom Wing* which help students to develop the problem-solving skill

Competition Wing has been integrated chapter-wise in the exercise part to prepare students for various competitive examinations.

Graded as per complexity: Level 1; Level 2; and Level 3

PRACTICE QUESTIONS COMPETITION WING

Level 1: Apply Your Concepts

Direction for questions from 1 to 5:
Answer the following questions briefly:

1. What value represents the energy released by a unit mass of fuel when burnt?
2. What are the primary compounds in petroleum called?
3.

15. Energy sources like wind and tidal are replenished naturally and are thus termed as ________ energy sources.
16. The splitting of a uranium nucleus in a reactor to produce a tremendous amount of heat energy is an example of ________.

energy contained within chemical bonds, which

Level 2: Review Your Concepts

40. Given the consistent motion of air (wind) renewable nature, why isn't wind energy ca replacing all other energy sources?
41. Why might geothermal energy be abundant regions and scarce in others, even if the Earth uniformly hot?

Level 3: Assess Your Conce

60. While both nuclear fission and nuclear fusi enormous amounts of energy, they're not us in current energy production methods. Why fission predominantly used in power pla fusion is not, even though fusion reactions p like our Sun?
61. Tidal energy and solar energy both origi astronomical bodies (the Moon and the Su tively). However, their impacts on Earth's e ance differ. How do these energy sources dif

Short Answer Type Questions

25. How can wind energy be converted to electrical energy?
26. Write a short note on various types of fuels (with reference to their physical presence).
27. Give the characteristics of sources of energy.
28. Explain the production of geothermal electricity.
29. Write a short note on natural gas.
30. What are the different types of sources of energy? G two examples for each.
31. What is a calorific value? Which gaseous substance the highest calorific value?

33. What are the types of fuels? G each.
34. Give the differences between b

48. Find the electrical power generated in 1s by a windmill that is erected in a location when air flows with an average speed of 54 $km \cdot h^{-1}$. Assume that the moving air is completely stopped by the blades of the wind turbine of area 10 m^2, over which air flows normally and the energy conversion from wind energy to electrical energy is only 50%. (Take density of air = 1.3 kg/m^{-3})
49. The solar energy incident normal to the surface of the water in a container raises its temperature from 10°C to 20°C, in one minute. If the mass of water in the container is 1400 g, then find the surface area of the

The icons are used for categorisation of the questions in Classroom Wing and Competition Wing

PRACTICE QUESTIONS JEE-NEET SPECIAL WING

Multiple-Answer Type Questions

Directions for Questions 1 to 5: Each question has FOUR options (a), (b), (c), and (d). ONE OR MORE THAN ONE of these four option(s) is/are the correct answer(s).

1. The constituents of biogas are ________.
   (a) Methane (b) Carbon dioxide
   (c) Hydrogen (d) Nitrogen
2. The value of solar constant is ________.
   (a) 1.4 kJ m^{-2} s^{-1} (b) 4.1 kJ m^{-2} s^{-1}
   (c) 1.4 kW m^{-2} (d) 1.4 kW m^{-2} s^{-1}
3. Which of the following sources of energy can provide energy over a long period of time?
   (a) Sun (b) Wind
   (c) Coal (d) Petrol
4. Which of the following types of coal contains the highest percentage of carbon?
   (a) Peat (b) Lignite
   (c) Bituminous (d) Anthracite
5. The energy received on the periphery of the atmosphere of an area of 75 m^2 in one hour is ____.

JEE-NEET Special Wing is curated specifically for targeted preparation of JEE and NEET examinations

Hints and Explanations

CLASSROOM WING

Very Short Answer Type Questions

1. Non-renewable
2. Renewable
3. Ignition temperature
4. Geothermal

22. Petrol – presence of hydrogen.
23. A device that converts wind energy to mechanical or electrical energy.
24. A device which directly converts solar energy into electrical energy.

Hints and Explanations for key questions of classroom wing, competition wing and JEE-NEET special wing along with highlights on the common mistakes that students usually make in the examinations

Competition Wing

Level 1: Apply Your Concepts

Explanation for questions from 1 to 5:

1. Calorific value.
2. Hydrocarbons
3. Ignition temperature
4. Solar energy.
5. The minimum temperature at ... begins to burn.

Explanation for questions from 6 to 10

6. False. Ignition temperature is th... ture at which a substance begin...
7. True.
8. False. Tidal energy is renewable ... itational effects of the moon and ... tive and consistent.
9. True.
10. False. This description is for nu...

Explanation for questions from 21 to 2...

21. (b). Nuclear fission involves th... nucleus, while nuclear fusion in... of lighter nuclei.

Explanation for questions from 36 to 44:

36. Silver is the metal which is used for connecting wires that connect solar cells in a solar panel, due to its large conductivity.
37. The most suitable fuel burns completely and does not

JEE-NEET SPECIAL WING

Multiple-Answer Type Questions

1. Refractive index and relative density are the ratios of similar quantities.

   i.e., $\text{Refractive index} = \dfrac{\text{Velocity of light in vacuum (c)}}{\text{Velocity of light in medium (v)}}$

   $\text{Relative density} = \dfrac{\text{Density of substance} - 1}{\text{Density of substance} - 2}$

   Therefore, both quantities do not have units. Hence, no dimensional formula for them.
   Hence, the correct option are (a, b)

2. We have, $\text{Pressure} = \dfrac{\text{Force}}{\text{Area}}$
   → SI unit is newton m^{-2}
   Now, $\text{Longitudinal stress} = \dfrac{\text{Force}}{\text{Area}}$
   → SI unit is newton m^{-2}
   Now, $\text{Young's modulus} = \dfrac{\text{Stress}}{\text{Strain}}$
   As strain does not have unit, SI unit of Young's modulus is newton m^{-2}.
   Hence, the correct option are (a, b, c)

3. Practical units of mass are ton (1000 kg), quintal (100 kg)

$= \dfrac{\text{Distance moved by screw}}{\text{No. of rotations} \times \text{No. of divisions on circular scale}}$

Hence, the correct option are (a, b, c)

Comprehension-Based Questions

6. The dimensional formula of acceleration is $[M^0 L^1 T^{-2}]$.
   Hence, the correct option is (c)
7. The force required to set the body at rest on the table to motion must at least be little greater than the static friction between the body and the surface.
   The static friction in this case depends on the normal force, which again depends on the weight of the body. Weight of the body is given by 'mg', where 'g' is acceleration due to gravity and is constant at a given place.
   The coefficient of friction (μ) between the body and the surface is also constant.
   Hence, the magnitude of the force required to put the body at rest on the surface to motion, F = (μ)mg.
   As 'μ' and 'g' are constant, the force is proportional to the mass of the body. body.
   Hence, the correct option is (a)
8. Normal reaction force is a derived quantity and vector quantity.

WORKSHEET
CHAPTER 2: DYNAMICS

Directions for questions from 1 to 5:
Select the correct alternative from the following options.

1. A bullet of mass 100 g moving with a velocity of 100 m s^{-1} is stopped by a plank. If the bullet travels a distance of 10 cm in the plank before it comes to rest, find the average force exerted by the plank.
   (a) 100 N (b) 1000 N
   (c) 2500 N (d) 5000 N
2. Find the power developed by an engine in filling water

a rough surface, the total work done by the frictional force is zero.

8. The orbital velocity of a satellite is inversely proportional to the radius of the orbit.
9. When a stone is tied to a string and rotated in a circular path, the work done by the tension of the string is zero.
10. A satellite revolving in an orbit closer to the surface of the earth has more speed than one which is moving in an orbit of higher radius.

DW

DW: Downloadable worksheets supplementing textual exercises for hand-on learning

AI Assessments

Which of the following is larger unit of density?

- g m^{-3}
- g km^{-3}
- kg m^{-3}
- g cm^{-3}

Questions 1 of 4 Next

AT

AT: Attemptable Tests for assessing understanding of concepts and getting a clear picture of your exam readiness

19. A standard vernier callipers with positive zero error of 0.03 cm is used to measure the diameter of a sphere. If the MSR is 5.5 cm and the diameter observed is 5.56 cm, then what is the true VCD?
20. The main scale of a vernier callipers has 10 divisions for each 1 cm and 10 divisions on its vernier scale such that N VSD = (N–1) MSD. What is the least count of the vernier callipers?
21. If the least count of a screw gauge is 0.001 mm and if the screw advances by 0.5 mm for its two complete rotations, how many divisions does the circular scale of

Video icon: **Audio and visual** learning to difficult **questions for effective learning** and retention

Unit I

Basic Physics

In this Unit

CHAPTER

1

Units and Measurements

Remember

Before beginning this chapter, you should be able to:

- Define physical quantity and should be able to identify different physical quantities in Physics.
- Define Unit of a physical quantity and should be able to identify different units of different physical quantities.
- Identify the different system of units, their significance and the conversions between them.
- Identify different instruments and methods used to measure the physical quantities like length, mass, time, weight, area, volume, etc.
- Understand the significance of measuring a physical quantity to a high accuracy.

Key Ideas

After completing this chapter, you should be able to:

- Identify the fundamental and derived physical quantities, their units and dimensional formulae.
- Write the units of fundamental and derived physical quantities by following proper rules.
- Know how to measure the length of an object by using a Vernier Calipers and Screw Gauge to higher accuracies.
- Understand the principles behind the working of Vernier Calipers and Screw Gauge which give more accurate readings.
- Identify the different applications of Vernier Calipers and Screw Gauge in the fields of Science and Industry.

Scientific Crypt

A Tribute to Pierre Vernier (1580 – 1637)

Pierre Vernier was taught mathematics and science by his father who was a lawyer and engineer. His father introduced him to the works of Claviers and Brahe. This great scientist was born in Franche-Comte (Free country), which was under the control of the Spanish Habsburgs.

Vernier held various official positions in government such as military engineer for the Habsburgs and director-general of the treasury in Dole and Basancon, the capital of Franche-Comte. He also held various posts in the government of Spain. Most of the time he worked as an engineer, working on the fortifications of various cities.

Like other scientists, Vernier also worked on cartography and on surveying. His interest in surveying led to the development of instruments used for surveying. His famous publication is *La construction, I'usage, et les propriet'es du Quadrant nouveau de mathematiques (1631).* In this, Vernier gives a table of sines and a method for deriving the angles of a triangle if its sides are known. In this he also describes his most famous invention, "Vernier calipers", an instrument meant to measure the length accurately.

FUN TIME

CROSSWORD

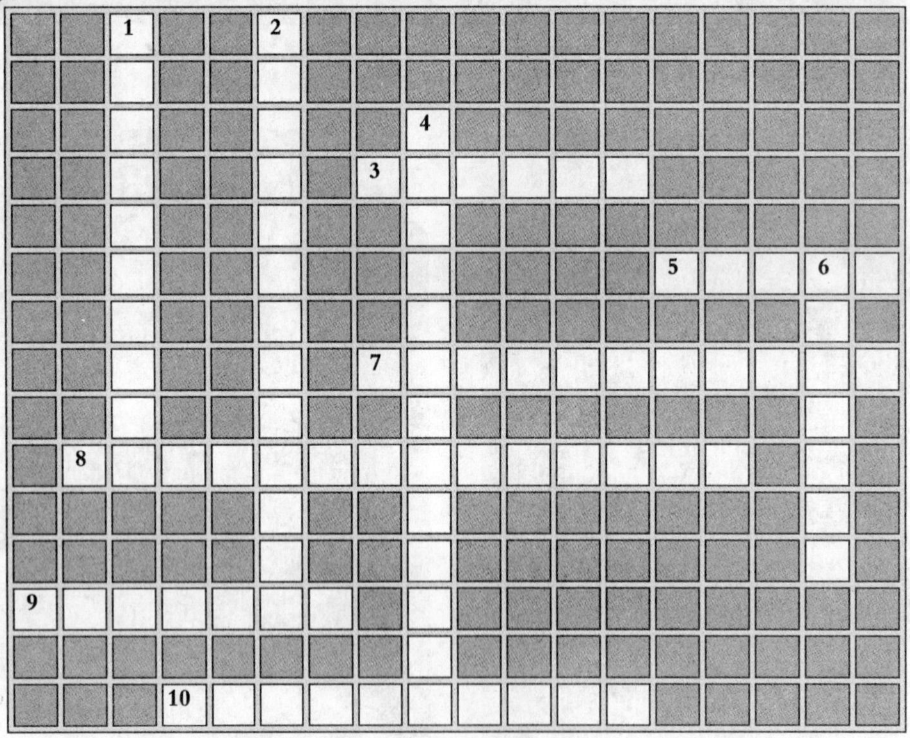

Across

3. SI unit of temperature.
5. The advancement in the screw tip of the screw on complete rotation of its head.
7. The smallest length that can be accurately measurable.
8. Present on the screw of the screw gauge.
9. Attached to the screw of a screw gauge by a spring.
10. If zero of the head scale is not coinciding with the index line.

Down

1. Equally spaced divisions on the tapered end of thimble.
2. Auxiliary scale of vernier calipers.
4. The scale that slides over the main scale.
6. S.I unit of intensity of light.

INTRODUCTION

A nut and its bolt should be tightly affixed for effective functioning. This is made possible by making accurate measurements during the process of manufacturing itself. One knows very well, what happens when defective bolts and nuts are used in a ceiling fan. It can be dangerous. This simple example is enough to emphasise the importance of 'Measurements'.

The topic, 'Measurements', enables a student to take measurements accurately up to a fraction of a millimetre by using measuring devices and this is going to help a lot in his/her future activities. This topic covers the ways on how to rectify the errors in the readings that are made by using defective instruments. The knowledge related to fundamental and derived physical quantities, their units and the dimensional formulae are also imparted in this chapter.

Physical Quantities and Units

Physics is a fascinating and wonderful, yet challenging branch of science, where the student explores and fathoms the wonders of the universe through a systematic study of the laws governing the natural phenomena. In this quest, the theoretical hypotheses have to be validated time and again through accurate experimentation and measurement of the physical quantities. In consequence, thereof proper systems for measurement, standards and notations, well-defined fundamental quantities and reliable instrumentation gain the utmost importance.

Before we take up the study of the underlying principles in the working of two instruments widely used in laboratories and industrial units, we will review some fundamentals, standards and regulations observed by the scientific fraternity.

Units of Physical Quantities

The seven fundamental quantities are taken as the seven dimensions for every other physical quantity. Thus, every derived quantity can be represented in terms of these dimensions. For example, speed being the ratio of distance to time, can be represented as $[M^0L^1T^{-1}]$, in which 'L' represents the dimension of length and 'T' represents the dimension of time. The following table gives the list of the fundamental quantities, the symbols used for their respective dimensions, as well as the corresponding S.I units.

Similarly, the dimensional formulae of some other physical quantities are,

1. Area = $[L^2]$
2. Density = $[M^1 L^{-3}]$
3. Force = $[M^1 L^1 T^{-2}]$

Generally, a dimensional formula is enclosed in square brackets and by convention the three fundamental quantities of mass, length and time are indicated even if they are not involved in the derived quantity. For example, the dimensional formula of acceleration is written as $[M^0L^1T^{-2}]$, the dimensional formula of density is $[M^1L^{-3}T^0]$, etc.

Rules to be Followed in Writing Units

1. The symbol for a unit, which is named after a scientist, should start with an upper-case letter.

   Example: Newton – N, Joule – J, Pascal – Pa, Kelvin – K, etc.

2. The symbol for a unit, which is not named after a person, is written in lower case.

   Example: metre – m, mole – mol, second – s, etc.

3. If the unit is named after a scientist or not, the full form of the units should start with a lower-case letter.

   Example: newton, metre, joule, second, hertz, etc.

4. Symbol of a unit should not be in plural form.
   Example: 500 metres should be written as 500 m and not 500 ms.

Physical quantities	Wrong notation	Correct notation
Force	Ns	N
Temperature	Ks	K
Amount of substance	mols	mol

5. A compound unit (obtained from units of two or more physical quantities) is written either by putting a dot or leaving a space between symbols of two units.
   Example: Unit of torque – N m or N.m.
   Unit of impulse – N s or N.s.
   Pole strength of magnet – A m or A.m.
6. The denominators in a compound unit should be written with negative powers.
   Example: Unit of density is kg m^{-3}, not kg/m^3.
   Unit of acceleration is m s^{-2} not m/s^2.

Konnect

There are seven base SI units: meter, kilogram, second, ampere, kelvin, mole, and candela. All other units are derived from these!

EXAMPLE 1.1 Write the CGS and SI unit of the physical quantities having the following dimensional formulae.

(A) $[ML^2T^{-2}]$ **(B)** $[M^0LT^0]$ **(C)** $[ML^{-1}T^{-1}K^0]$

SOLUTION

(A) For CGS: M = Gram (g); L = Centimetre (cm); T = Second (s)
Unit: g × cm^2 × s^{-2} = g.cm^2 / s^2
For SI: M = Kilogram (kg); L = Meter (m); T = Second (s)
Unit: kg × m^2 × s^{-2} = kg. m^2 / s^2

(B) Here only the length dimension is present.
For CGS: L = Centimetre (cm)
Unit: cm
For SI: L = Meter (m)
Unit: m

(C) For CGS: M = Gram (g); L = Centimetre (cm); T = Second (s); K = Kelvin (K)
[Again, even though Kelvin is a SI base unit, it remains unchanged in the CGS system]
Unit: g × cm^{-1} × s^{-1} = g / cm. s^{-1}
For SI: M = Kilogram (kg); L = Meter (m); T = Second (s)
Unit: kg × m^{-1} × s^{-1} = kg / m. s^{-1}

Vernier Calipers

Vernier Calipers are used for the measurement of length.

Measurement of Length

To find the length of the rod shown in the figure below in which block A in each case is fixed to the scale, while block B can slide along the scale.

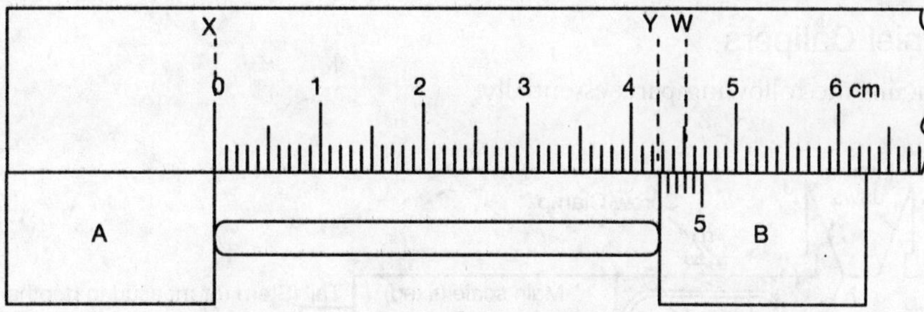

Figure 1.1 A rod between the blocks A and B

The length of the rod corresponds to XY. Here, X corresponds to zero but Y lies between the 42nd and 43rd divisions of the scale. Hence, the length of the rod would be a fraction of a millimetre greater than 42 mm. This fraction cannot be estimated with the given blocks. However, if we construct another scale on block B in which each division is slightly less than 1 mm, then we can possibly estimate this fraction more accurately as shown in figure (2) below, in which 5 divisions on block B are equal to 4 mm.

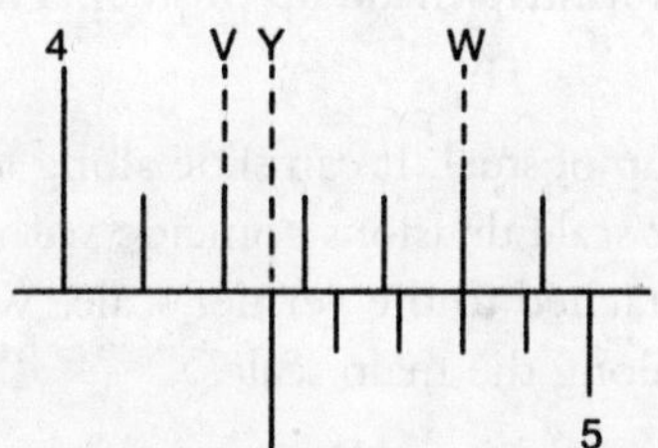

Figure 1.2 Magnified reading on the scale

> **Info Bytes!**
> The Vernier scale on callipers can measure dimensions up to one-hundredth of a millimetre!

Hence, one division on this scale is $\frac{4}{5}$ mm = 0.8 mm.

The length of the rod now corresponds to $XY = XV + VY$.

But $VY = VW - WY$

$= 3 \text{ mm} - 3 \times 0.8 \text{ mm} = 3 \text{ mm} - 2.4 \text{ mm} = 0.6 \text{ mm}.$

Thus, we are able to read the length of the rod more accurately by making a reasonably accurate estimation of VY. This is the principle on which Paul Vernier constructed an instrument now popularly known as the '**Vernier Calipers**'.

Main Scale Division (M.S.D.)

The markings on the actual scale in fig (1) is known as Main scale and each division on the main scale is known as Main Scale Division (M.S.D.).

Vernier Scale Division (V.S.D.)

The secondary scale marked on the sliding block is called the vernier scale and the divisions on it are called Vernier scale division (VSD).

Least Count (L.C.)

The smallest fraction of a millimetre (Main scale division or MSD) is the difference between 1 MSD and 1 VSD. This smallest fraction is also called the '**Least Count**'.

∴ Least count of a Vernier Calipers = 1 MSD − 1 VSD.

Description of a Vernier Calipers

The Vernier Calipers contains the following parts essentially:

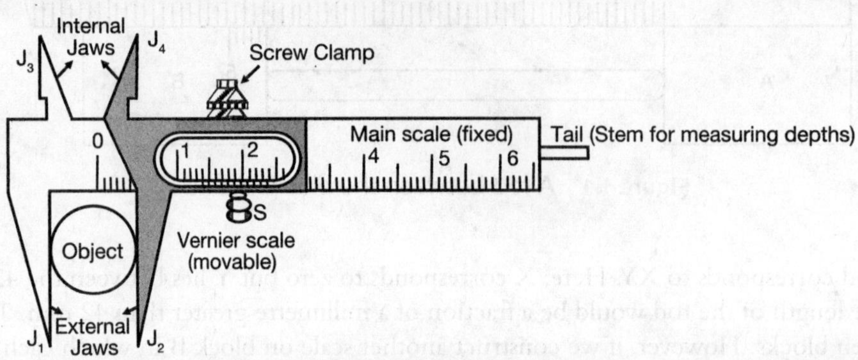

Figure 1.3 Vernier Calipers

1. **Main Scale:** The main scale is generally a 15 cm long thin strip made up of steel. The main scale is etched in mm. This scale is a fixed scale.
2. **Vernier Scale:** A vernier scale is a movable scale made up of steel. It can slide along the main scale and 10 divisions are marked on the vernier scale, such that the 10 vernier scale divisions coincide with 9 main scale divisions in case of a standard vernier caliper. A tightening screw (S) is attached to the vernier scale. With the help of the tightening screw, vernier scale can be fixed in any desired position along the main scale.
3. **External Jaws (J_1, J_2):** The jaws J_1 and J_2 are called external jaws. By using these external jaws, we can find the external dimensions of a sphere, a cylinder, etc., by fixing the object between these jaws. The jaw J_1 is fixed to the main scale, called fixed jaw and the jaw J_2 is fixed to vernier scale, called movable jaw.
4. **Internal Jaws (J_3, J_4):** The jaws J_3 and J_4 are together known as internal jaws. These jaws are used to measure the internal dimensions of an object such as the internal diameter of a hollow cylinder. The jaw J_3 is fixed to the main scale and is called the fixed internal jaw, the jaw J_4 is fixed to the vernier scale and is called the movable internal jaw.
5. **Tail:** It is used to measure the depth of cylinders or hollow tubes. It is connected to the vernier scale from behind, which slides back and forth along with the vernier scale.

Konnect

Generally, the standard vernier scale is provided with 10 graduations to coincide with 9 main scale divisions, i.e., the 10 divisions of the vernier scale measure 9 mm and 1 VSD = 0.9 mm.

Principle of Vernier Calipers

The principle of a vernier is to make 'N' vernier scale divisions equal to (N – 1) main scale divisions.

Procedure for Taking a Measurement Using a Vernier Calipers

1. Determine the least count of the vernier calipers:

   Least count (L.C.) = 1 M.S.D. – 1 V.S.D. = 1 mm – 0.9 mm = 0.1 mm = 0.01 cm

   $$\text{Least count (L.C.)} = \frac{1\text{ M.S.D.}}{\text{No of V.S.Ds}} = \frac{1\text{ mm}}{10} = 0.1\text{ mm} = 0.01\text{ cm}$$

2. To measure the external dimensions of an object it should be held tightly between the external jaws J_1 and J_2 and to measure the inner dimensions it should be held with internal jaws J_3 and J_4.

3. Note the main scale reading (M.S.R.). The main scale reading is always the smaller of the two values, between which the zero of the vernier scale lies.

4. Note the vernier-scale division which coincides with any main scale division. This is known as vernier coinciding division (VCD).

5. The length of rod, AB = $(y - x)$

$$= (z - x) + (y - z) = (z - x) + (w - z) - (w - y)$$
$$= \text{M.S.R.} + (\text{V.C.D.} \times \text{M.S.D.}) - (\text{V.C.D.} \times \text{V.S.D.})$$
$$= \text{M.S.R.} + \text{V.C.D.}\ (\text{M.S.D.} - \text{V.S.D.})\ (\because \text{L.C} = 1\ \text{M.S.D} - 1\ \text{V.S.D})$$

$\therefore$ Total reading (Length of the rod, AB) = M.S.R. + (V.C.D. × L.C.).

In case of any zero error in the instrument, the corresponding correction is to be added to the measurement calculated in step 5.

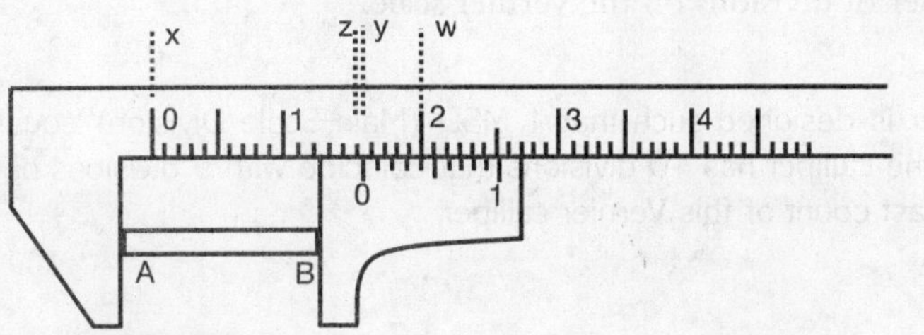

Figure 1.4 Total Reading of Vernier Calipers

Konnect

Zero error can either be positive or negative, depending on whether the zero mark on the Vernier scale is above or below the zero mark on the main scale.

Zero Error

When the fixed and the movable jaws of a vernier calipers are made to come in contact and if the zeroes of both the main scale and the vernier scale do not coincide with each other, then the instrument is said to have a **zero error.**

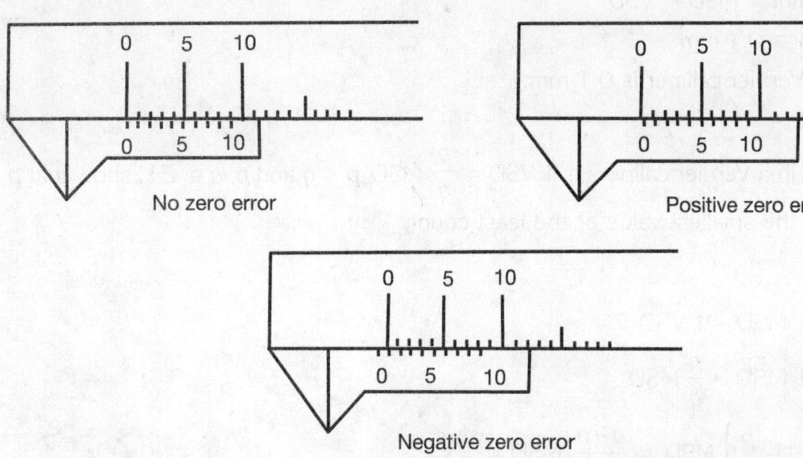

Figure 1.5 Zero errors of a Vernier Calipers

Positive Zero Error

If the zeroth division of the vernier scale is to the 'right' of the zeroth division of the main scale when the two jaws are brought in contact with each other, then the error is said to be positive and the correction is negative.

If the nth division of the vernier scale coincides with some division on the main scale, then the

Positive zero error = (+n × Least count)

and the **Correction = (−n × Least count).**

Negative Zero Error

If the zeroth division of the vernier scale is to the 'left' of the zeroth division of the main scale, the error is said to be negative and the correction is positive.

If the nth division of the vernier scale coincides with some division on the main scale, then the

Negative zero error = −(N − n) × Least Count

and the **Correction = +(N − n) × Least Count**

where, N = number of divisions on the vernier scale.

EXAMPLE 1.2

A Vernier calliper is designed such that 1 MSD (Main Scale Division) equals 1 mm. If the sliding scale of the calliper has 10 divisions that coincide with 9 divisions of the main scale, determine the least count of this Vernier calliper.

SOLUTION

Given, 1 MSD = 1 mm

The relation between MSD and VSD is given by the fact that 10 VSDs (Vernier Scale Divisions) are equal to 9 MSDs.

10 × VSD = 9 × MSD

10 × VSD = 9 × 1mm

10 × VSD = 9 mm

$$VSD = \frac{9 \text{ mm}}{10} = 0.9 \text{ mm}$$

Now, using the relation: Least Count = MSD − VSD

Least Count = (1 mm − 0.9 mm) = 0.1 mm

Therefore, the least count of the Vernier calliper is 0.1 mm.

EXAMPLE 1.3

In a Vernier calipers if 1 VSD = $\frac{p}{q}$ MSD, $p < q$ and $p, q \in Z+$, show that $p = q - 1$ to achieve the smallest value of the least count.

SOLUTION

We know that the least count = 1 MSD − 1 VSD

$$= 1 \text{ MSD} - \frac{p}{q}\text{MSD}$$

$$= \left(1 - \frac{p}{q}\right)\text{MSD} = \frac{q-p}{q}\text{ MSD.}$$

For a given q, the least count is smallest when $(q - p)$ is the smallest positive integer (=1)

$$\therefore q - p = 1 \text{ or } p = q - 1.$$

This forms the principle of a Vernier caliper, 'N divisions on the Vernier scale correspond to $(N - 1)$ divisions on the main scale'.

Thus, the least count = $\frac{1\,MSD}{q}$ $(\because q - p = 1)$

EXAMPLE 1.4 Find the zero error in the two figures given.

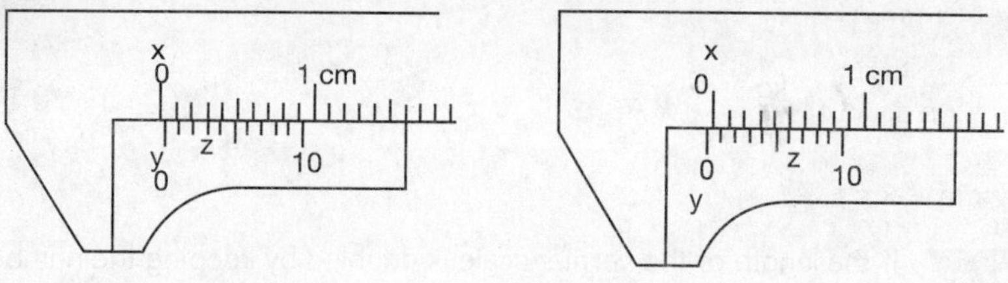

SOLUTION

For the first picture, the zero line of the vernier scale is on the right of the zero line of the main scale. Therefore, vernier calipers is having positive zero error.

We have, **Positive zero error = (+*n* × Least count)**

From figure, $n = 3$ and Least count = 0.1 mm

Therefore, Positive zero error = +3 × 0.1 = +0.3 mm

For the second picture, the zero line of the vernier scale is on the left of the zero line of the main scale. Therefore, vernier calipers is having negative zero error.

We have, **Negative zero error = −(*N* − *n*) × Least Count**

From figure, $n = 6$ and Least count = 0.1 mm

Therefore, Negative zero error = −(10 − 6) × 0.1 = − 0.4 mm

EXAMPLE 1.5 While measuring the inner diameter and outer diameter of a hollow tube to determine its thickness by using a Vernier callipers, the main scale readings are found to be 20 mm and 60 mm respectively. What are the minimum and maximum possible thickness if one main scale division = 1 mm, the number of the vernier scale division = 10.

SOLUTION

The maximum possible thickness:

To get the maximum thickness the inner diameter should be minimum and outer diameter should be maximum.

The maximum possible outer diameter is 60.9 mm.

The minimum possible inner diameter is 20 mm.

∴ 2 (thickness) = (60.9 – 20) = 40.9

$$\text{Maximum thickness} = \frac{40.9}{2} = 20.45 \text{ mm}$$

The minimum possible thickness:

To get the minimum thickness the inner diameter should be maximum, and the outer diameter should be minimum.

The maximum inner diameter = 20 mm

Minimum outer diameter = 60 mm

∴ 2 (thickness) = 60 – 20.9 = 39.1

$$\therefore \text{Thickness} = \frac{39.1}{2} = 19.55 \text{ mm}$$

EXAMPLE 1.6 The dimensional formula of a physical quantity is $[M^1L^{-1}T^{-2}I^2]$. What is its SI unit?

SOLUTION

$[M^1]$ whose SI unit is kilogram (kg); $[L^{-1}]$ whose SI unit is meter raised to the power of -1 (m^{-1} or $\frac{1}{m}$); $[T^{-2}]$ whose SI unit is second raised to the power of −2 (s^{-2} or $\frac{1}{s^2}$); and, I^2 whose SI unit is ampere squared (A^2).

Combining all these units, the SI unit for the physical quantity with dimensional formula $[M^1L^{-1}T^{-2}I^2]$.

Now, $[M^1L^{-1}T^{-2}I^2] \Rightarrow \frac{\text{mass}}{\text{length}} \times \frac{1}{(\text{Time})^2} \times (\text{Electric Current})^2$

Thus, the SI unit is $kg \times m^{-1} \times s^{-2}. A^2$ or $\frac{kg}{m} \times \frac{1}{s^2} \times A^2$

Therefore, the SI unit is $kg \times m^{-1} \times s^{-2}. A^2$

EXAMPLE 1.7 If the length of the vernier scale is doubled by keeping the number of divisions the same, how does its least count vary?

SOLUTION

If the length of the vernier scale is doubled and the number of VSD are the same

$$(VSD)' = 2(VSD) = 2 \times 0.9 = 1.8 \text{ mm}$$

$$\text{But } N \times VSD = (N - 1) \text{ MSD}$$

If $N = 10$, $10 \times 1.8 = (9) \times 1 \text{ MSD}$

$$1 \text{ MSD}' = \frac{10}{9} \times 1.8 = 2 \text{ mm.}$$

$$\therefore L.C' = 1 \text{ MSD}' - 1 \text{ VSD}' = 2 - 1.8 = 0.2 \text{ mm}$$

That is, the new L.C. is double the original L.C.

EXAMPLE 1.8 Determine the length of the object from the following diagram. 1 division on scale X is 1 mm and 10 divisions on scale Y is equal to 9 mm.

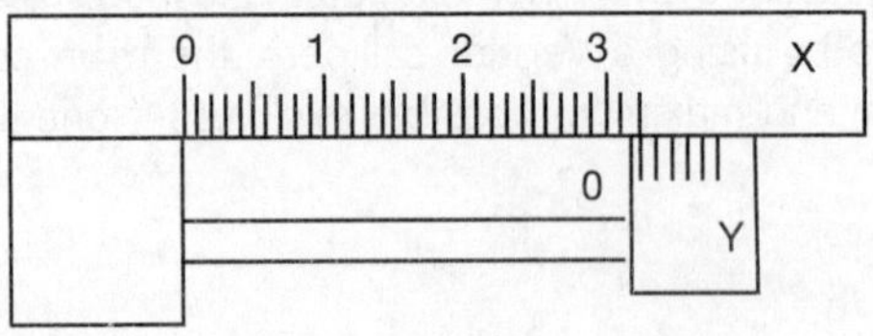

SOLUTION

The reading on scale X is 3.1 cm = 31 mm

The reading on scale Y is calculated as follows

Since $n = 1$ and L.C. = 0.1 mm, $n \times$ L.C. = 1 × 0.1 = 0.1 mm

∴ Total Length of the object = 31 + 0.1 = 31.1 mm

Screw Gauge

Principle of Screw

A screw consists of a shaft or a metallic cylinder and a spiral like thread cut on it along its axis. One end of it is called the head and the other end of it is known as the tip of the screw.

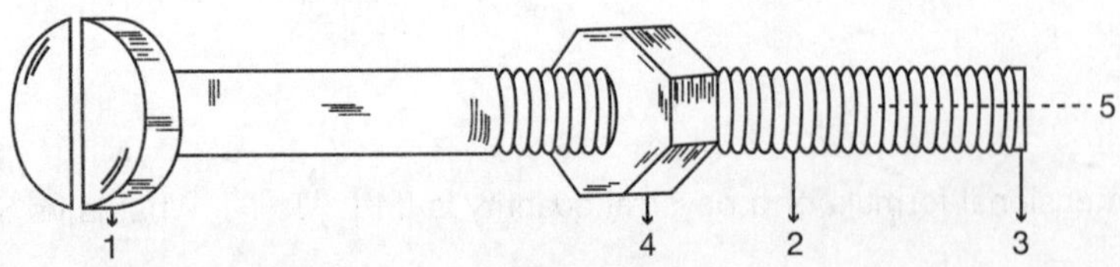

1. Screw head
2. Helical thread
3. Tip of the screw
4. Nut
5. Axis of the screw

Figure 1.6 Principle of a Screw

When the head is rotated, the tip of the screw makes a linear motion either in the forward or in the backward direction, depending upon the direction in which the head of the screw is rotated. When the head of the screw is rotated in the clockwise direction, the tip of the screw moves in the forward direction.

Principle of Screw Gauge

A screw gauge works on the principle of a screw in a nut, i.e., when the head of a screw makes one complete rotation then its tip moves by a distance equal to the gap between two successive threads of it called its pitch. Thus, the pitch of a screw may also be defined as the distance that the tip of the screw advances when its head is given one complete rotation.

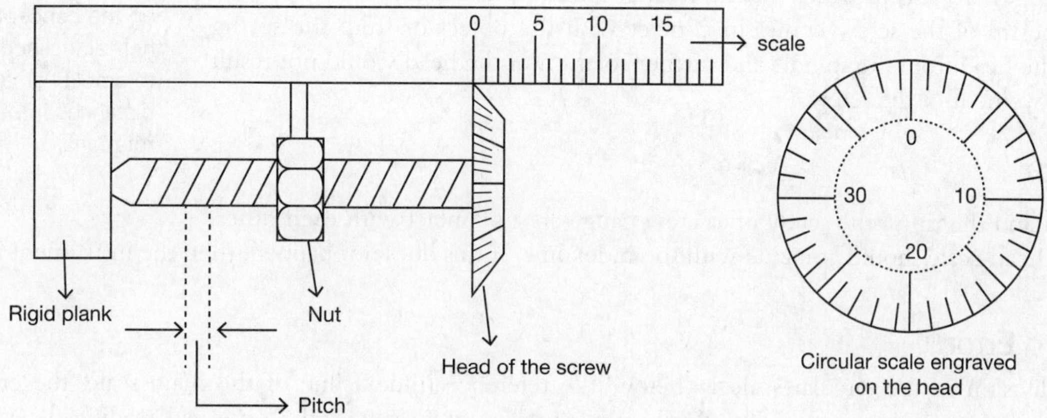

Figure 1.7 Principle of a Screw Gauge

In the above figure, let the head of the screw (having fine edge and able to slide along the length of scale) coincide with the zero division of the main scale (scale shown) when its tip is in contact with the rigid plank. When the head of the screw rotates, the head and the tip of the screw move by equal distances. Using the scale, the displacement of head and that of the screw can be determined.

If the head is provided with N equally spaced divisions, then for one complete rotation of head N - divisions of it pass over the edge of scale and the head advances by one pitch. But if head rotates such that only one of its divisions passes over edge of scale, then the tip advances by part of the pitch. Thus, the displacement of the tip can be calculated accurately up to part of the pitch.

Description of Screw Gauge

1. It has a U - shaped metallic frame with a fixed stud A and a nut at the other end.
2. The nut is attached with a coaxial hollow cylinder called sleeve cylinder.
3. Through this cylinder and nut, a long screw of 1 mm pitch having milled head (M), passes and can slide through them by the rotation of the head.
4. A barrel tapered at one end is attached with the milled head of the screw at the other end and forms a jacket to sleeve. This is called thimble.

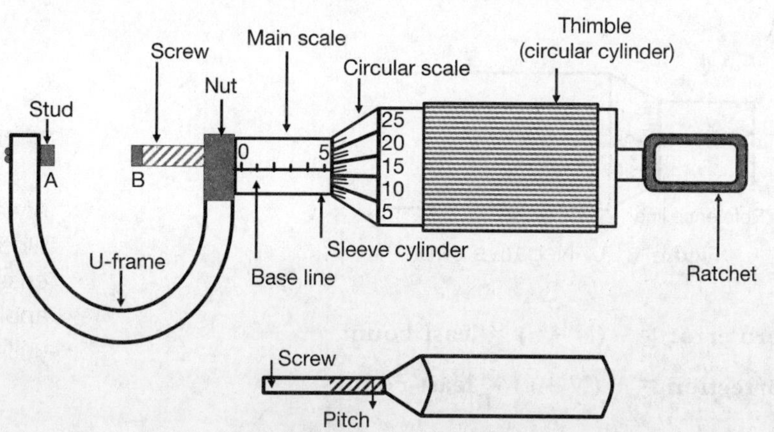

Figure 1.8 Screw Gauge

5. On the sleeve cylinder a line called index line graduated in mm (equal to the pitch of the screw) is drawn. This is called main scale or pitch scale.
6. The tapered end of the thimble is engraved with N-equally spaced divisions and is called head or thimble or circular scale.
7. Screw gauges are also provided with a ratchet attached to the screw by a spring. When the tip of the screw comes in contact with the object or stud, the spring releases the head from the spindle and further rotation of the head would not result in the movement of the screw.

Info Bytes!

The principle of screw gauge relies on the concept of a helical inclined plane to amplify small distances into large rotations.

Zero Error

When the stud and the tip of the screw of a screw gauge are in contact with each other, the zero of the head-scale should coincide with the index line. If this does not happen, then the instrument is said to have a **zero error.**

Positive Zero Error

If the zeroth division of the circular scale is 'below' the reference (index) line of the main scale, the error is said to be positive and the correction is negative. While using such a screw gauge, the observed reading determined would correspond to a measurement from 0, whereas it should be from *X*.

Thus, the distance OX should be subtracted from the observed reading.

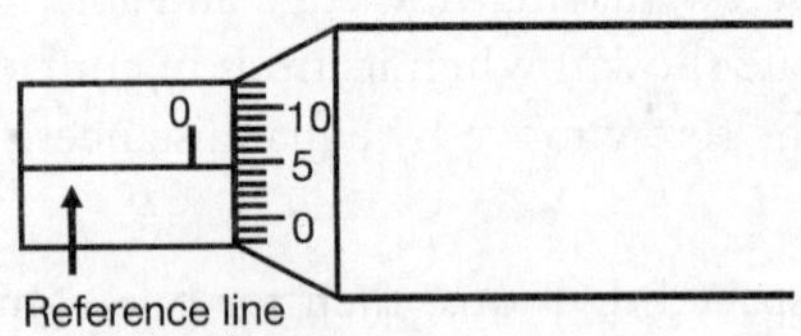

Figure 1.9 Positive error

If n is the circular scale division coinciding with the index line of the main scale, then we have

$OX = 0 + (n \times L.C) = n \times L.C.$

Thus, we have,

$$\textbf{Zero error} = +n \times \textbf{least count}$$

and

$$\textbf{Correction} = -n \times \textbf{least count}$$

Negative Zero Error

Similarly, if the zeroth division of the circular scale is 'above' the reference line of the main scale, the error is said to be negative and the correction is positive. If n is the circular scale division coinciding with the index line of the main scale, then the

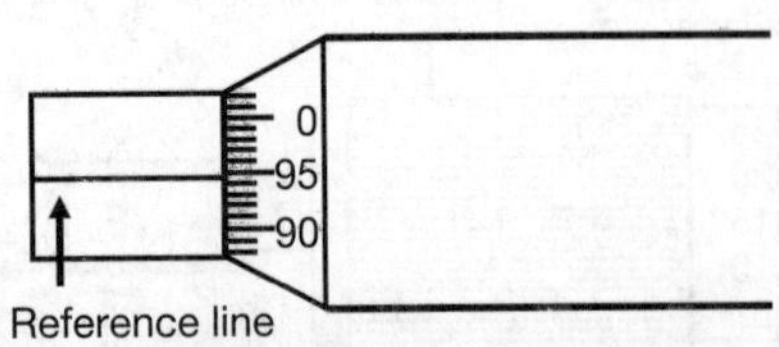

Figure 1.10 Negative error

$$\textbf{Zero error} = -(N - n) \times \textbf{least count}$$

and

$$\textbf{Correction} = +(N - n) \times \textbf{least count}$$

Konnect

Always release the ratchet when it begins to slip, ensuring that the pressure applied to the object is uniform and doesn't deform it.

Procedure for Taking a Measurement Using Screw Gauge

1. Determine zero error (Z.E.) and the zero correction (Z.C.) of the screw gauge.
2. To determine the pitch of the screw of a screw gauge:

$$\text{Pitch} = \text{Distance travelled by the thimble along the main scale for one complete rotation of the head.}$$

$$= \frac{\text{Distance of the tip advances for } n \text{ complete rotations}}{n}$$

3. To determine the least count:

$$\text{Least count (L.C.)} = \frac{\text{Pitch of the screw}}{\text{Number of head scale divisions } (N)}$$

4. Hold the item, whose measurement is to be taken, in between the stud and the tip of the screw.
5. Note down the M.S.R and H.S.R.

The main scale reading (M.S.R) is the value of the right most pitch scale division that is visible outside the barrel. In the figure below, 'Z' is the M.S.R. The main scale reading is also known as Pitch Scale Reading (P.S.R).

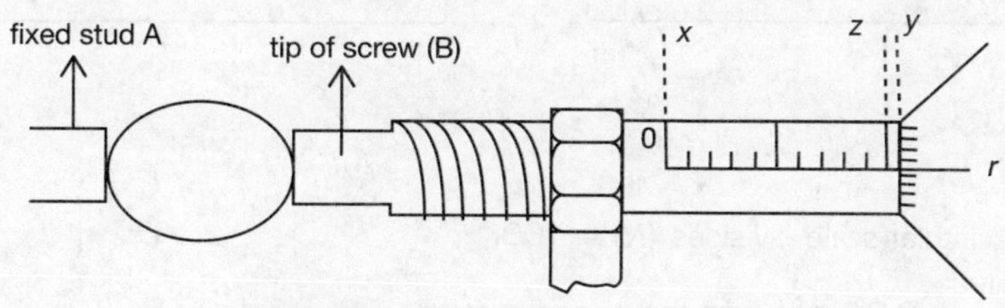

Figure 1.11 Pitch scale reading

H.S.R. (Head scale reading) is the division of head scale coinciding with base line (index line). In the above figure 'r' is the H.S.R.

Thus, the observed reading $= xy = (z - x) + (y - z) = z$ M.S.D $+ (r \times \text{L.C.}) =$ M.S.R. + (H.S.R. × L.C.)

6. Determine the corrected head scale reading.

$$\text{C.H.S.R.} = \text{H.S.R.} + \text{Z.C.}$$

Repeat the experiment by placing the different parts of the object between the studs and note down the H.S.R and M.S.R in each case.

The readings obtained can be tabulated in the table given below, and the diameter of the sphere is measured in each case as M.S.R + (C.H.S.R × L.C.)

S. No	P.S.R/ M.S.R.	H.S.R.	C.H.S.R × L.C.	Diameter, d = M.S.R + (C.H.S.R × L.C)

The average value of the diameter of the object is determined to reduce the experimental errors.

Back - Lash Error

Sometimes the tip of the screw does not move backward for a part of rotation of head in reverse direction, because of wear and tear of threads. This is called backlash error. This backlash error can be avoided by not rotating the head in the reverse direction once the object is held between the two studs.

EXAMPLE 1.9 The readings of a screw gauge when the tip of the screw is in contact with the stud and the object placed between the screw and the stud is as shown in the figure. Find the diameter of the object if the pitch of the screw gauge is 1.0 mm and the number of circular scale divisions is 100.

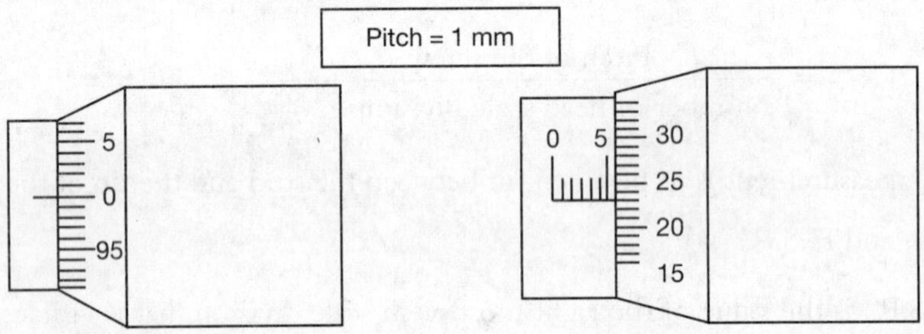

Reading with the tip of the screw in contact with the stud

Reading with the object held between the screw and the stud.

SOLUTION

Given, pitch (p) = 1.0 mm.

Number of circular scale divisions (N) = 100

$\therefore$ Least count $= \dfrac{p}{N} = \dfrac{1.0\text{ mm}}{100} = 0.01$ mm, from the given figure.

P.S.R = 6 mm; H.S.R = 23 divisions

$\therefore$ Diameter of the sphere = P.S.R + (H.S.R × L.C) = 6 + 23 × 0.01 = 6.23 mm

EXAMPLE 1.10 A screw gauge with a negative zero error of 3 divisions is used to measure the diameter of a thin wire. When the wire is placed between the two studs, the main scale reading is 2 mm and the head scale coinciding division is 15. If the least count of the screw gauge is 0.01 mm, find the diameter of the wire.

SOLUTION

Given,

P.S.R = 2 mm; H.S.R = 15; L.C = 0.01 mm

Error = 3 × 0.01 mm = 0.03 mm

Since it's a negative zero error, the true value is always more than the observed value. Hence, the correction is positive:

Correction = + 0.3 mm

$\therefore$ Diameter = P.S.R + (H.S.R × L.C) + Correction

= [2 + (15 × 0.01)] + 0.03

= 2.15 + 0.03

= 2.18 mm

EXAMPLE 1.11

(a) The head scale of a screw gauge has 200 divisions and its thimble moves by 0.5 mm along the main scale for one complete rotation of the screw. Find its least count.

(b) While measuring the thickness of a glass plate using a screw gauge, the main scale reads 2 mm and head scale coinciding division is 57. If the least count of the screw gauge is 0.01 mm, find out the thickness of glass plate (Zero error of the screw gauge is zero).

SOLUTION

(a) $N = 200$; $P = 0.5$ mm

$$\text{L.C} = \frac{P}{N} = \frac{0.5}{200} = \frac{5}{2000} = 0.0025 \text{ mm} = 0.00025 \text{ cm}$$

(b) MSR = 2 mm

H.S.R = 57

L.C = 0.01 mm

Thickness = MSR+ (HSR × LC) = 2 + 57 × 0.01 = 2.57 mm

EXAMPLE 1.12

Suppose the diameter of a small metal rod is measured using a screw gauge, and the reading is found to be 4.287 cm. If we measure the diameter using a standard vernier calliper and an ordinary scale, what would be the reading obtained?

SOLUTION

Vernier Calliper Reading:

The least count of vernier callipers is 0.01 cm. Therefore, the reading that can be taken from a vernier calliper will be up to two decimals.

Rounding 4.287 cm to two decimal places: Diameter = 4.29 cm.

Ordinary Scale Reading:

The least count of an ordinary scale is 0.1 cm. Thus, the reading that can be taken from an ordinary scale is rounded to the nearest tenth.

Rounding 4.287 cm to one decimal place: Diameter = 4.3 cm.

POINTS TO REMEMBER

- ✔ The power to which the units of fundamental quantities are raised to obtain the unit of a physical quantity is known as dimensions of the given quantity. The three fundamental quantities, namely mass, length and time are denoted by M, L and T respectively.
- ✔ Least count (L.C) of a vernier caliper.

  L.C = 1 Main Scale Division (M.S.D.) – 1 Vernier Scale Division (V.S.D.)

  and $\text{L.C} = \dfrac{1\ \text{M.S.D}}{\text{No. of VSD's}}$
- ✔ When the external jaws of a vernier calliper are in contact and if the zeroth division of the main scale is not in contact with the zeroth division of the vernier scale, the vernier calliper is said to have zero error.
- ✔ The pitch of a screw gauge is equal to the distance travelled by the thimble along the main scale for one complete rotation of the head.

  $$\text{Least Count (L.C.)} = \frac{\text{Pitch of the screw}}{\text{The number of head scale divisons } (N)}$$

  $$\text{Observed reading} = \text{MSR} + (\text{HSR} \times \text{LC}).$$
- ✔ If M.S.R is the main scale reading, L.C is the least count and C.V.C.D is the corrected vernier coinciding division, the length of an object is ℓ = M.S.R + (C.V.C.D × L C).
- ✔ If the studs of a screw gauge are in contact, and the zeroth division of the head scale is not in contact with the index line, then the screw gauge is said to have a zero error.
- ✔ When the studs of a screw gauge are in contact, if the zeroth division of the head scale is above the index line, the error is said to be negative and the correction is positive.
- ✔ When the studs of a screw gauge are in contact, if the zeroth division of the head scale is below the index line, the error is said to be positive and the correction is negative.

PRACTICE QUESTIONS CLASSROOM WING

Very Short Answer Type Questions

Directions for questions 1 to 5:
True or false.

1. The length measured by a standard Vernier Calipers is more accurate compared to the length measured by a standard Screw Gauge.

2. The difference between one Main Scale Division (M.S.D.) and one Vernier Scale Division (V.S.D.) of a vernier calipers gives its Least Count (L.C.).

3. One pitch is the distance covered by the tip of the screw for one complete rotation of the head scale.

4. For a Screw Gauge having positive zero error, the measured length is more than that of the actual length.

5. The length measured by Vernier Calipers having negative zero error is greater than that of actual length. So, the correction is positive.

Directions for questions 6 to 17:
Fill in the blanks.

6. The unit of ________ is g cm s^{-2}.

Note: Take the value of 'g' as 10 m s^{-2} wherever required.

7. If the dimensional formula of a physical quantity is [MLT^{-2}], then ____ will be its SI unit?

8. If the length of vernier scale in a standard Vernier calipers is minimum, then the length of the vernier scale is ______.

9. If $\frac{x}{y}$ has no dimensional formula and dimensional formula of x is [$M^1 L^1 T^{-2}$] then y is ________ (write its name).

10. The length of a body measured by a vernier calipers (A) is 4.3 cm. If the length of the same body measured by a vernier calipers 'B' is 4.33 cm and the vernier calipers (A) has no error, then the error in the vernier calipers B is ______.

11. ________ error can be avoided by not rotating the head of the screw gauge in the reverse direction when an object is placed between studs.

12. The distance between index line and zeroth division of head scale when two studs of a screw gauge having no zero error are in contact is ______.

13. If the number of head scale divisions of screw gauge is doubled then its least count ________.

14. The least count of a screw gauge is 0.0002 mm. The tip of the screw advances 0.1 mm when the screw is rotated through 2 rotations. Then the thimble of the screw gauge contains ________ divisions.

15.

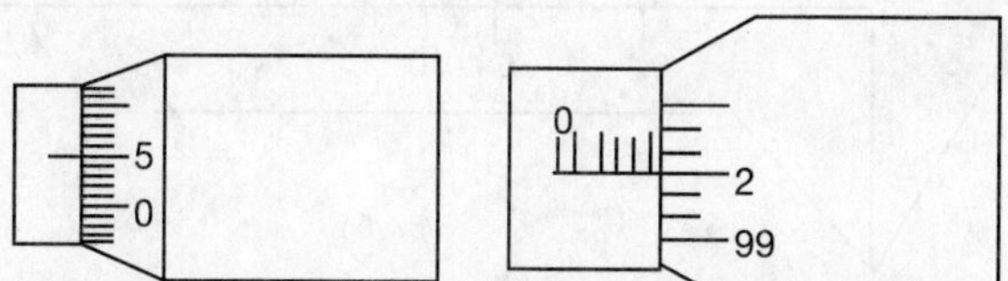

The readings of a screw gauge when two studs are in contact and when sphere is placed between two studs are shown in the above figures (a) and (b) respectively. If the pitch of the screw is 1 mm, then the radius of the sphere is _____ mm.

16. While measuring the diameter of a sphere using a screw gauge, the PSR, HCD are 3 mm and 47 respectively. If the least count of the screw gauge is 0.01 mm, then the diameter of the sphere is ______.

17. When two studs of standard screw gauge are in contact HCD is 56 and one division of the main scale is outside the edge of the head scale, then the zero error is ______.

Directions for questions 18 to 27:
Multiple choice questions.

18. What is the length of the object shown in the figure given below?

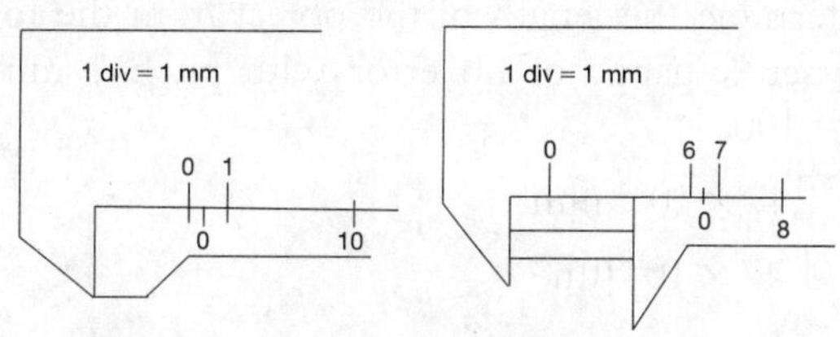

(a) 6.8 mm (b) 7.2 mm
(c) 6.7 mm (d) 6.4 mm

19. If A, B, C and T are displacement, velocity, acceleration and time respectively, then which of the following equations is dimensionally correct?

(a) A = BT (b) B = AT
(c) B = CT (d) Both (a) and (c)

20. Which of the following has the unit equal to kg m^2 s^{-2}?

(a) power (b) energy
(c) force (d) momentum

21. Which of the following is suitable for relative density among the given choices?

(a) $[ML^{-3}]$ (b) $[M^1L^{-3}T^0]$
(c) Both (a) and (b) (d) None of the above

22. The zero error in a Vernier calipers shown in the following diagram is ______.

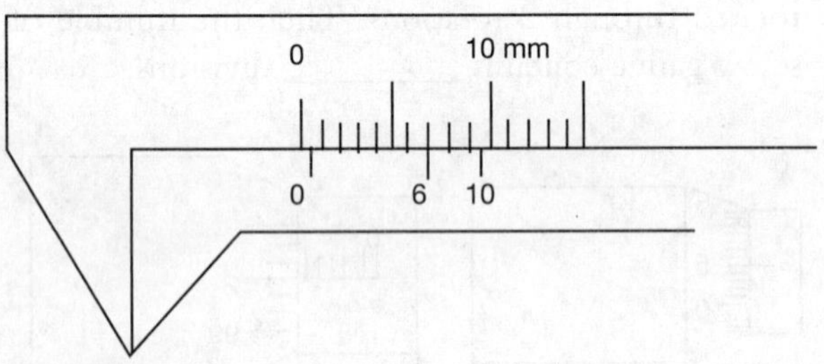

(a) 0.6 mm (b) –0.6 mm
(c) 0.8 mm (d) –0.8 mm

23. Which of these instruments gives an accurate value when the length of an object of 4 cm is measured?

(a) metre scale
(b) screw gauge
(c) vernier calipers
(d) all the above

24. Which of the errors given below is possible in Vernier Calipers and screw gauge both?

(a) zero error
(b) back-lash error
(c) manual error
(d) both (a) and (c)

25. Determine the length of the object from the following screw gauge of no error with pitch 1 mm and N = 100.

(a) 1.47×10^{-4} mm
(b) 1.47×10^{4} μm
(c) 1.47×10^{-7} μm
(d) 1.47×10^{-7} mm

26. Arrange the following steps to determine the diameter of a wire by screw gauge in a proper sequence.

(a) Place the wire between the studs and note down the PSR and HSR.
(b) Determine the zero error if any and find out the zero correction.
(c) Determine the C.H.S.R and determine the length of the object using
L = PSR + CHSR × LC
(d) Determine the pitch of the screw, the number of the head-scale divisions and the least count.

(a) b d c a (b) b d a c
(c) d b a c (d) a b c d

27. Match the following.

Column – A	Column – B
(A) Zeroth division of head scale below index line	a. Negative zero error
(B) Zeroth division of head scale above index line	b. Zero error
(C) Zeroth division of head scale coincides with index line	c. Positive zero error
(D) Correction is negative	d. No zero error

(a) A → a, B → c, C → d, D → c
(b) A → c, B → a, C → d, D → c
(c) A → c, B → a, C → d, D → b
(d) None of the above

Short Answer Type Questions

28. Out of the four equations, $v^2 = as$, $s = ut$, $s = at$ and $s = at^2$, which of the following is dimensionally incorrect?

29. Define fundamental quantity.

30. Give the dimensional formula of density.

31. What is positive zero error of a vernier calipers?

32. When thimble of a screw gauge is given 40 complete rotations, the tip of the screw advances 20 mm and when the studs of the screw gauge are in contact, the 85th division of the head scale is on the index line. What will be the zero correction of the screw gauge?

33. What are the uses of dimensional analysis?

34. Define pitch and give its formula.

35. What is head scale coinciding division (n) in screw gauge?

36. What are the principles behind the working of Vernier Calipers and Screw Gauge?

37. Mention the rules to write units.

38. The notations of physical quantities given below are incorrect. Give the correct notations.

Wrong notations
(a) Force = 10N.s
(b) Impulse = 20ns
(c) Acceleration = 10M/s²

39. The speeds of three vehicles moving in a straight line are 20 m s^{-1}, 90 km h^{-1} and 10^{-14} ly s^{-1} respectively. Arrange them in the ascending order.

40. Give the dimensional formula to the physical quantities having the following units.

(a) newton (b) joule (c) watt

41. What is mass? Write its dimensional formula and units? Is it vector or not and why? Explain.

42. Give the relation between 1 newton and 1dyne.

43. Discuss the types of errors in a screw gauge.

44. Define least count of an instrument in general terms. How can you find the least count of a screw gauge?

45. Differentiate Vernier calipers and screw gauge with at least 4 points.

46. Match the following.

Column – A	Column – B
(A) Time period/ frequency	a. Number of H.S.D. = 50
(B) $Density^2$ × Relative Density	b. $[M^2L^{-6}T^0]$
(C) Acceleration/ $Velocity^2$	c. Number of V.S.D. = 20
(D) $Force^2$/Energy	d. $[M^1L^0T^{-2}]$
(E) Vernier Calipers: L.C. = 0.05 mm; 1 M.S.D.= 1mm	e. $[M^0L^0T^2]$
(F) Screw Gauge: L.C. = 0.02; Pitch = 1 mm	f. $[M^0L^{-1}T^0]$

Essay Answer Type Questions

47. Describe Vernier Calipers with a neat diagram and give the procedure for taking measurement using Vernier Calipers.

48. Describe Screw Gauge with a neat diagram and give the procedure for taking measurement using Screw Gauge.

PRACTICE QUESTIONS COMPETITION WING

Level 1: Apply Your Concepts

1. What is the length of the object shown in the figure given below?

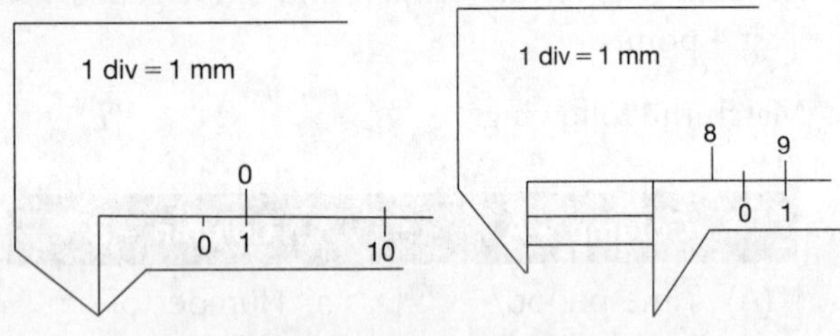

2. If the dimensional formula of a physical quantity is $[MLT^{-1}]$, then what will be its CGS unit?

3. In a vernier caliper, 20th division on the vernier scale coincides with the seventeenth division on the main scale when the two external jaws are in contact. If 1 cm on the main scale is divided into 20 equal parts, then what is the least count of the calipers.

4. Determine the
   (a) least count
   (b) zero error
   (c) zero correction of the vernier calipers shown in figure.

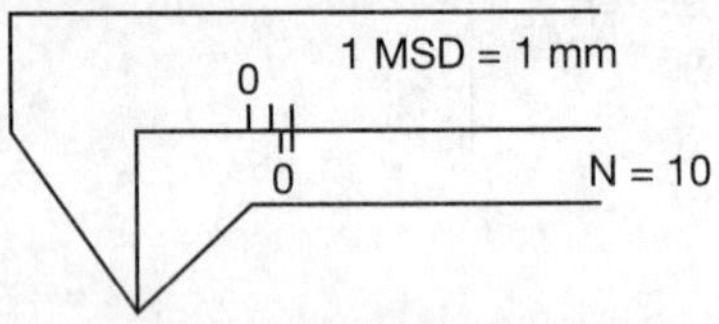

5. In the below figures the zero error of vernier calipers shown in figure (b) is equal to the zero error of vernier calipers shown in figure (a) but in opposite sign. Find the length of the object placed between the jaws of the vernier calipers shown in figure (b).

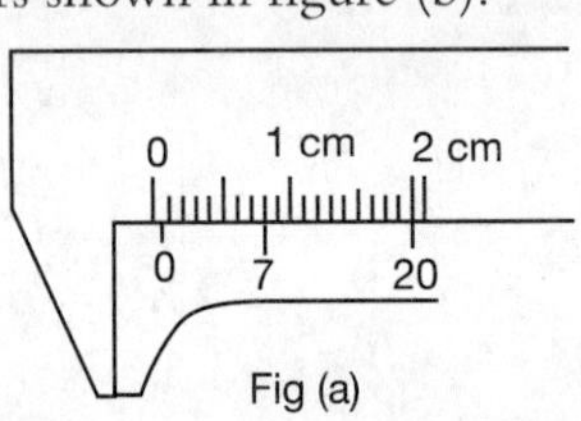

Fig (a)

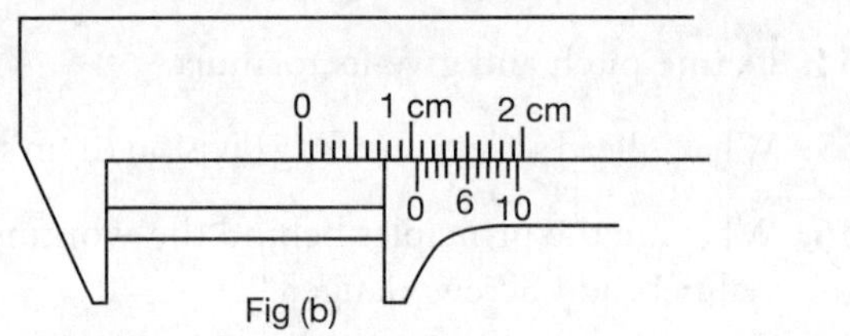

Fig (b)

6.

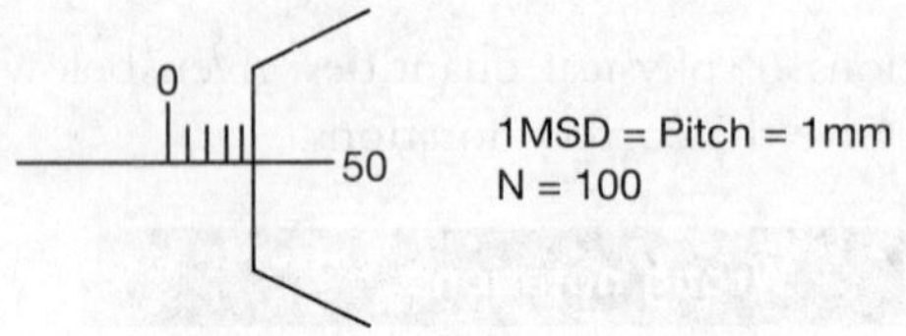

When two studs of a screw gauge are in contact, the divisions of the main scale are outside of the edge as shown above. Find the zero error.

7. If the pitch of the screw of a screw gauge is $^1/_2$ mm and the number of head scale divisions is 100, what is the least count?

8. (a) A screw gauge has 500 divisions on its head scale and the head scale moves 5 mm when rotated 10 times, then determine the pitch and the least count of the screw gauge.

   (b) The pitch of a screw gauge is 0.5 mm and its least count is 0.01 mm. Find the number of divisions on the head scale.

   (c) When the tip of the screw of a screw gauge is in contact with the stud, 96th head scale division coincides with the base line. If the least count of this screw gauge is 0.01 mm then find out the value and nature of correction to be made on observations. (Take the number of divisions on the head scale as 100).

Level 2: Review Your Concepts

9. Out of the four equations, $v = \sqrt{2as}$, $v = at$, $v = st$ and v = as, which equation is dimensionally incorrect?

10. $1\ J\ s^{-1} = 10^7\ g^p\ cm^q\ s^r$. Find p, q, and r values.

11. A screw gauge has a zero error of +0.24 mm when the number of head scale divisions are 100, and the least count is 0.01 mm. Find the head scale coinciding division of head scale with same radius but number head scale divisions are 50 to get the same error (pitch = 1 MSD = 1 mm).

12. An object having a length of 2.07 mm is placed between the jaws of a screw gauge A and another screw gauge B separately. Find the ratio of readings shown by screw gauge A to screw gauge B if zero error of screw gauge A and B are –0.02 mm and 0.08 mm respectively.

13. The main scale reading and head scale coinciding division of a screw gauge (of 1 pitch = 1 mm, and the number of head scale divisions 100) are 8 mm and 12 respectively when an object is placed between studs. If another screw gauge of pitch = 1 mm and the number of head scale divisions 50 is used to find the length of the same object, what is the H.C.D of it?

14. While measuring the diameter of a lead shot using a screw gauge, the pitch scale reading, and the head scale reading were found to be 4.0 mm and 50 respectively. If the least count of the instrument is 0.01 mm and zero error is – 0.45 mm, then what is the diameter of the lead shot?

15. When the thimble of a screw gauge is given 10 complete rotations, the tip of the screw advances 20 mm. When the studs of the screw gauge are in contact, the 90th division of the head scale is on the index line. What is the zero error of the instrument?

16. Determine the diameter of the object from the following diagram.

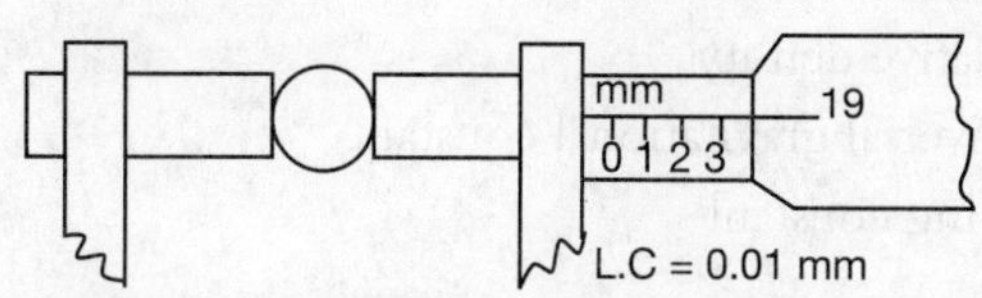

Level 3: Assess Your Concepts

17. Ramu constructed a vernier calipers as shown in the figure to measure the length of an object. When an object of length 10.5 mm is kept between the jaws, then the reading of A is 7.6 mm. Determine the MSR and VCD of B (Both A and B are standard vernier callipers).

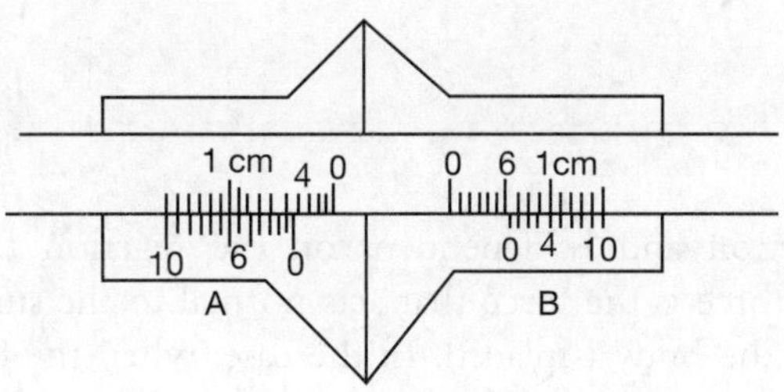

18. A screw gauge, as shown in the figure is used to measure the diameter of a rod. When the Jaws are in contact, the main scale readings on screw A and B are 7 mm and 5 mm respectively and head scale readings of A and B are 27 and 41 respectively. When a rod of diameter 12.53 mm is kept between the jaws, the reading of A is 8.43 mm. Determine the MSR and HCD of B. (Take N = 100, 1 MSD = 1 mm for both screw gauges A and B).

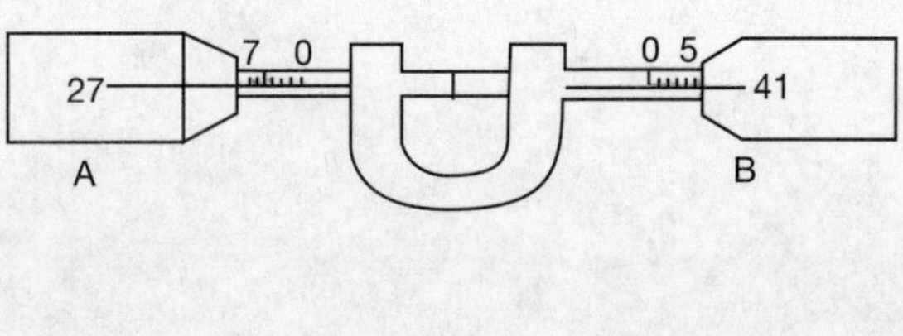

19. A standard vernier calliper with positive zero error of 0.03 cm is used to measure the diameter of a sphere. If the MSR is 5.5 cm and the diameter observed is 5.56 cm, then what is the true VCD?

20. The main scale of a vernier callipers has 10 divisions for each 1 cm and 10 divisions on its vernier scale such that N VSD = (N–1) MSD. What is the least count of the vernier callipers?

21. If the least count of a screw gauge is 0.001 mm and if the screw advances by 0.5 mm for its two complete rotations, how many divisions does the circular scale of the gauge has?

22. A screw gauge with a positive zero error of 5 divisions is used to find the thickness of a glass plate. When the glass plate is held between the two studs, the main scale reading is 6 mm, and the head scale coinciding division is 30. If the least count of the screw gauge is 0.01 mm, then what is the thickness of the glass plate?

23. If 1 MSD of a Vernier calliper is 0.25 mm and its least count is 0.01 mm, then how many divisions does its Vernier scale have?

PRACTICE QUESTIONS JEE-NEET SPECIAL WING

Multiple-Answer Type Questions

***Directions for Questions number 1 to 5:* Each question has FOUR options (A), (B), (C), and (D). ONE OR MORE THAN ONE of these four option(s) is/are the correct answer(s).**

1. Which of the following is (are) dimensionless?
   (a) Refractive index
   (b) Relative density
   (c) Universal gravitational constant
   (d) Spring constant

2. Which of the following can be expressed as newton m^{-2}?
   (a) Pressure
   (b) Longitudinal stress
   (c) Young's modulus
   (d) Viscosity

3. Which of the following is/are the units of mass?
   (a) gf (b) ton
   (c) quintal (d) dyne

4. The main scale division of a given vernier caliper is 1 mm. The vernier calipers give the least count equal to 0.01 cm if
   (a) the length of 10 vernier scale divisions is equal to that of 9 main scale divisions
   (b) the length of 9 vernier scale divisions is equal to that of 10 main scale divisions
   (c) its principle is N VSD = (N – 1) MSD
   (d) 9 mm of the main scale is divided into 10 divisions

5. The least count of a screw gauge is given by
   (a) $\frac{\text{Smallest division on pitch scale}}{\text{No. of divisions on circular scale}}$
   (b) $\frac{\text{Pitch}}{\text{No. of divisions on circular scale}}$
   (c) $\frac{\text{Distance moved by screw}}{\text{No. of rotations} \times \text{No. of divisions on circular scale}}$
   (d) $\frac{\text{Distance moved by screw}}{\text{No. of rotations}}$

Comprehension-Based Questions

***Direction for Questions 6 to 11:* Read the paragraph given below and answer the questions.**

The force acting on a body is a pull or push and its magnitude is given by the product of mass and acceleration. i.e., F = ma. Here mass is a fundamental quantity and acceleration is a derived quantity. When the body is placed on the surface of a table, the force due to gravity, i.e., the weight of the body (which always acts towards the centre of the earth). The surface of the table exerts normal reaction force which balances weight of the body. This reaction force is directly proportional to frictional force. This force which opposes the relative motion between the body and the surface is called friction and is dependent on the reaction force. Reaction force is the force that acts normal to the surface on which the body is placed. In the case, when the body is placed on a horiztontal surface, the magnitude of the normal reaction force is equal to that of weight and its direction is opposite to that of weight.

6. The dimensional formula of acceleration is _______.
   (a) $[M^1 L^1 T^{-2}]$
   (b) $[M^1 L^1 T^{-1}]$
   (c) $[M^0 L^1 T^{-2}]$
   (d) $[M^1 L^0 T^{-2}]$

7. The force acting on the body to bring it to motion, assuming the surface on which it is placed is rough, is directly proportional to ___.
   (a) mass of the body
   (b) weight of the body
   (c) density of the body
   (d) All of these

8. Normal reaction force is a __________.
   (a) fundamental quantity
   (b) derived quantity
   (c) vector quantity
   (d) Both (b) and (c)

9. If W and R are the weight and normal reaction force of a body, then vectorially they are represented as
   (a) $\bar{W} = \bar{R}$
   (b) $\bar{R} = n\bar{W}$
   (c) $\bar{W} = n\bar{R}$
   (d) $\bar{W} = -\bar{R}$

10. The mass of a body is measured using the principle __________.
   (a) principle of masses
   (b) principle of weights
   (c) principle of moments
   (d) principle of torques

11. Using the data given in the previous paragraph, match the following.

Column – A	Column – B
A. If the mass of the body is increased by 4 times	a. dyne
B. CGS unit of normal reaction force	b. acceleration produced is inversely proportional to the mass of the body
C. When a constant force is applied to the body	c. Force applied to move it also increased by 4 times
D. CGS unit of acceleration due to gravity	d. mass × Acceleration due to gravity
E. Magnitude of normal reaction force	e. dyne/g

ANSWER KEYS

Crossword

Across

3. Kelvin 5. Pitch 7. Least count 8. Helical thread
9. Ratchet 10. Zero error

Down

1. Head scale 2. Vernier scale 4. Vernier scale 6. Candela

Classroom Wing

Very Short Answer Type Questions

1. False 2. True 3. True 4. True 5. False
6. Force 7. kg m s^{-2} 8. 9 mm 9. Force
10. + 0.3 mm 11. Back lash 12. Zero 13. Becomes half of initial L.C.
14. 250 15. 2.985 mm 16. 3.47 mm 17. 1.56 mm 18. (c)
19. (d) 20. (b) 21. (d) 22. (a) 23. (d)
24. (d) 25. (b) 26. (c) 27. (b)

Competition Wing

Level 1: Apply Your Concepts

1. 9mm 2. $[MLT^{-1}] \Rightarrow g\ cm\ s^{-1}$ 3. 0.0075 cm
4. (a) 0.1 mm (b) 1.1 mm (c) −1.1 mm 5. 10.25 mm 6. +4.5 mm
7. 0.001 mm 8. (a) P = 0.5 mm; L.C = 0.01 mm (b) 50 (c) +0.04 mm

JEE-NEET SPECIAL WING

Multiple-Answer Type Questions

1. (a, b) 2. (a, b, c) 3. (b, c) 4. (a, c, d) 5. (a, b, c)

Comprehension-Based Questions

6. (c) 7. (a) 8. (d) 9. (d) 10. (c)
11. A-c, B-a, C-b, D-e, E-d

For answer key of Classroom wing and Competition wing, refer to Hints and Solutions

Hints and Explanations

CLASSROOM WING

Very Short Answer Type Questions

1. The length measured by a standard Screw Gauge is more accurate compared to the length measured by a standard Vernier Calipers because Screw Gauge can measure up to of 1 mm.

2. The difference between one Main Scale Division (M.S.D.) and one Vernier Scale Division (V.S.D.) of a vernier calipers gives its Least Count (L.C.)

3. One pitch is the distance covered by the tip of the screw for one complete rotation of the head scale.

4. For a Screw Gauge is having positive zero error, the measured length is more than that of the actual length.

5. The length measured by Vernier Calipers having negative zero error is less than that of actual length. So, the correction is positive.

6. $g\ cm\ s^{-2} \Rightarrow MLT^{-2}$

   $\Rightarrow$ mass × acceleration = Force

7. $[MLT^{-2}] \Rightarrow kg\ m\ s^{-2}$

8. The minimum length of vernier scale = N × VSD

   = 10 × 0.9 mm = 9 mm.

9. Dimensional formula of y is also $M^1L^1T^{-2}$.

   So, y is Force.

10. Error in vernier calipers B = 4.33 – 4.3

    = 0.03 cm or 0.3 mm

    Error in B = + 0.3 mm

11. Back lash error

12. Zero

13. Becomes half of initial L.C.

14. LC = 0.0002 mm

    Distance = 0.1 mm

    Number of rotations = 2

    Let N be the number of divisions on thimble.

    Pitch = 0.05 mm

    $N = \frac{Pitch}{LC} = \frac{0.05}{0.0002}$

    $= \frac{500}{2} = 250$

    N = 250

15. Pitch = 1 mm

    N = 100

    LC = 0.01

    Zero error = (n × LC)

    = 5 × 0.01

    = 0.05 mm

    Diameter of sphere

    = PSR + (n × LC) – error

    = 6 + (2 × 0.01) – 0.05

    = 5.97 mm

    $Radius = \frac{5.97}{2} = 2.985$ mm

16. P.S.R. = 3 mm; H.C.D. = 47; L.C. = 0.01 mm

    Diameter = P.S.R. + (H.C.D. × L.C.) = 3 + (47 × 0.01) = 3.47 mm

17. Screw Gauge has positive zero error as one division of the main scale is outside the edge of the head scale. Therefore, the positive zero error is given by

    Positive zero error = 1 + (n × L.C.) = 1 + (56 × 0.01) = 1 + 0.56 = 1.56 mm

18. Zero error = +(1 – 0.9) = 0.1 cm

    Zero correction = –0.1 cm

    Length = M.S.R. + V.S.R. × L.C + Z.C

    = 6 + (8 × 0.1) + –0.1

    = 6.7 mm

    Hence, the correct option is (c).

19. 1. A = BT

Displacement = Velocity × Time

$= \frac{\text{Displacement}}{\text{Time}} \times \text{Time}$

= Displacement

2. B = AT

Velocity = Displacement × Time

Dimensionally incorrect

3. B = CT

Velocity = Acceleration × Time

$= \frac{\text{Velocity}}{\text{Time}} \times \text{Time} = \text{Velocity}$

Dimensionally correct.

Hence, the correct option is (d).

20. kg m^2 s^{-2} = $[ML^2 T^{-2}]$

⇒ (Mass × acceleration) × length

= Force × Displacement = Energy.

Hence, the correct option is (b).

21. The dimensional formula for relative density is $[M^0 L^0 T^0]$.

Hence, the correct option is (d).

22. $LC = \frac{1 \text{ M.S.D.}}{N} = \frac{1\text{mm}}{10} = 0.1 \text{ mm}$

Positive zero error = (n × LC) = 6 × 0.1 = 0.6 mm.

Hence, the correct option is (a).

23. Metre scale, vernier calipers and screw gauge can measure 4 cm length accurately.

Hence, the correct option is (d).

24. Zero error and manual error

Hence, the correct option is (d).

25. $LC = \frac{1 \text{ mm}}{100} = 0.01 \text{ mm}$

Length = MSR + n × LC

= 14 + (70 × 0.01)

= 14.7 mm = 1.47×10^4 μm

Hence, the correct option is (b).

26. Correct order is d b a c.

Hence, the correct option is (c).

27. Correct match is

A → c, B → a, C → d, D → c.

Hence, the correct option is (b).

Short Answer Type Questions

Note: This is how you should frame your answer covering.

28. $v^2 = as$

LHS = $[LT^{-1}]^2 = [L^{-2} T^{-2}]$

RHS = as = $[LT^{-2}][L] = [L^2 T^{-2}]$

LHS = RHS: Equation is correct

Similarly, $s = ut$

LHS = [L] RHS = $[LT^{-1} T] = [L]$

$s = at^2$

LHS = [L] RHS = $[LT^{-1}] \times [T^2] = [L]$

$s = at$

LHS = [L] RHS = $[LT^{-2}][T] = [LT^{-2}]$

As, LHS ≠ RHS

These three equations are incorrect.

29. A physical quantity that does not depend on other physical quantities is known as fundamental physical quantity.

30. The dimensional formula for density is $[M^1 L^{-3} T^0]$

31. A Vernier Calipers is said to be having positive zero error if the zeroth division of the vernier scale is on the right side of the zeroth division of the main scale.

32. No. of rotations = 40

Distance travelled = 20 M.S.D.

Pitch = 20 M.S.D. = 0.5 mm

$L.C = \frac{0.5}{100} = \frac{5}{1000}$

Zero = error = –15 dvi = –15 × 0.005

Zero correction = +15 × 0.005

= 0.075 mm

33. (i) Relation between different physical quantities can be found using dimensional analysis.

(ii) The correctness of a given equation can be checked using dimensional analysis.

34. The distance travelled by the thimble along the main scale for one complete rotation of the head is called pitch.

$$\text{Pitch} = \frac{\text{Distance travelled by the thimble}}{\text{Number of rotations made by head scale}}$$

35. The division on the head scale that is coinciding with the index line is known as Head scale Coinciding Division (H.C.D.).

36. **Principle of Vernier Calipers:** The principle of a vernier is to make 'N' vernier scale divisions equal to (N – 1) main scale divisions.

Generally, a standard vernier scale is provided with 10 graduations to coincide with 9 main scale divisions, i.e., 10 divisions of the vernier scale measure 9 mm and 1 VSD = 0.9 mm.

Principle of Screw Gauge: A screw gauge works on the principle of a screw in a nut, i.e., when the head of a screw makes one complete rotation then its tip moves by a distance equal to the gap between two successive threads of it called its pitch.

37. **Rules to be Followed in Writing Units**

(i) The symbol for a unit, which is named after a scientist, should start with an upper-case letter.

Example: Newton - N, Joule - J, Pascal - Pa, Kelvin - K, etc.

(ii) The symbol for a unit, which is not named after a person, is written in lower case.

Example: metre - m, mole - mol, second – s.

(iii) If the unit is named after a scientist or not, the full form of the units should start with a lower-case letter.

Example: newton, metre, joule, second, hertz, etc.

(iv) Symbol of a unit should not be in plural form.

Example: 500 metres should be written as 500 m and not 500 ms.

38. Force = 10 N

Impulse = 20 N s

Acceleration = 10 m s^{-2}

39. $V_1 = 20 \text{ m s}^{-1}$

$V_2 = 90 \text{ km h}^{-1} = 90 \times \frac{5}{18} \text{ m s}^{-1} = 25 \text{ m s}^{-1}$

$V_3 = 10^{-14} \times 9.46 \times 10^{15} \text{ m s}^{-1} = 94.6 \text{ m s}^{-1}$

$V_1 < V_2 < V_3$

$20 \text{ m s}^{-1} < 90 \text{ km h}^{-1} < 10^{-14} \text{ ly s}^{-1}$

40. (a) Newton is unit of force and its dimensional formula is $[M^1 L^1 T^{-2}]$.

(b) Joule is unit of work or energy and its dimensional formula is $[M^1 L^2 T^{-2}]$.

(c) Watt is unit of power and its dimensional formula is $[M^1 L^2 T^{-3}]$.

41. Mass: The amount of matter contained in a body is called mass.

Dimensional formula of mass is $[M^1L^0T^0]$ or [M]. Units: kilogram and gram.

It is a scalar because it has only magnitude but no direction.

42. $1 \text{ N} = 1 \text{ kg} \times 1 \text{ m s}^{-2} = 1000 \text{ g} \times 100 \text{ cm s}^{-2} = 10^5 \text{ cm s}^{-2} = 10^5$ dyne.

43. (1) **Positive Zero Error**: If the zeroth division of the circular scale is below the reference line of the main scale, when the tip and stud are in contact, the error is said to be positive error.

(2) **Negative Zero Error**: If the zeroth division of the circular scale is above the reference line of the main scale when the tip and stud of screw gauge are in contact, then the error is said to be negative zero error.

(3) **Back-lash Error**: If the tip of screw does not move backward for a part of rotation of head in reverse direction. It is called back-lash error.

44. The smallest measurement that can be done by an instrument is called its least count.

$$\text{Least count of a screw gauge} = \frac{\text{Pitch}}{\text{Number of head scale divisions}}$$

45. i. Least count of vernier caliper is 0.1 mm but least count of screw gauge is 0.01 mm.

ii. In a vernier caliper there is a vernier scale but in a screw gauge there is head scale.

iii. A screw gauge gives more accurate values than those of vernier calipers.

iv. In a vernier caliper an object is placed between the jaws, in a screw gauge, the object is placed between the stud and the tip.

46. A – e; B – b; C – f; D – d; E – c; F – a

Essay Answer Type Questions

Note: This is how you should frame your answer covering.

47. **Description of a Vernier Calipers**

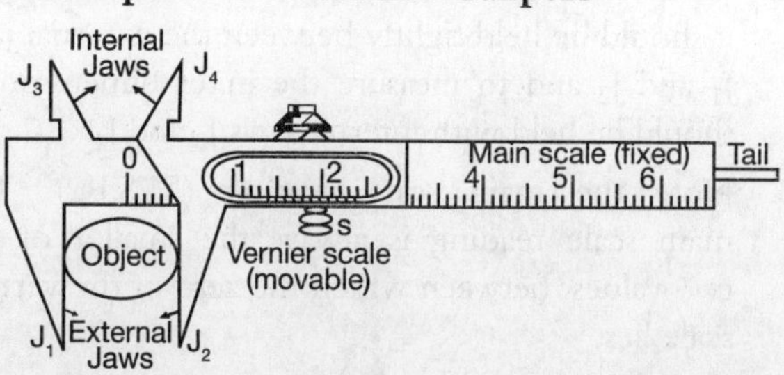

(i) **Main Scale:** The main scale is generally a 15 cm long thin strip made up of steel. The main scale is etched in mm. This scale is a fixed scale.

(ii) **Vernier Scale:** A vernier scale is a movable scale made up of steel. It can slide along the main scale and 10 divisions are marked on the vernier scale, such that the 10 vernier scale divisions coincide with 9 main scale divisions in case of a standard vernier caliper. A tightening screw (S) is attached to the vernier scale. With the help of the tightening screw, vernier scale can be fixed in any desired position along the main scale.

(iii) **External Jaws (J_1, J_2):** The jaws J_1 and J_2 are called external jaws. By using these external jaws, we can find the external dimensions of a sphere, a cylinder, etc., by fixing the object between these jaws. The jaw J_1 is fixed to the main scale, called fixed jaw and the jaw J_2 is fixed to vernier scale, called movable jaw.

(iv) **Internal Jaws (J_3, J_4):** The jaws J_3 and J_4 are together known as internal jaws. These jaws are used to measure the internal dimensions of an object such as the internal diameter of a hollow cylinder. The jaw J_3 is fixed to the main scale and is called the fixed internal jaw, the jaw J_4 is fixed to the vernier scale and is called the movable internal jaw.

(v) **Tail:** It is used to measure the depth of cylinders or hollow tubes. It is connected to the vernier scale from behind, which slides back and forth along with the vernier scale.

Procedure for taking a measurement using a Vernier Calipers

1. Determine the least count of the vernier calipers:

   Least count (L.C.) = 1 M.S.D. – 1 V.S.D.

   = 1 mm – 0.9 mm = 0.1 mm = 0.01 cm

   $$\text{Least count (L.C.)} = \frac{1\text{ M.S.D.}}{\text{No of V.S.Ds}} = \frac{1\text{ mm}}{10}$$

   = 0.1 mm = 0.01 cm

2. To measure the external dimensions of an object it should be held tightly between the external jaws J_1 and J_2 and to measure the inner dimensions it should be held with internal jaws J_3 and J_4.

3. Note the main scale reading (M.S.R.). The main scale reading is always the smaller of the two values, between which the zero of the vernier scale lies.

4. Note the vernier-scale division which coincides with any main scale division. This is known as vernier coinciding division (VCD).

5. The length of rod, AB = $(y - x) = (z - x) + (y - z)$ $= (z - x) + (w - z) - (w - y)$

   = M.S.R. + (V.C.D. × M.S.D.) – (V.C.D. × V.S.D.)

   = M.S.R. + V.C.D. (M.S.D. – V.S.D.)

   ($\because$ L.C = 1 M.S.D – 1 V.S.D)

   $\therefore$ Total reading (Length of the rod, AB) = M.S.R. + (V.C.D. × L.C.).

In case of any zero error in the instrument, the corresponding correction is to be added to the measurement calculated in step 5.

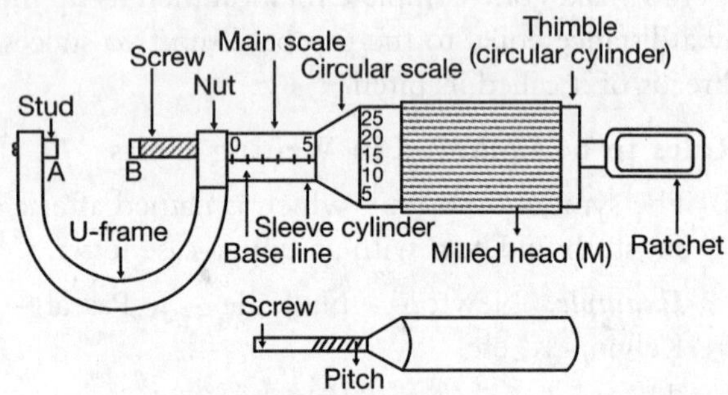

Screw gauge

48. Description of Screw Gauge

1. It has a U - shaped metallic frame with a fixed stud A and a nut at the other end.
2. The nut is attached with a coaxial hollow cylinder called sleeve cylinder.
3. Through this cylinder and nut, a long screw of 1 mm pitch having milled head (M), passes and can slide through them by the rotation of the head.
4. A barrel tapered at one end is attached with the milled head of the screw at the other end and forms a jacket to sleeve. This is called the thimble.
5. On the sleeve cylinder a line called index line graduated in mm (equal to the pitch of the screw) is drawn. This is called main scale or pitch scale.
6. The tapered end of the thimble is engraved with N-equally spaced divisions and is called head or thimble or circular scale.
7. Screw gauges are also provided with a ratchet attached to the screw by a spring. When the tip of the screw comes in contact with the object or stud, the spring releases the head from the spindle and further rotation of the head would not result in the movement of the screw.

Procedure for taking a measurement using Screw Gauge

1. Determine zero error (Z.E) and the zero correction (Z.C) of the screw gauge.
2. To determine the pitch of the screw of a screw gauge:

   Pitch = Distance travelled by the thimble along the main scale for one complete rotation of the head.

   $$= \frac{\text{Distance of the tip advances for } n \text{ complete rotations}}{n}$$

3. To determine the least count:

   $$\text{Least count (L.C.)} = \frac{\text{Pitch of the screw}}{\text{Number of head scale divisions } (N)}$$

4. Hold the item, whose measurement is to be taken, in between the stud and the tip of the screw.
5. Note down the M.S.R and H.S.R.

   The main scale reading (M.S.R) is the value of the right most pitch scale division that is visible outside the barrel. In the figure below, 'Z' is the M.S.R. The main scale reading is also known as Pitch scale reading (P.S.R).

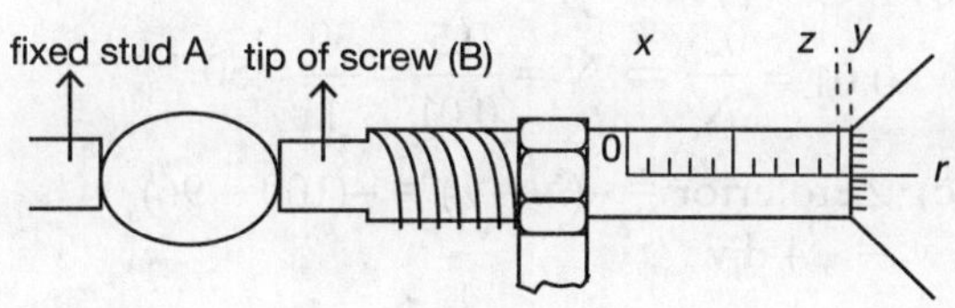

H.S.R. (Head scale reading) is the division of head scale coinciding with base line (index line). In the above figure '*r*' is the H.S.R.

Thus, the observed reading = $xy = (z - x) + (y - z) = z$ M.S.D + ($r \times$ L.C.)

= M.S.R. + (H.S.R. × L.C.)

6. Determine the corrected head scale reading.

   C.H.S.R. = H.S.R. + Z.C.

Repeat the experiment by placing the different parts of the object between the studs and note down the H.S.R and M.S.R in each case.

The readings obtained can be tabulated in the table given below, and the diameter of the sphere is measured in each case as M.S.R + (C.H.S.R × L.C.)

S. No	P.S.R/ M.S.R.	H.S.R.	C.H.S.R × L.C.	Diameter, d = M.S.R + (C.H.S.R × L.C)

The average value of the diameter of the object is determined to reduce the experimental errors.

Competition Wing

Level 1: Apply Your Concepts

1. Zero error = −0.9 mm, zero correction = +0.9 mm

Length = M.S.R. + V.S.R. × L.C + ZC

$= 8 \text{ mm} + 1 \times 0.1 + (0.9) = 8.1 + 0.9$

= 9 mm.

2. $[MLT^{-1}] \Rightarrow g\ cm\ s^{-1}$

3. 20th division on the vernier scale coincide with seventeenth division on the main scale

20 VSD = 17 MSD

$1 \text{ VSD} = \frac{17}{20} \text{MSD} \quad (1)$

1 cm on the main scale is divided into 20 parts

20 parts → 1 cm

$1 \text{ part} \rightarrow \frac{1}{20} \text{ cm} = 0.05 \text{ cm}$

1 MSD = 0.05 cm

$\text{L.C.} = 1 \text{ MSD} - 1 \text{ VSD} = 0.05 \text{ cm} - \frac{17}{20} \times 1 \text{ MSD}$

$= 0.05 \text{ cm} - \frac{17}{20 \times 20} \text{ cm} = 0.05 \text{ cm} - \frac{0.17}{4} \text{ cm}$

L.C. = 0.05 cm − 0.0425 cm = 0.0075 cm.

4 (a) $\text{Least count} = \frac{1 \text{ MSD}}{N} = \frac{1 \text{ mm}}{10} = 0.1 \text{ mm}$

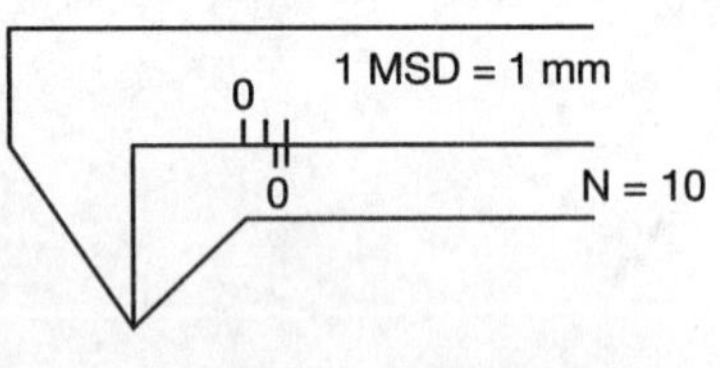

In the given figure 1 mm is towards left and the first division of the vernier scale is in contact with one of the divisions on the vernier scale.

(b) Zero error = 1 + 1 × 0.1 = 1.1 mm

(c) Zero correction = − 1.1 mm

5. From figure A

$\text{LC} = \frac{1 \text{ MSD}}{N} = \frac{1 \text{ mm}}{20} = 0.05 \text{ mm}$

Zero error = + (n × LC) = 7 × 0.05 = 0.35 mm

correction = −0.35 mm

By figure (b)

Length = MSR + (n × LC) − 0.35 = 10 + (6 × 0.1) − 0.35 = 10.25 mm

6. Positive zero error

$= 4 + (n \times \text{LC}) = 4 + 50 \times 0.01 = +4.5 \text{ mm}$

7. $\text{L.C} = \frac{P}{N} = \frac{0.5}{100} = \frac{5}{1000} = 0.005 \text{ mm}$

The number of divisions on the head scale (n) = 500.

Distance moved by the tip of the screw for 10 rotations of head = 5 mm.

10 rotation → 5 mm

1 rotation − ?

∴ Distance moved by the tip of the screw for 1 complete rotation of the head of the screw is called pitch of the screw.

$\text{Pitch} = \frac{5 \text{ mm}}{10} = 0.5 \text{ mm}$

$\text{Least count (L.C.)} = \frac{\text{Pitch}}{\text{Number of divisions on head scale}}$

$= \frac{0.5 \text{ mm}}{500} = 0.001 \text{ mm}$

8. (a) P = 0.5 mm

L.C = 0.01 mm

(b) L.C = P/N

$0.01 = \frac{0.5}{N} \Rightarrow N = \frac{0.5}{0.01} = \frac{50}{1} = 50$

(c) Zero error = −(N − n) = −(100 − 96) = −4 div

L.C = 0.01 mm

∴ Zero error = −4 × 0.01 = −0.04 mm and zero correction = + 0.04 mm

Level 2: Review Your Concepts

Note: This is how you should frame your answer covering.

9. $v = \sqrt{2as}$ is correct

$v = at$

$\text{LHS} = [LT^{-1}]$

$\text{RHS} = [LT^{-2}] \times [T] = [LT^{-1}]$

$v = st$

$\text{LHS} = [LT^{-1}]$

$\text{RHS} = [LT]$

$v = as$

LHS = $[LT^{-1}]$

RHS = $[LT^{-2}] \times [LT]$

LHS ≠ RHS.

10. $1\ J\ s^{-1} = 10^7\ g^p\ cm^q\ s^r$

$\Rightarrow 1 kg\ m^2 s^{-2}\ s^{-1} = 10^7\ g^p\ cm^q\ s^r$

$\Rightarrow 10^3\ g \times (10^2 cm)^2\ s^{-3} = 10^7\ g^p\ cm^q s^r$

$\Rightarrow 10^7\ g^1\ cm^2\ s^{-3} = 10^7\ g^p\ cm^q\ s^r$

By above equation,

$\therefore p = 1, q = 2, r = -3$

11. $n \times LC = +$ zero error

$n \times 0.01 = 0.24$

$n = 24$

HCD = 24

$$LC = \frac{1\text{ mm}}{50} = 0.02\text{ mm}$$

$n \times LC = 0.24$

$$n = \frac{0.024}{0.02} = \frac{24}{2} = 12$$

HCD = 12

12. The actual length of an object = 2.07 mm

$ZE_A = -0.02$ mm

$ZE_B = +0.08$ mm

$R_A = 2.07 - 0.02 = 2.05$

$R_B = 2.07 + 0.08 = 2.15$

$$\frac{R_A}{R_B} = \frac{2.05}{2.15} = \frac{41}{43}$$

$R_A : R_B = 41 : 43$

13. I case

1 MSD = 1 mm, $N = 100$

MSR = 8 mm, $n = 12$

$$LC = \frac{1\text{ mm}}{100} = 0.01\text{ mm}$$

Length = MSR + $n \times$ LC

= 8 + (12 × 0.01)

= 8.12 mm

II case

Length = 8.12 mm

1 MSD = 1 mm

$N = 50$

$$LC = \frac{1\text{ mm}}{50} = 0.02\text{ mm}$$

Length = MSR + $n \times L$

8.12 = MSR + ($n \times$ LC)

$\therefore$ MSR = 8 mm

$n \times LC = 0.12$

$$n = \frac{0.12}{0.02} = 6$$

VCD = n = 6

14. Pitch scale reading (PSR) = 4.0 mm.

Head scale reading (HSR) = 50.

Least count (L.C.) = 0.01 mm

Zero error = –0.45 mm; Correction = +0.45 mm

Diameter = P.S.R. + H.S.R. × L.C. + correction
= 4.0 mm + 50 × 0.01 mm + 0.45 mm
= (4 + 0.5) mm + 0.45 mm = (4.5 + 0.45) mm = 4.95 mm

15. Number of rotations = 10

Distance travelled = 20 M.S.D.

$$\text{Pitch} = \frac{\text{Distance travelled}}{\text{Number of rotations}} = \frac{20}{10} = 2\text{ mm}$$

$$L.C = \frac{2\text{ mm}}{100} = 0.02\text{ mm}$$

$\therefore$ zero error = –10 div = –10 × 0.02

= –0.20 mm

16. H.S.R = 19 div

P.S.R = 3 mm

L.C = 0.01 mm

Diameter = PSR + (HSR × L.C) = 3 + (19 × 0.01) = 3 + 0.19 = 3.19 mm

Level 3: Assess Your Concepts

Note: This is how you should frame your answer covering.

17. From the figure, initial reading of A

$(R_{A1}) = 4.6$ mm

Initial reading of B

$R_{B1} = 6.4$ mm

When object is placed between two jaws of A and B

Reading on A = 7.6 mm

Part of length of object measured by A = 7.6 mm – 4.6 mm = 3 mm

Part of length of object measured by B 10.5 – 3 = 7.5

New reading B

$R_B = 6.4 + 7.5 = 13.9$

$\therefore MSR_B = 13$ mm and

VCD = 9

18. $R_{A1} = 7 + (27 \times 0.01)$

= 7.27 mm

$R_{B1} = 5 + (41 \times 0.01)$

= 5.41 mm

When an object is placed between studs

$R_{A2} = 8.43$ mm given,

The length contributed by A to place the object is

= 8.43 – 7.27 = 1.16 mm

Then, the length given by B is

= 12.53 – 1.16 = 11.37 mm

$\therefore R_B = 5.41 + 11.37$

= 16.78 mm

MSR = 16 mm

N × LC = 0.78

$$N = \frac{0.78}{0.01} = 78$$

∴ MSR = 16 mm, HCD = 78

19. Given, positive zero error of the vernier calipers = + 0.03

MSR = 5.5 cm

Total Reading (diameter), observed = 5.56 cm

∴ Actual reading = Observed reading – Error = 5.56 cm – 0.03 cm = 5.53 cm

We have,

Total actual reading (d) = MSR + (VCD×LC)

⇒ 5.53 = [5.5 + (VCD × 0.01)]

⇒ 5.53 – 5.5 = (VCD × 0.01)

$$\Rightarrow 0.03 = (VCD \times 0.01) \Rightarrow VCD = \frac{0.03}{0.01} = 3$$

20. No. of division for 1 cm of main scale = 10

$$\therefore \text{One main scale division (1MSD)} = \frac{1cm}{10}$$

= 0.1 cm = 1 mm

No. of vernier scale divisions, N = 10

Principle of vernier callipers is N VSD = (N-1) MSD

$$\therefore \text{One vernier scale division (1VSD)} = \frac{N-1}{N}\text{ MSD}$$

$$= \frac{10-1}{10} \times 1 \text{ mm} = 0.9 \text{ mm}$$

Least count = 1MSD – 1VSD = 1 mm – 0.9 mm = 0.1 mm

21. Given the least count of the screw gauge, LC = 0.001 mm

Screw advances by 0.5 mm for its two complete rotations.

Hence, the pitch of the screw, p = 0.5 mm/2 = 0.25 mm

Let N be the number of divisions on the circular scale of the gauge.

Least count of the screw gauge,

$$\text{L.C.} = \frac{p}{N} \Rightarrow N = \frac{p}{\text{L.C.}} = \frac{0.25\,\text{mm}}{0.001\,\text{mm}} = 250$$

22. Given, P.S.R = 6 mm, H.S.R = 30, L.C = 0.01 mm

Error = 5 × 0.01 mm = 0.05 mm

∴ Correction = –0.05 mm

∴ Thickness of the glass plate = P.S.R + (H.S.R × L.C) + correction

= 6 + 30 × 0.01 – 0.05 = 6 + 0.30 – 0.05 = 6.25 mm

23. Given, the least count of the Vernier callipers, L.C. = 0.01 mm

Value of 1 MSD of the callipers = 0.25 mm

We have, LC = 1 MSD – 1 VSD · 1 VSD = 1 MSD – LC = 0.25 mm – 0.01 mm = 0.24 mm

We know, N VSD = (N–1) MSD · 1 VSD = $\frac{N-1}{N}$ MSD · 0.24 mm = $\frac{N-1}{N}$ ×0.25 mm

$$\Rightarrow \frac{N-1}{N} = \frac{24}{25} \Rightarrow 1 - \frac{1}{N} = \frac{24}{25}$$

$$\Rightarrow \frac{1}{N} = 1 - \frac{24}{25} = \frac{1}{25} \Rightarrow N = 25$$

Alternately,

If N VSD = (N–1) MSD · LC = 1MSD / N · N = 1 MSD / LC = 0.25 mm/ 0.01 mm = 25

JEE-NEET SPECIAL WING

Multiple-Answer Type Questions

1. Refractive index and relative density are the ratios of similar quantities.

i.e., Refractive index $= \dfrac{\text{Velocity of light in vacuum (c)}}{\text{Velocity of light in medium (v)}}$

Relative density $= \dfrac{\text{Density of substance} - 1}{\text{Density of substance} - 2}$

Therefore, both quantities do not have units. Hence, no dimensional formula for them.

Hence, the correct option are (a, b)

2. We have, Pressure $= \dfrac{\text{Force}}{\text{Area}}$

$\rightarrow$ SI unit is newton m^{-2}

Now, Longitudinal stress $= \dfrac{\text{Force}}{\text{Area}}$

$\rightarrow$ SI unit is newton m^{-2}

Now, Young's modulus $= \dfrac{\text{Stress}}{\text{Strain}}$

As strain does not have unit, SI unit of Young's modulus is newton m^{-2}

Hence, the correct option are (a, b, c)

3. Practical units of mass are ton (1000 kg), quintal (100 kg)

Hence, the correct option are (b, c)

4. Given, the main scale division of a given vernier caliper is 1 mm.
The least count of the vernier callipers = 0.01 cm
To get the least count 0.01 cm
the length of 10 vernier scale divisions should be equal to that of 9 main scale divisions
i.e., N VSD = (N – 1) MSD
9 mm of the main scale is divided into 10 divisions.

Hence, the correct option are (a, c, d)

5. For a screw gauge,
Pitch = Smallest division on the pitch scale

Pitch $= \dfrac{\text{Distance moved by screw}}{\text{No. of rotations}}$

Least count $= \dfrac{\text{Pitch}}{\text{No. of divisions on circular scale}}$

$= \dfrac{\text{Smallest division on pitch scale}}{\text{No. of divisions on circular scale}}$

$= \dfrac{\text{Distance moved by screw}}{\text{No. of rotations} \times \text{No. of divisions on circular scale}}$

Hence, the correct option are (a, b, c)

Comprehension-Based Questions

6. The dimensional formula of acceleration is $[M^0 L^1 T^{-2}]$.

Hence, the correct option is (c)

7. The force required to set the body at rest on the table to motion must at least be little greater than the static friction between the body and the surface.
The static friction in this case depends on the normal force, which again depends on the weight of the body. Weight of the body is given by 'mg', where 'g' is acceleration due to gravity and is constant at a given place.
The coefficient of friction (μ) between the body and the surface is also constant.
Hence, the magnitude of the force required to put the body at rest on the surface to motion, F = (μ)mg.
As 'μ' and 'g' are constant, the force is proportional to the mass of the body. body.

Hence, the correct option is (a)

8. Normal reaction force is a derived quantity and vector quantity.

Hence, the correct option is (d)

9. If W and R are the weight and normal reaction force of a body, then vectorially they are represented as $\bar{W} = -\bar{R}$.

Hence, the correct option is (d)

10. The mass of a body is measured using the principle called principle of moments.

Hence, the correct option is (c)

11. If the mass of the body is increased by 4 times, then the force applied to move it also increased by 4 times. i.e., **A → c**
CGS unit of normal reaction force is dyne. i.e., **B → a**
When a constant force is applied to the body, the acceleration produced is inversely proportional to the mass of the body. i.e., **C → b**
CGS unit of acceleration due to gravity is dyne/g. i.e., **D → e**
Magnitude of normal reaction force = mass × Acceleration due to gravity. i.e., **E → d**

Unit II

Mechanics

In this Unit

CHAPTER

2

Dynamics

Remember

Before beginning this chapter, you should be able to:

- State Newton's three laws of motion.
- Understand the different factors that affect the friction, the advantages and disadvantages of friction.
- Study how energy is conserved and to understand the term power..
- Learn the terms associated with a simple pendulum and to verify the laws of simple pendulum.

Key Ideas

After completing this chapter, you should be able to:

- Learn laws of motion and their application in mechanics.
- Understand the terms work, energy and power and to learn the different factors affecting them.
- State some laws such as Law of conservation of momentum, Newton's universal law of gravitation, Principle of moments, Principle of orbiting satellite, etc..
- Study the different terms associated with the working of simple machines and to understand their working.
- Find differences between centripetal force and centrifugal force and study their applications in everyday life.
- Understand the different terms related to circular motion.

Scientific Crypt

A Tribute to Sir Isaac Newton (1643 – 1727)

Who discovered the concept of universal law of gravitation and laws of motion? Who invented the first practical reflecting telescope? Who along with Gottfried Leibniz was responsible for the development of calculus? Who gave the generalized binomial theorem? Surely all of us must have got it right, it is none other than Sir Issac Newton. He was a mathematician, physicist and astronomer. He was also an alchemist and theologian. His work "Mathematical Principles of Natural Philosophy", published in 1687, laid the foundation for most of the classical mechanics that we know today. In physics, Newton contributed to classical mechanics, built the first practical reflecting telescope, formulated an empirical law to study the speed of sound. In mathematics, he was instrumental in the development of the concept of calculus and also contributed to the study of power series. The epitaph written by the english poet, Alexander Pope is a true tribute to Newton's accomplishments, the epitaph reads: Nature and nature's laws lay hid in night; God said "Let Newton be" and all was light. While the humble Newton remarked "I do not know what I may appear to the world, but to myself I seem to have been only like a boy playing on the sea-shore, and diverting myself in now and then finding a smoother pebble or a prettier shell than ordinary, whilst the great ocean of truth lay all undiscovered before me".

FUN TIME

CROSSWORD

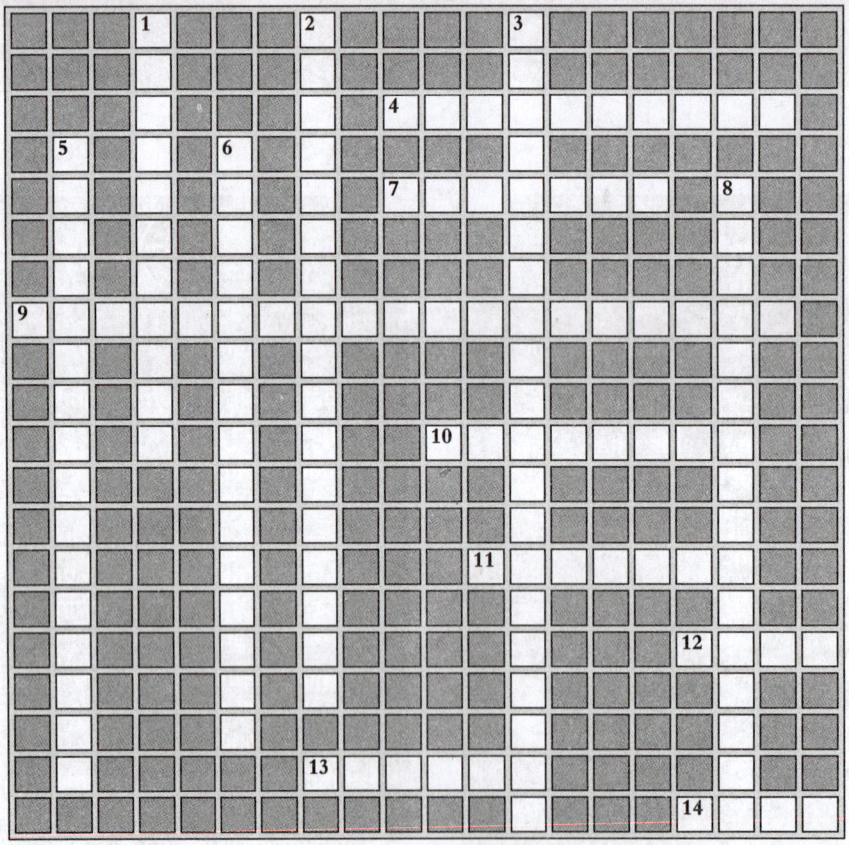

Across

4. The ratio of mechanical advantage of a simple machine to its velocity ratio.
7. Fixed part of a simple machine around which other parts rotate.
9. Cylinder taking rest on its curved surface.
10. Example of simple machine which act as a 1st and 2nd order lever.
11. Change in the momentum.
12. Change in kinetic energy.
13. The ratio of load to mechanical advantage.
14. C.G.S unit of force.

Down

1. To and fro motion of a particle.
2. For every action there is an equivalent or equal and opposite reaction.
3. The sum of clockwise moments is equal to the sum of anti-clockwise moments.
5. Angle made by the outer edge of the road with inner edge.
6. The force which always acts perpendicular to the surfaces which are in contact.
8. The ratio of angular displacement to the time taken.

INTRODUCTION

Dynamics deals with the effect of forces on bodies and is an important branch of physics. Newton's laws of motion relate the type of motion of the body that results from the action of the forces and is of great importance.

SECTION A: WORK, POWER AND ENERGY

When a force acts on a body causing the body to be displaced, then work is said to be done by the force.

When we try to push a wall, the wall does not move even a bit, i.e., there is no displacement and no work is done. Thus, work is done only if a force acts on a body and if the body is displaced. Hence, work done in a body is a product of force applied on it and displacement of the body in the direction of force.

Work

Work done is directly proportional to the force applied on the body.

$$W \propto \vec{F} \tag{2.1}$$

Mathematically, this can be expressed as, Work done is directly proportional to displacement of the body.

$$W \propto \vec{s} \tag{2.2}$$

From equations (2.1) and (2.2), and keeping in mind that work is a **scalar quantity.**

$$W \propto \vec{F}.\vec{s}$$

$$W = k\left(\vec{F}.\vec{s}\right)$$

where, k is proportionality constant. By defining the unit of work, k is taken as one.

Unit Work

When a unit force acting an a body displaces it through one unit, then the work done is one unit. Thus, $k = 1$. If $F = 1$ unit and $s = 1$ unit, then, $W = 1$ unit and $k = 1$.

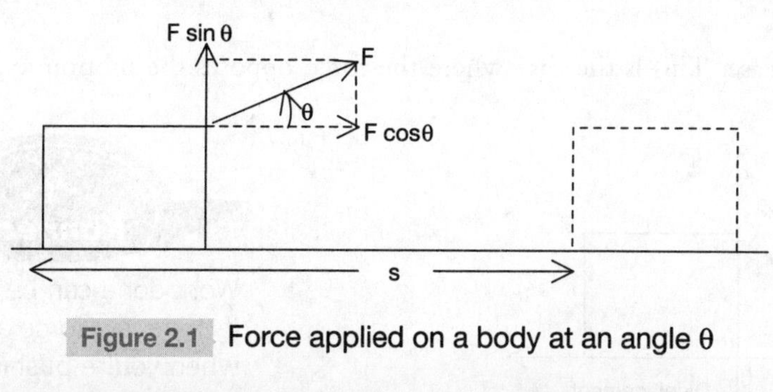

Figure 2.1 Force applied on a body at an angle θ

Info Bytes!

The unit of work in the International System of Units (SI) is the joule, named after the physicist James Prescott Joule.

If the direction of applied force on a body makes an angle θ with the direction of its displacement, then the component of the force along the direction of displacement is $F \cos\theta$, and the work done is

$$W = F\cos\theta \times s$$

$$W = F \times s\cos\theta$$

OR

Thus, the work is said to done when a force or its component acting on a body displaces it in its direction.

$$W = F \times s \cos\theta$$

or

$$W = \vec{F}.\vec{s}$$

where, $\vec{F}.\vec{s} = Fs \cos\theta$.

Thus, work is the dot product of force and displacement since work is a scalar quantity. Dot product of two vectors is a scalar.

Special Cases

Case (i)

If the displacement is in the direction of force, then $\theta = 0°$ and $\cos 0° = 1$,

$$W = Fs \cos\theta$$

$$W = Fs$$

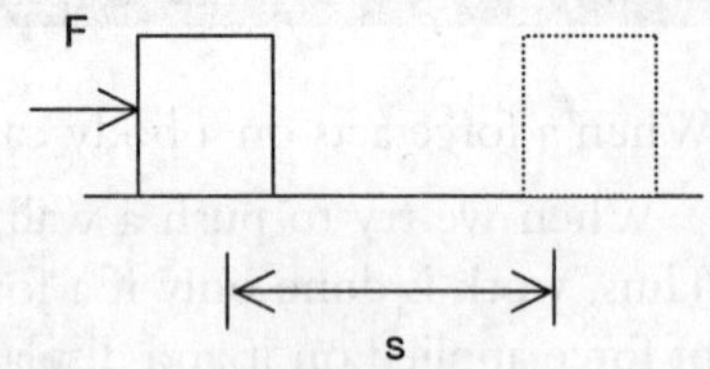

Figure 2.2

Example: In case of a horse pulling a cart, force exerted by the horse on the cart and the displacement of the cart are in the same direction.

Case (ii)

If the displacement vector is at right angles to the applied force, then, $\theta = 90°$.

$$W = Fs \cos 90°$$

$$W = 0 \text{ (zero)}$$

$\because \quad \cos 90° = 0$

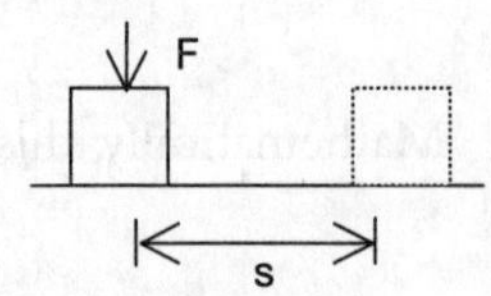

Figure 2.3

Example: A porter walking with a load on his head. Work done by the porter is equal to zero.

Case (iii)

If the displacement is along a direction opposite to that of the force, then $\theta = 180°$.

$$W = Fs \cos 180°$$

$$W = -Fs$$

$(\because \cos 180° = -1)$

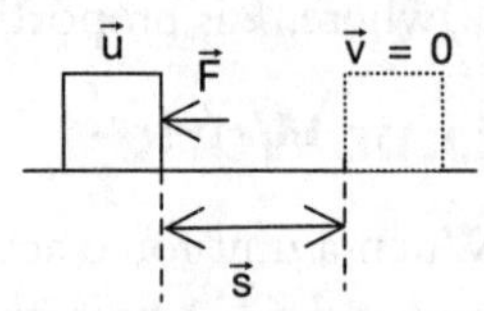

Figure 2.4

Work done by the force is negative in this case. This is the case where the force opposes the motion, e.g., the truck driver applies brakes to his moving vehicle.

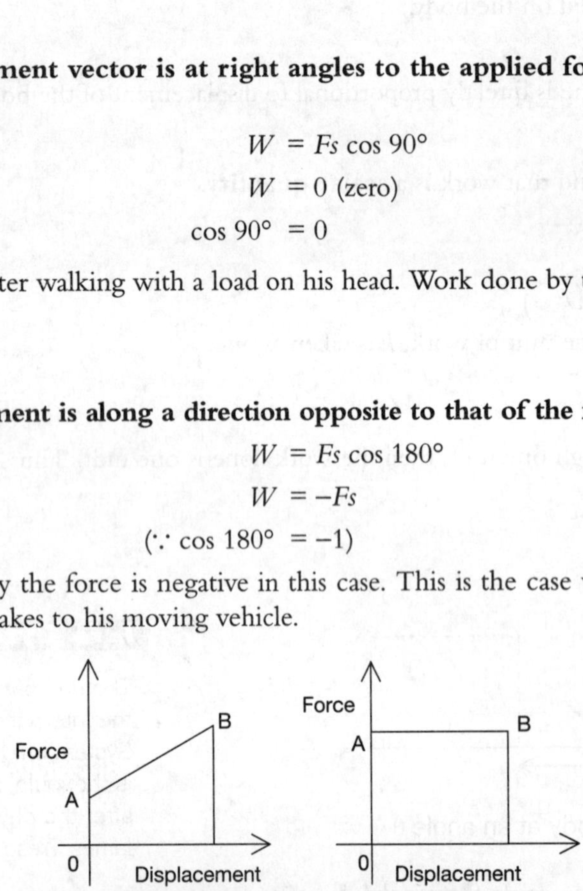

Figure 2.5 Graphs of work done

Konnect

Work done can be zero even if there is a force applied, like when you're pushing a wall but it's not moving.

If the force varies with displacement, then the work done is obtained by plotting a graph. Force is plotted along the Y-axis and displacement along the X-axis. The area enclosed by the curve gives the work done. If a constant force acts on the body, then the graph is a straight line parallel to *X*-axis. Work done by constant force is equal to the area of rectangle formed in the *F*–*s* graph.

Work Done by the Force of Gravity

All bodies are attracted towards the centre of Earth due to force of gravity. If a body moves short distance horizontally over the surface of the Earth or in a circular path around the Earth, like satellites, work done by the force of gravity is zero because the displacement of the body at any instant is perpendicular to the direction of force of gravity. If a body of mass '*m*' falls vertically down through a height '*h*', then the work done will be equal to *mgh*, i.e., the change in the gravitational potential energy.

$\because$ Force due to gravity on the body

$$F = mg \text{ and } \theta = 0°$$

$$\therefore \cos 0° = 1$$

If *h* is the displacement, i.e., the height through which the body falls,

$$W = Fs\cos\theta$$

$$W = (mg)\,(h)\,(\cos 0°) = mgh$$

This can also be obtained from work-energy theorem, work done = change in potential energy = *mgh*.

> **Konnect**
>
> (i) No work is done when $\theta = 90°$ ($\cos 90° = 0$), i.e., when force and displacement are perpendicular to each other.
>
> (ii) No work is done when a body undergoes circular motion.

Units of Work

Work = Force × Displacement

1 J = 1 N × 1 m

S.I. unit of work is joule (J).

Definition of Joule

One joule of work is said to be done when a force of 1 newton acting on a body displaces it through 1m in its direction. C.G.S. unit of work is erg; 1 erg = 1 dyne × 1 cm.

If a force of 1 dyne acting on a body displaces it through 1 cm in its direction, then the work done in said to be 1 erg.

Dimensional Formula for Work

Work = Force × Displacement. Thus, [Work] = [Force] [Displacement]

$$= [M^1L^1T^{-2}] \times [L^1]$$

$$= [M^1L^2T^{-2}]$$

Relation between Joule and Erg

1 J = 1 N × 1 m

1 J = 10^5 dyne × 10^2 cm

1 J = 10^7 dyne cm

But 1 dyne × 1 cm = 1 erg

$\therefore$ 1 J = 10^7 erg

> **Info Bytes!**
>
> When work is done against gravity, like lifting an object, it's negative work.

Power

Work done does not depend on time. For example, If a person A lifts 10 kg load through 5 m in 2 minutes and person B lifts the same load through the same height in 1 minute, the work done by both the persons is the same, but the rate at which the work is done is not the same. We say that the second person is stronger and has more power. Thus, power is defined as the rate at which work is done.

$$\text{Power} = \frac{\text{Work}}{\text{Time}}$$

$$\text{Power} = \frac{\text{Force} \times \text{Displacement}}{\text{Time}}$$

∵ Work = Force × Displacement

$$P = \frac{F \times s}{t}$$

$$\left(\frac{s}{t} = \text{Average Velocity}\right)$$

$$P = F \times v$$

If the displacement makes an angle 'θ' with the force, then the power

$P = F \times v \cos\theta = \vec{F}.\vec{v}$

$P = \vec{F}.\vec{v}$

Thus, power is a dot product of force and velocity, and a scalar quantity.

Unit of Power

S.I. unit of power is watt or J s^{-1}. Watt is denoted by W.

$$\text{Power} = \frac{\text{Work}}{\text{Time}}$$

$$1\text{W} = \frac{1\text{J}}{1\text{s}}$$

Definition of Watt

If one joule of work is done in one second, then the power is said to be one watt.

$$1\text{W} = \frac{1\text{J}}{1\text{s}} = \frac{1\text{N} \times 1\text{m}}{1\text{s}} = \frac{1\ \text{kg} \times 1\text{m s}^{-2} \times 1\text{m}}{1\text{s}} = \text{kg m}^2\text{s}^{-3}$$

C.G.S. unit of power is erg per second $\frac{1\ \text{erg}}{1\ \text{second}} = \frac{1\ \text{dyne} \times 1\text{cm}}{1\ \text{second}}$

$$= \frac{1\text{g} \times \text{cm s}^{-2} \times \text{cm}}{\text{s}}$$

$$= 1\ \text{g cm}^2\ \text{s}^{-3}$$

Multiple units or bigger units of power are:

1. kW – kilo watt = 10^3 W
2. MW – mega watt = 10^6 W
3. GW – giga watt = 10^9 W
4. hp – Horse power = 746 W

Dimensional Formula for Power

$$\text{Power} = \frac{\text{Work}}{\text{Time}}$$

Hence,
$$[\text{Power}] = \frac{[\text{Work}]}{[\text{Time}]}$$

$$= \frac{[M^1L^2T^{-2}]}{[T]} = [M^1L^2T^{-3}]$$

Energy

A body which is capable of doing work possesses energy. Thus, energy is the ability or the capacity of a body to do work.

Unit of Energy

The unit of energy is the same as that of work. Thus, S.I. unit of energy is joule (J) and its C.G.S. unit is erg. Energy appears in various forms namely, heat, light, sound, electricity, etc.

Types of Energy

The various types of energy are discussed as follows:

Heat Energy

It is the energy which causes a sensation of hotness or coldness.

Example: Energy obtained by burning wood. Heat energy is measured in calories or kilo calories.

Calorie: It is the amount of heat energy required to raise the temperature of one gram of water through 1°C. It is denoted by 'cal'.

$$1 \text{ calorie} = 4{\cdot}2 \text{ J}$$

Kilo Calorie: It is the amount of heat energy required to raise the temperature of one kilogram of water through 1°C.

$$1 \text{ kilo calorie} = 4{\cdot}2 \text{ kJ}$$

Electrical Energy

Energy possessed by charged particles in motion is referred to as **electrical energy.**

Units of Electrical Energy: It is the energy spent/used in 1 hour at the rate of 1 W.

1. **Watt Hour (W h):** It is the electric energy used in 1 hour at the rate of 1 W.

$$1 \text{ W h} = 1 \text{ watt} \times 1 \text{ hour} \qquad (\because \text{Energy} = \text{power} \times \text{time})$$

$$= \frac{1 \text{ J}}{1 \text{ s}} \times 3600 \text{ s}$$

Thus, 1 W h = 3600 J

Konnect

- Heat energy flows from a body at a higher temperature to one at a lower temperature.
- Electrical energy can be converted into other forms of energy such as light or thermal energy.

Kilowatt hour is a multiple of Wh and is a bigger unit of energy.

1 kilo watt hour $= 10^3$ watt hour

$= 3600 \times 10^3$ J

$= 3{\cdot}6$ MJ

2. **One Electron Volt:** It is the work required to move an electron or a proton (in an electric field) through a potential difference of exactly one volt. It is denoted by eV.

1 electron volt = charge of 1 electron × 1 volt

$= 1{\cdot}6 \times 10^{-19}$ C × 1 V

$= 1{\cdot}6 \times 10^{-19}$ J

Light Energy

It is the energy which causes sensation of sight.

Example: Light energy emitted by sun.

Info Bytes!

- The speed of light is 299,792,458 meters per second.
- Sound energy requires a medium to travel.
- Magnetic energy can be stored in a magnetic field.
- Mechanical energy is the sum of kinetic and potential energy.

Sound Energy

It is the energy which produces sensation of hearing.

Example: The ringing of a bell.

Magnetic Energy

Energy possessed by a magnet is called **magnetic energy.**

Example: Energy possessed by motors.

Chemical Energy

Energy released or absorbed by atoms or molecules during chemical reaction is called **chemical energy.**

Example: Energy released during combustion.

Nuclear Energy

Energy released during fission or fusion of nucleus is called **nuclear energy.** In nuclear fusion or fission, nuclear mass is converted to energy ($E = mc^2$ where m is the mass, c is velocity of light in air).

Example: Atom bomb and hydrogen bomb release energy in the form of heat and radiation. Nuclear energy is used in nuclear reactor to generate electric power.

Mechanical Energy

Energy possessed by a body due to its position or motion is known as **mechanical energy.** Mechanical energy is classified into potential energy and kinetic energy.

Potential Energy

The form of energy possessed by a body due to its position or configuration, is known as potential energy.

Example: Wound spring of a clock possesses potential energy. When the spring unwinds, it uses this energy for the movement or rotation of the hands of the clock. Stretched bow, stretched elastic band and compressed gas molecules possess elastic potential energy.

Elastic Potential Energy

Elastic potential energy is the potential energy possessed by an elastic body in a deformed state, i.e., it is the amount of work done in deforming the body within its limit of elasticity and is stored in the body as elastic potential energy. This potential energy possessed by the spring is called elastic potential energy.

Water stored at a height possesses potential energy due to its position. This energy is used to rotate a turbine which in turn generates electric energy. Energy possessed by water stored at height is called gravitational potential energy. Thus, gravitational potential energy is the amount of work done in lifting the body against gravity.

Expression for Gravitational Potential Energy

When a body of mass 'm' is lifted to a height 'h', work is done against the gravity. This work done is stored as gravitational potential energy in the body.

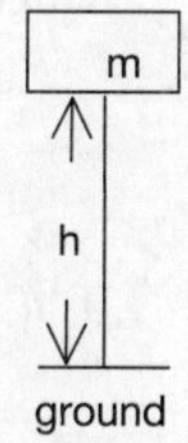

Work done in lifting a body = Force × Displacement

W = Mass × Acceleration due to gravity × Displacement

$W = mgh$

Thus, gravitational potential energy = mgh

Kinetic Energy

Energy possessed by a body due to its motion is called **kinetic energy.**

Example: Wind possesses kinetic energy and this energy is used to rotate the blades of a wind mill. For a body of mass m and velocity v, kinetic energy is given by,

$$K = \frac{1}{2} mv^2$$

Kinetic energy of a body increases if the velocity or speed of the body increases. To increase the kinetic energy of a body, net force has to be applied. Thus, the work done by this force is equal to the change in the kinetic energy of the body. This is known as work-energy theorem.

Work-Energy Theorem

The work done on a body by a force is equal to the change in its kinetic or potential energy when change in speed of the body is the effect of the foce on the body.

Konnect

Surface of the Earth is taken as reference for height in calculations of gravitational potential energy. By this assumption, gravitational potential energy of a body on the surface of the Earth at mean sea level is considered to be zero.

Consider a body of mass m moving with a velocity 'v'. Let a retarding force 'F' be applied on it causing it to come to rest after a distance 's'.

From equation of motion, we get

$$v^2 = u^2 + 2as$$

$$0 = v^2 - 2as$$

(negative sign is used because the body is retarding)

$$v^2 = 2as$$

or

$$\frac{v^2}{2} = as \tag{2.5}$$

Work done by the body before coming to rest = Force × Displacement

$$= ma \times s$$

$$= mas \tag{2.6}$$

Substituting equation (2.5) in equation (2.6), we get

Work done by the body before coming to rest $= \dfrac{mv^2}{2}$

Kinetic energy = Work done by the retarding force

$$\therefore \; K = \frac{1}{2}mv^2$$

If 'u' is the initial velocity of the body and 'v' is the final velocity, then the change in kinetic energy,

$$K_f - K_i = \frac{1}{2}mv^2 - \frac{1}{2}mu^2$$

$$= \frac{1}{2}m(v^2 - u^2) = \frac{1}{2}m2as$$

$(v^2 - u^2 = 2as)$

$$= (ma)s = \text{(Force)} \times \text{(Displacement)} = \text{Work done}$$

Thus, change in kinetic energy of the body = Work done on the force

This is the mathematical expression of work-energy theorem.

Different Forms of Kinetic Energy

The three types of motion that a body may display are:

1. Translatory motion
2. Rotatory motion
3. Vibrational motion

1. **Translational Kinetic Energy:** It is the kinetic energy possessed by a body moving along a straight line.
   Example: Energy possessed by a freely falling body.
2. **Rotational Kinetic Energy:** It is the kinetic energy possessed by a rotating body.
   Example: Wheels of a car in motion have rotational kinetic energy along with translational kinetic energy whereas the blades of a rotating fan have rotational kinetic energy only.
3. **Vibrational Kinetic Energy:** It is the energy possessed by a body, which executes to-and-fro motion about its mean position.
   Examples: Energy possessed by an oscillating pendulum, and energy possessed by a vibrating stretched string.

Relationship between Kinetic Energy and Momentum

Kinetic energy of a body, $K = \dfrac{1}{2}mv^2$ (2.7)

Momentum, $p = mv$ (2.8)

From (2.7) and (2.8)

$$K = \frac{1}{2}\frac{p^2}{m}$$

$$p^2 = 2m.K$$

where, K is the kinetic energy.

$$\therefore \quad p = \sqrt{2mK} \text{ or } K = \frac{p^2}{2m}$$

Law of Conservation of Energy

Energy can neither be created nor destroyed but it can be transformed from one form to another form, i.e., the total energy of a system remains constant.

Examples of interconversion of energy:

1. In solar cells, light energy is converted into electrical energy.
2. In fans, electrical energy is converted into mechanical energy.
3. In plants, light energy is converted into chemical energy.
4. In burning fuel like wood, etc., chemical energy is converted into light and heat energy.
5. In microphone, sound energy is converted into electrical energy.

Conservation of Mechanical Energy

Total mechanical energy of an isolated system always remains constant.

Mechanical energy is the sum of potential energy and kinetic energy. According to law of conservation of mechanical energy, if potential energy of a body increases, its kinetic energy decreases and vice versa such that the total mechanical energy always remains constant.

Info Bytes!

Law of Conservation of energy applies in systems with no non-conservative forces.

Applications of Law of Conservation of Energy

1. In the case of a freely falling body.

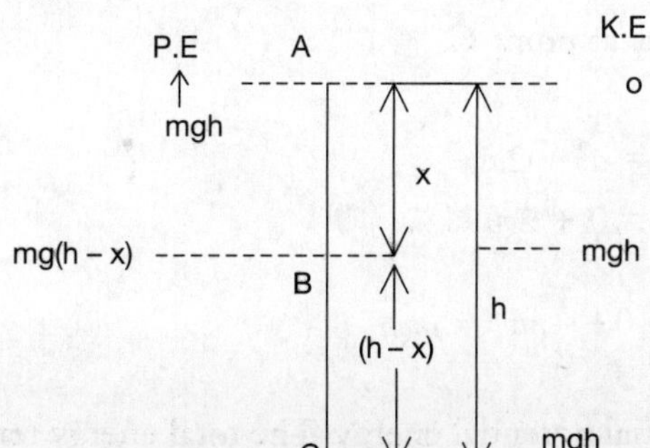

Figure 2.6

Konnect

It is always the kinetic energy which is converted into other forms, i.e., during the conversion of mechanical energy into other forms.

Consider a body of mass m at 'A' falling freely under gravity dropped from 'A' at height h. At the point 'A', energy of the body is purely potential because it is momentarily at rest.

$$\therefore \quad \text{Total energy at } A = \text{Potential energy} + \text{Kinetic energy}$$

$$\text{Total energy at } A = mgh + 0 \tag{2.9}$$

As the body falls through a distance x, its potential energy decreases because its height from the ground decreases but the kinetic energy increases as its velocity increases.

$$\therefore \text{Total energy at } B = \text{Potential energy} + \text{Kinetic energy} = mg(h - x) + \frac{1}{2}mv_B^2 \tag{2.10}$$

where, v_B is the velocity at B.

Substituting $u = 0$, $v = v_B$, $a = g$ and $s = x$ in the equation of motion $v^2 = u^2 + 2as$, we get

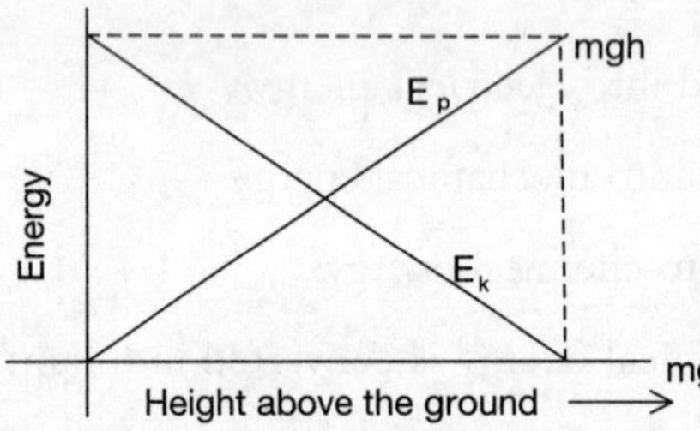

Figure 2.7 Energy graph of the object at a certain height

$$v_B^2 = 2gx \tag{2.11}$$

Substituting equation (2.11) in (2.10), we get

$$\text{Total energy at } B = mg(h - x) + \frac{1}{2}m\,2gx$$

$$= mgh - mgx + mgx$$

$$\therefore \text{Total energy at } B = mgh \tag{2.12}$$

At the instant when the body strikes the ground, entire energy of the body is kinetic. Potential energy is equal to zero at the ground.

$$\therefore \text{Total energy at } C = \text{Potential energy} + \text{Kinetic energy}$$

$$\text{Total energy at } C = 0 + \frac{1}{2}mv_c^2 \text{ where } v_C \text{ is the velocity at point } C. \tag{2.13}$$

From equations,

$$v_c^2 = u^2 + 2as$$

$$v_c^2 = 0 + 2gh$$

Equation (2.13) can be written as total energy at $C = 0 + \frac{1}{2}mv_c^2 = mgh$

Thus, the kinetic energy of the body is equal to initial potential energy. The total energy remains constant and is independent of height of fall.

Note: Resistance of air is neglected in verifying the above law.

2. Conservation of energy in the case of a simple pendulum

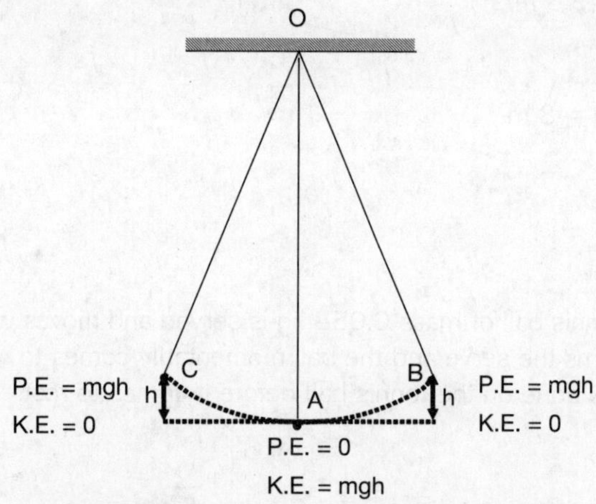

Figure 2.8 Motion of a simple pendulum

O is the point of suspension of the simple pendulum. When the pendulum is made to swing, it reaches equal heights on either side of the mean position A. B and C are called extreme positions of the pendulum.

At an extreme position, the bob of the pendulum is momentarily at rest, hence, its energy is entirely potential.

$\therefore$ Total energy at extreme position = P.E + K.E. = mgh (2.14)

As it swings from extreme position to mean position, potential energy decreases and its kinetic energy increases such that the total energy remains constant. At the mean position, energy of the bob is purely kinetic.

Total energy at mean position = $P.E + K.E.$

$$= 0 + \frac{1}{2}mv^2 \tag{2.15}$$

But $v^2 = u^2 + 2as$ $(u = 0, s = h, a = g)$ $v^2 = 0 + 2gh$

$\therefore$ Total energy at mean position $= 0 + \frac{1}{2}mv_c^2 = \left(\frac{1}{2}\right)mv^2 = \left(\frac{1}{2}\right)m\left(\sqrt{2gh}\right)^2 = mgh$

$$= mgh \tag{2.16}$$

Thus, kinetic energy at the mean position is equal to initial potential energy at the extreme position. As it moves from mean position to the other extreme position, its kinetic energy decreases but potential energy increases as the height increases.

Hence, at extreme position, energy of the bob is entirely potential and at any intermediate position, total energy of the bob is the sum of potential energy and kinetic energy.

Thus, total energy of the bob remains constant throughout the swing.

Note: Air friction is neglected in the above discussion.

EXAMPLE 2.1 A block is pushed by a force of 5 N for a distance of 3 m at an angle of 30° to the direction of displacement. How much work is done by the force?

SOLUTION

Work done = $F \times s = F_s \cos\theta$

Given, $F = 5N$, $s = 3m$, and $\theta = 30°$

$W = 5 \times 3 \times \cos(30°) = 15 \times \left(\frac{\sqrt{3}}{2}\right) = 7.5\sqrt{3} \Rightarrow 13J$

So, the work done by the force on the block is approximately 13 Joules.

EXAMPLE 2.2 Calculate the work done in lifting a mass of 15 kg through a height of 8 m from the ground. ($g = 9.8 \text{ m/s}^2$)

SOLUTION

Given, $m = 15\text{kg}$; $g = 9.8 \text{ m/s}^2$; and h = 8 m

Work done $W = mgh$

$w = 15 \times 9.8 \times 8 = 1176$

Thus, the work done is 1176 joules (J).

EXAMPLE 2.3 A tennis ball of mass 0.058 kg is served and moves with a velocity of 45 m/s. The opponent returns the serve and the ball momentarily comes to rest before being hit back. Calculate the work done on the tennis ball before it comes to rest.

SOLUTION

According to the work-energy theorem,

Work done = Change in kinetic energy

$$\text{Work} = \frac{1}{2}mv^2 - \frac{1}{2}mu^2$$

$$= 0 - \left(\frac{1}{2} \times 0.058 \text{ kg} \times (45 \text{ m/s})^2\right)$$

$$= -(0.029 \text{ kg} \times 2025) = -59.725 J$$

The negative sign indicates that the work done is in the direction opposite to the tennis ball's motion. This is consistent with the ball being slowed down and brought to a stop. The work done on the tennis ball is $-59.725 J$.

EXAMPLE 2.4 What is the work done by a porter in carrying a load of 50 kg?

(i) While walking along the platform

(ii) While climbing up a slope of height 10 m ($g = 10 \text{ m s}^{-2}$)?

SOLUTION

While carrying a load, the porter applies a force equal to mg vertically upwards.

(i) Work done by a porter along the horizontal

$$W \propto \vec{F}.\vec{s} = Fs\cos\theta$$

Where F is the force, s is the displacement and θ is angle between F and s.

Since $\theta = 90°$, work done $(W) = F \cdot s \cos 90° = 0$ (zero).

$\therefore$ Work done when the porter walks along the platform = 0

(ii) Work done when the porter walks along the slope

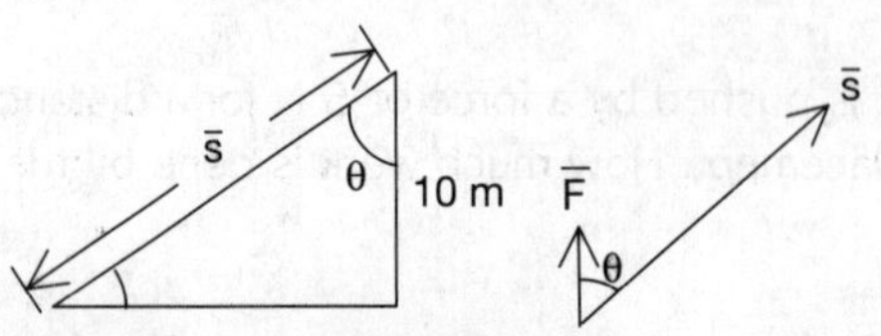

Figure 2.9

$$W = \vec{F}.\vec{s} = Fs\cos\theta$$

Work is done by force of gravity, $F = mg$ and $s\cos\theta = h$

$\therefore W = mgh$

$\therefore W = 50 \times 10 \times 10 = 5000 \text{ J} = 5 \text{ kJ}.$

EXAMPLE 2.5 What is the power developed by an engine in lifting 3000 L of water from a well 20 m deep in one minute (1 L water = 10^3 kg; g = 10 m s^{-2})?

Assume that there is no loss of energy in the conversion of energy.

SOLUTION

$$\text{Power} = \frac{\text{Work}}{\text{Time}}$$

Work = Force × Displacement

$W = \vec{F}.\vec{s}$ work is done by the force of gravity = $F\, s \cos\theta$

$\therefore F = mg$, $s = h$ and $\theta = 0°$

$W = mgh \cos 0°$

$= 3 \times 10^3 \times 10 \times 20 = 6 \times 10^5$ joules

$$\text{Power} = \frac{\text{Work}}{\text{Time}}$$

Time = 1 minute = 60 s

$\therefore \text{Power} = \dfrac{6 \times 10^5}{60} = 10^4 \text{ W} = 10{,}000 \text{ W}$

The power of the engine is 10 kW.

EXAMPLE 2.6 In a hydroelectric power station, water is allowed to fall at the rate of 2000 kg per second on a turbine kept 100-m below the water level.

(i) Calculate the potential energy of water falling every one second.

(ii) Find kinetic energy of this water when it falls through a height of 25 m.

(iii) If 80% of initial potential energy is converted into electrical energy, calculate the power output in 1 second (g = 10 m s^{-2}).

SOLUTION

(i) From definition of potential energy (P.E)

P.E = mgh

P.E = 2000 × 10 × 100

= 2 × 10^6 J.

From law of conservation of energy,

Total energy at the highest point

E_1 = potential energy + kinetic energy

$E_1 = mgh + 0$ (K.E at the highest point = 0)

$\Rightarrow E_1 = 2 \times 10^6$ J

(ii) When water falls through a height of 25 m, its velocity (v) is given by:

$v^2 = u^2 + 2gs$

$v^2 = 0 + 2 \times 10 \times 25$

$v^2 = 500$

$\therefore$ K.E. = 1/2 mv^2

K.E. = 1/2 × 2000 × 500

K.E. = 5 × 10^5 J

(iii) 80% of initial potential energy is converted into electrical energy

$$80\% \text{ of } E_1 = \frac{80}{100} \times 2 \times 10^6$$

$$= 16 \times 10^5 \text{ J is converted into electrical energy}$$

$$\text{Power output} = \frac{\text{Work}}{\text{Time}} = \frac{\text{Energy}}{\text{Time}}$$

$$= \frac{16 \times 10^5}{1} = 16 \times 10^5 \text{ W}$$

Thus, the power output is 16×10^5 W = 1.6 MW.

Parallel Forces

Let us look at the following examples to understand the concept of parallel forces.

A 5-N force acting along east can be represented by a ray 5-cm long with the arrow pointing towards east (Fig. 2.10).

Figure 2.10 Force denoted by ray OA.

1. The point of application of the force is represented by the point O.
2. The length of line OA is proportional to the magnitude of the force.
3. The direction of the arrow indicates the direction of the force. Thus, a force can be represented graphically.

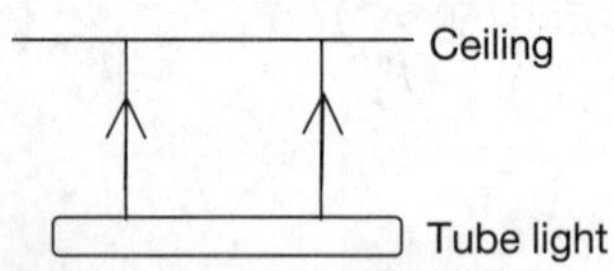

Figure 2.11 A tube-light fixed with ceiling

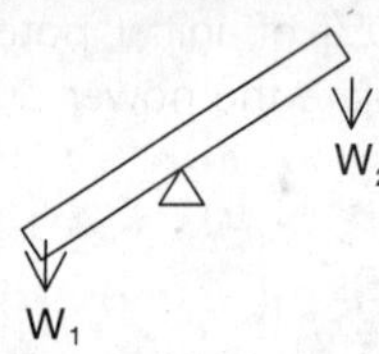

Figure 2.12 See-saw

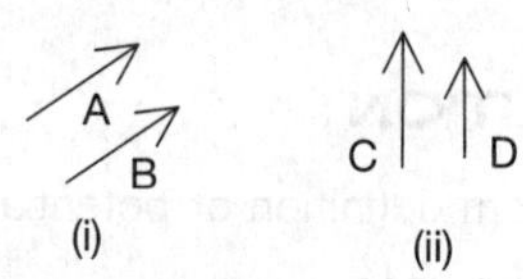

Figure 2.13

When a tube light fixture is suspended from two points symmetrical about its centre from the ceiling of a room as shown (Fig. 2.11), two equal forces act along the strings by which the fixture is suspended. These two forces act along the parallel lines are called parallel forces.

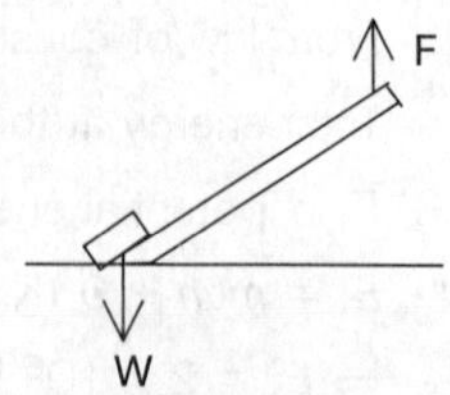

Figure 2.14

When two lads sit on either side of a see-saw, the weights of the lads act vertically downwards along the parallel lines (Fig. 2.12). These parallel forces are called like parallel forces.

In the Fig. 2.13 (i), *A* and *B* represent a set of like parallel forces. Similarly in Fig. 2.13 (ii), *C* and *D* also represent another set of like parallel forces. Thus, the forces acting along parallel lines in the same direction are called like parallel forces.

When we want to a lift a load using a wooden plank as shown (Fig. 2.14), the weight of the load acts vertically downwards and the force exerted acts vertically upwards. These two forces act along the parallel lines in opposite direction. These types of parallel forces are called unlike parallel forces.

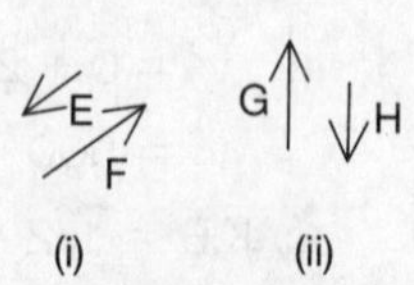

Figure 2.15

In the adjacent Fig. 2.15 (i), *E* and *F* represent a set of unlike parallel forces. Similarly in Fig. 2.15 (ii), G and *H* also represent another set of unlike parallel forces. Thus, unlike parallel forces are forces acting along parallel lines in opposite directions.

Therefore, parallel forces are classified into like parallel forces and unlike parallel forces.

Consider a ring pulled by two persons P and Q in two diametrically opposite directions with forces F_1 and F_2, respectively (Fig. 2.16).

The ring moves in the direction of F_2 when F_2, is greater than F_1. Then, the resultant of the forces of F_1 and F_2 is $F_2 - F_1$ and acts in the direction of F_2.

If the magnitude of F_2 is equal to F_1 then the body does not move, then the resultant of the two forces is zero. Therefore, resultant of two or more (parallel) forces is that single force whose effect is the same as that of the combination of all forces.

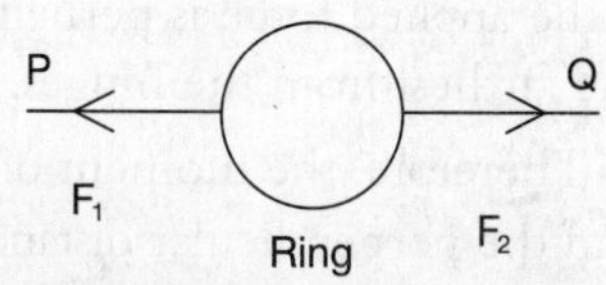

Figure 2.16 A ring pulled by P and Q

When unequal weights F_1 and F_2 are placed on the pans of a balance, the resultant of the weights acts along R (Fig. 2.17). If the balance is suspended by a string, the tension in the string F_3 is equal in magnitude and opposite in direction to that of the resultant. This force F_3 is called equilibrant.

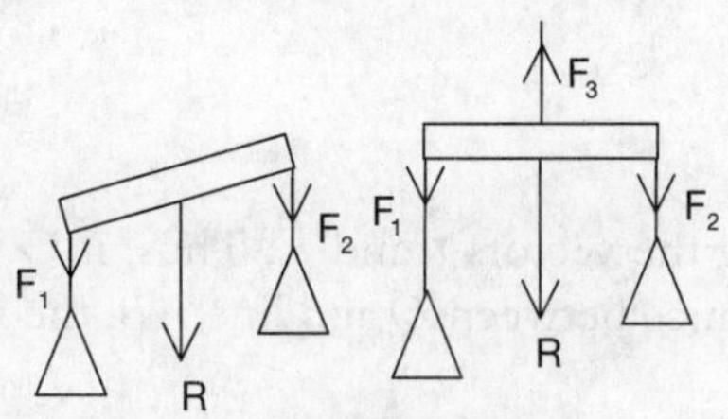

Figure 2.17

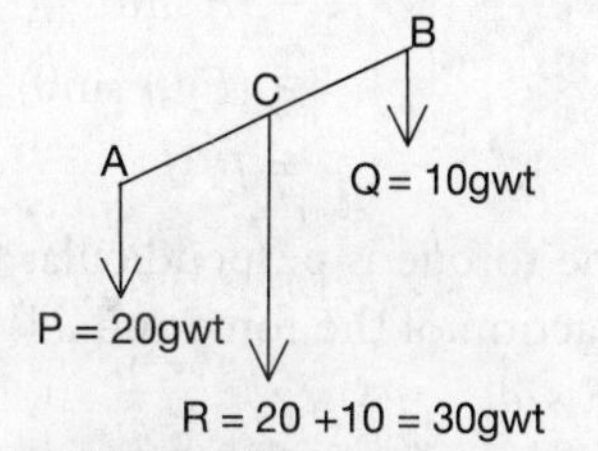

Figure 2.18 Two forces A & B suspended to a beam

When 20 gwt and 10 gwt are suspended to a beam or a rod, the two forces act along the parallel lines vertically downwards (Fig. 2.18). The resultant of these two forces is equal to 20 + 10 = 30 gwt and it acts vertically downwards near the greater force such that the point of action of the resultant divides the line joining the point of action of the two forces internally in the inverse ratio of the forces.

Thus, the magnitude of the resultant of two parallel forces is equal to the sum of individual forces, i.e., $R = P + Q$. The direction of the resultant is the same as the direction of either force. The resultant force R divides the line joining the point of action of P and Q in the inverse ratio of the forces.

$$\Rightarrow P \times AC = Q \times BC,\ \text{i.e.,}\ \frac{P}{Q} = \frac{BC}{AC}$$

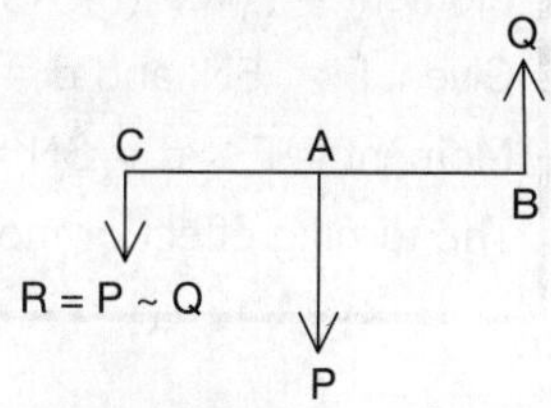

Figure 2.19 Unlike parallel forces A & B

When a body is lifted by a wooden plank by applying a force 'F' at 'B', which acts vertically upwards, half the weight of the body 'W', acts vertically downwards on the plank at A (Fig. 2.19). These two forces constitute unlike parallel forces and the resultant of these forces acts in the direction of the greater force. Its magnitude is equal to $(W/2) \sim (F)$.

The point of action of the resultant divides the line joining the point of action of the two forces externally in an inverse ratio of the forces.

Thus, the magnitude of the resultant of the two unlike parallel forces is equal to difference of the magnitudes of the individual forces. Direction of the resultant is in the direction of the greater force and the point of action of the resultant divides the line joining the point of action of the two forces externally in the inverse ratio of the forces (Fig. 2.20).

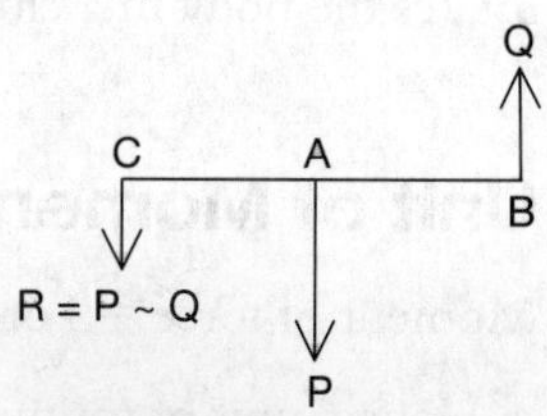

Figure 2.20 Direction of resultant of two unlike parallel forces

$$P \times AC = Q \times BC$$

Moment of a Force

When a force is applied on a door handle, it tends to turn (open or close) the door about the hinges.

This rotating or turning effect of a force about a fixed point or fixed axis is called moment of the force about that point. This moment of the force, i.e., the turning effect is maximum if the applied force is perpendicular to the plane of the door and the point of application is the farthest from the hinges.

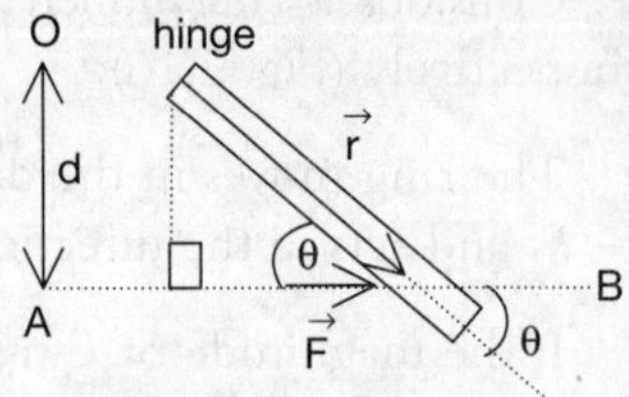

Figure 2.21 Moment of a force

Therefore, the moment of force is measured by the product of the magnitude of the force and the perpendicular distance between the fixed point or the fixed axis and the line of action of the force.

This moment of force, also called torque, is a vector quantity and is given as a cross product of the force vector, $\vec{F}$ and the radius vector, $\vec{r}$ as,

$\vec{\tau} = \vec{r} \times \vec{F}$ and the magnitude of torque is given by,

$$\tau = rF\sin\theta$$
$$= (F)(r\sin\theta)$$
$$= F.\,d$$

The direction of the torque is perpendicular to the plane containing the vectors $\vec{r}$ and $\vec{F}$. Thus, if O is the fixed point and AB is the line of action of the force and d is the perpendicular distance between O and line AB, the magnitude of the moment of force = $F \times d$.

If the perpendicular distance between the line of action of the applied force and the fixed point is greater, greater will be the turning effect.

Example: Door handles are provided far away from the hinges so that less force is required to obtain greater turning effect.

EXAMPLE 2.7 A child pushes a swing with a force of 5 N. If the force is applied perpendicular to the swing seat's chain at a distance of 1.5 meters from the pivot point (where the chain is attached to the frame), what is the moment (or turning effect) of the force?

SOLUTION

Moment = Force (F) × Perpendicular distance from fixed axis (d)

Given: F = 5N, and d = 1.5m

Moment = F × d = 5N × 1.5m= 7.5Nm

The turning effect or moment of the force is 7.5 N m.

Similarly, it is easier to tighten or unwind a screw using a long spanner or a screw driver with a bigger handle. By convention, moment of force is taken as positive if it rotates the body in an anti-clockwise direction and negative if it rotates the body in a clockwise direction.

Unit of Moment of Force

Moment of force = Force × Perpendicular distance

Hence, unit of torque = (unit of force) (unit of distance)

Thus, the S.I. unit of moment of force is N m and in C.G.S. system it is dyne cm.

Konnect

Turning effect is zero when forces are applied on the fixed point or on the fixed axis.

Dimensional Formula of Moment of Force

Moment of force = Force × Perpendicular distance

Thus, [torque] = [Force] [Distance]

$= [M^1L^1T^{-2}] \times [L]$

$= [M^1L^2T^{-2}]$

Konnect

The dimensional formula of torque is the same as that of work.

Principle of Moments or Theorem of Moments

When a number of parallel forces act on a rigid body and the body is in equilibrium, then the algebraic sum of the moments of the individual forces about any point is equal to zero, i.e., sum of anti-clockwise moments is equal to sum of clockwise moments.

If $\vec{F_1}, \vec{F_2}$ and $\vec{F_3}$ are three parallel forces acting about O under which the body is in equilibrium, then according to the principle of moments (Fig. 2.22), $F_1d_1 + F_3d_3 = F_2\, d_2$ or $F_1d_1 + F_3d_3 - F_2d_2 = 0$

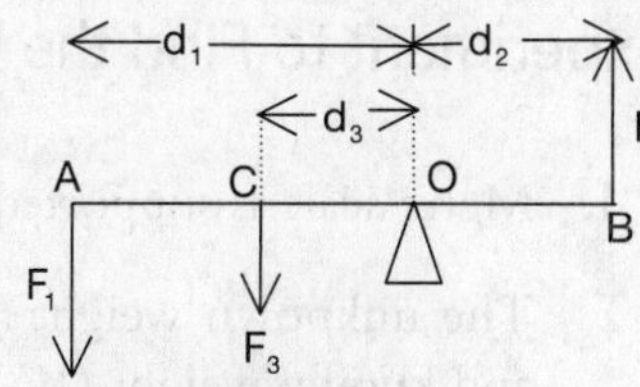

Figure 2.22 Three parallel forces in equilibrium

Consider a wooden plank of length 4 m supported at its ends by two supports whose tensions are 40 kgwt and 30 kgwt. Weight of 50 kg is suspended at the centre of the plank and 20 kgwt is suspended at a distance 1m from the end (Fig. 2.23).

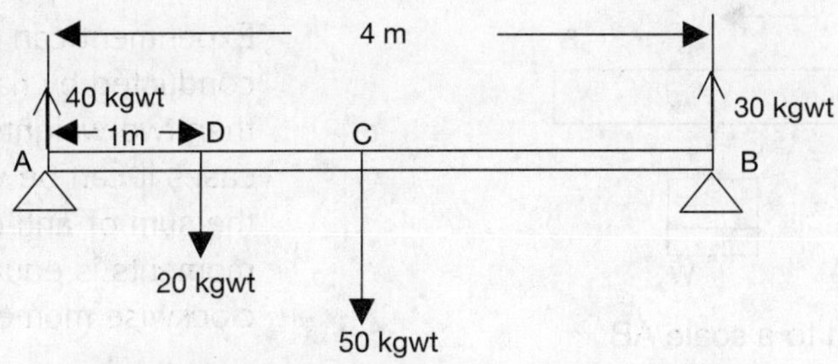

Figure 2.23 A wooden plank by two supports

Konnect

The principle of moments states that for a body to be in equilibrium, the sum of clockwise moments about a pivot must equal the sum of anticlockwise moments about the same pivot.

If the plank is in equilibrium, then algebraic sum of the moment about any point should be equal to zero. Taking moments about A, we get

$$(40 \times 0) - (20 \times 1) - (50 \times 2) + (30 \times 4) = -20 - 100 + 120 = 0$$

Experiment to Verify the Principle of Moments

1. Metre scale is supported at its centre by a knife edge so that the scale remains horizontal.
2. Slotted weights W_1 and W_2 are added to the weight hangers, which are suspended to the scale, such that the scale remains in equilibrium.
3. Distances between slotted weights and the centre of the scale are measured. Let the distances from the knife edge to the weights W_1 and W_2 be d_1 and d_2, respectively.
4. Moment of the force is calculated using the formula.

   Moment of force = Force × Distance

   Clockwise moment = $W_2 \times d_2$

   Anti-clockwise moment = $W_1 \times d_1$

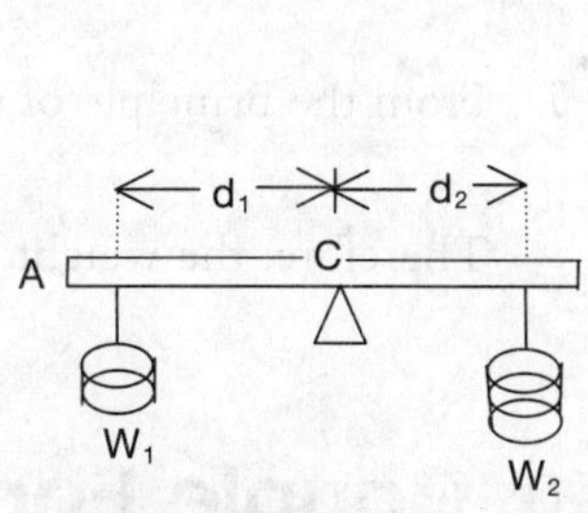

Figure 2.24 Weights suspended to a scale

Trial No	W_1 kgwt	W_2 kgwt	d_1 m	d_2 m	Anti-clockwise moment ($W_1 \times d_1$)	Clockwise moment ($W_2 \times d_2$)

5. Experiment is repeated for different weights and different distances and the result is tabulated.

Observation

In all the cases, it is found that the anti-clockwise moment is equal to the clockwise moment.

Experiment to Find the Weight of a Body Using the Principle of Moments

1. Metre scale is supported at its centre by a knife edge, so that the scale is horizontal.
2. The unknown weight (W_1) is suspended on one side of the scale as shown and known weight (W_2) is suspended on the other side.

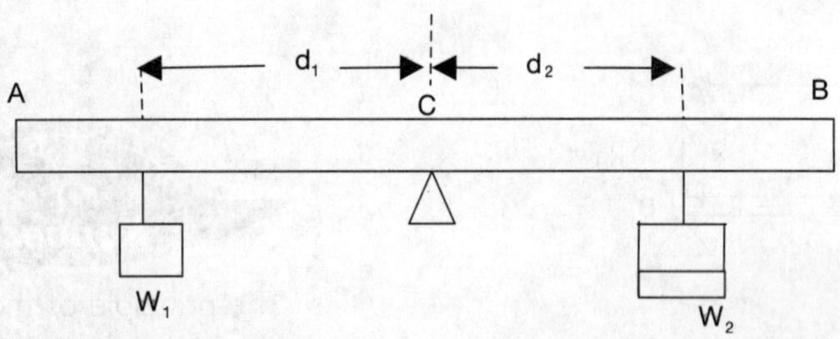

Figure 2.25 W_1 & W_2 suspended to a scale AB

Konnect

Experiment can be conducted by having more than two weights. In all the cases it can be verified that the sum of anti-clockwise moments is equal to sum of clockwise moments.

3. The two weights are adjusted and positioned on the scale, until the scale remains horizontal (equilibrium position).
4. Distance d_1 between unknown weight and the centre of the scale is noted down. Similarly, distance d_2 between the known weight and the centre of the scale is also noted down.
5. From the principle of moments $W_1 \times d_1 = W_2 \times d_2$ or $W_1 = \frac{W_2 \times d_2}{d_1}$

   Therefore, the weight of the unknown body is determined.

Couple Force

Two equal and unlike parallel forces constitute a couple. A couple does not produce translatory motion since the resultant of the forces is zero. Rotating effect of the couple is known as moment of couple.

Example: Couple is applied in turning (opening or closing) a tap and winding or unwinding a screw, etc.

Moment of couple is measured by product of either force and the perpendicular distance between the two forces (arm of couple).

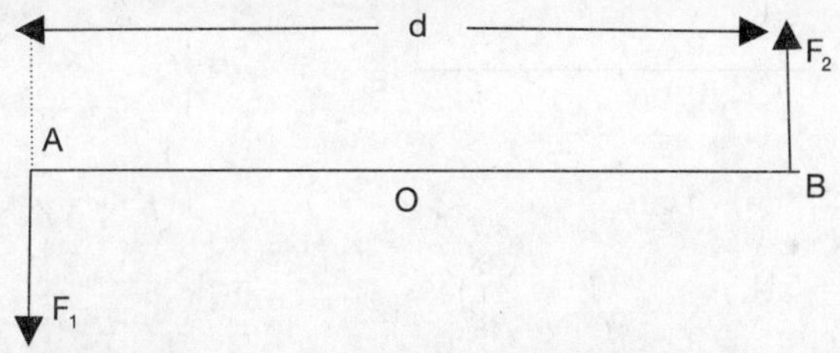

Figure 2.26 2 Equal and unlike parallel forces

In the Fig. 2.26, F_1 and F_2 would constitute a couple if $F_1 = F_2 = F$ (say)

$\therefore$ Moment of couple $= F \times AB$

$= F \times d$

> **Konnect**
> - A couple cannot be balanced by a single force. It has to be balanced by another couple.
> - A couple consists of two parallel forces that are equal in magnitude but opposite in direction.

Moment of couple is taken as positive if the couple rotates the body in an anti-clockwise direction and negative if it rotates the body in a clockwise direction. Unit of moment of couple is N m in S.I. system and dyne cm in C.G.S. system.

EXAMPLE 2.8 AB is a rigid rod of uniform cross-section and length 6 m. Two forces, $P = 5$ N and $Q = 3$ N act at the ends A and B of the rod. Find the magnitude, direction and point of application of the resultant if the

(i) two forces are like parallel forces.

(ii) two forces are unlike parallel forces.

SOLUTION

(i) For like parallel forces

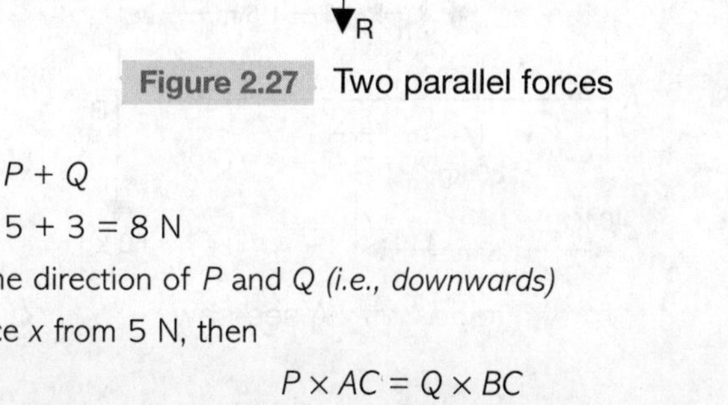

Figure 2.27 Two parallel forces

Magnitude of the resultant, $R = P + Q$

$R = 5 + 3 = 8$ N

Direction of the resultant is in the direction of P and Q *(i.e., downwards)*

Let the resultant act at a distance x from 5 N, then

$$P \times AC = Q \times BC$$

$$5 \times x = 3\ (6 - x)$$

$\Rightarrow 5x = 18 - 3x \Rightarrow 5x + 3x = 18$

$\Rightarrow 8x = 18$ or $x = 2.25$ m

$\therefore$ The resultant acts at a distance 2.25 m from 5 N.

(ii) Unlike parallel forces

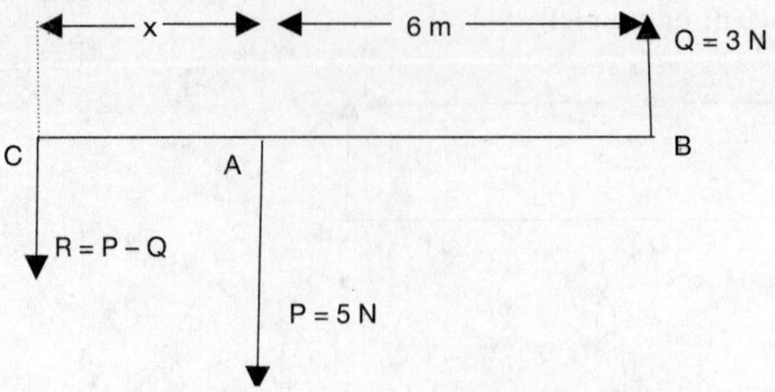

Figure 2.28 Two unlike parallel forces

Magnitude of the resultant of two unlike parallel forces is

$$R = P \sim Q$$

$$\Rightarrow R = 5 - 3 = 2 \text{ N}$$

Direction of the resultant is along the greater force.

⇒ Direction of the resultant R is in the direction of P.

If the resultant acts at a distance x from 5 N, then

$$P \times AC = Q \times BC$$

$$5 \times x = 3\ (6 + x)$$

$$5x = 18 + 3x$$

$$5x - 3x = 18$$

$$2x = 18 \Rightarrow x = 9 \text{ m}$$

i.e., resultant acts at a distance 9 m from 5 N.

EXAMPLE 2.9

Two lads of 40 kg and 60 kg sit on either side of a see-saw of length 3 m which is supported at its centre. Where should a third lad of 30 kg sit so as to balance the see-saw?

SOLUTION

Let the third lad sit at a distance 'x' from the support to balance the see-saw. From the principle of moments, the sum of anti-clockwise moments is equal to the sum of clockwise moments. (Moment = Force × Perpendicular distance) Anti-clockwise moment is taken as positive.

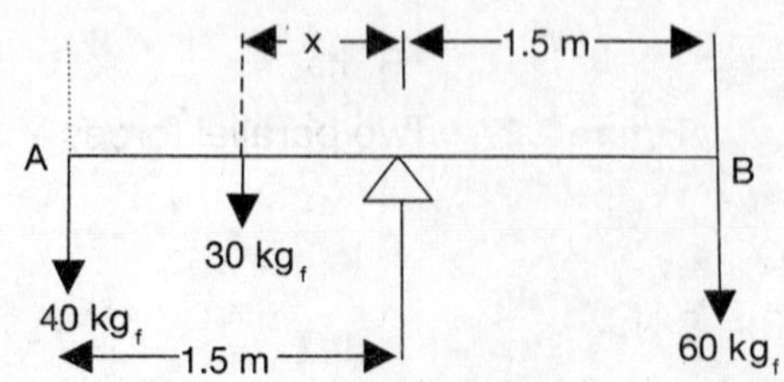

Figure 2.29 A see-saw

$$(40 \times 1{\cdot}5) + (30 \times x) - (60 \times 1{\cdot}5) = 0$$

$$60 + 30x - 90 = 0$$

$$30x - 30 = 0$$

$$30x = 30 \Rightarrow x = 1 \text{ m}$$

EXAMPLE 2.10 A painter of 50 kg stands on a wooden plank of length 5 m and negligible mass. The plank is suspended at its ends by ropes. The painter stands at a distance 2 m from one end of the plank. Find the tensions (force) in the ropes.

SOLUTION

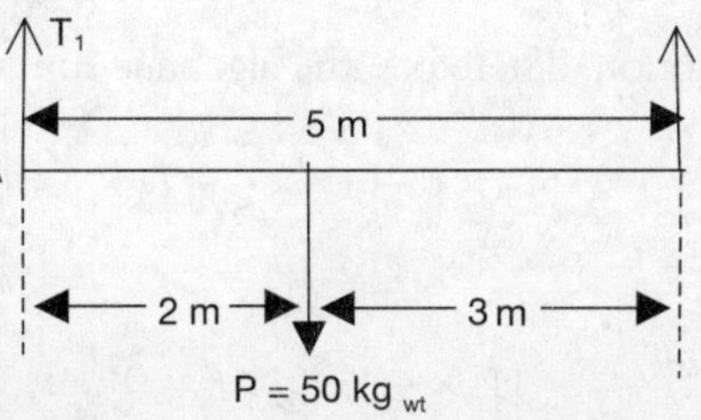

Figure 2.30 A wooden plank of length AB

(i) Let T_1 and T_2 be the tensions in the ropes. Painter P stands at a distance 2 m from the end A. From the principle of moments, the algebraic sum of the moments about any point is equal to zero. Anti-clockwise moment is taken positive. Applying theorem of moments about point A, we get

$$(T_1 \times 0) - (50 \times 2) + (T_2 \times 5) = 0$$

$$-100 + 5T_2 = 0$$

$$5T_2 = 100 \Rightarrow T_2 = 20 \text{ kg wt}$$

(ii) For equilibrium of the plank, condition is upward force = downward force

$\therefore T_1 + T_2 = P$

$\Rightarrow T_1 + 20 = 50$

$\Rightarrow T_1 = 50 - 20 = 30$ kgwt

Alternately, applying principle of moments about B;

$$(T_1 \times 5) - (50 \times 3) + (T_2 \times 0) = 0$$

$$5T_1 - 150 = 0$$

$$\Rightarrow T_1 = 30 \text{ kg wt}$$

Static Equilibrium

A body is said to be in equilibrium if it does not change its state of rest or uniform motion. If the body does not possess translatory motion and rotatory motion, then the body is said to be in static equilibrium. Hence, the conditions for a body to be in equilibrium are:

1. The algebraic sum of the forces acting on the body should be equal to zero.
2. The algebraic sum of the moments of forces about any point should be equal to zero.
3. All forces must be coplanar forces.

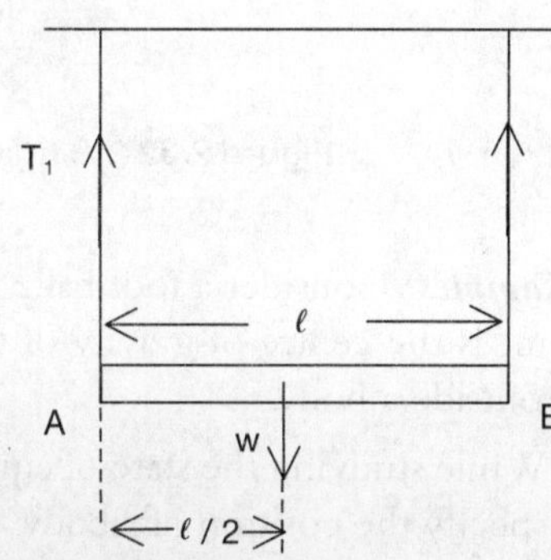

Figure 2.31 A wooden plank suspended by 2 ropes

Consider a wooden plank suspended by two parallel ropes at its ends A and B as shown. The wooden plank is in equilibrium under the action of forces. The upward forces acting on the plank are T_1 and T_2, where T_1 and T_2 are the tensions in the ropes. The weight of the plank W acts vertically downwards. The plank is in equilibrium because:

$$T_1 + T_2 = W \tag{2.17}$$

$$T_1 + T_2 - W = 0$$

Thus, the upward force = downward force

The plank does not possess any rotatory motion. Therefore, the algebraic sum of moment of the forces about $A = 0$.

i.e.,
$$T_1 \times 0 - W \times \frac{\ell}{2} - T_2 \times \ell = 0$$

where, ℓ is the length of the plank

$$W \times \frac{\ell}{2} - T_2 \times \ell = 0$$

$$\therefore T_2 = \frac{W}{2} \tag{2.18}$$

By substituting equation 2.18 in 2.17,

$$T_1 = \frac{W}{2}$$

$$T_2 = \frac{W}{2}.$$

Centre of Gravity

Consider a rigid body. It consists of a number of particles and these particles are attracted towards the earth due to gravity. The forces acting on the particle are F_1, F_2, F_3, etc. These forces act downwards along parallel lines. These are called like parallel forces. These like parallel forces can be replaced by a single force whose effect is the same as the combination. This is called resultant. The resultant force acts at a particular point. This point can be assumed as the point where the whole weight, W of the body acts. This point is known as centre of gravity (C.G).

Thus, $\overline{W} = \overline{F_1} + \overline{F_2} + \overline{F_3} + \ldots\ldots..$

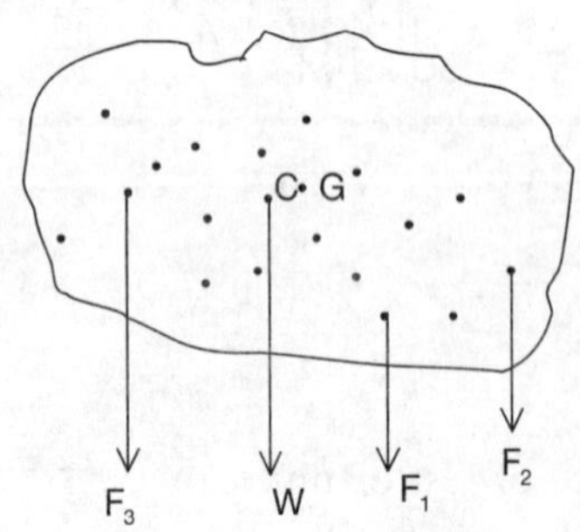

Figure 2.32 A rigid body consisting of many particles

The center of gravity is the point where all weight is evenly distributed.

Examples: Consider a foot ball. The whole weight of the ball acts through the centre of the ball. This point is the centre of gravity of the ball. Therefore, in general, centre of gravity (C.G) may lie inside or outside a body.

While studying the state of equilibrium of a body, we often refer to the position of C.G. of the body to specify the position of a body. Therefore, when we say the position of the body is changed, we mean that the position of the C.G. is changed.

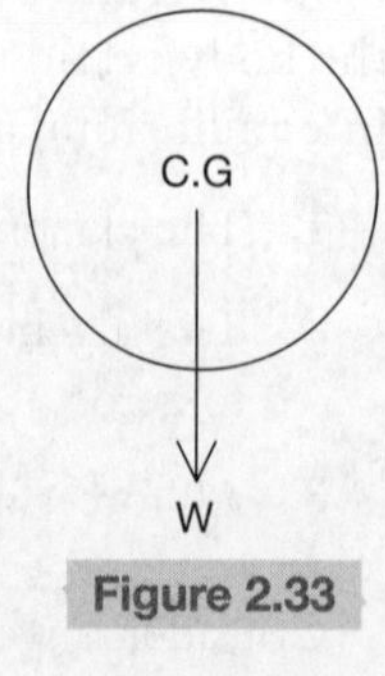

Figure 2.33

A funnel is placed on a table top with its base in contact with the horizontal surface because the tip of the funnel has smaller area of cross-section and when the funnel is made to stand on the tip, it topples down. Thus, for the funnel to be stable, it should be rested with its broader base in contact with the horizontal surface.

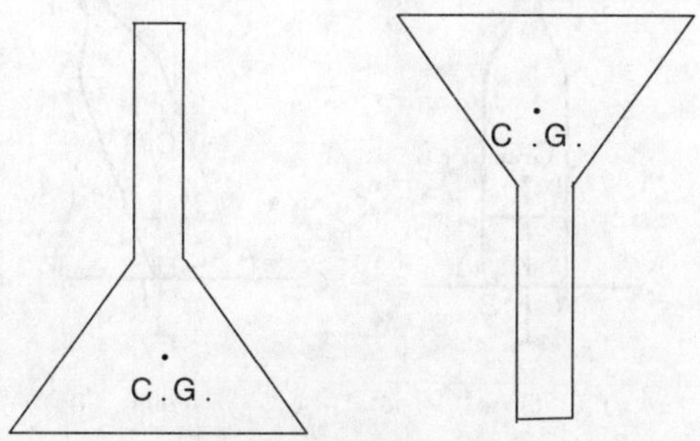

Figure 2.34 Funnel

Formula race cars are shorter in height and have broader and heavier base. Thus, the height of their centre of gravity from their base is lesser. Even if the car tilts due to high speed, it can regain its original position because the vertical line from the centre of gravity falls within the base and the centre of gravity of the car is almost at the base.

The height of centre of gravity of an empty bottle from its base is higher when compared to the height of centre of gravity in the case when the bottle is half filled with a liquid. Hence, the stability of the bottle is more when it is half filled compared to that when it is empty.

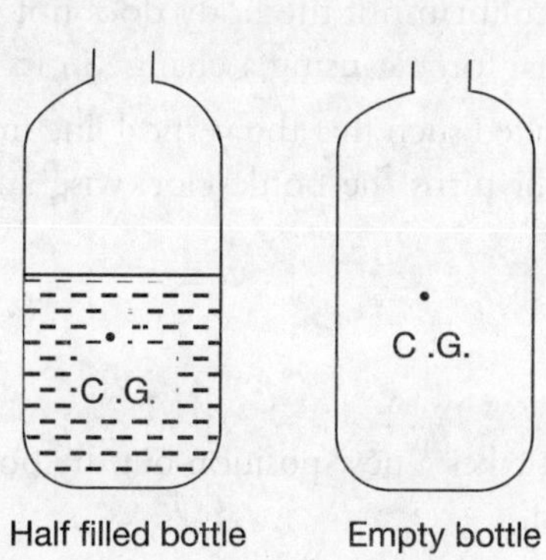

Figure 2.35 Empty and Half-filled Bottle

The famous leaning tower of Pisa is stable even though it is slightly tilted from the vertical, as the line joining its centre of gravity and the centre of the earth falls within its base.

Thus, for a body to be stable,

1. it should have a broader base,
2. the height of the centre of gravity should be lowered (C.G can be lowered by having heavy base), and
3. the vertical line drawn from the centre of gravity of the body to the centre of the earth should fall within the base of the body.

Stable Equilibrium

When the base of a water bottle is in contact with the horizontal surface, the centre of gravity of the bottle falls within the base. If the bottle is tilted slightly, centre of gravity of the bottle is raised. As a result, the stability of the bottle decreases. If the vertical line drawn from the centre of gravity to the centre of the Earth passes between A and B, the moment of weight restores the bottle its initial position, then the bottle is said to be in stable equilibrium.

Thus, a body is said to be in stable equilibrium if the body returns to its original state after the external force causing the change of position of the body is withdrawn.

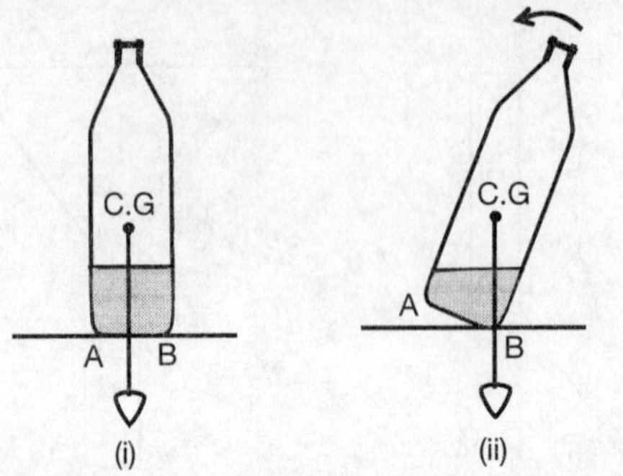

Figure 2.36 A bottle placed straight and tilted

Unstable Equilibrium

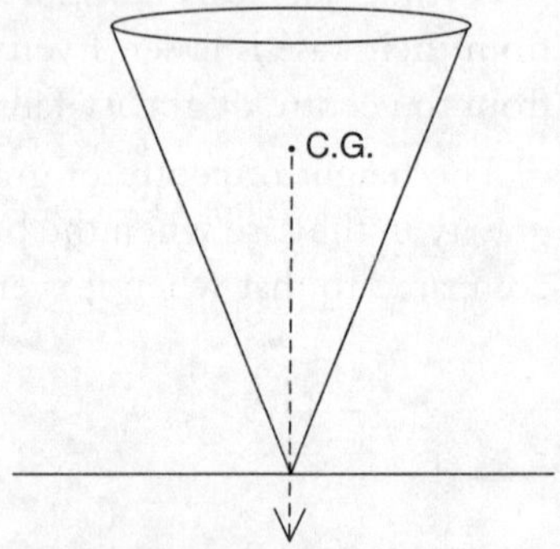

Figure 2.37 A cone placed upside down on its tip

A cone resting on its apex would topple when the slightest of disturbances cause the vertical line drawn from the C.G. to centre of the Earth to fall outside the base.

Thus, the cone cannot regain its original position. This is known as unstable equilibrium. Therefore, a body is said to be in unstable equilibrium if the body does not return to its initial position after the removal of the external force causing a change in its position.

In the example of the bottle, if the bottle is tilted such that the vertical line from the C.G. passes to the right of B, the moment of weight turns the bottle clockwise and the bottle topples.

Neutral Equilibrium

When a ball is rolled on a horizontal surface, it takes a new position but the position of centre of gravity remains intact. This state of the ball is known as neutral equilibrium.

Thus, a body is said to be in neutral equilibrium if it takes a new position without the change in its position of centre of gravity.

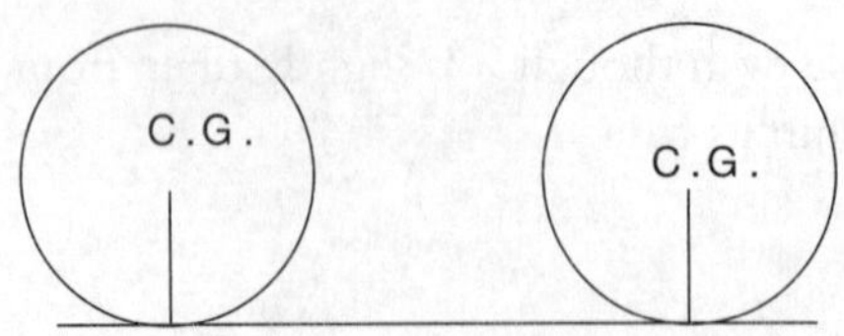

Figure 2.38 Change of position of ball on a horizontal surface when rolled

Some more examples to understand centre of gravity:

1. Kids or infants stand with their legs apart, so that the centre of gravity falls between the legs. This gives them the stability.
2. Vessels like jugs, mugs, water bottles, candles, candle stand, etc., have a broad base to prevent toppling.
3. The base of the ships, pedestal fans and formula cars are made heavy in order to lower centre of gravity which gives them stability.

Konnect

The position of centre of gravity remains unchanged, whether the body is at rest or in motion.

POINTS TO REMEMBER

- ✔ Work done is directly proportional to the force applied on the body.
- ✔ Power is defined as the rate at which work is done.
- ✔ Energy is the ability or the capacity of a body to do work.
- ✔ Energy can neither be created nor destroyed but it can be transformed from one form to another form, i.e., the total energy of a system remains constant.
- ✔ Mechanical energy is the sum of potential energy and kinetic energy.
- ✔ The rotating or turning effect of a force about a fixed point or fixed axis is called moment of the force about that point.
- ✔ A body is said to be in equilibrium if it does not change its state of rest or uniform motion.
- ✔ A body is said to be in unstable equilibrium if it does not return to its initial position after the removal of the external force causing a change in its position.
- ✔ When a ball is rolled on a horizontal surface, it takes a new position but the position of centre of gravity remains intact.
- ✔ Ratio of useful work done by the machine to the work done on the machine is known as efficiency.

SECTION B: SIMPLE MACHINE

Principle of Simple Machine

In order to cut paper or cloth, we make use of scissors. To squeeze lemon, we use a squeezer. Slopes or inclined planes connecting higher floors to the lower floors are usually seen in tall buildings or hospitals. These slopes are used to carry load easily. These devices make our work easier and convenient.

In all these devices, we apply a small force at some convenient point and a greater force acts on the body at another point in desired direction. These devices are known as simple machines.

Nut cracker on its own cannot crack a nut. Energy or the force has to be applied to the nut cracker to crack the nuts. This force applied to the machine to overcome resistance is called effort or power, which is denoted by P.

In the above case of nut cracker, the force exerted on the machine or the cracker to overcome resistance is called effort and the force required to crack the nut is called load.

For any machine, the effort applied or the energy supplied to the machine is used to move machine parts. It is partly used to overcome friction and the remaining part of the energy is used to do useful work. Thus, all the energy supplied to the machine is not used in doing useful work. Hence, the useful work done by the machine is always less than the actual work done on the machine.

The machine whose parts are weightless and frictionless is called ideal machine. In an ideal machine, the output energy is equal to the input energy or in other words, all the work done on the machine is used in overcoming resistance or the load.

Thus, in an ideal machine or perfect machine, output is equal to input.

$$\text{Work done by the machine} = \text{Work done on the machine}$$

This is known as the principle of a machine. Ideal machine cannot be realized in practice because it is impossible to have a machine whose parts are weightless and frictionless.

Mechanical Advantage

The ratio of load to effort is known as mechanical advantage (M.A.).

$$\therefore \text{M.A.} = \frac{\text{Load } (W)}{\text{Effort } (P)}$$

If a large load is lifted with small effort, then the mechanical advantage is greater than one. The effort applied on the machine is used to run the machine parts, to overcome friction and to do useful work. Thus, the total load is the sum of the force to overcome the moveable parts, load due to friction and the useful load.

This ratio of total load to effort is called ideal mechanical advantage (I.M.A.)

Therefore, $$\text{I.M.A.} = \frac{\text{Total load}}{\text{Effort}}$$

The ratio of useful load to effort is called actual mechanical advantage (A.M.A.)

Therefore, $$\text{A.M.A.} = \frac{\text{Useful load}}{\text{Effort}}$$

Info Bytes!

Mechanical Advantage is the factor by which a machine multiplies the force put into it.

Velocity Ratio

Consider a load W lifted using a crow bar as shown in the Fig. 2.39. The effort P moves a certain distance 'x', then the load moves through a distance 'y' in the same interval of time in which the effort moves. The ratio of displacement of effort to the displacement of load is called velocity ratio (V.R.).

$$\text{V.R.} = \frac{\text{Displacement of the effort}}{\text{Displacement of the load}} \Rightarrow V.R. = \frac{x}{y}$$

Dividing the displacement of effort and load by time, we get V.R. = $(x/t) \div (y/t)$, where, t is time in which the load or the effort moves.

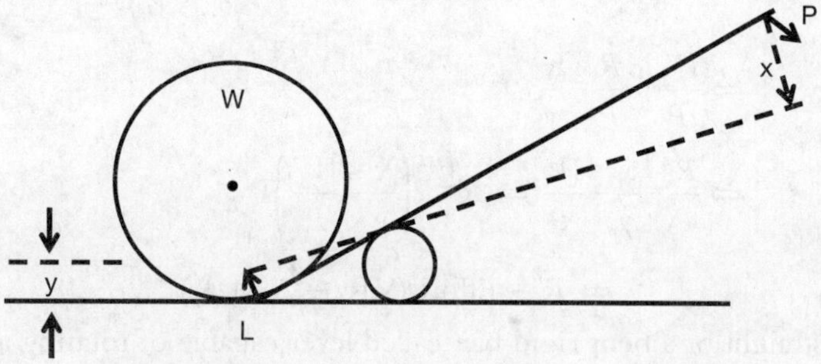

Figure 2.39 A load *W* lifted using a crow bar

$$\therefore \quad \text{V.R.} = \frac{\text{Velocity of the effort}}{\text{Velocity of the load}}$$

Efficiency (η)

It has already been pointed out that the actual work done by a machine is always less than the work done on the machine. The ratio of useful work done by the machine to the work done on the machine is known as efficiency.

$$\text{Efficiency} = \frac{\text{Useful work done by the machine}}{\text{Work done on the machine}}$$

Useful work done by the machine is the work done to overcome useful load (the output) and the work done on the machine is called input.

$$\therefore \text{ Efficiency} = \eta = \frac{\text{Output}}{\text{Input}}$$

In practice, since the output is less than input, efficiency of a machine is always less than one or 100%. For ideal machines, output is equal to input. Hence, the efficiency of an ideal machine is 100%.

Efficiency is defined as.

$$\left(\frac{\text{Mechanical Advantage}}{\text{Velocity Ratio}}\right) \times 100$$

$$\eta = \frac{\text{Work done in overcoming load}}{\text{Work done on the machine}}$$

If P, is the effort which displaces through x in overcoming a load W, and y is the displacement of the load, then output $= W \times y$ and input $= P \times x$.

Hence,

$$\text{Efficiency, } \eta = \frac{W \times y}{P \times x}$$

$$\eta = \frac{W/P}{x/y} \qquad (\because \text{Work} = \text{Force} \times \text{Displacement})$$

$$\eta = \frac{\left(\dfrac{\text{Load}}{\text{Effort}}\right)}{\left(\dfrac{\text{Displacement of effort}}{\text{Displacement of the load}}\right)} \Rightarrow \eta = \frac{\text{Mechanical advantage (M.A)}}{\text{Velocity ratio (V.R)}}$$

This gives the relation between efficiency, mechanical advantage and velocity ratio.

If W_1 is the useful load and R is the resistance due to moveable parts and the friction, then the total load $W = W_1 + R$.

In the case of a machine having friction and weight, work done in overcoming the total load is equal to work done by the effort.

$$\Rightarrow (W_1 + R) \times y = P \times x$$

$$\Rightarrow \frac{W_1}{P} + \frac{R}{P} = \frac{x}{y}$$

$$\Rightarrow \frac{R}{P} = \frac{x}{y} - \frac{W_1}{P} \Rightarrow R = P\left(\frac{x}{y} - \frac{W_1}{P}\right)$$

$$\Rightarrow R = \text{Effort (V.R.} - \text{A.M.A.)}$$

A simple machine can be a straight or a bent rigid bar, called lever capable of rotating about a fixed point, or it might be a rigid flat surface inclined at an angle called inclined plane. Thus, simple machines can be classified into levers and inclined planes.

Pulley and wheel-and-axle are modifications of lever. Inclined plane is modified into wedge and screw.

Levers

It is a rigid bar, straight or bent rigid body. The fixed point about which the lever rotates is called fulcrum (F).

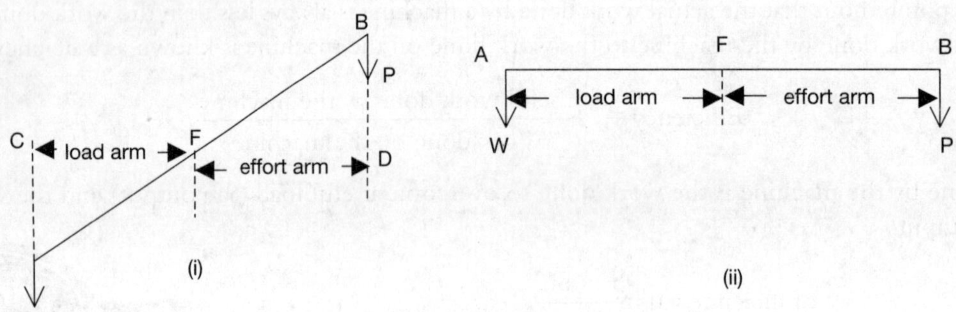

Figure 2.40 A See-Saw

In a see-saw, the load is applied at the end A and the effort P to lift the load is applied at B. The perpendicular distance between the load and the fulcrum is called load arm and the perpendicular distance between the effort and the fulcrum is called effort arm. Thus, in the above diagram (ii), load arm is CF, the effort arm is DF.

In the above example, for the see-saw to be in equilibrium, the algebraic sum of the moment of forces about the fulcrum should be equal to zero.

$$\Rightarrow W \times AF - P \times BF = 0 \text{ or } W \times AF = P \times BF$$

Thus, $\quad \text{Load} \times \text{Load arm} = \text{Effort} \times \text{Effort arm}$

This is called principle of lever. From principle of lever,

$$\frac{\text{Load}}{\text{Effort}} = \frac{\text{Effort arm}}{\text{Load arm}}$$

But $\quad \text{Load/Effort} = \text{Mechanical advantage (M.A.)}$

$$\therefore \quad \text{M.A} = \frac{\text{Effort arm}}{\text{Load arm}}$$

Thus, mechanical advantage of a lever increases with increase in the length of its effort arm. In the case of cutting pliers or a nut cracker, the length of the effort arm is greater than that of the load arm, so, less effort is used to cut a wire or crack a nut.

Depending upon the relative positions of load, effort and fulcrum, levers are classified into first order, second order and third order levers.

First-order Lever

In the case of a see-saw, cutters, crowbar, pliers, scissors, etc., fulcrum lies between the effort and the load. This type of lever is known as a first-order lever. It is shown in figure given below.

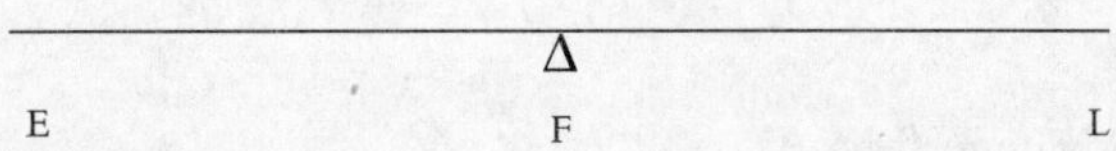

Usually in a first-order lever, the length of the effort arm is greater than that of the load arm. Thus, the mechanical advantage of a first-order lever, in general, is greater than or equal to one. But in scissors, the effort arm is shorter than the load arm, and the mechanical advantage is less than one.

Second-order Levers

In nutcracker, squeezer, hinges, etc., load lies between effort and fulcrum. These type of levers are called second-order levers. In a second-order lever, the effort arm is greater than the load arm. Hence, the mechanical advantage of second-order lever is always greater than one. It is shown in figure given below.

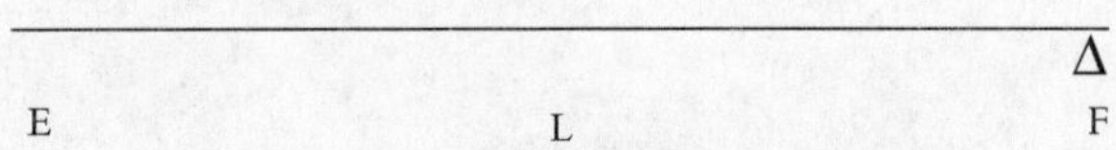

Third-order Lever

In forceps, tongs, knife or when a person swims, the effort lies between load and the fulcrum. This type of lever is called third-order lever. In third-order lever the load arm is longer than the effort arm. Thus, the mechanical advantage of the third-order lever is always less than one. First and second-order levers are force multipliers and the third-order levers are speed multipliers.

Pulley

It is a wheel or a flat disc which has a grooved edge or a rim. A pulley rotates about a fixed axis which passes through the centre. The axle is fixed to a frame or a block. If the block is clamped, the pulley is called fixed pulley and if the block is not clamped, the pulley is called moveable pulley.

Single Fixed Pulley

It is a single pulley which is usually used to draw water from well. The frame of the pulley is clamped.

A rope is passed through the groove. To one end of the rope, a load is tied and effort is applied at the other end. The effort is applied in the downward direction. The tension '*T*' of the rope acts on both the sides of the rope upward.

If the pulley is not rotating and the load due to friction and moveable parts is neglected, then both the load and the effort are equal to the tension in the string.

Thus, $W = P = T$

$$\text{Mechanical advantage} = \frac{\text{Load}}{\text{Efforts}} = \frac{W}{P} = \frac{T}{T} = 1$$

In practice, the effort applied is greater than load due to friction in the moveable parts of the pulley.

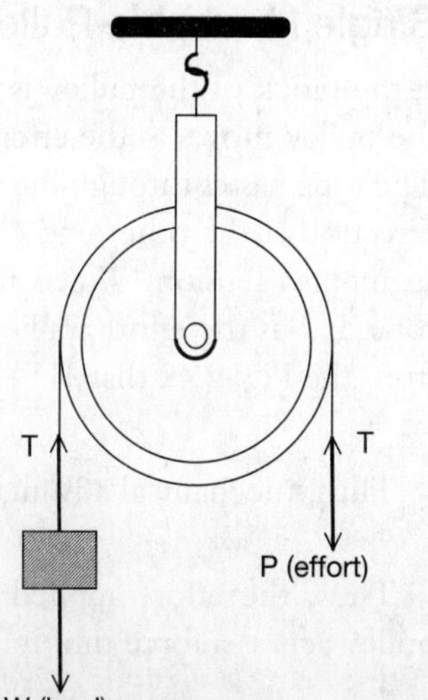

Figure 2.41 Single fixed pulley

If the effort moves through a distance 'x', load is lifted through the same distance also.

$$\text{Hence, velocity ratio} = \frac{\text{Distance moved by the effort}}{\text{Distance moved by the load}} = 1$$

Thus, there is no gain in mechanical advantage or in velocity ratio of the pulley. It is used only to change the direction of effort. It is easier to exert effort in the downward direction, i.e., in the direction of gravity which makes lifting of loads convenient.

Efficiency of an Ideal Pulley

$$\eta = \frac{\text{Ideal mechanical advatage (I.M.A)}}{\text{Velocity ratio}}$$

I.M.A. = 1 and V.R. = 1

$\eta = 1$ or 100%

Thus, the efficiency of an ideal pulley is 100%.

Info Bytes!

A single pulley changes the direction of the force required to lift a load.

In practice, the effort applied is used to lift useful loads, to overcome loads due to friction and load due to moveable parts. But the total load is equal to effort. If the useful load is W_1 and R is the load due to friction and moveable parts, then total load = $W_1 + R$.

$$\Rightarrow W_1 + R = P$$

$$\Rightarrow \frac{W_1+R}{P} = 1 \Rightarrow \frac{W_1}{P} + \frac{R}{P} = 1$$

$$\Rightarrow \frac{W_1+R}{P} = 1 - \frac{R}{P}.$$

$$\text{But } \frac{W_1}{P} = \frac{\text{Useful load}}{\text{Effort}} = \text{Actual Mechanical Advantage (A.M.A)}$$

$$\therefore \text{A.M.A.} = 1 - \frac{R}{P}$$

Single Moveable Pulley

If the block of the pulley is not clamped, it is called moveable pulley. In this case, the pulley moves as the effort pulls the rope. One end of a rope is fixed to a hook. The rope passes through the rim of the pulley and the effort is applied in the upward direction at the other end of rope. The moveable pulley divides the rope into two segments. Tension 'T' acts in an upward direction along the two segments of the rope. If P is the effort applied to overcome total load, then $P = T$ and it is obvious from the Fig. 2.42 that $W = T + T = 2T$, where W is the total load.

$$\text{Thus, mechanical advantage} = \frac{\text{Load}}{\text{Effort}} = \frac{W}{P} = \frac{2T}{T} = 2$$

Thus, the effort applied is equal to half the load. Hence, a single moveable pulley acts as a force multiplier. If the effort moves through a distance 'x', the load is lifted through a distance $\frac{x}{2}$.

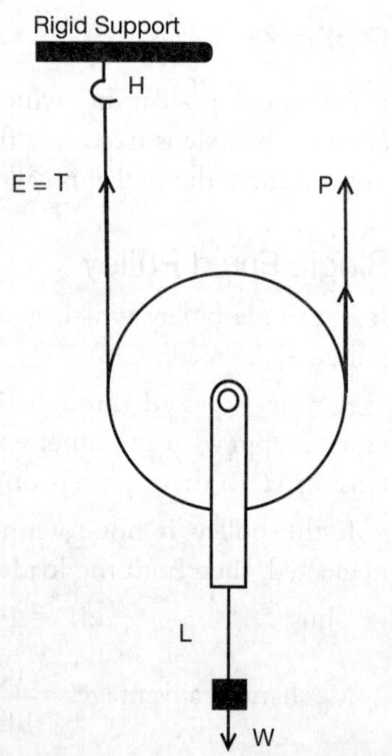

Figure 2.42 Single moveable pulley

Thus, velocity ratio of the single moveable pulley

$$\text{V.R.} = \frac{\text{Displacement of the effort}}{\text{Displacement of the load}}$$

$$\text{V.R.} = \frac{x}{\frac{x}{2}} = \frac{2x}{x} = 2.$$

The efficiency of a single moveable pulley

$$\eta = \frac{\text{M.A.}}{\text{V.R.}} = \frac{2}{2} = 1 \text{ or } 100\%$$

If W_1 is the useful load and R is load due to friction and moveable parts of the machine,

$$\text{Mechanical advantage} = \frac{\text{Total load}}{\text{Efforts}} \Rightarrow \text{M.A.} = \frac{W_1 + R}{P}$$

Since $$\text{M.A.} = \frac{\text{Total load}}{\text{Effort}} = \frac{W}{P} = 2\text{, we get}$$

$$\frac{W_1}{P} + \frac{R}{P} = 2 \text{ or } \frac{W_1}{P} = 2 - \frac{R}{P}$$

where, $\frac{W_1}{P}$ is the actual mechanical advantage.

Hence, $$\text{A.M.A.} = 2 - \frac{R}{P}$$

Since the ratio of R to P is a positive quantity, A.M.A. of a single moveable pulley is always less than 2.

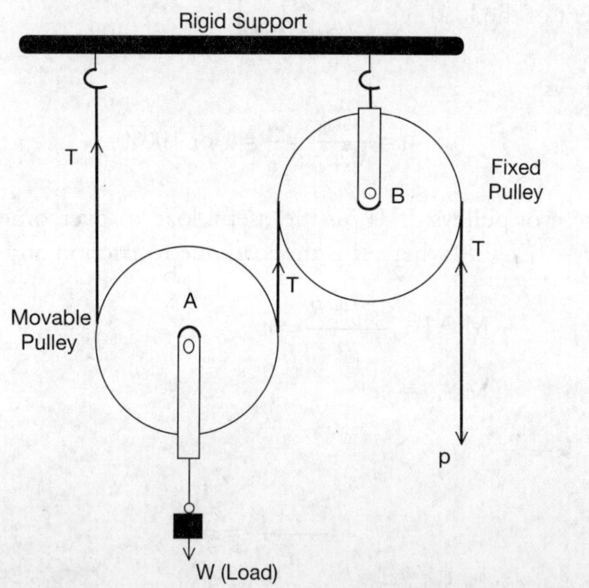

Figure 2.43 Single movable pulley with a fixed pulley

Since it is not convenient to apply effort in the upward direction, a single moveable pulley is combined with a fixed pulley to give the same M.A. and V.R. and it is easier to apply the effort using the combination of the fixed pulley and moveable pulley because the effort is applied in the downward direction. It consists of two pulleys. One pulley (B) is fixed and this pulley helps to change the direction of effort. The other pulley (A) moves along with the rope. The load is attached to the moveable pulley.

So, one end of rope is fixed to a hook and the rope passes through the moveable pulley and the fixed pulley. The moveable pulley moves along the two segments of the rope. If the effort moves through a distance x, each length of the segment of rope is decreased by an amount equal to $(x/2)$.

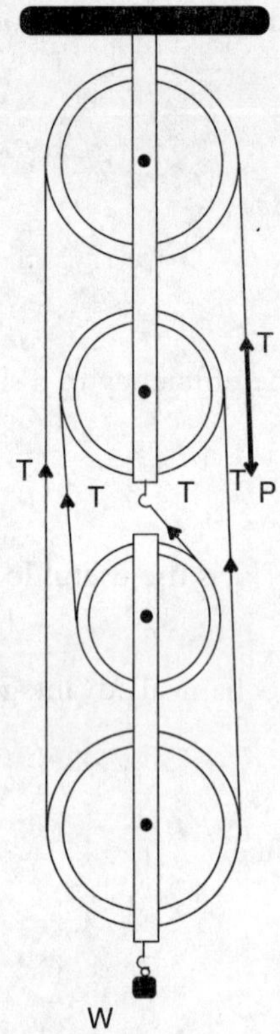

Figure 2.44 Block and tackle for four

Sheath Pulley System or Block and Tackle System

It consists of two sets of pulleys. One set of pulleys is attached to a rigid support at the top and is called block. The lower set of pulleys carries a load and is called tackle.

One end of the string or rope is fixed to a hook of the tackle. The rope passes round the rim of all the pulleys and the effort is applied at the free end of the rope in the downward direction, as shown in the Fig. 2.44.

Tackle is supported by 'n' segments of the rope, where 'n' is the number of pulleys in the system. Tension on each segment of the rope is T and it acts vertically upwards.

If P is the effort used to overcome load W, then $W = nT$ and $P = T$. Thus, the ideal mechanical advantage of the pulley system, $= \dfrac{W}{P} = \dfrac{nT}{T} = n$

Thus, the I.M.A. of a pulley system is equal to number of pulleys in the system. The effort required to lift the load is (W/n). Thus, the system of pulleys acts as a force multiplier and it also changes the direction of force.

Thus, the larger the number of pulleys, the lesser is the effort. If the effort moves through a distance x, then length of each segment of the rope is decreased by (W/n).

Konnect

Since M.A. = n, there is no gain in energy.

Thus, the velocity ratio of the pulley system (V.R.)

$$= \frac{\text{Displacement of the effort}}{\text{Displacement of the load}} \Rightarrow \text{V.R.} = \frac{x}{\left(\frac{x}{n}\right)} = n$$

The efficiency of system of pulleys

$$\eta = \frac{\text{M.A}}{\text{V.R.}} = \frac{n}{n} = 1 \text{ or } 100\%$$

η is 100% only in an ideal system of pulleys. If W_1 is the useful load to overcome by the effort, then M.A. = (W/P), where W is the total load. But $W = W_1 + R$ where R is the load due to friction and moveable parts of the system.

Then,
$$\text{M.A.} = \frac{W_1 + R}{P} = n$$

Since
$$\text{M.A.} = n$$

We get

$$\frac{W_1 + R}{P} = n$$

$$\frac{W_1}{P} + \frac{R}{P} = n$$

But (W_1/P) is the actual mechanical advantage of the pulley system A.M.A.

$$\Rightarrow \qquad \text{A.M.A} + \frac{R}{P} = n$$

Hence,
$$\text{A.M.A.} = n - \frac{R}{P}$$

Since (R/P) is positive, A.M.A. of the pulley system is always less than n.

Effect of Weight of Pulleys in Tackle

If W_2 is the weight of the pulleys in the tackle, then the load and weight is balanced by nT, where n is the number of pulleys and T is the tension on each part of the rope. Thus,

$$W + W_2 = nT = nP \qquad (\because T = P)$$

where, P is the effort

$$\Rightarrow W + W_2 = nP$$

$$\Rightarrow \frac{W}{P} + \frac{W_2}{P} = n \Rightarrow \frac{W}{P} = n - \frac{W_2}{P}$$

Hence,
$$\text{M.A} = n - \frac{W}{P} \qquad \left(\because \frac{W}{P} = M.A\right)$$

The efficiency of the system of pulleys,

$$\eta = \frac{\text{M.A.}}{\text{V.R.}}$$

$$\Rightarrow \qquad \eta = \frac{n - \frac{W_2}{P}}{n} \qquad (\because \text{V.R} = n)$$

$$\Rightarrow \qquad \eta = 1 - \frac{W_2}{nP}$$

Therefore, to achieve higher efficiency in the system of pulley, the weights of the pulleys in the tackle should be lesser.

Wheel and Axle

Let us study the following figure to understand the concept of wheel and axle.

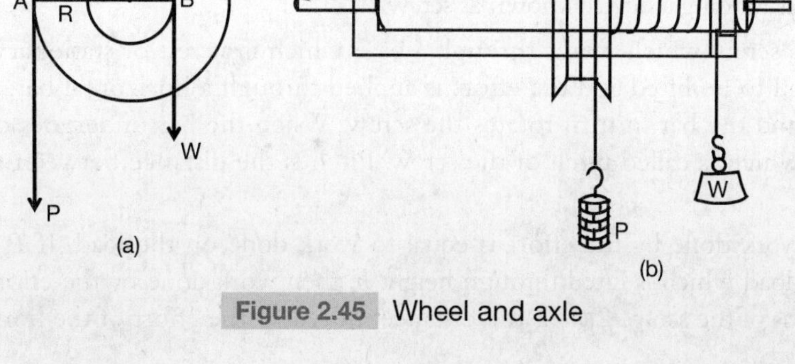

Figure 2.45 Wheel and axle

A wheel is fixed to a strong cylindrical axle such that they have a common axis. The radius of the wheel (R) is greater than the radius of the cylindrical axle (r). A string is wound around the cylinder. Load is attached to the free end of this string. Effort is applied to the free end of the string which is wound round the wheel. The windings of the rope on the wheel is in the opposite direction to that of the windings on the axle. The rotating effect of the wheel is equal to the rotating effect of the cylinder.

$\Rightarrow$ Moment of the wheel about the axis = Moment of the axle about the axis

$\Rightarrow P \times R = W \times r$, where, P is the effort and W is the load.

$$\Rightarrow \frac{W}{P} = \frac{R}{r}$$

But (W/P) is the M.A.

$$\text{M.A.} = \frac{R}{r}$$

$$\text{M.A} = \frac{\text{Radius of the wheel}}{\text{Radius of the axle}}$$

Screw Jack

Let us study the following figure to understand the concept of screw jack.

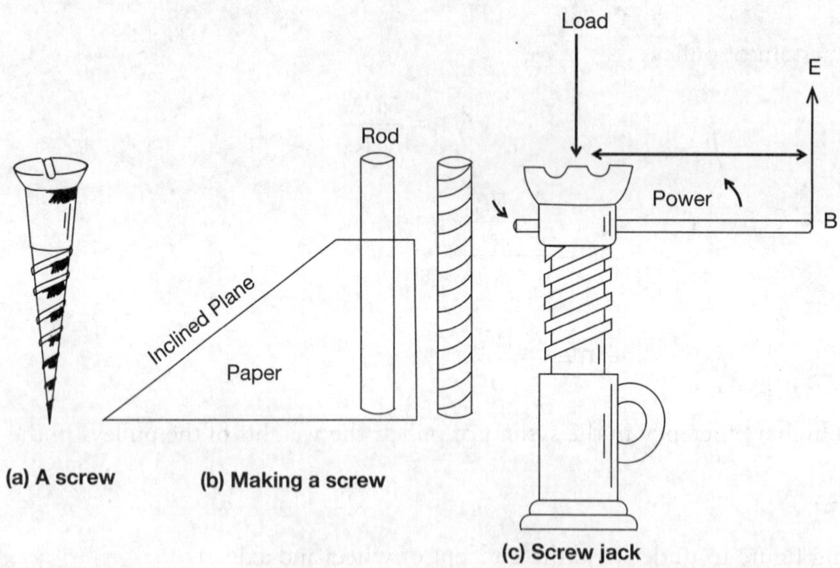

Figure 2.46 (a) A Screw, (b) Making a Screw, (c) Screw jack

When a tyre of a car or a heavy vehicle is punctured, the vehicle should be lifted up so as to remove or replace the tyres. These vehicles are lifted up easily using a device known as screw jack.

A screw jack consists of a screw which works through a base which is at rest or stationary. The screw jack is placed under the vehicle or the load to be lifted and the effort is applied through a horizontal bar. The effort E applied gives a turning effect to the bar and the bar in turn rotates the screw. When the bar undergoes one complete rotation, the screw is raised by a height which is called pitch of the screw. Pitch is the distance between two consecutive threads of the screw.

For an ideal screw jack, work done by the effort is equal to work done on the load. If P is the effort applied to the horizontal bar and W is the load which is lifted through height h, then work done by the effort is $2\pi\ell \times P$ where ℓ is the length of the bar from the axis of the screw. $2\pi\,\ell$ is the distance moved by the effort of the horizontal bar.

Work done on the load = $W \times h$, where 'h' is the pitch of the screw.

Work done by effort = Work done on the load.

$$\Rightarrow 2\pi\ell \times P = W \times h$$

$$\Rightarrow \frac{W}{P} = \frac{2\pi\ell}{h}$$

Ratio of load to effort (W/P) is the M.A. of the screw jack.

Thus, M·A. of the screw jack $= \dfrac{2\pi\ell}{h}$

Inclined Plane

Let us study the following figure to understand the concept of inclined plane.

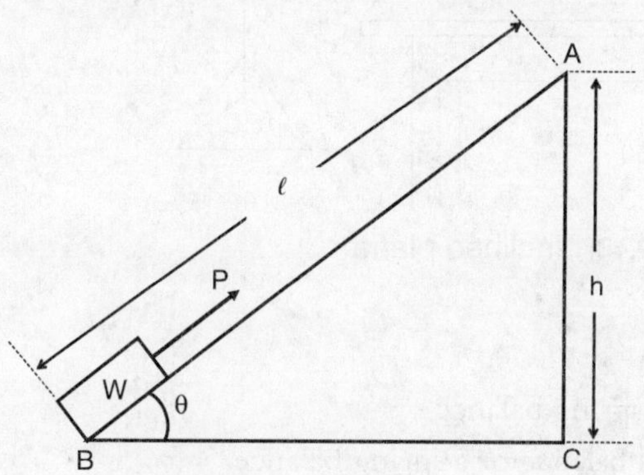

Figure 2.47 Inclined plane

Info Bytes!

An inclined plane reduces the effort needed to lift an object to a certain height.

In order to climb up a hill or top of a building, we make use of slopes or a ladder or a staircase. We make use of slopes to take vehicles in and out of the house, garage or parking slots at higher level. Flyovers are constructed with slopes. Thus, by using the slopes, we can easily move the load against gravity to a higher location. Inclined plane is a smooth rigid plane inclined to the horizontal.

Mechanical Advantage of an Inclined Plane When Efforts Act Parallel to the Plane

Consider an inclined plane AB inclined to the horizontal at an angle θ. Let W be the load to be moved along the plane AB by applying effort P.

If the surface of the plane is considered to be frictionless, then the output work is equal to the input work, i.e., work done by the effort is equal to work done on the load.

$$\Rightarrow \quad P \times AB = W \times AC$$

$$\frac{W}{P} = \frac{AB}{AC}$$

$$\frac{W}{P} = \frac{\text{Length of the plane } (\ell)}{\text{Height of the plane } (h)}$$

From Fig. 2.47, $\dfrac{AC}{AB} = \sin\theta$

$$\therefore \frac{W}{P} = \frac{1}{\text{Sin}\theta} = \frac{\ell}{h}$$

But (W/P) is the M.A. of the inclined plane.

$$\therefore \text{M.A.} = \frac{W}{P} = \frac{\ell}{H} = \frac{1}{\text{Sin}\theta}$$

From the above expression, it is obvious that lesser the inclination of the slope, lesser is the effort to raise a given load along the inclined plane. Thus, greater effort is required to climb a steep hill.

Experiment to Determine Mechanical Advantage of an Inclined Plane

Apparatus Required: Inclined plane, meter scale, physical balance, scale pan, roller and weights.

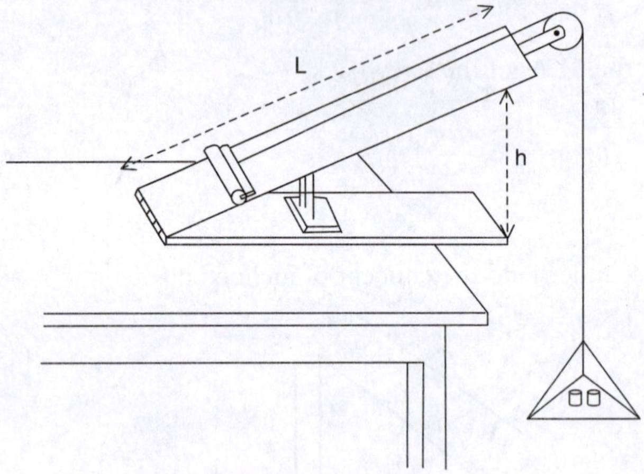

Figure 2.48 Inclined plane

Procedure

1. Inclined plane is inclined at a suitable angle or a spring balance.
2. Weight of the roller '*W*' is found using a physical balance or a spring balance.
3. The roller is attached to one end of the string and the string is passed over a pulley. To the free end of the string, is attached a scale pan whose mass (*S*) is known.
4. The length '*L*' of the plane and the height '*H*' is measured using a metre scale.
5. Suitable weights are added in the scale pan, so that the roller just ascends the plane. The weight W_1 in the scale pan is noted down.
6. The weights in the scale pan are gradually decreased until the roller just descends. The weight W_2 in the scale pan is noted down.
7. Experiment is repeated for different heights of the plane and the results are tabulated.

Observation

Weight of the roller, $W =$ ______ g^{-wt}

Weight of the scale pan, $S =$ ______ g^{-wt}

Length of the plane, $L =$ ______ cm

Trial No.	W_1 (g)	W_2 (g)	L (m)	$P = S + \left(\frac{W_1 + W_2}{2}\right)$	L/H	$\frac{W}{P}$
1						
2						
3						
4						
5						

P is the effort $= S + \left(\frac{W_1 + W_2}{2}\right)$ kg^{-wt}.

Result: It is found that $\frac{W}{P} \approx \frac{L}{H}$ and M.A. $= \frac{W}{P}$.

EXAMPLE 2.11 A machine is used to displace a load of 400 N through 50 cm by an effort of 100 N. If the efficiency of the machine is 80%,

(i) find its mechanical advantage and velocity ratio.

(ii) find the distance moved by the effort.

(iii) find the resistance due to the moveable parts of the machine and friction.

SOLUTION

(i) In the given problem

Load, $W = 400$ N.

Distance moved by the load $= y = 50$ cm $= 0{\cdot}5$ m.

Effort, $P = 100$ N.

Efficiency $= \eta = 80\%$.

$$\text{M.A.} = \frac{\text{Load}}{\text{Effort}} = \frac{W}{P} = \frac{400}{100} = 4$$

Thus, the M.A. of the machine is 4.

To find V.R, we can use the relation,

$$\eta = \frac{\text{M.A}}{\text{V.R}}$$

$$\Rightarrow \frac{80}{100} = \frac{4}{\text{V.R.}}$$

$$\therefore \text{V.R.} = \frac{4 \times 100}{8}$$

$$\text{V.R.} = 5.$$

V.R. of the machine is 5.

(ii) To find the distance moved by the effort, we use the relation

$$\text{V.R.} = \frac{\text{Distance moved by the effort}}{\text{Distance moved by the effort}} = \frac{x}{y}$$

where, x is the distance moved by the effort, and y is the distance moved by the load.

$$\Rightarrow 5 = \frac{x}{0.5}$$

$$\therefore x = 0{\cdot}5 \times 5 = 2{\cdot}5 \text{ m}$$

Hence, distance moved by the effort = 2·5 m.

(iii) Resistance due to moveable parts of the machine and friction.

$R = P$ (V.R – A.M.A)

where R is the resistance due to moveable parts and friction.

A.M.A. is the actual mechanical advantage.

$$\text{A.M.A.} = \frac{\text{useful load}}{\text{effort}}$$

Useful load = 400 N

$$\therefore \text{A.M.A.} = \frac{400}{100} = 4$$

$$\therefore R = 100\,(5 - 4) = 100 \text{ N}.$$

Thus, the load due to moveable parts and friction is 100 N.

EXAMPLE 2.12 A nutcracker is used to crack open a walnut. When an effort of 0.5 N is applied at the end of the handles (effort arm) of the nutcracker, the nut still doesn't crack. The effort arm of the nutcracker is 15 cm, while the load arm (where the nut is placed) is 2 cm in length. Calculate the resistance offered by the walnut.

SOLUTION

According to the principle of a simple machine (lever principle),

Load × Load arm = Effort × Effort arm

Now, given is, Effort, P = 0.5N; Effort arm = 15 cm (0.15 m); and Load arm = 2 cm (0.02m)

$$\text{Load} = \frac{\text{Effort} \times \text{Effort Arm}}{\text{Load Arm}}$$

$$\text{Load} = \frac{0.5 \times 0.15}{0.02} = \frac{0.075}{0.02} = 3.75 \text{ N}$$

Hence, the resistance offered by the walnut is 3.75 N.

EXAMPLE 2.13 A farmer lifts a 20 kg sack of grain from a depth of 7 m using a single fixed pulley by applying an effort of 240 N. Determine the mechanical advantage, velocity ratio, and efficiency of the pulley system. (Assume g = 10 m/s^2)

SOLUTION

Weight of grain (W) = 20 kg

Depth from which the grain is lifted (d) = 7 m

Effort (P) = 240 N

Load (W) = Weight of grain × Acceleration due to gravity = 20 kg × 10 m/s^2 = 200N

$$\text{Mechanical Advantage, M.A.} = \frac{W}{P} = \frac{200\text{ N}}{240\text{ N}} = 0.8333$$

For a single fixed pulley, the Velocity Ratio (V.R.) is the ratio of the distance moved by the effort to the distance moved by the load. Since both distances are equal in a single fixed pulley: V.R. = 1

$$\text{Efficiency (h)} = \frac{\text{M.A.}}{\text{V.R.}} = \frac{0.8333}{1} = 0.8333$$

Therefore, the efficiency is approximately 83.33%

EXAMPLE 2.14 A block and tackle system of pulleys consists of 8 pulleys. A load of 1000 kgf is lifted by an effort of 250 kgf. Find the mechanical advantage, velocity ratio and efficiency.

SOLUTION

In the given problem

Number of pulleys, $n = 8$

Load = W = 1000 kgf

Effort, P = 250 kgf

$$\therefore \text{M.A.} = \frac{\text{load}}{\text{efforts}} = \frac{1000}{250} = 4$$

If the effort moves through a distance 'x', then the load moves through a distance x/n.

$$\text{V.R.} = \frac{\text{Distance moved by the effort}}{\text{Distance moved by the load}} = \frac{x}{x/n} = n = 8$$

$$\text{Efficiency, } \eta = \frac{\text{M.A}}{\text{V.R}} = \frac{4}{8} = 0.5 = 50\%$$

Thus, the efficiency of the given system of pulleys is 50%.

EXAMPLE 2.15 A screw jack is used to lift a vehicle of weight 10,000 N through a height of 0·25 m from the ground. If the length of the rod is 0·3 m, find the effort and mechanical advantage used to lift the load. (Assume the jack to be ideal.)

SOLUTION

Given, load (W) = 10,000 N

Height through which the load is lifted, (h) = 0·25 m

Length of the rod = 0·3 m

For an ideal machine, work done on the load is equal to work done by the effort.

$\Rightarrow W \times h = 2\pi\ell \times P$, where P is the effort.

$$\therefore P = \frac{W \times h}{2\pi\ell}$$

$$= \frac{10{,}000 \times 0.25}{2\pi\ell \times 0.3} = \frac{25000}{0.6\pi} = 1326.29\text{N}$$

$$\text{M.A.} = \frac{\text{load}}{\text{effort}} = \frac{10{,}000}{1326.29} = 7.539$$

Thus, the M.A. = 7·539

POINTS TO REMEMBER

- ✔ The ratio of load to effort is known as mechanical advantage (M.A.).
- ✔ Force exerted on the machine or the cracker to overcome resistance is called effort and the force required to crack the nut is called load.
- ✔ The machine whose parts are weightless and frictionless is called ideal machine.
- ✔ Total load is the sum of the force to overcome the moveable parts, load due to friction and the useful load.
- ✔ Ratio of useful work done by the machine to the work done on the machine is known as efficiency.
- ✔ Lever is a rigid bar, straight or bent rigid body. The fixed point about which the lever rotates is called fulcrum (F).
- ✔ A pulley rotates about a fixed axis which passes through the centre.
- ✔ If the block of the pulley is not clamped, it is called moveable pulley.
- ✔ The efficiency of an ideal pulley is 100%.
- ✔ If the block is clamped, the pulley is called fixed pulley and if the block is not clamped, the pulley is called moveable pulley.

SECTION C: CIRCULAR MOTION

When a Body is Said to be in Circular Motion

When we open or close a door, the door rotates about a fixed axis (hinges). Each particle or point on the door describes an arc with its centre at the foot of the perpendicular line drawn from the particle to the axis of rotation. Thus, the particles of the door undergo a circular motion.

Hence, a body is said to be in circular motion if every particle in it moves along a circular path and the centre of all these circles lies on the axis of rotation.

If a particle moves along a circle with uniform speed, then the motion of the particle is called uniform circular motion.

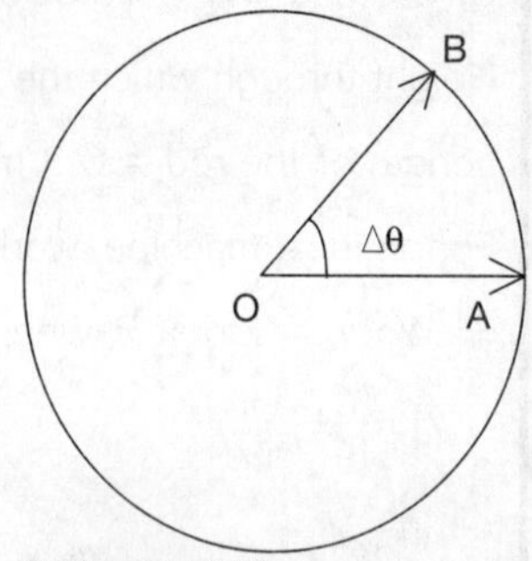

Figure 2.49 A particle in uniform circular motion

Examples:

1. Motion of a person in a giant wheel or a merry-go-round.
2. Motion of the Moon round the Earth.

Consider a particle in a rigid body undergoing uniform circular motion along a circle of radius r. In uniform circular motion, though the speed of the particle is constant, its linear velocity is not constant. The magnitude of linear velocity is constant but its direction is along the tangent to the circumference of the circular path. Thus, the direction of the linear velocity changes continuously. According to Newton's first law, the particle should move along the tangent due to inertia of direction. Instead the particle changes its direction and moves along a circular path due to a net external force acting on it. Thus, the particle undergoes displacement along the curve.

Thus, the radius vector $\vec{OA}$ drawn from the centre of circular path to the particle rotates. The angle through which the radius vector turns is known as 'angular displacement'. The angular displacement, $\Delta\theta = \angle AOB$. Its value can be found out using $\Delta\theta = \frac{\lambda}{r}$ = length of arc AB/radius r. Its unit is radian. (2π radian = 360°)

Let the particle be at point 'A' at time t_1. Due to the net external force acting on it, the particle undergoes uniform circular motion and let the particle after time t_2 be at B. Let $\Delta\theta$ be the angular displacement of the radius vector,

The rate of angular displacement is called angular velocity. It is represented by ω.

$$\omega = \frac{\Delta\theta}{t_2 - t_1} = \frac{\Delta\omega}{\Delta t}$$

where, Δt is small interval of time.

Hence,

$$\omega = \frac{\text{Change in angular position}}{\text{Time}} = \frac{\text{Angular displacement}}{\text{Time}}$$

Angular displacement is measured in radian and time in second. Hence, the S.I. unit of angular velocity is radian per second. When the time interval Δt tends to zero, then the ratio of $\Delta\theta$ to Δt is called instantaneous angular velocity.

Instantaneous angular velocity,

$$\omega = \underset{\Delta t \to 0}{Lt} \frac{\Delta\theta}{\Delta t} = \frac{d\theta}{dt}$$

Relation among *v*, *r* and ω

Consider a particle moving with constant speed v along a circular path of radius r. Let θ be angular displacement in time interval t, then the angular velocity,

$\omega = \frac{\theta}{t}$, s = APB = Length of the minor arc.

But $\theta = \frac{s}{r}$

$\therefore\ \omega = \frac{s}{rt}$

But displacement/time = Linear velocity, v

$\Rightarrow w = \frac{v}{r}$ or $v = w\ r$

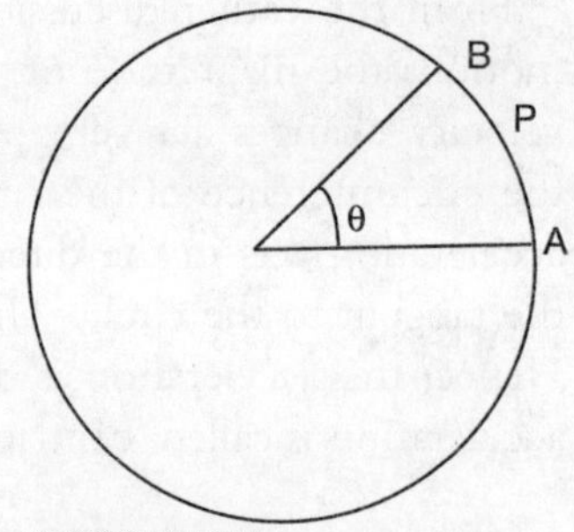

Figure 2.50 A particle moving along a circular path

Alternative Method

Consider a particle moving in a circular path of radius r with uniform speed 'v'. Let $\Delta\theta$ be an extremely small angular displacement of the radius vector $\overline{OA}$ in time interval Δt.

Length of the arc AB = $s = r\Delta\theta$

Linear velocity of the particle = $\frac{\text{arc length}}{\Delta t} = \frac{r\Delta\theta}{\Delta t}$

But $\frac{\Delta\theta}{\Delta t}$ = angular velocity = ω

$\therefore\ v = r\omega$

Thus, the above equation gives the relation between linear velocity and angular velocity.

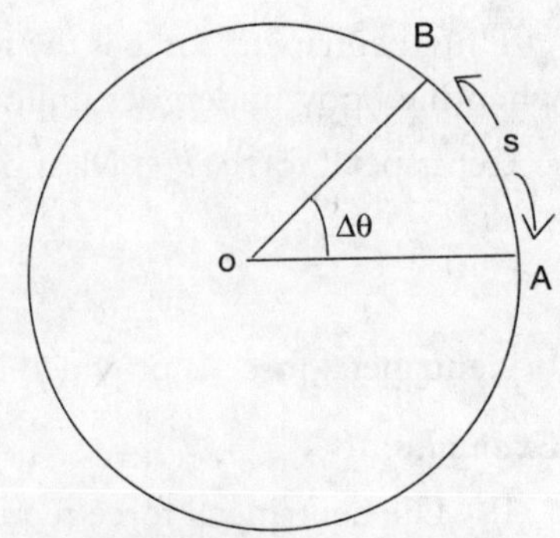

Figure 2.51 A particle moving along a circular path

Angular Momentum

Momentum gained by the body during rotation angular momentum. The angular momentum is defined as $\vec{L} = \vec{r} \times \vec{p}$, where $\vec{P}$ is the linear momentum, $\vec{r}$ and $\vec{P}$ are perpendicular to each other, where r is radius of rotation.

$$L = mvr$$

Thus, angular momentum = mvr

$\because$
$$v = \omega r$$

$$L = mr^2\omega$$

S.I. unit of L= kg m^2 s^{-1} or Js and C.G.S. unit is g cm s^{-2}.

> **Konnect**
> Angular momentum is a measure of the amount of rotation an object has, taking into account its mass and shape.

Period

The time taken by a body to complete one revolution is called its time period of revolution. It is denoted by T.

We know, $\omega = \frac{\Delta Q}{\Delta t}$ and $\Delta Q = 2\pi$

$$\therefore \text{Period} = \frac{2\pi}{\text{Angular velocity}}$$

$$T = \frac{2\pi}{\omega} \text{ or } \omega = \frac{2\pi}{T}$$

From the earlier discussion, we know that when a particle undergoes a circular motion, the magnitude of the velocity remains the same but the direction of the velocity changes at every point. The direction of velocity is along the tangent to the circumference of the circle. Thus, the particle is continuously accelerated. This acceleration acts in the direction of the force. This force is always perpendicular to the tangent to the circle. Thus, the force is directed towards the centre of the circle. Hence, the acceleration is directed towards the centre of the circular path and this acceleration is called 'centripetal acceleration' or normal acceleration or 'radial acceleration'.

Konnect

2π radians = 360°

Centripetal acceleration 'a' is given by, $a = \frac{v^2}{r}$, where, v is the magnitude of linear velocity and r is the radius of the circular path.

Also, since $v = r\omega$, $a = \omega^2 r$

Centripetal Force

It is seen that when a particle undergoes uniform circular motion, a force is required to make the particle change its direction of motion continuously to move along the circular path with a constant speed. This force is always directed towards the centre of the circular path. This force is called centripetal force or radial force (inward force).

Thus, centripetal force is the force which is always directed towards the centre of the circle (i.e., along the radius vector) when the body undergoes uniform circular motion.

Centripetal force, F = Mass of body × Centripetal acceleration

$$\therefore \quad F = m\frac{v^2}{r} = m\omega^2 r \qquad (\because v = \omega r)$$

Centripetal force is provided by an external agency.

Examples:

1. The centripetal force required for a planet to go round the Sun is provided by the gravitational force applied by the Sun on that planet.
2. The centripetal force required for electrons to move round the nucleus is provided by electrostatic force of attraction between the nucleus and the electron.

Centrifugal Force

In kinematics, we have studied that rest or motion is defined depending on a reference. For example, a bird flying is said to be in motion when the reference frame is attached to the ground. But for another bird flying alongside, the first bird appears to be at rest.

Thus, we find that Newton's first law can be applied depending on the reference frame. Hence, whenever no net force acts on a body producing a change of rest or of uniform motion, then there always exists a reference frame in which a body has no acceleration. Such a reference frame is called inertial reference frame or inertial frame.

Example: A car moving with uniform velocity can be considered as an inertial frame, since no force acts on any body placed in the car.

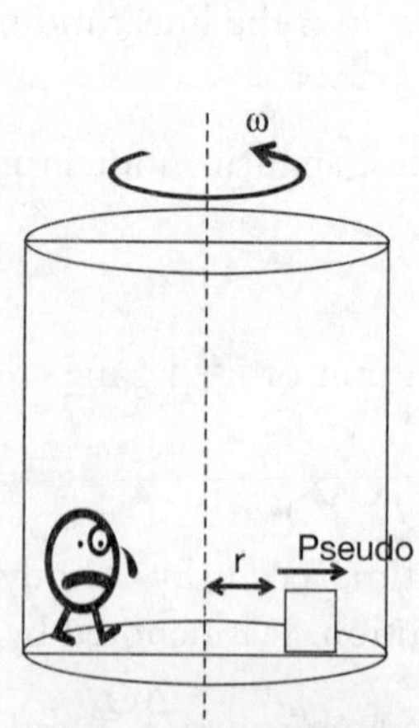

Figure 2.52

However, travelling in a train accelerating forwards, you would observe objects like a box placed on the floor of the coach sliding backward as if a force is acting on them. Thus, a reference frame attached to an accelerating train is a non-inertial reference frame, and the force which appears to be acting on the box is referred to as a pseudo force or a fictitious force. (The force which exists without any external agent is called pseudo force.)

Example: Standing passengers in a bus are thrown forwards when the driver suddenly applies brakes.

Similarly, standing on the rotating platform of a merry-go-round, the hanging seats along the circumference appear to be pushed outward as if a radially outward force acts on them. This pseudo force arising from a circular motion or rotatory motion is referred to as centrifugal force.

Example: Consider a man sitting in a circular chamber rotating about a central vertical axis at a uniform angular velocity, ω rad s^{-1}.

Let a box be resting on the floor at a distance of *r* from the centre.

As the chamber continues to rotate at uniform angular velocity, the man would observe that the box would slide and move towards the wall of the chamber. The box would remain at rest only after it comes into contact with the wall.

Similarly, every particle of the chamber also experiences such a force directed radially outwards.

The centripetal force and centrifugal force are equal in magnitude but opposite in direction.

$$\text{Centrifugal force} = \frac{mv^2}{r} = m\omega^2 r$$

Centripetal force	Centrifugal force
It is always directed towards the centre.	It is directed away from the centre.
It is a real force.	It is a pseudo force.
It is always associated with an external agent, e.g., tension in the string, etc.	Being a pseudo force, it is not associated with any external agent.
It is the cause of a circular motion.	It is the effect of circular motion.
It is the pull on the body towards the centre of the circle.	It is a tendency to move away from the centre of the circle.

Similarities between Centripetal Force and Centripetal Acceleration

1. Magnitude of both the forces is given by the expression $\frac{mv^2}{r}$ or $m\omega^2 r$.
2. In uniform circular motion, their magnitude is constant.
3. The magnitude of each force depends on the mass and the speed of rotation.

Application of Centrifugal Force

Centrifuge

Centrifuge is a device used to separate minute particles of varying densities which cannot be separated by sedimentation.

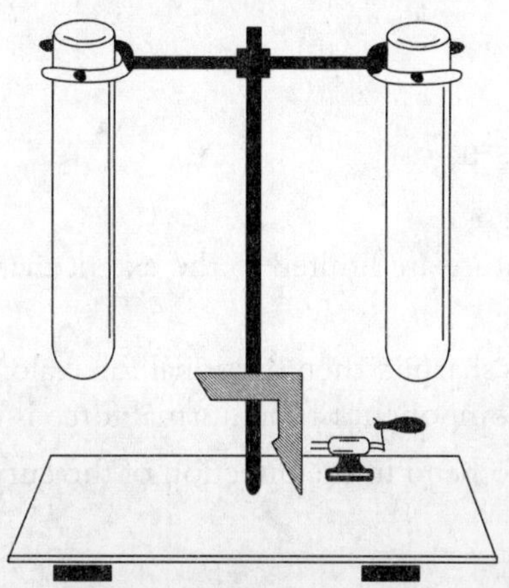

Figure 2.53 Centrifuge

Konnect

- Centripetal force and centrifugal force are not action - reaction pair since both are acting on the same body.
- Centrifugal force is a 'fictitious' force that appears to act on all objects when viewed in a rotating frame.

Its working is similar to the butter churn used to churn curds. It consists of a number of vials suspended to a horizontal frame which is supported by a vertical stand. The vials are filled with solid liquid mixture from which solid particles are to be separated and the vials are rotated in a horizontal plane at a very high speed by an electric motor. Higher density particles move towards the bottom of the vials (small lubes) because centrifugal force for heavier particles is greater than the lighter particles. Thus, the lighter particles move towards the axis and can be easily skimmed off. Thus, particles of different densities are separated.

Centrifuge is used to separate cream from milk, to separate hormones, viuses proteins, etc., from blood.

Laundry Drier or Washing Machine Dryer

It consists of a perforated cylindrical vessel which can rotate about its axis at a very high speed. The clothes to be dried are placed in the cylinder and are rotated with high speed. The adhesive force between water and the cloth is less compared to the centrifugal force acting on the water molecules.

This centrifugal force, forces the water molecules to escape through the holes of the cylindrical vessel. Thus, the wet clothes get dried.

Centrifugal Governor

It works on the principle of a centrifugal force. This device was applied to a steam engine by James Watt. It is a special governor that controls the speed of an engine by regulating the fuel intake into it, irrespective of load or fuel supply conditions, and thus, maintains a near constant speed.

Centrifugal Pump

This device is used to transfer liquids or gases from low-pressure regions. This device works on the principle of centrifugal force. Exhaust fans and blowers are centrifugal pumps.

Banking of Roads

The centripetal force that helps a vehicle to negotiate a curve is the frictional force between the tyres and the road. Since the vertical displacement of the vehicle moving along a circular path is zero, the frictional force involved is only static frictional force, which is limited by $\mu_s N$.

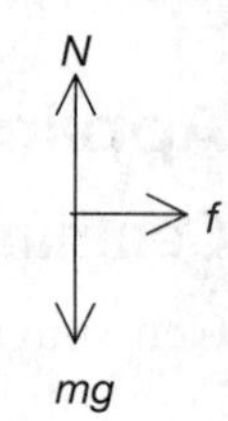

Since $$N = mg,$$

$$f \leq \mu_s mg$$

Equating f to centripetal force, $\frac{mv^2}{R}$,

We get $$\frac{mv^2}{R} \leq \mu_s mg$$

$$\frac{v^2}{R} \leq \mu_s g$$

Thus, both the speed of the vehicle and the radius of curvature are limited to the extent that the ratio $\frac{v^2}{R}$ must be less than $\mu_s g$.

If either the speed increases or the curve to be negotiated is sharper, then frictional force alone would not be sufficient to produce the corresponding centripetal acceleration and a component of the normal force is utilized.

This is the reason a cyclist negotiating a curve would tend to bend in the direction of the curve; and roads are provided with banking.

Banking is the inclination given to roads and rail tracks at turnings or along curved paths, by raising the outer edge of the path slightly above the inner edge towards the centre of the curvature.

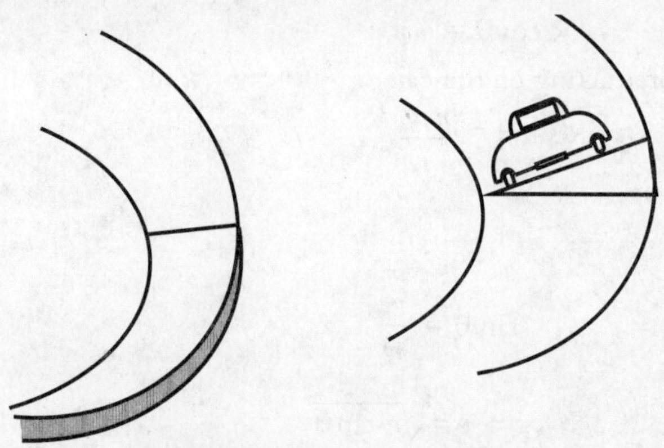

Figure 2.54 Banking of road

Consider a body moving along a horizontal circular path, where no banking is provided.

A car moving on a road (or a train moving on the rails) requires a centripetal force while taking a turn. To some extent, this centripetal force is provided by the friction between the road and tyre. When the vehicles are heavy, the required centripetal force may not be provided by the frictional force, as it is limited.

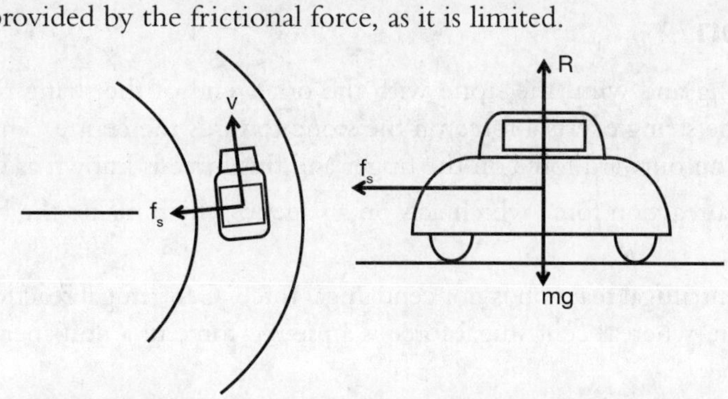

Figure 2.55 A car moving on a road while taking a turn

As the magnitude of f_s cannot exceed $\mu_s R$, where μ_s is the coefficient of static friction,

$$\therefore \qquad f_s \le \mu_s R$$

$$f_s \le \mu_s mg, \text{ i.e., } \frac{mv^2}{r} \le \mu_s mg$$

$$\mu_s \ge \frac{v^2}{rg}$$

If this condition is not satisfied, the car or train would skid outwards.

Now, consider a curved road with banking. The angle made by the road with the horizontal line is called 'angle of banking'.

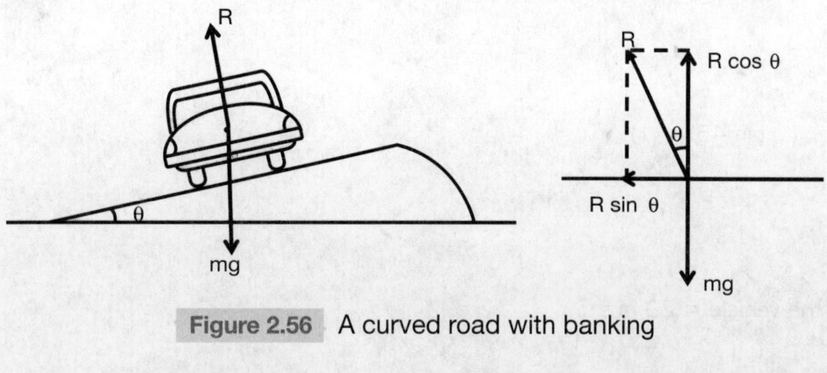

Figure 2.56 A curved road with banking

Let the angle of banking be θ. On resolving, the normal reaction 'R' into components, we can say that normal reaction is equal to the weight of the car.

i.e., $$R \cos \theta = mg \tag{2.19}$$

and $R \sin \theta$ acts as centripetal force acting on the car.

i.e., $$R \sin \theta = \frac{mv^2}{r} \tag{2.20}$$

By dividing Eq. (2.19) and (2.20)

Thus, we have $$\tan \theta = \frac{v^2}{rg}$$

$$\Rightarrow v = \sqrt{rg \tan \theta}$$

Above formula is used to find expected speed at a curve.

The roads are banked, i.e., the angle of banking is provided for the average expected speed of the vehicles. If the speed of the vehicle v is less, then the average expected speed (v_0) for a given banking, the vehicle would skid towards the centre. If $v > v_0$, the car would skid outwards.

Centrifugal Reaction

Take a stone and tie it to a string and whirl the stone with the other end of the string tied to the forefinger so that it describes a horizontal circle. The string exerts a force on the stone towards the centre. This force is centripetal force. At the same time, the string exerts an outward force on the finger and this force is known as centrifugal reaction.

Thus, centrifugal reaction is a reaction force which acts on an agent, which makes the body to move along a curve or a circular path.

It is important to note that centrifugal reaction is not centrifugal force. Centrifugal reaction is a reaction force according to Newton's third law of motion, whereas centrifugal force is a pseudo force in a non-inertial frame.

EXAMPLE 2.16 A car takes a turn along a curved road of radius 40 m and the angle of banking of the road is 45°. At what maximum speed, can the car be driven so that it may not skid (g = 10 m s^{-2})?

SOLUTION

The maximum speed for the car is given by v.

$$\tan \theta = \frac{v^2}{rg}$$

where r is the radius of the road, g is the acceleration due to gravity and θ is the angle of banking = 45°.

r = 40 m

g = 10 m s^{-2}

$$\tan \theta = \frac{v^2}{rg}$$

$$\tan 45° = \frac{v^2}{40 \times 10} \Rightarrow \quad (\because \tan 45° = 1)$$

$$v^2 = 400$$

$$v = \sqrt{400} = 20$$

The maximum speed of the vehicle = 20 m s^{-1}

EXAMPLE 2.17 A ceiling fan rotates at a speed of 150 revolutions per minute (rpm). Determine its angular velocity and its period.

SOLUTION

Number of revolutions per minute (n) = 60 rpm.
First, we need to convert revolutions per minute into revolutions per second:

$$n = \frac{60 \text{ revolutions}}{60 \text{ seconds}} = 1 \text{ revolution per second (rps)}$$

Angular velocity, w= 2p × (n)= 2p × (1)= 2p radians per second

$$\text{Now, } T = \frac{\text{Time}}{\text{No. of revolutons}} = \frac{60 \text{ seconds}}{60 \text{ revolutions}} = 1 \text{ second/revolution}$$

So, the angular velocity of the record player is 2π radians per second and its period is 1 second.

EXAMPLE 2.18 A figure skater spins on her toes with her arms stretched out. If the length of each arm is 60 cm and if she spins at a uniform linear speed of 4 m s^{-1}, measured at the tip of the arm, find the

(i) angular velocity.

(ii) period.

(Consider, length of arm = distance from tip of the arm to the axis of rotation)

SOLUTION

(i) In the above problem, since the ballet dancer spins on her toe, the length of the arm

= radius = r.

r = 60 cm = 0·6 m

Linear speed = v = 4 m s^{-1}

Angular velocity, $\omega = \frac{v}{r}$ rad s^{-1}

$$\omega = \frac{4}{0.6} = \frac{40}{6} = 6.66 \text{ rad s}^{-1}$$

(ii) Period, that is time taken for one revolution,

$$T = \frac{2\pi}{\omega} = \frac{2\pi}{6.66} = 0.9425 \text{ s}$$

EXAMPLE 2.19 A block of mass 150 g moves with a uniform speed in a circular groove of radius 30 cm. Find its centripetal acceleration and centripetal force acting on the block if the linear speed of the block is 0·8 m s^{-1}.

SOLUTION

In the given problem

Mass, m = 150 g = 0·150 kg

Radius, r = 30 cm = 0·3 m

Linear speed, v = 0·8 m s^{-1}

Hence, centripetal acceleration, $a = \frac{v^2}{r}$

$$\therefore\ a = \frac{(0.8)^2}{(0.3)} = \frac{0.64}{0.3} = \frac{6.4}{3} = 2.13 \text{ms}^{-2}$$

Centripetal force, $F = \frac{mv^2}{r} = m\omega^2 r$ or

$$F = m \cdot a$$

$$= 0{\cdot}15 \times 2{\cdot}13 = 0{\cdot}315 \text{ N}$$

EXAMPLE 2.20 A bucket containing water is fastened to a rope and is whirled in a vertical circle of radius 50 cm. Find the minimum speed at the highest point, so that the water does not spill.

SOLUTION

The bucket should be rotated such that the weight of the bucket and the water in it are balanced by the centrifugal force.

Let the mass of the bucket filled with water be = m

$\therefore$ Weight = mg

Weight = Centrifugal reaction acting on the bucket filled with water

$$\Rightarrow mg = \frac{mv^2}{r} \qquad \left(\because \text{Centrifugal reaction} = \frac{mv^2}{r}\right)$$

where, r is radius or the length of the rope = 500 cm = 0·5 m

$\therefore v^2 = rg$

$v = \sqrt{rg}$

$v = \sqrt{0.5 \times 9.8} = \sqrt{4.90}$

$v = 2{\cdot}214 \text{ m s}^{-1}$

Planetary Motion

Motion of the planets, moon, sun, etc., puzzled many scientists. It was Ptolemy in the second century A.D. who put forward a theory known as geo-centric theory. According to his theory, Sun along with the other planets revolves round the stationary Earth, which is the centre of the universe.

Geo-centric theory is also known as Ptolemic theory. Geo-centric theory was accepted until Copernicus, a Polish monk proposed a theory known as 'helio-centric theory'. According to helio-centric theory, Earth along with other planets revolves round the Sun in a circular orbit. Helio-centric theory was accepted for many years. It was Kepler, assistant of Tycho Brahe who analysed the observations of Brahe and supported the helio-centric theory and put forward his results in the form of laws called Kepler's laws.

Konnect

Asteroid: These are the rocky- metallic bodies which orbit the Sun between planet Mars and Jupiter.

Comet: These are small dusty snowballs which revolve round the sun.

First Law of Kepler

First law of Kepler states that all planets revolve round the Sun in an elliptical orbit of different radii with the Sun at one of their focal points.

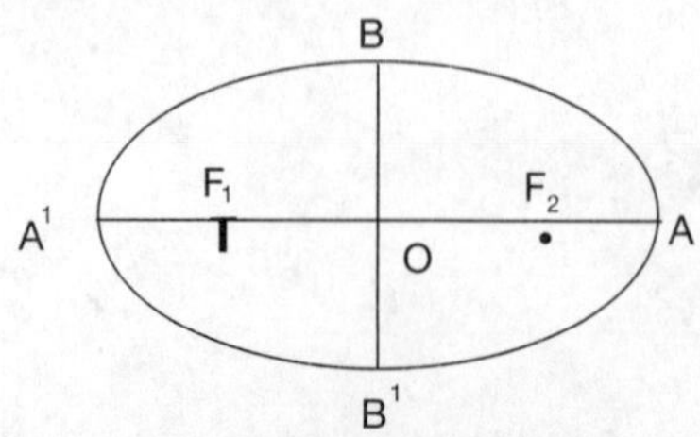

Figure 2.57 Ellipse

Ellipse consists of two axes, longer axis ($A\,A^1$) is called major axis and the shorter axis ($B\,B^1$) is called minor axis. Two points F_1 and F_2 which are at fixed positions on the major axis are called focii.

Kepler's first law is also called law of orbits.

Second Law of Kepler

According to the second law of Kepler, an imaginary line drawn from sun to the planet, also called radius vector, sweeps out equal areas in equal intervals of time.

Consider a planet orbiting around the sun as shown in the Fig. 2.58. Let P_1 and P_2 be the positions of the planet at the beginning and end of a given time interval, say a month. After a certain duration, let P_3 and P_4 be the positions of the planet at the beginning and end of a month duration. Then according to Kepler's second law, the area SP_1P_2 is equal to the area SP_3P_4.

This law is called law of areas.

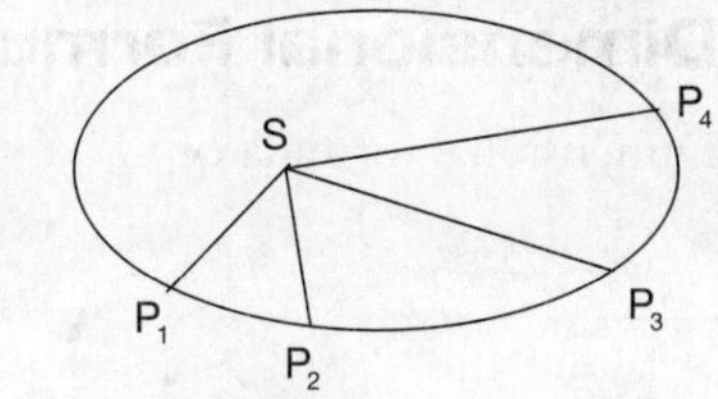

Figure 2.58 A planet orbiting around the sun with different positions

Third Law of Kepler

Square of the time period of revolution of a planet is directly proportional to cube of mean distance of that planet from the Sun.

If T is period of revolution of the planet and d is the mean distance of the planet from the Sun, then $T^2 \propto d^3$.

If T_1 and T_2 are periods of revolutions of two planets, and d_1 and d_2 are the mean distances of the planets from the sun, respectively, then according to Kepler's third law,

$$\frac{T_1^2}{T_2^2} = \frac{d_1^3}{d_2^3}.$$

Info Bytes!

When two asteroids collide with each other, upon which there is a small piece that breaks off from them. These pieces from asteroids after the collision are called as meteorites.

When a meteorite hits the earth's atmosphere with a high velocity, it looks flashy and like a fireball.

Newton's Universal Law of Gravitation

Newton was investigating the nature of force that makes the Moon go round the Earth. His observation of an apple falling towards the Earth led him to conclude that Earth attracts all bodies towards it and he found that the force of attraction is not limited only to terrestrial bodies, but to all bodies in the universe. Force between the bodies is known as gravitational force. Newton made use of Kepler's second law in stating the universal law of gravitation.

Every body in the universe attracts every other body with a force which is directly proportional to the product of their masses and inversely proportional to the square of the distance between them.

If m_1 and m_2 are masses of two bodies separated by a distance d, then according to universal law of gravitation, the gravitational force between them, F is given by,

$$F \propto m_1 m_2 \qquad (2.21)$$

and

$$F \propto \frac{1}{d^2} \qquad (2.22)$$

Combining (2.21) and (2.22), we get

$$F \propto \frac{m_1 m_2}{d^2}$$

$\Rightarrow$

$$F = G\frac{m_1 m_2}{d^2}$$

where, G is the universal gravitational constant.

S.I. unit of G:

$$G = \frac{F \times d^2}{m_1 m_2}$$

$$\text{Unit of } G = \frac{\text{Unit of } F \times (\text{Units of distance})^2}{(\text{Unit of mass}) \times (\text{Unit of mass})} = \frac{\text{N} \times \text{m}^2}{\text{kg} \times \text{kg}}$$

Thus, the unit of G in S.I. system is N m^2 kg^{-2} and the value of $G = 6{\cdot}67 \times 10^{-11}$ N m^2 kg^{-2}.

Dimensional Formula of *G*

Dimensional formula of G,

$$= \frac{[\text{Force}]\times[\text{Distance}]^2}{[\text{Mass}]^2} = \frac{[M^1L^1T^{-2}]\times[L^2]}{[M^1]\times[M^1]}$$

$$= [M^{-1}L^3\,T^{-2}]$$

Hence, the dimensional formula of G is $[M^{-1}\,L^3T^{-2}]$.

$G = F$ when $m_1 = m_2 = 1$ unit and the distance between the two bodies is one.

$$G = \frac{F\times 1^2}{1\times 1} = F$$

Thus, universal gravitational constant is equal to the gravitational force acting between two bodies each of unit mass and separated by a unit distance.

When a ball or any object is thrown up, it is pulled towards the earth due to Earth's gravitational force. As a result, the velocity of the body increases by 9·8 m s^{-1} for every second at sea level near the equator of the Earth. Thus, the body is uniformly accelerated.

This uniform acceleration of a freely falling body due to Earth's gravitational force is known as acceleration due to gravity. Acceleration due to gravity is denoted by '*g*'.

Konnect

Acceleration due to gravity is the same for all bodies irrespective of their mass, shape and size.

Relation between G and g

Consider an apple of mass *m* falling from a tree. The apple is acted upon by gravitational force due to Earth, and hence, it is attracted towards the Earth. From Newton's law of gravitation, the gravitational force acting on the apple is given by,

$$F = \frac{GMm}{R^2} \qquad (2.23)$$

Where, *M* is the mass of the earth and *R* is the radius of the Earth.

From Newton's second law, the apple is accelerated towards centre of the Earth due to gravitational force.

$$\therefore\ F = mg \qquad (2.24)$$

From equations (2.23) and (2.24), we get

$$mg = \frac{GMm}{R^2} \quad \text{or} \quad g = \frac{GM}{R^2}$$

This equation shows the relation between *g* and *G* and it shows that *g* is independent of mass of the body, i.e., all bodies irrelevant of their masses are accelerated to the same extent. Thus, when we drop a wooden ball and a solid iron ball of different masses simultaneously from the same height, both reach the Earth at the same time.

From the relation $g = \frac{GM}{R^2}$, the value of *g* can be found out.

Mass of the Earth = 6×10^{24} kg

Radius of the Earth = $6{\cdot}4 \times 10^3$ km = 6.4×10^6 m.

$$\therefore\ g = \frac{GM}{R^2} = \frac{6.67\times 10^{-11}\times 6\times 10^{24}}{(6.4\times 10^6)^2} = 9.77\ \text{m s}^{-2}$$

The value of '*g*' calculated above is near the equator at sea level. The value of '*g*' varies with height, depth and latitude.

Variation of 'g' with Height

Consider a body of mass '*m*' at a height '*h*' above the surface of the Earth. If *M* and *R* are mass and radius of the Earth, respectively, then acceleration due to gravity at height '*h*' is given by,

$$g_h = \frac{GM}{(R+h)^2} \tag{2.25}$$

On the surface of the Earth

$$g = \frac{GM}{R^2} \tag{2.26}$$

From equations (2.25) and (2.26), we get

$$\frac{g_h}{g} = \frac{R^2}{(R+h)^2}$$

$$\frac{g_h}{g} = \frac{R^2}{R^2\left(1+\frac{h}{R}\right)^2}$$

$$g_h = \frac{g}{\left(1+\frac{h}{R}\right)^2}$$

Expanding $\left(1+\frac{h}{R}\right)^{-2}$ using binomial theorem and neglecting the higher powers.

When $h << R$, i.e., close to the Earth's surface,

We get $\left(1+\frac{h}{R}\right)^{-2} \approx 1-\frac{2h}{R}$

$\Rightarrow$ $g_h = g\left(1-\frac{2h}{R}\right)$

Thus, acceleration due to gravity decreases with height.

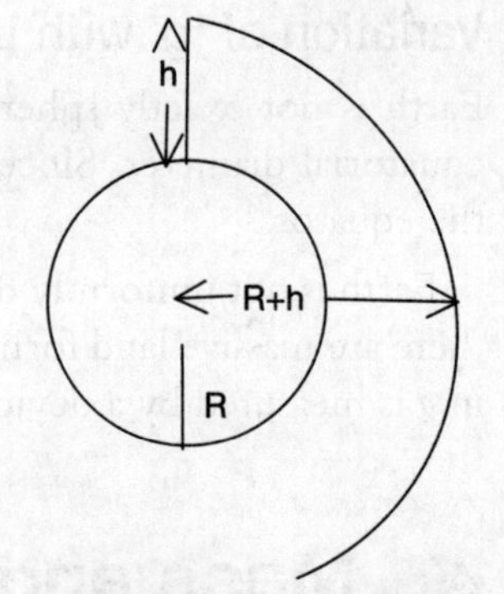

Figure 2.59 A body of mass '*m*' at a height '*h*' above the surface of the Earth

Variation of 'g' with Depth

As we go deep into the earth, the effective mass of the Earth decreases. Effective mass of the Earth at a depth '*h*' is given by,

$$M_d = \frac{4}{3}\pi(R-h)^3\rho,$$

where ρ is the average density of the Earth.

Thus, acceleration due to gravity decreases with depth and the acceleration at depth '*h*' is given by,

$$g_d = g\left(1-\frac{h}{R}\right)$$

At the centre of the Earth, depth, $h = R$. Therefore, $g_d = 0$.

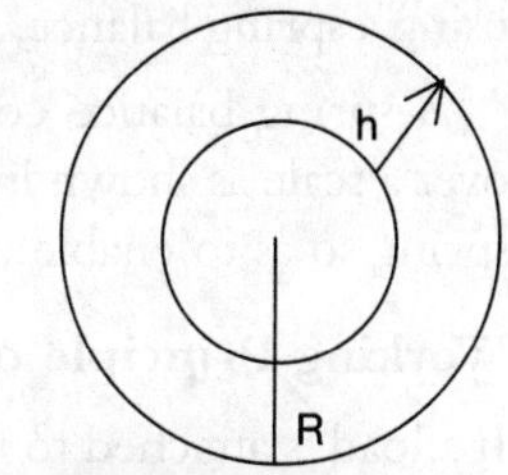

Figure 2.60 The earth at a depth '*h*'

Variation of 'g' with Latitude

Earth is not exactly spherical in shape, but is ellipsoidal. Its polar diameter is lesser by 40 km approximately than the equatorial diameter. Since $g \propto (1/R^2)$ acceleration due to gravity is greater or maximum at the poles and minimum at the equator.

Earth is not uniformly dense. There are a variety of mineral deposits, water, oil, etc., inside the Earth and on the surface there are massive land formations like mountains, etc. Hence, the value of g is affected by all these factors. Small variations in g is measured by a device known as gravity meter.

Mass and Weight

The force exerted by the Earth on a body is called weight. Thus, the weight of a body (w) is equal to mg where 'm' is the mass of the body and 'g' is acceleration due to gravity. From earlier discussion, it is seen that g varies from place to place, hence, the weight of the body also varies from place to place and is different on different planets since 'g' is different on different planets, whereas the mass is the amount of matter contained in the body, and thus, mass of a body remains constant everywhere.

Suppose we measure the mass and the weight of a body using a common balance and a spring balance, respectively, at two places, say Kanyakumari and Mount Everest, we observe that mass of the body at the two places is same but its weight on Mount Everest is less than that at Kanyakumari.

Table 2.1 Difference between mass and weight

Mass	Weight
It is the amount of matter contained in the body.	It is the force exerted by the earth on the body, i.e., $W = mg$.
Mass remains same anywhere in the universe.	Weight changes or varies from place to place.
S.I. unit of mass is kilogram.	S.I. unit of weight is newton and gravitational unit is kgf or kgwt.
Mass is measured by a common balance or physical balance.	Weight is measured by spring balance.

Measurement by Weight-Spring Balance

The weight of a body (mg), as discussed earlier, can be determined using a spring balance. Before we proceed to know about how the measurement of weight is done by using a spring balance, we need to know about the balance and the principle behind it.

A spring balance consists of a spring and a pointer attached to the spring sliding over a scale as shown in the Fig. 2.61. There is a hook attached to the lower end of the spring so as to enable us to attach the given load to the balance.

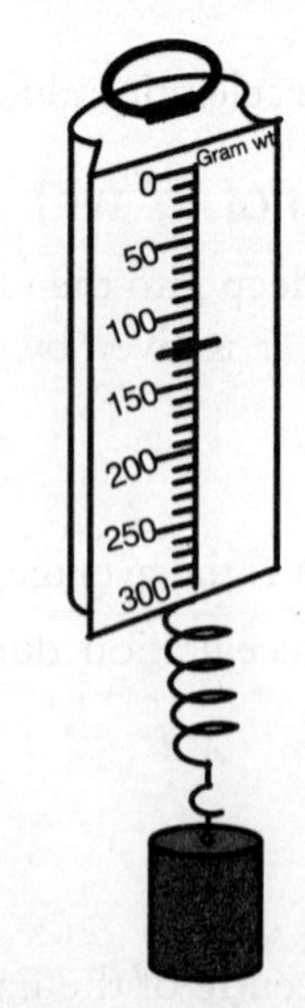

Figure 2.61 Spring balance

Working Principle of a Spring Balance

If a load is attached to the hook of a spring balance, there is an extension in the length of the spring due to the attached load. Thus, there is a downward force acting on the spring all along its length. The force acting per unit area of cross-section of the spring is called stress. If 'F' is the downward force acting on the spring and 'A' is the area of cross section of the spring, then stress (F/A). Due to this stress, there is an extension ($\Delta\ell$) in the length of the spring. This extension or elongation of the spring takes place throughout its length (ℓ). The ratio of elongation to its original length or elongation per unit length is called 'strain'. Thus, strain = ($\Delta\ell/\ell$).

The amount of strain produced in the spring is directly proportional to the stress applied on it. This proportionality is applicable to the spring within the elastic limit (the condition in which the spring tends to loose its elastic property) only. Thus, within the elastic limit, for an elastic body, stress is proportional to the strain. This is known as Hooke's law.

Thus, according to Hooke's law

$$\text{Stress} \propto \text{Strain} \Rightarrow \frac{\text{Stress}}{\text{Strain}} = \text{Constant}$$

$$\therefore \frac{F/A}{\Delta\ell/\ell} = \text{Constant}$$

$$\Rightarrow \frac{F}{A} \times \frac{\ell}{\Delta\ell} = \text{Constant}$$

$$\Rightarrow \frac{F}{\Delta\ell} \times \frac{\ell}{A} = \text{Constant}$$

Konnect

A spring balance measures force in newtons, which can be converted to weight.

As 'ℓ' the initial length of the spring and 'A' the area of cross-section of the spring are constant, we have $(F/\Delta\ell)$ = constant. The downward force 'F' acting on the spring is the weight of the load 'w' and so $(w/\Delta\ell)$ = constant.

Experiment to Determine Weight of a Body using a Spring

Consider a spring of considerable length suspended from a rigid support as shown in the Fig. 2.62. Let 'ℓ' be its length, when no load is attached to the free lower end of the spring. When a load is attached at the lower end of the spring, it has an extension $\Delta\ell$. According to Hooke's law, within the elastic limit, the weight of the load attached at the bottom of the spring (w) is directly proportional to the extension ($\Delta\ell$). Thus, $w \propto \Delta\ell$ and so $(w/\Delta\ell)$ constant. This is the principle used in measuring the weight of a substance.

Attach a pan of negligible weight at the bottom of the spring. Let 'ℓ_o' be the length of the spring shown by the pointer on the scale. Now place 10g weight in the pan, and note the pointer reading. Let it be 'ℓ_1'.

Then the extension in the spring is $\Delta\ell = \ell_1 - \ell_o$. Now, increase the weight in the pan in steps of 10 g and in each case note the pointer reading 'ℓ_1', so that the extension $\Delta\ell$ in each case can be calculated. The procedure is repeated till the weight in the pan is around 100 g. Now gradually decrease the weight in the pan in steps of 10g and again note the pointer reading 'ℓ_2' in each case. Calculate the mean of the pointer readings while loading and unloading the pan so that extension $\Delta\ell$ is calculated accurately. In each case, calculate $\frac{\Delta\ell}{\text{weight}}$.

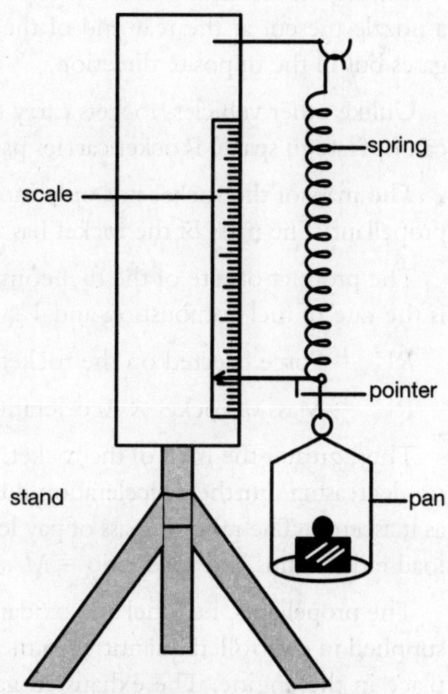

Figure 2.62 Spring balance

The observations are tabulated as below.

S. No.	Weight in the pan (w) (g)	Pointer positions: While loading ℓ_1 (cm)	Pointer positions: While unloading ℓ_2 (cm)	Mean position $\ell = \frac{\ell_1+\ell_2}{2}$ (cm)	Extension $\Delta\ell = \ell - \ell_o$ (cm)	$\frac{\Delta\ell}{w}$ (cm g^{-1})
1	10					
2	20					
3	30					
4	40					
5	50					
6	60					
7	70					
8	80					
9	90					
10	100					

A graph is plotted between w (in gwt) along the X-axis and Δl (in cm) along the Y-axis. The graph obtained is a straight line making a positive angle with the X-axis and passing through the origin, as shown in the Fig. 2.63.

To determine the weight of a body, the body is kept in the pan; then the extension in the spring is measured. From the graph of weight versus extension, the weight of the body is determined.

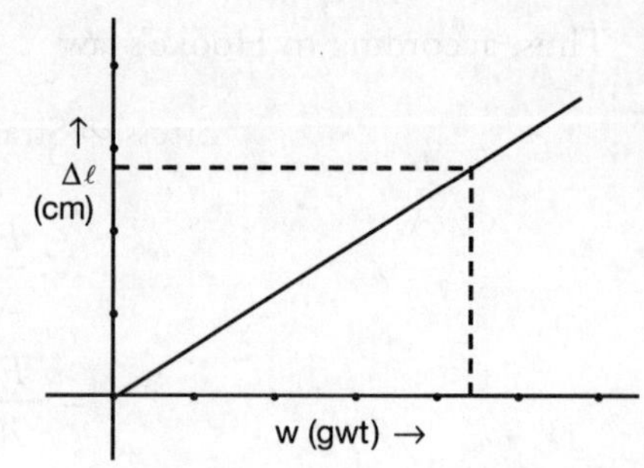

Figure 2.63 w versus Δℓ graph

Rockets

Rockets are vehicles which are used to carry objects having heavy mass like space craft, satellite, etc. The mass of rocket plays an important role in accelerating the rocket. Rocket works on the principle of conservation of linear momentum which states that when net external force acting on the system is zero, the total momentum of the system remains constant.

During the launching of a rocket, fuels are burnt and the gases escape with a high speed. These gases are ejected through a nozzle present at the rear end of the rocket. The rocket acquires the same momentum as that of the ejected or exhaust gases but in the opposite direction.

Unlike other vehicles, rockets carry their own oxidant which provides oxygen for combustion of the fuel. Hence, rockets can operate in space. Rocket carries payload or space-craft, which is usually placed in the front portion of the rocket.

The mass of the rocket not only includes the mass of the space craft but also mass of the fuels and oxidants called rocket propellant. The mass of the rocket has an effect in its acceleration.

The product of rate of the fuel consumption and its escape velocity gives the force or thrust exerted on the rocket. If R is the rate of fuel combustion and V_{ex} is the exhaust velocity of the fuel, then

RV_{ex} = Force exerted on the rocket.

RV_{ex} = Mass of rocket × Acceleration of the rocket.

Thus, greater the mass of the rocket, lesser is its acceleration. But as the rocket consumes fuel, the mass of the rocket keeps on decreasing. Further, acceleration due to gravity decreases as the rocket goes higher and the resistance of air also decreases as it ascends. The ratio of mass of pay load (M) to mass of propellant (m) is called 'pay load ratio'. Thus, pay load ratio $= M/m$.

The propellants, i.e., fuel and oxidant are kept in different chambers and they are supplied in controlled quantities to the engine and the combustion of the fuel takes place in the engine. The exhausted gases come out through the nozzle present at the rear end.

Multi-stage Rockets

In order to carry heavy load, multi-stage rockets are used. A multi-stage rocket consists of a number of parts of a rocket which are placed (joined) one above the other. As the rocket ascends to a height say about 100 km, it discards the chambers of propellants which have been used. Thus, the mass of the rocket is reduced. This is the first stage. The second stage carries the rocket to a still greater height and at a certain height the chambers of the propellant get detached from the rocket. The next stage takes over and the process continues. Thus, the fuel consumed is reduced. This increases the efficiency of the rocket.

Rockets which are used to launch space vehicles or scientific instruments are multi-stage rockets and generally have massive first booster stage and two smaller stages.

Rockets are used to launch space-craft or satellites and missiles. Rockets are equipped with radio transmitters which help in transmission of data collected back to the Earth.

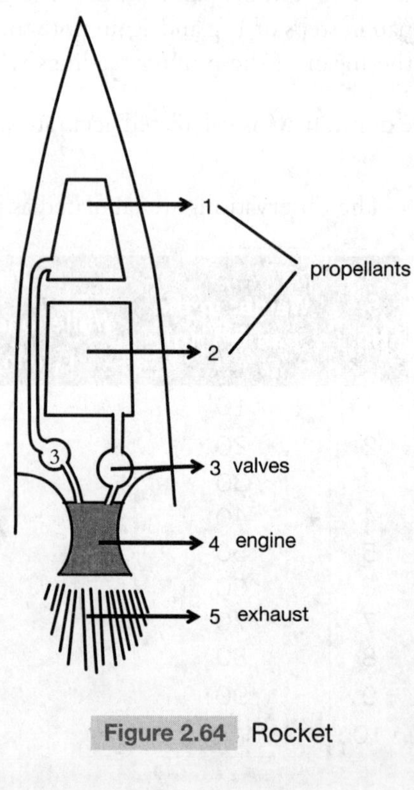

Figure 2.64 Rocket

Satellite

Moon is the natural satellite of the Earth. INSAT, Aryabhatta, Sputnik, etc., are artificial satellites. Thus, satellites are celestial or artificial objects which revolve round a body of larger mass.

Artificial satellites are man-made satellites and these are launched using multi stage rockets. A rocket takes a satellite to the desired height and places the satellite in an orbit by giving sufficient horizontal velocity.

Principle of Orbiting Satellite

When an object is dropped, it reaches the earth along the vertical line in the absence of air resistance (free fall). If the object is thrown horizontally with the same initial velocity, it takes a curved path, but still it reaches the Earth.

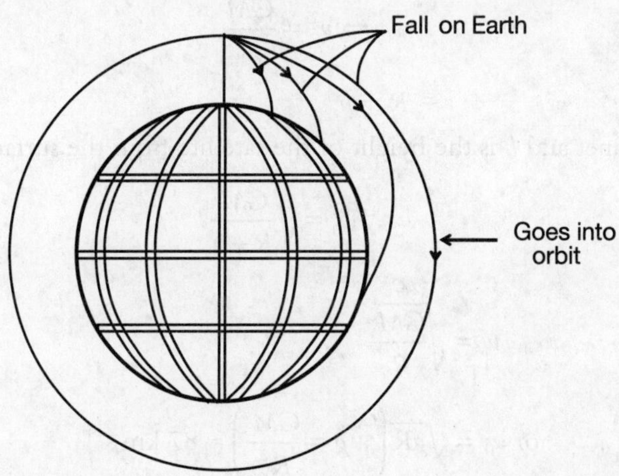

Figure 2.65 An object moving around the earth in an orbit

If the initial horizontal velocity is further increased, the object takes a less curved path and the object would fall on the earth at a farther point or the range increases. Thus, as the initial velocity increases, greater is the radius of the curved path.

If the object is given an initial horizontal velocity such that the radius of the curved path described by the object is equal or greater than the radius of the Earth, the object will never return to Earth. Instead, it orbits round the Earth and the object becomes an artificial satellite. The value of initial velocity of the object is less than the required value the object falls to Earth.

Orbital Velocity (v_0)

Satellites are taken to a required height and are given required horizontal velocity such that it revolves round the planet. This horizontal velocity with which the satellite revolves round the planet is called orbital velocity.

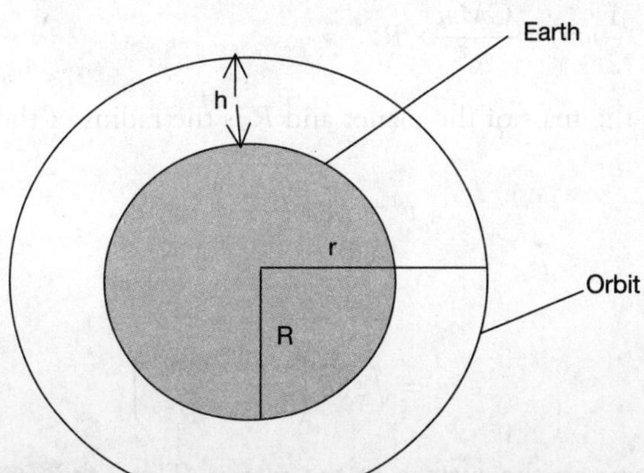

Figure 2.66 Satellites moving in an orbit around the Earth

For any satellite to go around the planet, it requires a centripetal force. The centripetal force required for the satellite is provided by gravitational force of attraction between the satellite and the planet.

∴ Centripetal force = Gravitational force between satellite and the planet.

$$\frac{mv_0^2}{r} = \frac{GMm}{r^2} \tag{2.25}$$

where, M is the mass of the planet,
r is the radius of the orbit,
m is the mass of the satellite,
G is universal gravitational constant, and
v_0 is the orbital velocity of the satellite.

$$\Rightarrow v_0^2 = \frac{GM}{r}$$

But $$r = R + h,$$

where, R is the radius of the planet and h is the height of the satellite from the surface of the planet.

$$\therefore V_0 = \sqrt{\frac{GM}{R+h}}$$

If $h << R$, then

$$v_o = \sqrt{\frac{GM}{R}}$$

$$\text{or } v_0 = \sqrt{gR}\left(\because g = \frac{GM}{R^2}\right) \approx 87 \text{ km s}^{-1}$$

Thus, the orbital velocity is independent of the mass of the satellite.

Example: Orbit velocity on the Earth is 7.6 km s^{-1}.

Escape Velocity (v_e)

It is the minimum velocity required for a satellite or any body to escape the Earth's gravitational pull. For any satellite to escape the Earth's gravitational pull, work has to be done against gravitational force. This work done appears as kinetic energy of the satellite. Thus, kinetic energy given to the satellite is equal to work done on the satellite against gravitational force.

(Here, $\frac{GMm}{R^2} \times R$ and so equal to P.E of the body w.r.t Earth's centre)

$$\therefore \quad \frac{1}{2}mv_e^2 = \frac{GMm}{R^2} \times R \qquad \text{(Work = Force × Displacement)}$$

where, v_e is the escape velocity, M is the mass of the planet and R is the radius of the planet.

$$\therefore \; v_e = \sqrt{\left(\frac{2GM}{R}\right)}$$

or

$$v_e = \sqrt{2gR}\left(\because g = \frac{GM}{R^2}\right)$$

where, g is acceleration due to gravity on the surface of the planet. Thus, the escape velocity is same for all bodies because it is independent of mass of the body.

Substituting the value of $g = 9{\cdot}8$ m s^{-2} and radius of the Earth, $R = 6400$ km, it is found that the escape velocity of a body on the Earth is 11.2 km per second. That is, in order to escape from Earth's gravitational pull, an object should possess a minimum speed of 11.2 km s^{-1}.

$\therefore$ V_e on the Earth's surface = 11.2 km s^{-1}

Relation between Orbital Velocity and Escape Velocity

Orbital velocity of a satellite orbiting close to Earth's surface is given by,

$$v_o = \sqrt{gR} \tag{2.26}$$

Escape velocity of a body on the surface of the Earth is given by,

$$v_e = \sqrt{2gR} \tag{2.27}$$

where, R is the radius of the Earth.

From equation (2.26) and (2.27),

$$v_e = \sqrt{2}.\sqrt{gR}$$

$$v_e = \sqrt{2}v_0$$

$$v_0 = \frac{v_e}{\sqrt{2}}$$

Uses of Artificial Satellites

1. **Communication Satellite:** Satellites are used for global communication, telephone communication, fax messages, TV transmission and internet. Communication satellites are geo-stationary satellites.

   A geo-stationary satellite appears to be at rest in space at a certain height above the equator. This satellite has the same period of revolution as that of the Earth, hence, this satellite appears to be at rest with respect to Earth. By placing three satellites in proper positions, the whole globe can be linked.

   INSAT series of satellites are geo-stationary satellites. Latest geo-stationary satellite launched by India is INSAT-3E. This was launched on 28 September 2003.

2. **Weather Forecasting:** These satellites are used to give information about weather changes, about cyclones, hurricanes, floods, etc.

3. **Remote Sensing Satellites:** These satellites are used to identify underground water resources, mineral resources, etc., to find the areas of ocean, forest, deserts, etc., to monitor air, water, sound and thermal pollution.

   IRS (Indian Remote Sensing) is a remote sensing satellite.

   Bhaskara was the first IRS. It was launched in 1979. After Bhaskara, many sophisticated remote sensing satellites are launched. These satellites are monitored at master control station of ISRO at Hassan.

4. Satellites and space-stations are used to obtain the information of the planets, stars, galaxies, comets, etc. Experiments conducted in such space shuttles and space station help in growth of science and technology. Satellites are also launched by many countries for espionage.

Indian Space Research Organisation (ISRO)

The Indian Space Research Organisation (ISRO) is India's national space agency. It was previously called the Indian National Committee for Space Research (INCOSPAR) and was established in 1962 by Jawaharlal Nehru, India's first prime minister, on the recommendation of Dr. Vikram Sarabhai. In 1972, the Indian government created a Space Commission and the Department of Space (DoS), which oversees ISRO and other institutions responsible for astronomy and space technology in India. ISRO is the primary research and development arm of DoS, and the Prime Minister of India directly supervises it. ISRO's responsibilities include space-based operations, space exploration, international space cooperation, and the development of related technologies.

India's first satellite, Aryabhatta, was built by ISRO and was launched by the Soviet space agency Interkosmos in 1975. Since then, ISRO has developed many medium-lift launch vehicles, rocket engines, and satellite systems which have enabled them to launch satellite RS-1 (First of the Rohini series) onboard SLV-3 (Satellite Launch Vehicle). This achievement made India the seventh country in the world to be capable of undertaking orbital launches. SLV-3 was followed by ASLV (Advanced Satellite Launch Vehicle). Today, the world's largest constellation of remote-sensing satellites is being operated by ISRO. It successfully launched satellite navigation systems named, GAGAN and IRNSS (NavIC). In 2008, ISRO launched Chandrayaan-1, the first probe to verify the presence of water on the Moon, and in 2013, the Mars Orbiter Mission, the first Asian spacecraft to enter Martian orbit. India was the first country who succeeded at this on its first attempt.

Satellite Programmes

1. **Indian Remote Sensing satellite (The IRS series):**

   The Indian Remote Sensing satellites (IRS) are country's earth observation satellites. These satellites are the largest collection of remote sensing satellites which is used for civilian operation, providing remote sensing services.

2. **Indian National Satellite System (The INSAT series):**

   The Indian National Satellite System (INSAT) is the India's telecommunication system. These are the series of geostationary satellites built and launched by ISRO to satisfy the broadcasting, telecommunications, meteorology, and search-and-rescue needs.

3. **Gagan Satellite Navigation System:**

   Gagan Satellite Navigation System is for satellite-based Communications, Navigation, Surveillance and Air Traffic Management plans for civil aviation.

4. **Navigation with Indian Constellation (NavIC):**

   NavIC is an independent regional navigation satellite system developed by India. This satellite is responsible for providing the accurate position information service to users in India. It provides two types of services, namely, Restricted Service (RS) and Standard Positioning Service (SPS, providing a position accuracy of better than 20 m (66 ft) in the primary service area.

Other Satellites

- Kalpana-1 (MetSat-1) was ISRO's first dedicated meteorological satellite.
- Indo-French satellite SARAL on 25 February 2013. SARAL (or "Satellite with ARgos and ALtiKa") is a cooperative altimetry technology mission, used for monitoring the oceans' surface and sea levels.

Launch vehicles

A launch vehicle is a rocket-powered vehicle designed for carrying the payload from Earth's surface or lower atmosphere to outer space.

1. **Satellite Launch Vehicle (SLV)**

   The Satellite Launch Vehicle (known as SLV-3) was the first space rocket to be developed by India. The initial launch in 1979 was a failure followed by a successful launch in 1980, making India the sixth country in the world with orbital launch capability.

2. **Augmented Satellite Launch Vehicle (ASLV)**

   Augmented or Advanced Satellite Launch Vehicle (ASLV) was another small launch vehicle released in the 1980s. The main purpose of the launch is to develop technologies required to place satellites into geostationary orbit.

3. **Polar Satellite Launch Vehicle (PSLV)**

   Polar Satellite Launch Vehicle or PSLV is the first medium-lift launch vehicle from India. It enabled India to launch all its remote-sensing satellites. PSLV has done more than 50 launches placing hundreds of Indian and foreign satellites into orbit.

4. **Geosynchronous Satellite Launch Vehicle (GSLV)**

   Geosynchronous Satellite Launch Vehicle was envisaged in the 1990s to transfer significant payloads to geostationary orbit.

5. **Launch Vehicle Mark-3 (LVM3)**

   The heaviest rocket in operational service with ISRO is Launch Vehicle Mark-3 (LVM3), previously known as GSLV Mk I. It is equipped with a more powerful cryogenic engine and boosters. It also has significantly higher payload capacity and allows India to launch all its communication satellites.

6. **Small Satellite Launch Vehicle (SSLV)**

   The Small Satellite Launch Vehicle (SSLV) is a small-lift launch vehicle developed by the ISRO with a payload capacity to deliver 500 kg (1,100 lb) to low Earth orbit (500 km (310 mi)) or 300 kg.

Lunar Exploration

India's series of lunar exploration spacecraft is called Chandrayaan. Its first mission, Chandrayaan-1, was launched by ISRO on 22 October 2008 from the Satish Dhawan Space Centre. The mission included a lunar orbiter, and an impactor called the Moon Impact Probe, and it entered lunar orbit on 8 November 2008. The spacecraft carried high-resolution remote sensing equipment for visible, near infrared, soft and hard X-ray frequencies. Its primary goal was to survey the lunar surface and produce a complete map of its chemical characteristics and three-dimensional topography. The polar regions were of special interest as they may have possible ice deposits. The mission lasted for 312 days, during which Chandrayaan-1 provided valuable insights into the Moon's surface.

On 22 July 2019, India launched the Chandrayaan-2 mission, which was the second mission to the Moon. The mission comprised an orbiter, a lander, and a rover. The GSLV Mk III rocket was used for the launch. The spacecraft had three components, a lunar orbiter, the Vikram lander, and the Pragyan lunar rover, all of which were developed in India. The mission was aimed at exploring the lunar south pole region, which had not been explored. The main purpose of the Chandrayaan-2 mission was to land a robotic rover on the Moon's surface to conduct various studies. The Vikram lander, carrying the Pragyan rover, was supposed to land on the near side of the Moon, in the south polar region on 7 September 2019. Unfortunately, the lander deviated from its intended trajectory and the telemetry was lost just before touchdown.

India made its second attempt to soft-land on the Moon with the Chandrayaan-3 mission, following the partial failure of Chandrayaan-2. This mission involved only a lander-rover set, which will communicate with the orbiter from the previous mission. On August 23, 2023, the Indian Space Research Organisation (ISRO) became the first space agency to successfully land a spacecraft on the lunar south pole region. This achievement also made ISRO the fourth space agency in history to successfully land on the Moon.

Mars Exploration

The Mars Orbiter Mission, also known as Mangalyaan, was launched by the Indian Space Research Organisation (ISRO) on 5th November 2013. After entering Earth's orbit, it reached Mars orbit on 24th September 2014. India became the first country to successfully put a space probe into Mars orbit on its first attempt. The Mars Orbiter Mission team was awarded the 2015 Space Pioneer Award by the National Space Society in the science and engineering category.

ISRO's Contribution to Other Fields

Access to high-quality healthcare is not universally available in some of the remote areas of India. To bridge this gap, ISRO has developed a telemedicine technology that connects patients in rural areas to medical professionals in urban locations via satellite. This technology allows doctors to diagnose and analyze patients in real-time via video conferencing. The doctors then advise the patient on medicine and treatment, and the patient is treated by the staff at one of the "super-speciality hospitals" as per instructions from those doctors.

ISRO's research has been utilized to develop various technologies for other sectors. These include bionic limbs for people without limbs, silica aerogel to keep Indian soldiers serving in extremely cold areas warm, distress alert transmitters for accidents, Doppler weather radar, and various sensors and machines for inspection work in engineering industries.

India's educational institutions, such as the Indira Gandhi National Open University and the Indian Institutes of Technology, utilize satellites for educational purposes. Back in 1975-76, India embarked on its biggest sociological program utilizing space technology, which was aimed at educational development in rural areas. The program, known as the Satellite Instructional Television Experiment (SITE), reached out to 2,400 villages through video broadcasting in local languages, using ATS-6 technology developed by NASA. As a result of this experiment, there was a significant improvement in rural education.

Info Bytes!

ISRO holds the record for launching 104 satellites in a single mission (PSLV-C37).

EXAMPLE 2.21 The time taken by Mars is 1.88 years to go round the Sun. Find the ratio of average distance between the Mars and the Sun to that between the Earth and the Sun.?

SOLUTION

From Kepler's third law:

$$\frac{T_1^2}{T_2^2} = \frac{d_1^3}{d_2^3}$$

where, T_1 and T_2 are the periods of Mars and Earth, respectively.

$$T_1 = 1{\cdot}88 \text{ years}$$

$$T_2 = 1 \text{ year}$$

$$\therefore \frac{T_1^2}{T_2^2} = \frac{d_1^3}{d_2^3}$$

$$\frac{(1.88)^2}{1^2} = \frac{d_1^3}{d_2^3} \quad \frac{3.534}{1} = \left(\frac{d_1}{d_2}\right)^3$$

Taking cube root,

$$\frac{d_1}{d_2} = 1.52$$

EXAMPLE 2.22

Two equal masses are separated by a certain distance and the force between them is 8 N. When the distance of separation is increased by 1 m, the force between them reduces to 2 N. Find the initial distance of separation and their masses.

SOLUTION

Let the mass of each body be = m kg

Given $m_1 = m_2 = m$ kg

Let the initial distance of separation be = d m

From universal law of gravitation the force between them is given by,

$$F = \frac{Gm_1m_2}{d^2}$$

where, G is the universal gravitational constant.

Let F_1 be the force when the bodies are separated by a distance, d.

$$F_1 = \frac{Gm_1m_2}{d^2} = \frac{Gm^2}{d^2}$$

Let F_2 be the force when the distance is increased by 1 m.

$$F_2 = \frac{Gm_1m_2}{(d+1)^2} = \frac{Gm^2}{(d+1)^2}$$

$$\frac{F_1}{F_2} = \frac{\frac{Gm^2}{d^2}}{\frac{Gm^2}{(d+1)^2}}$$

$$\Rightarrow \frac{8}{2} = \frac{(d+1)^2}{d^2} \Rightarrow 4 = \frac{(d+1)^2}{d^2}$$

Taking square root on both sides.

$$2 = \frac{d+1}{d}$$

$$2d = d + 1$$

$$\text{or } d = 1\ m$$

Since $m_1 = m_2 = m$ and $d = 1$ m and $G = 6.67 \times 10^{-11}$ N m^2 kg^{-2}, using

$$F = \frac{Gm^2}{d^2},$$

we get

$$8 = \frac{6.67 \times 10^{-11} \times m^2}{1^2}$$

$$\Rightarrow m^2 = \frac{8}{6.67 \times 10^{-11}} \Rightarrow m^2 = \frac{8 \times 10^{11}}{6.67}$$

$$\Rightarrow m^2 = 1{\cdot}199 \times 10^{11} = 0.1199 \times 10^{12}$$

$$m = \sqrt{0.1199 \times 10^{12}} = 0.346 \times 10^6 \text{ kg}$$

$$m_1 = m_2 = 0{\cdot}346 \times 10^6 \text{ kg}$$

EXAMPLE 2.23 What is the acceleration due to gravity on the top of Mount Everest, whose height is 8848 *m*, if acceleration due to gravity on the surface of the Earth is 9.8 m s^{-2}?
Radius of the Earth = 6400 km

SOLUTION

In the given problem, height h = 8848 m = 8.848 km

Acceleration due to gravity, $g^1 = g\left(1-\frac{2h}{R}\right)$

$$g^1 = 9.8\left(1-\frac{2\times 8.848\times 10^3}{6400\times 10^3}\right)$$

$g^1 = 9{\cdot}8\ (1 - 0{\cdot}0028) = 9{\cdot}8 \times 0{\cdot}9972$
$g^1 = 9{\cdot}77$ m s^{-2}

EXAMPLE 2.24 A satellite is to revolve round the Earth in an orbit of height 8000 km. With what speed should the satellite be projected into the orbit? What will be its time period?

SOLUTION
Radius of the orbit in which the satellite revolves $r = R + h$ = 6400 km + 8000 km = 14,400 km
where 'R' is the radius of the Earth and h is the height of orbit of the satellite.

The orbital velocity of the satellite is given by, $v_O = \sqrt{\frac{GM}{R+h}} = \sqrt{\frac{R^2 g}{R+h}}$

Where 'g' is acceleration due to gravity on the surface of Earth.

$\therefore\ v_O = 6.4 \times 10^6 \sqrt{\frac{9.8}{14.4\times 10^6}}$

$= 6.4 \times 10^6 \sqrt{0.68\times 10^{-6}}$
$= 6.4 \times 10^3 \times 0.825$
$= 5.28 \times 10^3$ m s^{-1}
$= 5.28$ km s^{-1}

Time period of the satellite, $T = \frac{2\pi r}{v_O}$

$\therefore\ T = \frac{2\times\pi\times 14400\times 10^3}{5280}$ s

$= 17127.3$
$= 285.5$ minutes
$= 4.76$ hours

POINTS TO REMEMBER

- ✔ If a particle moves along a circle with uniform speed, then the motion of the particle is called uniform circular motion.
- ✔ Momentum gained by the body during rotation is angular momentum.
- ✔ The time taken by a body to complete one revolution is called its time period of revolution.
- ✔ Centripetal force is the force which is always directed towards the centre of the circle
- ✔ Centrifugal reaction is a reaction force which acts on an agent, which makes the body to move along a curve or a circular path.
- ✔ According to the second law of Kepler, an imaginary line drawn from sun to the planet, also called radius vector, sweeps out equal areas in equal intervals of time.
- ✔ First law of Kepler states that all planets revolve round the sun in an elliptical orbit of different radii with the sun at one of their focal points.
- ✔ According to the Second law of Kepler, an imaginary line drawn from sun to the planet, also called radius vector, sweeps out equal areas in equal intervals of time.
- ✔ Square of the time period of revolution of a planet is directly proportional to cube of mean distance of that planet from the sun.
- ✔ Every body in the universe attracts every other body with a force which is directly proportional to the product of their masses and inversely proportional to the square of the distance between them.
- ✔ The force exerted by the earth on a body is called weight. Thus, the weight of a body (*w*) is equal to *mg* where '*m*' is the mass of the body and '*g*' is acceleration due to gravity.
- ✔ Rockets are vehicles which are used to carry objects having heavy mass like space craft, satellite, etc.
- ✔ Artificial satellites are man-made satellites and these are launched using multi stage rockets.
- ✔ Escape velocity is the minimum velocity required for a satellite or any body to escape the earth's gravitational pull.

DW

PRACTICE QUESTIONS CLASSROOM WING

Very Short Answer Type Questions

Direction for questions from 1 to 7:
Fill in the blanks.

1. The ratio of the weight of a body to its mass gives the ______ at the given place.
2. Sugar crystals can be separated from molasses, using a ______.
3. The weight of a body is minimum at ___ on the earth.
4. A body of mass '*m*' is dropped from a height '*h*'. The kinetic energy of the body on reaching the ground is ______.
5. Wheel and axle is a lever of _____ order.
6. The mechanical advantage of an inclined plane 2m long and 1m high is equal to ______.
7. The escape velocity on the surface of the Earth is ______ km s^{-1}.

Direction for questions from 8 to 25:
Answer the following questions briefly.

8. State Hooke's law.
9. Define work and power (write their dot product).
10. A force of 10 N is applied on a body of mass 1 kg. If the friction acting on it is 2 N, determine the acceleration of the body.
11. A body of mass 2 kg is dropped from 10 m height. Calculate the kinetic energy (in J) of the body on reaching the ground. (take $g = 10 ms^{-2}$)
12. What is the mechanical advantage of a sheath of pulleys?
13. What are parallel forces?
14. Define orbital velocity and escape velocity.
15. What is moment of a force or a torque?
16. What is centre of gravity?
17. What is the effect of weight of pulleys in the tackle?
18. Define centripetal acceleration.
19. What is meant by stable equilibrium?
20. The momentum of a body of mass 3 kg is 25 kg m s^{-1}. Calculate the kinetic energy (in J) of the body.
21. Give an expression which relates orbital velocity and escape velocity.
22. What is a simple machine?
23. An object of mass *m* is hanging from the ceiling of a cabin which is moving down with an acceleration '*a*'. Calculate the tension in the string.
24. Find the power developed by an engine if it imparts a velocity of 10 ms^{-1} . What is the maximum potential energy gained by the body?
25. The kinetic energy of a body of mass 5 kg is 200 J. Calculate the momentum of the body.

Short Answer Type Questions

26. Obtain the relation between angular velocity and linear velocity.
27. An object of mass 1 kg moves with an intitial velocity of 20 m s^{-1}. How much is the force (in N) required to change the velocity to 30 m s^{-1} in 1 ms?
28. A car of mass 1,500 kg takes a turn along a curved road of radius of curvature 20 m, with a speed of 36 km h^{-1}. Determine the static friction acting on it if the road is not banked.
29. A body starts to slide on a hemisphere of radius *R* from the topmost point as shown in the figure. If the surface is frictionless, determine the speed of the body at point B.

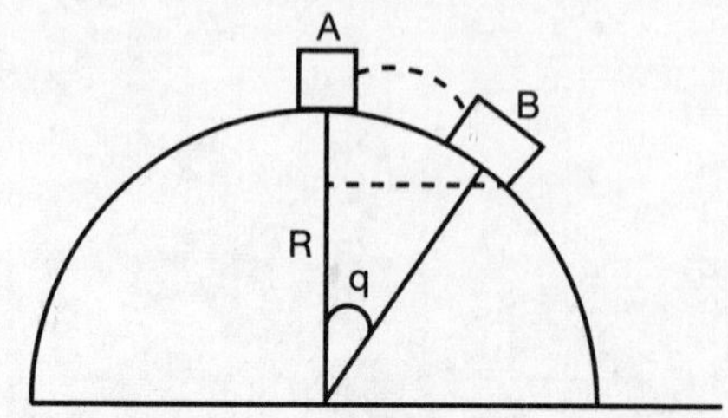

30. A force of 100 N acts on a body such that it makes an angle of 30° with the direction of displacement. If the displacement of the body is 2 m, find the work done.

31. A rocket with a mass of 20,000 kg is blasted upwards with an initial acceleration of 5 m s^{-2}. Calculate the initial force of the blast.

32. Find the power developed by an engine in filling water of 2000 L from a well of depth 20 m in 20 s.

33. State Newton's law of gravitation.

34. Calculate the work done by the gravity when an object of mass 50 kg is lifted upwards through a distance 20 m.

35. A car of mass 2000 kg is moving uniformly at a velocity of 20 m s^{-1}. If the engine gathers an extra momentum of 1000 kg m s^{-1}, calculate the new velocity of the car.

36. A particle moves in a circular path of radius 20 cm with an angular velocity of 2π rad s^{-1}. Find the speed of the particle.

Essay Answer Type Questions

37. A bullet of mass 100 g moving with a velocity of 100 m s^{-1} is stopped by a plank. If the bullet travels a distance of 10 cm in the plank before it comes to rest, find the average force exerted by the plank.

38. A particle of mass 25 kg is dropped from 5 m height into a liquid. If the distance travelled by the particle before it comes to the state of rest in the liquid, is 200 cm, calculate the average resistance force offered by the liquid (neglect the upthrust).

39. A swing is suspended from two parallel ropes at its ends. Two person weighing 50 kg wt and 30 kg wt sit at a distance 20 cm and 80 cm from one end. The weight of the swing is 20 kg wt. Find the tensions on the rope. Length of the plank of the swing is 100 cm.

40. A ball is tied to a string of length 1 m and is whirled in a horizontal circle with a linear speed of 5 m s^{-1}. If the mass of the ball is 1000 g, find its
   (a) angular velocity,
   (b) centripetal force acting on the ball, and
   (c) centrifugal force acting on the ball.

41. A block of mass 'm' is projected with a velocity 'v' towards a spring of spring constant 'k', which fixed on a rigid support. Determine the maximum compression of the spring. [The surface is frictionless]

42. Obtain an expression for banking angle.

43. A car moving with a speed of 72 km h^{-1} is stopped by applying brake. The mass of the car is 1000 kg and the average frictional force used to stop the car is 6000 N. Determine the distance travelled before it comes to the state of rest.

44. Explain the principle of an orbiting satellite.

45. Explain the working of a screw-jack.

PRACTICE QUESTIONS COMPETITION WING

Level 1: Apply Your Concepts

Direction for questions from 1 to 5:
Answer the following questions briefly.

1. A car of mass 2000 kg is initially moving at 18 km h^{-1}. How much is the force required to change the speed to 36 km h^{-1} in 2 s?
2. A body of mass 2 kg is thrown up with a velocity 10 m s^{-1}. What is the maximum potential energy gained by the body?
3. The kinetic energy of a body of mass 5 kg is 200 J. Calculate the momentum (in kg m s^{-1}) of the body.
4. Calculate the work done by the gravity on an object of 20 kg when it is moved horizontally by applying a force of 20 N to produce a displacement of 2 m.
5. An object of mass '*m*' is hanging from a lift which is moving down with a uniform velocity. Find the tension in the string.

Direction for questions from 6 to 12:
State whether the following statements are true or false.

6. The work done by the earth on a satellite revolving around it is zero.
7. The escape velocity of a body on a planet is always greater than the orbital velocity of the body around the planet in an orbit closer to it.
8. The gravitational potential energy of a body is directly proportional to its height above the surface of the earth.
9. The mechanical advantage of an inclined plane is always greater than unity.
10. The resultant of all internal forces acting on a body at rest is zero.
11. Centrifugal force is a reaction to centripetal force.
12. A 10 N force is applied at a distance of 1 m from the hinge of door such that the line of action of force is parallel to the plane of the door. The moment of force produced on the door is 10 N m.

Direction for questions from 13 to 19:
Fill in the blanks.

13. Two forces act on either side of a uniform rod AB of negligible mass suspended by string as ß shown in the figure. If *R* is the resultant force, the tension of the string, $T =$ _______ g_{wt}.

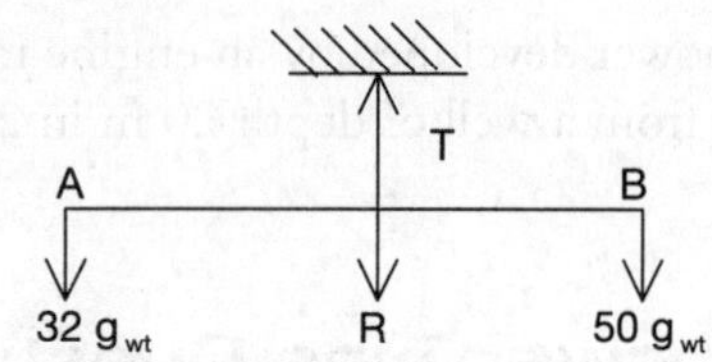

14. A metre scale is suspended at 50 cm mark to a rigid support with a weight of 150 g attached at 5 cm mark. To balance the scale, a weight of 450 g should be attached at _______ cm mark.
15. Two planets have average radii of their orbits of revolution in the ratio 64 : 9. Then, the ratio of their periods of revolution is _______.
16. A particle moves in a circle whose radius is 20 cm with a linear speed of 10 m s^{-1}. Then its angular velocity is _______ rad s^{-1}.
17. A particle moving along a circular path with the uniform angular velocity 'ω' is under the action of a force '*F*' directed towards the centre of the circular path. If the radius of the circular path is doubled without changing the linear velocity, the centripetal force acting on the body would be _______.
18. The ratio of escape velocity of a tennis ball to that of a basket ball on the surface of the earth is _______.
19. If I.M.A. and V.R. are the ideal mechanical advantage and velocity ratio of a pulley, then its efficiency is _______.

Direction for question 20:

20. Match the statements of Column A with those of Column B.

Column A	Column B
A. Aceleration due to gravity at the centre of the Earth	a. 1.63 m s^{-2}
B. Escape velocity on the Earth	b. 11.2 km s^{-1}
C. Orbital velocity on the Earth	c. 7.8 km s^{-1}
D. Acceleration due to gravity on the Moon	d. zero

Direction for questions from 21 to 48:
For each of the questions, four choices have been provided. Select the correct alternative.

21. A body is moving around another body of mass 'M' with a speed v m s^{-1} due to the gravitational force of attraction between them. Determine the Radius of the orbit (in m).
(a) $\frac{GM}{v}$ (b) $GM\,v$
(c) $\frac{GM}{v^2}$ (d) $\frac{GM^2}{v}$

22. The stability of a flexible body depends on
(a) height of the centre of gravity from the ground.
(b) base area of the body.
(c) shape of the body.
(d) all the above

23. The relation between momentum (P), mass (m), kinetic energy (KE) and velocity (V) of two bodies is
(a) $P_1V_1 = P_2V_2$ where KE is constant.
(b) $KE_1m_1 = KE_2m_2$ where P is constant.
(c) $KE_1P_2^2 = KE_2P_1^2$ when m is constant.
(d) All the above

24. In the adjacent diagram, the shaded regions A and B are the areas covered by a planet around the sun d_A and d_B, t_A and t_B are the distances traveled by the planet and the time taken by it to cover the paths PQ and RS, respectively. Choose the correct statement.

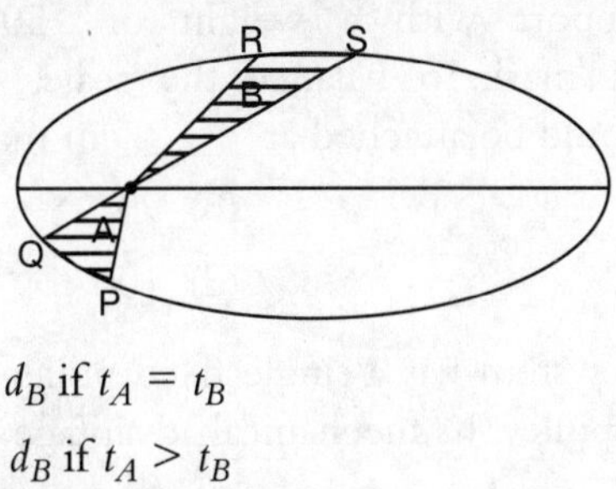

(a) $d_A = d_B$ if $t_A = t_B$
(b) $d_A < d_B$ if $t_A > t_B$
(c) $d_A = d_B$ if $t_A < t_B$
(d) $d_A > d_B$ if $t_A = t_B$

25. The gravitational force of attraction between two bodies at a certain distance is 10 N. If the distance between them is doubled, the force of attraction ______.
(a) decreases by 50%
(b) decreases by 75%
(c) increases by 50%
(d) increases by 75%

26. Action and reaction
(a) always act on two different bodies.
(b) are equal in magnitude.
(c) act in opposite directions.
(d) All the above

27. Two particles of equal mass are revolving with the same linear speed on circular paths of radii r_1 and r_2. The ratio of the centripetal force acting on them will be __.
(a) $\frac{r_2}{r_1}$ (b) $\sqrt{\frac{r_2}{r_1}}$
(c) $\left(\frac{r_1}{r_2}\right)^2$ (d) $\left(\frac{r_2}{r_1}\right)^2$

28. Choose the correct statement.
(a) In a simple machine, the input energy is always equal to output energy.
(b) Actual mechanical advantage > Ideal mechanical advantage.
(c) Velocity ratio = $\frac{\text{displacement of the efforts}}{\text{displacement of the load}}$
(d) The mechanical advantage of a single fixed pulley is greater than one.

29. While opening a tap with two fingers, the forces applied are
(a) equal in magnitude.
(b) parallel to each other.
(c) opposite in direction.
(d) All the above

30. A rubber ball of mass 250 g hits a wall normally with a velocity of 10 m s^{-1} and bounces back with a velocity of 8 m s^{-1}. The impulse is ______ N s.
(a) –0.5 (b) +0.5
(c) –4.5 (d) +4.5

31. The false statement about universal gravitational constant (G) among the following is ______.
(a) Its dimensional formula is [$M^{-1} L^3 T^{-2}$]
(b) It is a vector quantity
(c) Its value in SI system is 6.67×10^{-11}
(d) Its unit is N m^2 kg^{-2}

32. The weight of an object is zero at ______.
(a) a height equal to half of the radius of earth
(b) the centre of the earth
(c) the equator
(d) both (a) and (b)

33. A force acts on an object while in the state of motion. If the force acting on it is equal to the sum of all the resistance forces, then the object ______.
(a) stops after covering some distance
(b) moves with uniform acceleration
(c) moves with uniform velocity
(d) moves with uniform retardation

34. In the case of an oscillating simple pendulum, if the air resistance is taken into consideration, then ______.
(a) amplitude of oscillation remains the same
(b) frequency remains the same
(c) the resultant acceleration remains the same
(d) All the above

35. The magnitude of acceleration due to gravity decreases
(a) as the height from the surface of the earth increases.
(b) as the depth from the surface of the earth increases.
(c) as one moves from the pole of the earth to its equator.
(d) All the above.

36. A body of mass 1 kg moves with a velocity 5 m s^{-1}. A force is applied on it for 1 ms such that its velocity is increased to 7 m s^{-1}. The force applied on the body is______N.
(a) 2000 (b) 200
(c) 20 (d) 2

37. Force required to produce an acceleration of 1 m s^{-2} on a body of mass 1 kg is______N.
(a) 1 (b) 2
(c) 3 (d) 4

38. 1 dyne force can produce an acceleration of ______ cm s^{-2} on an object of mass 100 g.
(a) 1 (b) 0.1
(c) 10 (d) 0.01

39. An object A of mass of 0.1 kg exerts a force of 1N on a body B. Then, the acceleration of the body A is______m s^{-2}.
(a) zero (b) 10
(c) −10 (d) −5

40. The momentum of a body of mass 0.5 kg dropped from a certain height (h), when it reaches the ground is 10 N s. The value h is______m. (take $g = 10$ m s^{-2})
(a) 20 (b) 40
(c) 10 (d) 80

41. The momentum of a body is increased by 50%. If v_1 is the initial velocity of the body, the change in kinetic energy is
(a) $2mv_1^2$ (b) $\frac{5}{4}mv_1^2$
(c) $\frac{5}{8}mv_1^2$ (d) $\frac{3}{2}mv_1^2$

42. Work done on a body depends
(a) only on the magnitude of external force applied on the body.
(b) only on the displacement of the body.
(c) on both the displacement of the body and the component of the external force acting in the direction of its displacement.
(d) None of the above

43. The mechanical advantage of an inclined plane of angle of inclination 60° is equal to______.
(a) $\frac{2}{\sqrt{3}}$
(b) cosec 30°
(c) Both (a) and (b)
(d) None of the above

44. A metre scale is suspended at 50 cm mark to a rigid support with a weight of 150 g attached at 5 cm mark. To balance the scale, a weight of 450 g should be attached at______cm mark.
(a) 65 (b) 90
(c) 95 (d) 100

45. A pulley system has a single fixed pulley and a single movable pulley. Its mechanical advantage is______.
(a) 1 (b) 2
(c) 3 (d) 4

46. A particle moves in a circle whose radius is 40 cm with a linear speed of 5 m s^{-1}. Then its angular velocity is______rad s^{-1}.
(a) 100 (b) 12.5
(c) 25 (d) 125

47. A particle, moving in a circle of radius 10 cm with a uniform speed, completes a revolution in 4 seconds. The magnitude of the centripetal acceleration it experiences is______cm s^{-2}.

(a) 2.5 π^2 (b) 5 π^2

(c) 3 π^2 (d) $6\pi^2$

48. Gravity meters measure in units of mGal where 1 Gal (or 1 galileo) is the C.G.S. unit of acceleration due to gravity. A gravity meter shows a reading of +300 mGal at a place where the normal '*g*' is 9.78 m s^{-2}. The correct '*g*' at that place where the reading was taken is______m s^{-2}.

(a) 9.777 (b) 9.783

(c) 9.750 (d) 9.810

Level 2: Review Your Concepts

49. An object '*m*' of mass 50 kg is lifted by using an arrangement as shown in the figure. If the load due to the weight of the pulley and the resistance due to the friction of the pulley is 2.5 kgwt, calculate the effort required to lift the object. If $M.A_1$ and $M.A_2$ are the mechanical advantages of the inclined plane and the pulleys, respectively, derive an expression for the resultant mechanical advantage if the friction force between the object and the inclined plane is negligible.

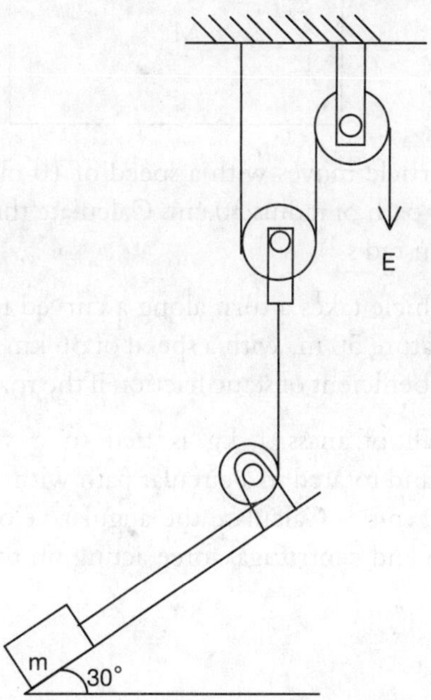

50. A load of 60 kg is lifted using a wheel and axle, the sum of whose diameters is 1.2 m, by a man and his son who can share their efforts in the ratio 2 : 1. If the radius of the axle is 10 cm, find the effort contributed by the son. (g = 10 m s^{-2}).

51. A body of mass '*m*' revolves around another body of mass '*M*' in a circular path of radius '*R*' due to the gravitational force of attraction. Arrange the following steps in sequential order to find the speed of the body:

(P) Determine the square of the speed of the body.

(Q) Determine the gravitational force on the body.

(R) Determine the centripetal force.

(S) Equate the gravitational force with the centripetal force.

52. A stone is tied to a massless and inextensible string and rotated in a vertical plane. Discuss the variation in centripetal force of the stone from the top to the bottom positions of the circular path if minimum speed is imparted to it so as to continue its circular motion.

53. An object of mass 20 kg is moving with a velocity 200 m s^{-1}. If a force is applied so that the momentum is decreased by 100 kg m s^{-1}, determine the new velocity of the object.

54. A metallic vessel having a shape that is a combination of a hemisphere and a truncated cone is placed on the ground in a position as shown in the figure. 'C' is the centre of curvature of the hemispherical part of the vessel. The height of the truncated conical part is less than the radius of curvature of the hemispherical part of the vessel.

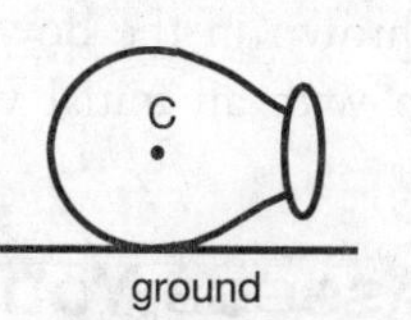

(i) Locate the centre of gravity of the vessel.

(ii) What is the state of equilibrium of the vessel in the position shown?

(iii) When the vessel is left in the position shown, what is the effect of the forces acting on the vessel? Discuss.

55. Find the power developed by an engine if it imparts a velocity of 10 m s^{-1} to a body of mass 2 kg in 0.1 s.

56. A spring balance whose spring can have a spring can have a maximum extension of 20 cm, can sustain a maximum load of 20 kg_{wt} within its elastic limit on the surface of the earth. Now the same balance is taken to the moon. Given that $g_{earth} = 6\, g_{moon}$, what is the maximum mass of the load that can be attached to the balance to have half its maximum extension?

57. A body is projected vertically upwards from ground with a velocity 'u' and it gains a maximum height 'H'm. At a point 'x'm height ($x <$ H), the ratio of its potential to Kinetic energy is 1 : 2. Now if the body is projected upwards with a velocity '$3u$' from the ground, find the ratio of its potential to kinetic energy at a point whose height is '$3x$'m.

58. The magnitude of acceleration due to gravity at an altitude 'h' from earth is equal to its magnitude at a depth 'd'. Find the relation between 'h' and 'd'. If 'h' and 'd' both increase by 50%, are the magnitudes of acceleration due to gravity at the new altitude and the new depth equal?

59. A ball of mass 500 g hits a wall with a velocity 10 m s^{-1} such that it makes an angle 60° with the normal. It bounces back with the same speed making an angle of 60° with the normal. Determine the change in momentum.

60. Why cannot an artificial satellite be parked in its orbit using a single stage rocket instead of using a multistage rocket for the purpose?

61. Find the power of a machine gun that can fire 240 bullets per minute, each weighing 50 g, with a velocity of 100 m s^{-1}.

62. A spirit level cannot be used to find out whether the top of the table placed on a rotating platform is horizontal. Explain.

63. An object thrown in the downward direction from a height 10 m with an initial velocity 15 m s^{-1} strikes the ground and bounces back to a height of 12 m. Determine the percentage loss of its energy during collision with the ground. (Take $g = 10 \text{ m s}^{-2}$).

64. A smaller block of mass 'm' is placed on another block of mass 'M'. When a horizontal force F is applied on the block of mass M as shown in the figure, the smaller block does not slide. If the magnitude of friction between the bigger block and the ground is 'f', determine the magnitude and direction of friction between the two blocks.

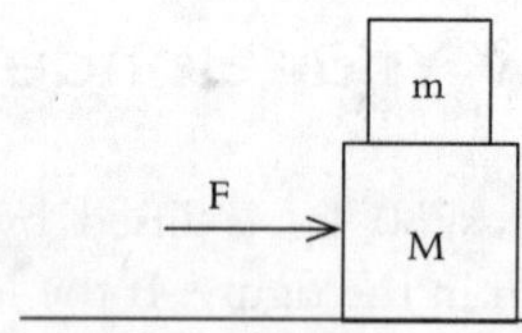

65. An object of mass M is hanging from the string as shown in the figure. If the uniform acceleration of the cabin in the upward direction is 'a', determine the tension in the string.

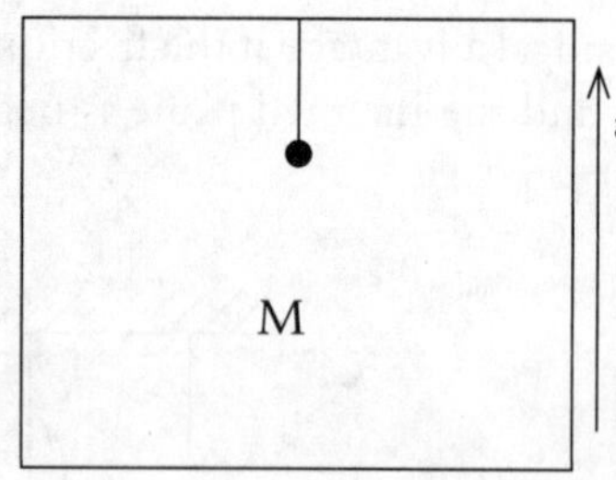

66. A particle moves with a speed of 10 m s^{-1} along a circular path of radius 30 cm. Calculate the angular velocity (in rad s^{-1}).

67. A vehicle takes a turn along a curved road of radius of curvature 50 m, with a speed of 36 km h^{-1}. Determine the coefficient of static friction if the road is not banked.

68. A ball of mass 1 kg is tied to a string of length 2 m and rotated in a circular path with a uniform speed of 10 m s^{-1}. Calculate the angular velocity, centripetal force and centrifugal force acting on the body.

Level 3: Assess Your Concepts

69. Two satellites of masses 'm' and '$2m$' are moving around two planets of masses $2M$ and M, respectively. If 'r' and $2r$ are the radii of their orbits, determine the ratio of their time periods.

70. A body of mass 5 kg is placed on an inclined plane as shown in the figure given below. Determine the magnitude of minimum force 'F' required to keep

the body under equilibrium. The coefficient of static friction is 1.

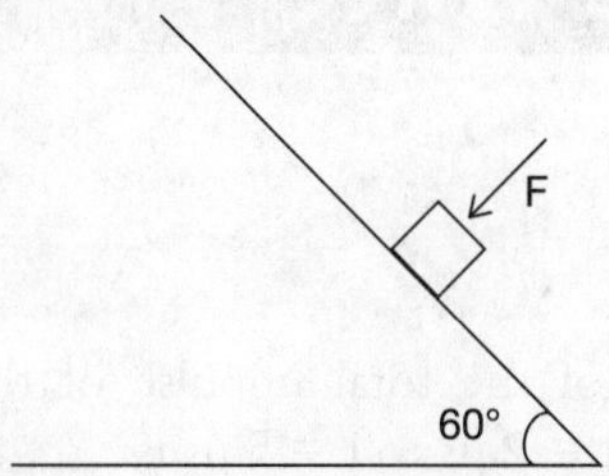

71. A bullet of mass 50 g is fired from a stationary rifle into a wooden block of mass 1.95 kg placed on a horizontal wooden surface. On striking, the bullet is embedded into the block and both together cover a distance of 200 m in a straight path before coming to rest. Given the coefficient of friction between the block and the surface is 0.2 and the mass of the rifle from which the bullet is triggered is 14 kg, find the magnitude of the velocity of the recoil of the rifle.(Neglect the resistance of air on the bullet).

72. When a pendulum of length 50 cm is set into oscillation, the maximum change in potential energy is found to be 4 J. If the mass of the bob is 200 g, determine the tension in the string when it is at the mean position.

73. A particle loosely held at the circumference of a platform rotating with a uniform velocity flies off during the rotatory motion. Explain its of motion,

(i) as seen by an observer on the ground.

(ii) as seen by an observer on the platform.

74. An object of mass 2 kg is moving with an initial velocity of 36 km h^{-1} on a rough inclined surface of angle of inclination 45°. If the maximum increase in potential energy is 80 J, determine the coefficient of sliding friction between the surfaces.

75. Two bodies A and B having masses in the ratio 1 : 2 are in uniform circular motion along two concentric circular paths. The angular velocity of A is four times that of B. If the centripetal force on both of them are equal, find the ratio of difference in the radii to the smaller radius.

76. The average radius of the orbit of the revolution of a planet around the sun is three times greater than that of the earth. How many years does the planet take to revolve once around the sun?

77. A metre scale '*PQ*' of uniform thickness and weighing 100 g_{wt} is suspended by means of a string to a rigid support at a point '*R*' on it such that *PR* : *QR* = 2 : 3. At the end '*P*' a load of 85 g_{wt} is attached. Find the load attached at Q such that the scale is in equilibrium. If '*S*' is a point on the scale such that *PR* : *SR* = 2 : 1 and the load at 'Q' is shifted to 'S', find the percentage change in the load, in shifting it from 'Q' and '*S*'; to maintain equilibrium state of the scale.

78. Find the power of a machine gun that can fire 240 bullets per minute, each weighing 50 g, with a velocity of 100 m s^{-1}.

79. A bullet of mass 0.02 kg moving with a muzzle velocity of 26 m s^{-1} reduces its velocity to 24 m s^{-1} on piercing through a wooden plank of thickness 3 mm. In total how many such planks are required to be piled up to bring the bullet to rest?

80. What is the power developed by an engine of a motor in lifting 4200 L of water from a well 25 m deep on to the surface in 5 minute? (1 L water = 1 kg; g = 10 m s^{-2}) Assume that there is no loss of energy in the conversion of energy.

81. Find the turning effect produced in opening a door, if a force 10 N is applied on the door, perpendicular to its plane at 60 cm from its hinge.

82. The work done on a body by applying a force of 40 N with an angle of 60° with the ground made a body to accelerate 2 m s^{-2} from rest gains the velocity of 40 m s^{-1}. Find the work done by the applied force.

83. Two bodies of masses 5 kg and 4 kg are attached to different strings of lengths 2 m and 4 m respectively. These are performing uniform circular motion about a fixed point with the same speed then find the ratio of tensions acting along the strings.

AT

PRACTICE QUESTIONS JEE-NEET SPECIAL WING

Multiple-Answer Type Questions

Directions for Questions 1 to 5: **Each question has FOUR options (A), (B), (C), and (D). ONE OR MORE THAN ONE of these four option(s) is/are the correct answer(s).**

1. Two blocks each of mass 2 kg are connected by a rope of mass 1 kg. If this arrangement is moved up as shown in the figure with an acceleration of 2 m/s^2, then force 'F' applied to lift the arrangement is ________.

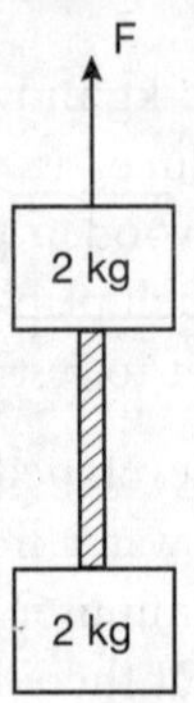

(a) 50 N (b) 60×10^5 dyne
(c) 60 N (d) 100×10^5 dyne

2. A block of mass 'm' is placed on a smooth inclined plane of mass 'M' as shown in the figure. A force F is applied on the inclined plane and the inclined plane moves with an acceleration 'a' as shown in the figure. If the block stays at the same position where it is kept during the motion of the inclined plane, then the acceleration of the block is ________.

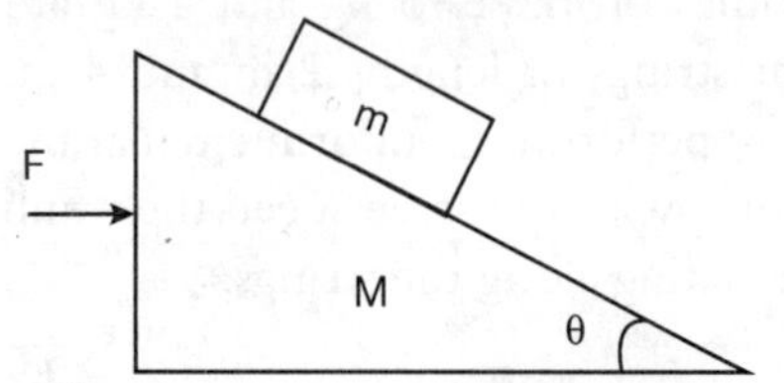

(a) g tan θ (b) g sin θ
(c) g cos θ (d) g

3. The magnitude of the force (in N) acting on a body varies with time t (in μs) as shown in the figure. The magnitude of the total impulse of the force on the body from t = 2 μs to t = 5 μs is

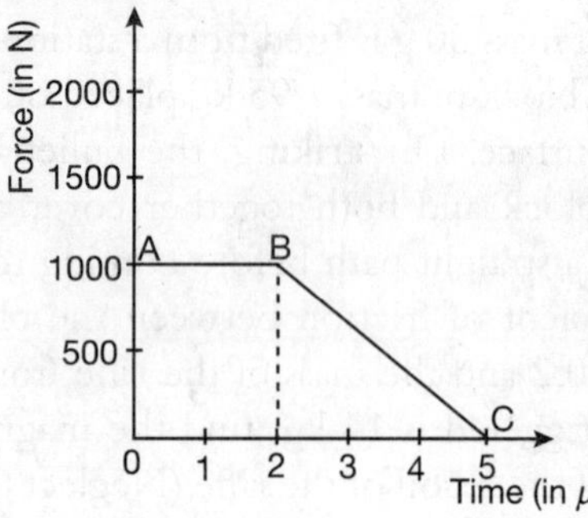

(a) 500 μ s (b) 15×10^5 ns
(c) 1500 μ s (d) 2500 μ s

4. When we pedal a bicycle, the direction of the frictional force between the ground and the two wheels (front and rear) is ________. Let F_1 be the friction between the ground and the front wheel, and F_2 be the friction between the ground and the back wheel.

(a) F_1 acts backward direction and F_2 acts forward direction.
(b) F_1 acts forward direction and F_2 acts backward direction.
(c) Both F_1 and F_2 act forward direction.
(d) Both F_1 and F_2 act backward direction.

5. A block of mass 10 kg is kept on a surface with a coefficient of friction of 0.2. A force F is applied on the block as shown in the figure. The maximum value of F for which the block does not move is ________. ($\sqrt{3} = 1.732$ and g = 10 m/s^2) (Approx.)

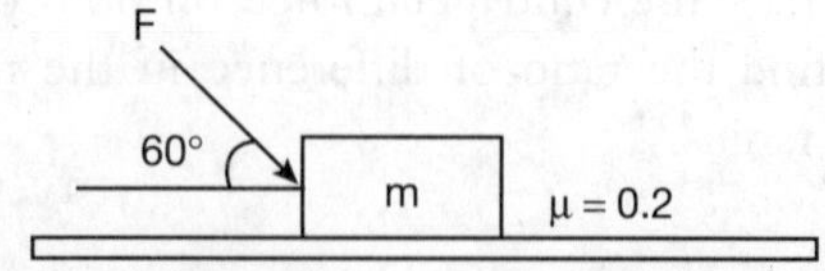

(a) 61 N (b) 51 N
(c) 41 N (d) 31 N

Comprehension-Based Questions

Direction for Question 6 to 11: **Read the paragraph given below and answer the questions.**

An inclined plane is placed as shown in the figure. A block of mass 20 kg is placed on the inclined plane and pulled with the help of a rope that is attached to it. The rope passes over a pulley as shown in the figure. The magnitude of the force used to pull the block is 100 N. ($g = 10\ m/s^2$)

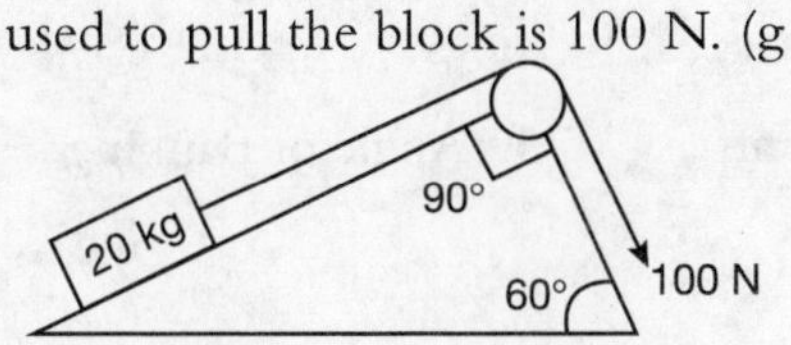

6. What is the tension in the rope?

(a) 50 N (b) 100 N
(c) 150 N (d) 200 N

7. What is the angle of the inclined plane?

(a) 30° (b) 45°
(c) 60° (d) 75°

8. Calculate the net force acting on the block.

(a) 20 N (b) 10 N
(c) 5 N (d) 0 N

9. What is the acceleration produced in the block?

(a) 0 m/s^2 (b) 5 m/s^2
(c) 10 m/s^2 (d) 20 m/s^2

10. If the force applied is doubled, then calculate the acceleration produced in the body.

(a) 0 m/s^2 (b) 5 m/s^2
(c) 10 m/s^2 (d) 20 m/s^2

11. Using the data given in the above paragraph, match the following.

Column – A	Column – B
A. Normal reaction acting on the block	a. 200 N
B. If coefficient of friction of the inclined plane, μ is 0.1, then the frictional force between the block and the inclined plane is	b. 100 N
C. When the inclined plane is a smooth surface, the load on the pulley is	c. $10\sqrt{3}$ N
D. When the inclined plane is a smooth surface, the mechanical advantage of the pulley is	d. $100\sqrt{3}$ N
E. If the mass of the block is doubled, then the effort required to hold the block at a given place is	e. 1

ANSWER KEYS

Crossword

Across

4. Efficiency
7. Fulcrum
9. Neutral Equilibrium
10. Crow Bar
11. Impulse
12. Work
13. Effort
14. Dyne

Down

1. Oscillation
2. Newton's third Law
3. Principle of Moments
5. Angle of Banking
6. Normal Reaction
8. Angular Velocity

Classroom Wing

Very Short Answer Type Questions

1. Acceleration due to gravity.
2. centrifuge
3. equator
4. mgh
5. first
6. 2 and cosec 30°
7. 11.2
8. 8 ms^{-2}
11. 200 J
20. 104.16 J
23. $T = m(g - a)$
24. 100 J
25. $20\sqrt{5}$

Competition Wing

Level 1: Apply Your Concepts

1. 5000 N
2. 100 J
3. $20\sqrt{5}$
4. 0
5. $T = mg.$
6. True
7. True
8. False
9. True
10. False
11. False
12. False
13. 82
14. 65
15. 512 : 27
16. 50
17. $\frac{F}{2}$
18. 1 : 1
19. $\frac{I.M.A}{V.R}$
20. $A \to d$, $B \to b$, $C \to c$, $D \to a$
21. (c)
22. (d)
23. (d)
24. (d)
25. (b)
26. (d)
27. (a)
28. (c)
29. (d)
30. (c)
31. (b)
32. (b)
33. (c)
34. (b)
35. (d)
36. (a)
37. (a)
38. (d)
39. (c)
40. (a)
41. (c)
42. (c)
43. (c)
44. (a)
45. (b)
46. (b)
47. (a)
48. (b)

JEE-NEET SPECIAL WING

Multiple-Answer Type Questions

1. (b, c)
2. (a)
3. (b, c)
4. (a)
5. (a)

Comprehension-Based Questions

6. (b)
7. (a)
8. (d)
9. (a)
10. (b)
11. A-d, B-c, C-b, D-e, E-a

For answer key of Classroom wing and Competition wing, refer to Hints and Solutions

Hints and Explanations

CLASSROOM WING

Very Short Answer Type Questions

1. Acceleration due to gravity.
2. centrifuge
3. equator
4. mgh
5. first
6. 2 and cosec 30°
7. 11.2
8. Within elastic limit, stress is directly proportional to strain.
9. Work is product of force and displacement. Power is rate of doing work.

   $W = \vec{F}.\vec{d}$, Power $= \vec{F}.\vec{v}$
10. $F = 10$ N, $f = 2$ N

    $F_{net} = 10 - 2 = 8 \text{ N} = m \times a$

    $a = 8 \text{ m } s^{-2}$.
11. Mass = 2 kg, $h = 10$ m

    $K = mgh = 2 \times 10 \times 10 = 200$ J.
12. MA = n (n = number of pulleys in sheath)
13. Two forces acting along parallel lines.
14. Orbital velocity – Minimum velocity to make a satellite revolve around the planet

    Escape velocity – Minimum velocity to make a body escape from Earth's surface.
15. Product of force and perpendicular distance.
16. The point where the total weight of a body acts.
17. They decrease the efficiency
18. The acceleration directed towards the centre of circular path.
19. A body regains its original position after application of slight force.
20. $K = \frac{1}{2m} p^2$

    $= \frac{1}{2 \times 3} \times (25)^2 = \frac{625}{6} = 104.16 \text{ J}$
21. $V_e = \sqrt{2}\, V_o$
22. A device which allows application of force conveniently to overcome force at on other point.
23. Put $F = ma = mg - T$

    $T = m(g - a)$.
24. 100 J
25. $20\sqrt{5}$

Short Answer Type Questions

Note: This is how you should frame your answer covering.

26. $V = r\omega$
27. $u = 20 \text{ m s}^{-1}$, $v = 30 \text{ m s}^{-1}$, $t = 1 \times 10^{-3}$ s.

    $m = 1$ kg

    $$F = m\left(\frac{v-u}{t}\right)$$

    $$= 1 \times \left(\frac{30-20}{10^{-3}}\right) = 1 \times 10 \times 10^3 = 10^4 \text{ N.}$$
28. $$F = \frac{mv^2}{R} = \frac{1500 \times (10)^2}{20}$$

    $= 7{,}500$ N.
29. Loss of potential energy = gain in kinetic energy

    $$Mg\,(R - R\cos\theta) = \frac{1}{2} M \times v^2$$

    $$v = \sqrt{2(R)(1-\cos\theta)g}$$
30. $F = 100$ N, $\theta = 30°$

    $W = Fs\cos\theta$

    $= 100 \times 2 \times \cos 30$

    $= 200\,\frac{\sqrt{3}}{2} = 100\sqrt{3}$ J.
31. (i) Force required

    (ii) Gravitational pull

    (iii) Upward force

    (iv) Resultant force

    Ans: Net force $= 2{\cdot}96 \times 10^5$ N

32. Power $= \frac{\text{work}}{\text{time}}$

$$= \frac{Fs\cos\theta}{\text{time}} = \frac{mas\cos\theta}{\text{time}}$$

$$\frac{2000 \times 10 \times 20}{20} = 20 \text{ kW}$$

33. $F = G\frac{m_1 m_2}{r^2}$

34. $W = Fs \cos \theta$
$= 50 \times 10 \times 20(\cos 180)$
$= -10 \times 10^3$ J
$= -10^4$ J.

35. Mass = 2000 kg, $u = 20$ m s^{-1}, $\Delta P = 1000$ kg m s^{-1}
$Pf = 2000 + 20 \times 1000 = m \times v$

$$u = \frac{40000 + 1000}{2000}$$

$$\frac{41}{2} = 20.5 \text{ m s}^{-1}$$

36. $S = 0.2$ m, $w = 2\pi$ rad s^{-1}
$V = sw = 0.2 \times 2\pi = 0.4\pi$ m s^{-1}.

Essay Answer Type Questions

Note: This is how you should frame your answer covering.

37. According to work energy theorem,
ΔK = work done

$$F \times 0.1 = \frac{1}{2} \times 0.1(100)^2$$

$$= \frac{104 \times 0.1}{2}$$

$$= \frac{10^3}{2} = 500$$

$F = 5{,}000$ N.

38. Mass = 20 kg

$h = 5$ m, distance = 2 m

$\Delta K = w$

$0 - 25 \times 10 \times 5 = 25 \times 10 \times 2 - f \times 2$

$-f(2) = -1250 - 500$

$$-f = \frac{1750}{2}$$

$f = 875$ N

39. (i) Theorem or principle of moment
(ii) Clockwise moment
(iii) Equilibrium

Ans: $T_2 = 44$ kg$_{wt}$
$T_1 = 56$ kg$_{wt}$

40. Ans: $\omega = 5$ rad s^{-1}
Centripetal force = 25 N
Centrifugal force = 25 N

"Efficiency is defined as the ratio of M.A. to V.R".

41.

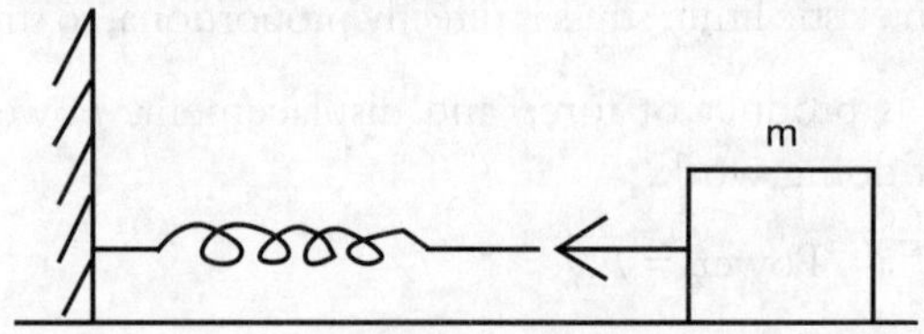

According to the work energy theorem

$\Delta K = W_{net}$

$K_f = 0; \quad k_i = \frac{1}{2} mv^2$

Work done by elastic force = work done by friction

$$0 - \frac{1}{2} mv^2 = -\frac{1}{2} kx^2$$

$$\frac{1}{2} mv^2 = \frac{1}{2} kx^2$$

$$mv^2 = kx^2$$

$$x^2 = \frac{mv^2}{k}$$

$$x = \sqrt{\frac{m}{k}}\,v$$

42. $\tan\theta = \frac{v^2}{rg}$

43. $v = 72$ km h^{-1} $= \frac{72 \times 5}{18} = 20$ m s^{-1}

$m = 1000$ kg, $f = 6000$ N
According to work energy theorem,
Δk = work done by friction

$K_f - k_i = f \times s$

$$\Rightarrow 0 - \frac{1}{2} \times 1000 \times 20^2 = -6000 \times s.$$

$$-\frac{1}{2}\ 400 = -6 \times s$$

$$s = \frac{200}{6} = \frac{100}{3} = \text{m} = 33.3 \text{ m}.$$

44. Horizontal speed

Curved path

45. Refer to Page-2.38 under Screw Jack

Competition Wing

Level 1: Apply Your Concepts

1. $u = 18$ km h^{-1}, $v = 36$ km h^{-1} $t = 2$

$$F = m\left(\frac{v-u}{2}\right) = 2000\left(\frac{10-5}{2}\right)$$

$= 5000$ N.

2. Mass = 2 kg, u =10 m s^{-1}

Potential energy = $\frac{1}{2}$ mv^2

$= \frac{1}{2} \times 2 \times 10^2 = 100$ J.

3. $P = \sqrt{2mk} = \sqrt{2 \times 5 \times 200}$

$= 20\sqrt{5}$

4. $W = Fs \cos \theta$

$= Fs \cos 90° = 0.$

5. As the body is moving with uniform velocity

$F_{net} = 0$

$Mg - T = 0$

$T =$ mg.

20. A → d, B → b, C → c, D → a

21. $\frac{GMm}{R^2} = \frac{mv^2}{R}$

$R = \frac{GM}{v^2}$

Hence, the correct option is (c).

36. Force $= m.a$

$$= m\left(\frac{v-u}{t}\right) = \frac{1(7-5)}{1 \times 10^{-3}} = 2000\text{N}$$

37. Force $F = ma = 1 \times 1 = 1$ N

38. Force $F = ma$

$$1 \text{ dyne} = 100 \times a \Rightarrow a = \frac{1}{100} = 0.01 \text{ cm s}^{-2}$$

39. According to Newton's third law of motion Action = – (Reaction)

$M_B a_B = -M_A \times a_A$

$1 = -0.1 \times a_A$

$a_A = -10$ m s^{-2}

40. Momentum p, $= mv = 10$ N s

Mass m, $= 0.5$ kg

$$10 = 0.5 \times v \Rightarrow v = \frac{10}{0.5} = 20 \text{ m s}^{-1}$$

Kinetic energy of the body reaching the ground = potential energy at the highest point

$\frac{1}{2} mv^2 =$ mgh

$$\frac{1}{2} \times (20)^2 = 10 \times h \Rightarrow h = 20 \text{ m}.$$

41. $K.E. = \frac{1}{2} mv^2 = \frac{1}{2} p.v. = \frac{1}{2}\frac{p^2}{2m}$

$p_1 = p, p_2 = p + \frac{p}{2} = \frac{3p}{2} = 1.5p$

$$K.E_2 = \frac{1}{2}\frac{p_2^2}{2m} = \frac{1}{2} \times \frac{(1.5p)^2}{m} = \frac{9p^2}{8m} = \frac{9}{4}\left(\frac{1}{2}\frac{p^2}{m}\right)$$

$$K.E_2 = \frac{9}{4} KE_1$$

∴ Change in K.E = $KE_2 - KE_1$

$$= \frac{9}{4} KE_1 - KE_1 = \frac{5}{4}.\frac{1}{2} mv_1^2 = \frac{5}{8} mv_1^2$$

42. The work done an a body due to net force = force × displacement.

Always the total force applied on a body may not be responsible for its motion. A component of force can also cause displacement in the body.

∴ Work done = (component of force acting in the direction of displacement of body) × displacement) = (F cos θ) × s

43. Mechanical advantage of an inclined

$$\text{Plane} = \frac{\text{Lenght of plane}}{\text{Height of plane}}$$

$$= \frac{\ell}{h} = \frac{1}{\sin\theta}$$

$$\therefore \text{M.A} = \frac{4m}{1m} = 4$$

$$\frac{1}{\sin 60} = \text{cosec } 60 = \frac{2}{\sqrt{3}}$$

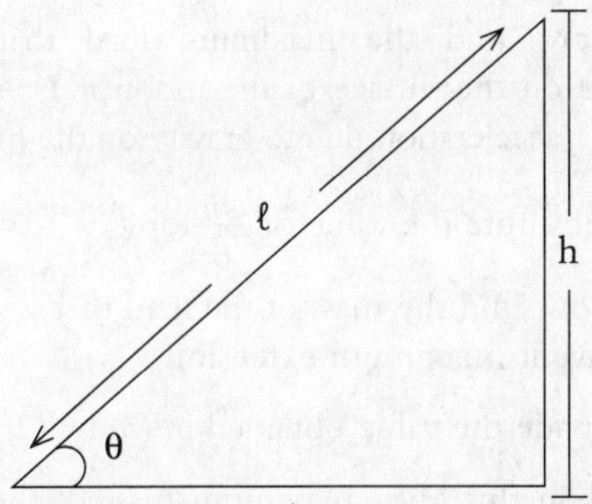

44.

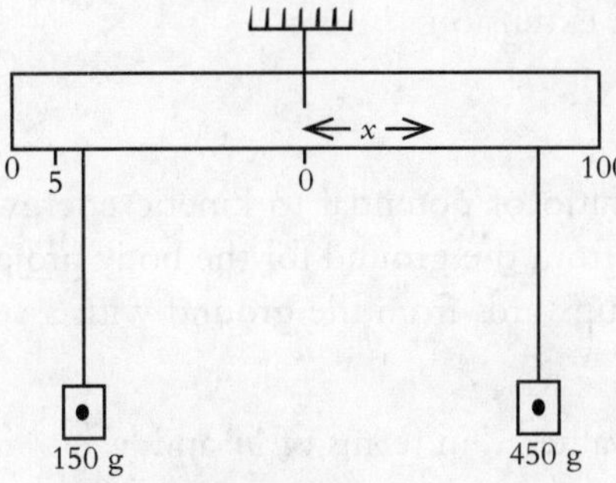

Let the weight 450g be attached at a distance of x cm from the point of suspension.

∴ According to the principle of moments. Sum of anti-clockwise moments = Sum of clockwise moments about the point of suspension

$\therefore 45 \text{ cm} \times 150 \text{ g} = x \times 450 \text{ g}$

$$x = \frac{45}{3} \text{ cm} = 15 \text{ cm}$$

∴ The weight should be attached at a distance of 15 cm from point of suspension (or) at (50 + 15) cm = 65 cm fmark of the scale.

45. The movable pulley divides the rope into two segments. Tension T acts in upwards direction along the two segments of the rope.

If 'p' is the effort applied to overcome total load, then $p = T$ and it is obvious that $w = T + T = 2T$ where, w is the total load.

$$\therefore \text{The mechanical advantage} = \frac{\text{Load}}{\text{Efforts}} = \frac{2T}{T} = 2$$

If pulley is not rotating and the load due to friction and movable parts is neglected, then both the load and the effort are equal to the tension in the sting.

Thus, $w = p = T$

$$\therefore \text{Mechanical advantage} = \frac{w}{p} = \frac{T}{T} = 1$$

Total mechanical advantage (M.A) = ($M.A_1$) × ($M.A_2$) = 2 × 1 = 2

46. The radius of circular path (r) = 40 cm = 0.40 m
Linear speed of the particle (v) = 5 ms^{-1}

The angular velocity

$\omega = v/r = 5/0.4 = 50/4 = 12.5 \text{ rad } s^{-1}$

47. Radius of circular path (r) = 10 cm
Time taken to complete a revolution (T) = 4s
Centripetal acceleration (a)?

$$\therefore \text{Angular speed} = \omega = \frac{2\pi}{T} \text{ rad } s^{-1}$$

$$= \frac{V^2}{r} = \frac{(rw)^2}{r} = rw^2$$

$$\therefore a = 10 \text{ cm} \times \frac{4\pi^2}{T^2} = 10 \text{ cm} \times \frac{4^{-2}}{16}$$

$$= 2.5\pi^2 \text{ cm s}^{-2}$$

48. +300 m Gal = 0.3 × 10^{-2} m s^{-2} = 0.003 m s^{-2}

$\therefore g = 9.78 + 0.003 = 9.783 \text{ m s}^{-2}$

Level 2: Review Your Concepts

Note: This is how you should frame your answer covering.

49. (i) For inclined plane, $\text{M.A.} = \dfrac{1}{\sin\theta}$

(ii) For single movable pulley, M.A. = 2

(iii) 13.75 kgwt, $M.A._1 \times M.A._2$

50. (i) From given information, find the load in newtons.

Find the radii of wheel and axle.

The mechanical advantage (M.A) of wheel and axle is, $\text{M.A} = \dfrac{R}{r} = \dfrac{\text{Load}}{\text{Efforts}}$.

Find the value of effort.

Here, the son contributes one-third of the total effort.

Then find the value of effort contributed by the son.

(ii) 40 N

51. Q → R → S → P

$$\frac{GMm}{R^2} = \frac{mv^2}{R}$$

$$v^2 = \frac{GM}{R}$$

$$v = \sqrt{\frac{GM}{R}}$$

52. At the top position of the circular path, is centrifugal force, $F = \frac{mv^2}{r}$ equal to the weight of the stone and tension (T) in the string.

At the bottom position of the circular path, the tension (T) in the string is equal to the weight of the stone and centrifugal force (F).

53. Mass = 20 kg, $u = 200$ m s^{-1}, $P_i = 1000$ kg m s^{-1}

$P_f = 4000 - 100 = 3900$ kg m s^{-1}

$P = mv$

$3900 = 20 \times v$

$V = \frac{3900}{20} = 195$ m s^{-1}.

54. Which portion of the metallic vessel, i.e., a hemisphere or a truncated cone, contains more mass?

Hemispherical portion has more metal. So, centre of gravity (G) of the vessel lies near the bottom.
Find whether the height of the centre of gravity remains constant in any position where the hemisphere part touches the ground.
Then find the state of equilibrium of the vessel.
Here, centre of gravity 'G' lies near to the base of the vessel, i.e., near the hemisphere. Then find the direction of moment of forces acting on the metallic vessel with respect to C.

55. $v = 10$ m s^{-1}, $m = 2$ kg, $t = 0.1$ s.

$$P = \frac{\frac{1}{2}mv^2}{t} = \frac{\frac{1}{2} \times 2 \times 1000}{0.1} = 1000 \text{ W}$$

= 1 kW.

56. (i) Find the maximum load, i.e., 20 kgwt, in terms of newtons.

Convert 20 cm length in terms of S.I.

Find the value of force constant (k) from the formula, $F = kx$. (1)

Now, find the maximum load that is possible on the surface of the moon if $F = mg_m = kx$ (g_m acceleration due to gravity on the moon).

Substitute the value of $\frac{g_E}{6}$ for g_m (2)

Now, find the mass of the load that is attached to have its maximum extension (3)

Divide the value obtained in (3) by (2).

Then this gives maximum mass of the load that can be attached to the balance to have half its maximum extension.

(ii) 60 kg

57. (i) Find the ratio of potential to kinetic energy at a height 'x' from the ground for the body projected vertically upwards from the ground with a velocity 'u'.

Find the value 'x' in terms of 'u' and 'g'.

For the same body, when projected up with a velocity $3u$, the ratio of potential to kinetic energy is at a height '$3x$' from the ground.
Find the velocity of the body at height '$3x$' in terms of u, g and x using the formula $v^2 = u^2 - 2gh$, and then simplify.

(ii) 1 : 8

58. (i) Here, acceleration due to gravity at height 'H', from earth is $g_h = g_o\left(1 - \frac{2h}{R}\right)$.

Then, acceleration due to gravity at a depth 'd' from earth is $g_d = g_o\left(1 - \frac{d}{R}\right)$.

If $g_h = g_d$, then find the relation between 'h' and 'd' – (1)

If the 'g' and 'd' both increase by 50%, then $h = h + \frac{h}{2}$ and $d^1 = d + d/2$.

Substitute the value obtained from (1) and find whether $g_{h'} = g_d$.

(ii) $d = 2h$

59. (i) Resolve momentum into horizontal and vertical components.

(ii) Change in momentum is due to change in vertical component osf the momentum.

(iii) –5 kg m s^{-1}

60. If the mass of the satellite is more, is it easily possible to lift it to higher altitudes?

Find the difference between the single stage rocket and multistage rocket.

61. (i) How many bullets are fired from the machine gun in one second?

What is the kinetic energy of the bullet?

The work done by the gun in one second is equal to the total amount of kinetic energy of the bullets fired in one second.

Find the value of the power.

(ii) 1 kW

62. What is centripetal force?

Will heavier particle move towards the centre of curvature?

Will air bubble move away from the centre of curvature?

63. (i) Total energy $= \frac{1}{2} mv^2 + mgh_1$

Change in energy $= \left(\frac{1}{2}mv^2 + mgh_1\right) - (mgh_2)$

% change in energy

$$= \frac{\left(\frac{1}{2}mv^2 + mgh_1\right) - (mgh_2)}{\frac{1}{2}mv^2 + mgh_1} \times 100$$

(ii) 43.5%

64. The net force acting on the two block system is

$F - f = (M + m)\, a$

$\therefore a = \frac{F - f}{(M + m)}$

The smaller block is moving forward and the only force acting on it in the horizontal direction is frictional force between the blocks. Thus, the frictional force acts along the direction of motion of the smaller block.

The magnitude of frictional force,

$$F^1 = m\left(\frac{F - f}{m + m}\right)$$

65. The forces acting on the object are mg downward, tension (T) upward

$\therefore$ Net force $F = T - mg$

$ma = T - mg \Rightarrow T = m(a + g)$

66. $v = 10 \text{ ms}^{-1}$ $r = 0.3$ m.

$$v = rw.\ w = \frac{v}{r} = \frac{10}{0.3} = \frac{100}{3} = 33.3 \text{.m s}^{-1}$$

67. $s = 3$ m, speed $= 10$ m s–1 $\mu = ?$

$$\frac{m \times (10)^2}{50} = \mu \times m \times 10$$

$$\mu = \frac{10}{50} = \left(\frac{1}{5}\right) = 0.2$$

68. Angular velocity, $\omega = \frac{v}{r} = \frac{10}{2} = 5 \text{ rad } s^{-1}$

Centripetal force, $F = \frac{mv^2}{r} = \frac{1 \times 10^2}{r} = 50$ N

The magnitude of centripetal force is equal to the magnitude of centrifugal force.

Hence, centrifugal force is 50 N but opposite in direction to centripetal force.

Level 3: Assess Your Concepts

Note: This is how you should frame your answer covering.

69. The centripetal force = gravitational force

$$\frac{mv^2}{r} = \frac{G \times m \times 2M}{(r)^2} \Rightarrow \frac{2GM}{r} = v^2$$

$$v_1 = \sqrt{\frac{2GM}{r}} = \frac{2\pi \times r}{T_1} \qquad (1)$$

For the second satellite

$$\frac{2mv_2^2}{2r} = \frac{G \times 2m \times M}{(2r)^2}$$

$$v_2^2 = \frac{GM}{2r}$$

$$v^2 = \sqrt{\frac{GM}{2r}} = \frac{2\pi(2r)}{T_2} \qquad (2)$$

$$\frac{(1)}{(2)} = \frac{\sqrt{\frac{2GM}{r}}}{\sqrt{\frac{GM}{2r}}} = \frac{2\pi(r)}{T_1} \times \frac{T_2}{2\pi(2r)} \Rightarrow 2 = \frac{T_2}{2T_1}$$

$$\frac{T_1}{T_2} = \frac{1}{4}$$

70.

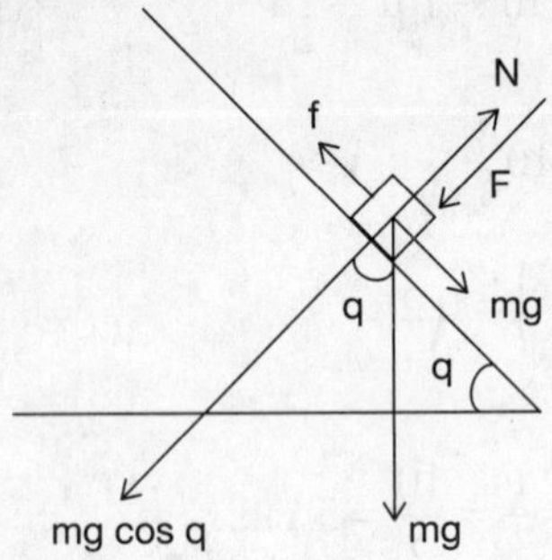

To keep the body under equilibrium, the net force required is zero.

That is $f = mg \sin \theta$

$mg \cos \theta + F = N$

$$5 \times 10 \times \frac{1}{2} + F = N$$

$$f = 5 \times 10 \times \frac{\sqrt{3}}{2} = \mu N = \mu\left(5 \times 10 \times \frac{1}{2} + F\right)$$

$$\Rightarrow 25\sqrt{3} = 25 + F \Rightarrow 25(\sqrt{3} + 1)$$

$$= 25 \times 0.7$$

$$= 17.5 \text{ N.}$$

71. (i) Find the masses of bullet (m_b) and block (m_w) in C.G.S. system.

According to the law of conservation of momentum:

$m_1 u_1 + m_2 u_2 = m_1 v_1 + m_2 v_2$

Then, take initial velocity of bullet and block as 'u' and 'zero', respectively.

When the bullet is embedded into the block, both have a common velocity.

Let 'v' be the common velocity.

Find the relation between 'u' and 'v'.

By law of conservation of momentum, when both bullet and block together cover 200 m before coming to rest, then, the frictional force,

$$F = \mu(m_b + m_w) g \quad (1)$$

Find the work done to overcome the friction.

The kinetic energy of the system = ½ $(m_b + m_w) v^2$ = Work done

Then,

$$\frac{1}{2}(m_b + m_w) v^2 = \mu(m_b + m_w) g s \quad (2)$$

Find the value of 'v' from (2).

Find the mass of the gun m_g from given information.

Apply the law of conservation of momentum.

$$u_g = u_b = 0$$

Then,

$$m_g u_g + m_b u_b = m_g v_g + m_b u_b \quad (3)$$

Find the value 'v_g' from (3).

(ii) 4 m s^{-1}

72.

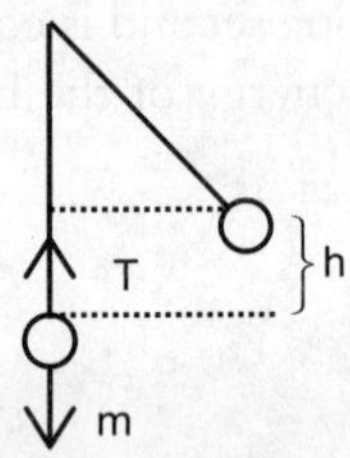

Length of the pendulum = 0.5 m

$mgh = 4$ J

The potential energy at the highest point = kinetic energy at the mean position

$$\frac{1}{2} mv^2 = 4$$

$$\frac{1}{2} \times 0.2 \times v^2 = 4$$

$$v^2 = 40 \Rightarrow v = \sqrt{40} \text{ m s}^{-1}$$

$$T - \text{mg} = \frac{mv^2}{R}$$

$$T = \frac{mv^2}{R} + mg = \frac{0.2 \times 40}{0.5} + 0.2 \times 10$$

$$= \frac{8}{0.5} + 2 = 18 \text{ N}$$

73. (i) How the motion appears from inertial and non-inertial frames of reference?

(ii) Direction of velocity is along the tangent.

(iii) How the centrigal force acts on the body?

74.

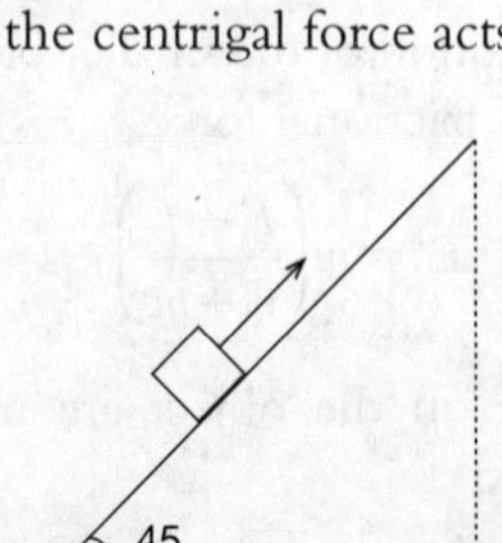

$$M = 2 \text{ kg}; \; V = \frac{36 \times 5}{18} = 10 \text{ m s}^{-1}$$

According to the work energy theorem

ΔK = work done by external forces.

$K_f - K_{-i}$ = work done by friction + work done by gravitational force

$$0 - \frac{1}{2} \times m(10)^2 = -\mu\, mg \cos 45° + -mgh$$

given $mgh = 80$ J

$$-\frac{1}{2} \times 2 \times 100 = -\mu \times 2 \times 10 \times \frac{1}{\sqrt{2}} - 80$$

$$100 - 80 = 10\sqrt{2}\,\mu$$

$$\mu = \frac{20}{10\sqrt{2}} = \sqrt{2}$$

75. Given, $m_A : m_B = 1 : 2$;

$\omega_A : \omega_B = 4 : 1$ and

$F_A = F_B$

Centripetal force $F = mr\omega^2$

$\therefore m_A r_A \omega_A^2$

$$\Rightarrow \frac{r_A}{r_B} = \left(\frac{m_B}{m_A}\right)\left(\frac{\omega_B}{\omega_A}\right)^2 = \left(\frac{2}{1}\right)\left(\frac{1}{4}\right)^2$$

$$\therefore \frac{r_B}{r_A} = 8$$

Hence, the required ratio is

$$\frac{r_B - r_A}{r_A} \Rightarrow \frac{r_B}{r_A} - 1 = 7 : 1$$

76. According to Kepler's law of periods,

$T^2 \propto R^3$

$$\Rightarrow \frac{T_2^2}{T_1^2} = \frac{R_2^3}{R_1^3}$$

$$\Rightarrow T_2 = T_1\left(\frac{R_2}{R_1}\right)^{\frac{3}{2}}$$

Given, $R_2 = R_1 + 3R_1 = 4R_1$

$\therefore = T_2 = T_1 (4)^{3/2} = 8T_1.$

$T_1 = 1$yr. $\quad \therefore T_2 = 8$ yrs.

77.

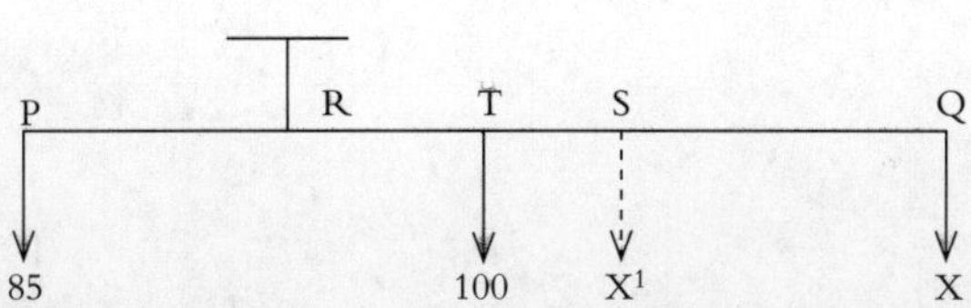

T is the midpoint of the scale and its weight 100 g acts at this point.

Given, PR : QR = 2 : 3

But PR + QR = 100 cm

$\therefore$ PR = 100 − QR

$$\text{PR} = 100 - \frac{3}{2}\text{PR}$$

$$100 = \text{PR} + \frac{3}{2}\text{PR}$$

$$100 = \frac{5}{2}\text{PR}$$

or,

PR = 40 cm

$\therefore$ QR = 60 cm.

If x is the load attached at Q, then for the scale to be in equilibrium,

(85 g) (PR) = x(QR) + RT(100) $\Rightarrow$ (85)(40) = x(60) + 1000

$\Rightarrow x = 40$ g.

$$\text{Given, } \frac{\text{PR}}{\text{SR}} = \frac{2}{1} \Rightarrow \text{SR} = \frac{\text{PR}}{2} = \frac{40}{2} = 20 \text{ cm}$$

Lt x^1 be the load attached at S.

Then (85)PR = (x^1) (SR) + 100(TR)

85(40) = x'^1(20) + 100(10) $\Rightarrow x'^1 = 120$ g

If the load at Q is shifted to S, the percentage change in the load

$$= \left(\frac{x^1 - x}{x}\right)100 = \left(\frac{120 - 40}{40}\right) \times 100 = 200\%$$

78. Number of bullets fired per minute = 240.

Time, $t = 60$ s

Mass of each bullet, $m = 50$ g.

$\therefore$mass of 240 bullets = nm = (240) (50) g.

$$= \frac{24 \times 5}{10} \text{kg} = 12 \text{ kg}$$

Initial velocity of the bullets (u) = 0 m s^{-1}.

Final velocity of the bullets (v) = 100 m s^{-1}.

$\therefore$Initial kinetic energy of the bullets

$$= \frac{1}{2}mnu^2 = 0$$

Final kinetic energy of the bullets

$$= \frac{1}{2}mnv^2 = \frac{1}{2}\left(\frac{240 \times 50}{1000}\right)(100)^2$$

∴ Change in kinetic energy

$$= \frac{1}{2}mnv^2 - 0 = \frac{1}{2}mnv^2$$

But the change in

Kinetic energy = Work done (W).

$$\therefore \text{Power} = \frac{\text{Work}}{\text{Time}} = \frac{W}{t} = \frac{1}{2}\frac{mnv^2}{t}$$

$$= \frac{1}{2}\left(\frac{240 \times 50}{1000}\right)\frac{(100)^2}{60} = 1000 \text{ W} = 1 \text{ kW}$$

79. Given, m = 0.02 kg, u = 26 m/s, v = 24 m/s, and s = 3 mm = 3×10^{-3} m

Let the resistive force offered by the single wooden plank be 'f' N.

In the first case, the velocity of the bullet is decreased from "u" to "v" on piercing through "s", where "s" is the thickness of a single plank.

Then the work done by the resistive force "f" on the bullet is given by

$$\frac{1}{2}mv^2 - \frac{1}{2}mu^2 = -fs \Rightarrow \frac{1}{2}m\left(v^2 - u^2\right) = -fs \rightarrow (1)$$

The negative sign is taken to indicate that the work is done on the bullet by the resistive force.

In the second case, if "n" such planks are piled up, then the distance the bullet travels before coming to rest = ns.

Thus, we have

$$\frac{1}{2}m0^2 - \frac{1}{2}mu^2 = -fns \Rightarrow -\frac{1}{2}mu^2 = -fns \rightarrow (2)$$

Dividing equation (2) by (1) we get

$$\frac{-\frac{1}{2}mu^2}{\frac{1}{2}m\left(v^2 - u^2\right)} = -n \Rightarrow n = \frac{u^2}{u^2 - v^2}$$

$$= \frac{26^2}{26^2 - 24^2} = \frac{676}{676 - 576} = \frac{676}{100} = 6.76$$

As the number is a fraction, we need to consider the round up value. Hence, we need 7 such planks to bring the bullet to rest.

80. Volume of water, V = 4200 L

Mass of water, m = 4200 kg

Acceleration due to gravity, g = 10 m/s^2

Height from which water is lifted, h = 25 m

Time taken, t = 5 min = 5×60 s = 300 s

Power, P = work / time

$$\Rightarrow P = \frac{mgh}{t} = \frac{4200 \times 10 \times 25}{300} = 3500W$$

81. Force applied, F = 10 N

Perpendicular distance of the point of application of the force, r = 60 cm = 0.6 m (radius vector)

Turning effect, $\tau = rF \sin\theta$, where θ is the angle between the direction of the applied force and the radius vector.

Here $\theta = 90°$ and $\sin 90° = 1$

Hence, we get $\tau = 0.6 \text{ m} \times 10 \text{ N} \times 1 = 6 \text{ N m}$

82. F = 40 N; $\theta = 60°$; a = 2 m s^{-2}

u = o; v = 40 m s^{-1} W =?

$$W = F\cos\theta \times s = F\cos\theta\left(\frac{v^2 - u^2}{2a}\right) = 40 \quad \cos 60$$

$$\left(\frac{40 \times 40}{2 \times 2}\right) = 40 \quad \frac{1}{2} \quad 10 \quad 40$$

W = 8000 J = 8 kJ

83. $m_1 = 5$ kg; $m_2 = 4$ kg

$r_1 = 2$ m; $r_2 = 4$ m

$v_1 = v_2$

tension = centripetal force

$$T = \frac{mv^2}{r}$$

$$\frac{T_1}{T_2} = \frac{m_1 v_1^2}{r_1} \times \frac{r_2}{m_2 v_2^2} = \frac{m_1}{m_2} \times \left(\frac{v_1}{v_2}\right)^2 \times \frac{r_2}{r_1}$$

$$= \frac{5}{4} \times 1 \times \frac{4}{2} = 5:2$$

JEE-NEET SPECIAL WING

Multiple-Answer Type Questions

1. Given,
Mass of each block, $m = 2$ kg
Mass of the rope, $m' = 1$ kg
Therefore, the mass of the system of masses
$= 2 + 2 + 1 = 5$ kg
Acceleration of the system, $a = 2$ m/s^2
Acceleration due to gravity, $g = 10$ m/s^2
The net force acting on the system of masses
$= F - (5 \times g)$
We have Newton's law,
$F - (5 \times g) = ma$
$\Rightarrow F - (5 \times 10) = 5 \times 2$
$\Rightarrow F - 50 = 10 \Rightarrow F = 60\ N = 60 \times 10^5$ dyne
Hence, the correct option is (b, c)

2. According to the question,

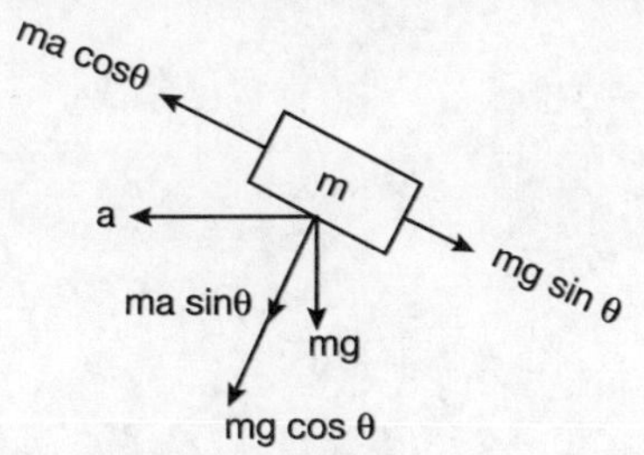

Given, mass of the block = m
Mass of the inclined plane = M
Force applied on the block = F
From the free body diagram,
For the block of mass 'm' to be at rest,
The net force acting along the plane of the inclined plane should be zero.
i.e., $mg \sin \theta = ma \cos \theta$
$\Rightarrow a = g \tan \theta$
Hence, the correct option is (a)

3. From the F-t graph,
The magnitude of the total impulse of the force on the body = Area of F-t graph for $t = 2\ \mu$ s to $t = 5\ \mu$ s,
The magnitude of the total impulse
$= \frac{1}{2} \times$ Base $\times$ Height
$= \frac{1}{2} \times (5 - 2)\ \mu s \times 1000\ N$
$= 1500\ \mu s$
Hence, the correct option is (b, c)

4. When we peddle the bicycle, the force is applied initially on the rear wheel. Therefore, the rear wheel moves in the forward direction but the point of contact of the wheel and the land surface moves in *a* backward direction hence, F_2 acts in the forward direction. Due to transitional motion, the front wheel moves in the forward direction. At the point of contact, the frictional force F_1 acts backward direction.
Hence, the correct option is (a)

5. Given,
Mass of the block, $m = 10$ kg
Coefficient of friction, $\mu = 0.2$.
From figure,
Component of F = Frictional force
$\Rightarrow F \cos 60° = \mu$ mg $+ \mu F \sin 60°$
$\Rightarrow F \times \frac{1}{2} = 0.2 \times 10 \times 10 + 0.2 \times F \times \frac{\sqrt{3}}{2}$
$\Rightarrow F \times \left(\frac{1}{2} - \frac{0.2 \times \sqrt{3}}{2}\right) = 20$
$\Rightarrow F \times \left(\frac{1 - 0.2 \times 1.732}{2}\right) = 20$
$\Rightarrow F \times \left(\frac{1 - 0.3464}{2}\right) = 20$
$\Rightarrow F \times \left(\frac{0.6536}{2}\right) = 20$
$\Rightarrow F = \frac{40}{0.6536} \sim 61N$
Hence, the correct option is (a)

Comprehension-Based Questions

6. The tension in the rope is the force applied on the rope to pull the block. Therefore, the tension (T) in the rope is 100 N.
Hence, the correct option is (b)

7. The angle of the inclined plane is the angle made by the plane with the horizontal. i.e.,
Angle of the inclined plane = 180 – (90 + 60) = 30°.
Hence, the correct option is (a)

8. Net force acting on the block = $T -$ mg sin θ
= 100 – (20 × 10 × sin30°)
= 100 – 100 = 0 (since sin30° $= \frac{1}{2}$)
Hence, the correct option is (d)

9. We have,
Net force acting on the block = ma

i.e., $T - mg \sin\theta = ma$

$\Rightarrow 100 - (20 \times 10 \times \sin 30°) = 20\,a$

$\Rightarrow 100 - 100 = 20\,a$ (since $\sin 30° = \frac{1}{2}$)

$\Rightarrow a = 0$

i.e., the net force acting on the block is zero.
Therefore, the acceleration produced is zero.
Hence, the correct option is (a)

10. If the force applied on the rope is doubled, i.e., 200 *N*.

Using Net force acting on the block = ma

i.e., $T - mg \sin\theta = ma$

$\Rightarrow 200 - (20 \times 10 \times \sin 30°) = 20\,a$

$\Rightarrow 200 - 100 = 20\,a$ (since $\sin 30° = \frac{1}{2}$)

$\Rightarrow a = \frac{100}{20} = 5\ m/s^2$

Hence, the correct option is (b)

11. Normal reaction force, $N = mg \cos\theta$
$= 20 \times 10 \times \cos 30° = 100\sqrt{3}$

A → d

The frictional force between the block and the inclined plane $= \mu\ mg \cos\theta$
$= 0.1 \times 20 \times 10 \times \cos 30° = 10\sqrt{3}\ N$

B → c

When the inclined plane is *a* smooth surface, the load on the pulley $= mg \sin\theta$
$= 20 \times 10 \times \sin 30° = 100\ N$

C → b

When the inclined plane is *a* smooth surface, the mechanical advantage of the pulley,
$M = L/E = 100/100 = 1$

D → e

If the mass of the block is doubled, then the effort required to hold the block at *a* given place is
Effort = load $= mg \sin\theta = 40 \times 10 \times \sin 30° = 200\ N$

E → a

CHAPTER 3

Sources of Energy

Remember

Before beginning this chapter, you should be able to:

- Understand renewable and non-renewable sources of energy.
- Understand uses of different sources of energy.
- Recognize causes and preventive measures of air pollution.

Key Ideas

After completing this chapter, you should be able to:

- Study in detail about different sources of energy and classification of these sources into renewable and non-renewable.
- Understand the advantages and disadvantages of different sources of energies like solar energy, wind energy, hydel energy, tidal energy, thermal energy, geothermal energy, etc.
- Learn about types of fuels such as solid fuels, liquid fuels, gaseous fuels and fossil fuels.
- Select a good fuel, the qualities of a good fuel, the advantages and disadvantages of different fuels.

Scientific Crypt

A Tribute to James Perscott Joule (1818 – 1889)

Joule was born in Salford, Lencashire on 11th December 1818. Upto 1834, he was tutored at the family home Broomhill, near Salford. Then he was sent to John Dalton, along with his brother, to learn geometry and arithmetic for two years. Later, he was tutored by John Davies. In 1838, his first scientific paper on electricity was published. The relationship between heat produced and electric current flowing through a resistor was formulated in 1840, which is known as Joules law. His work on heat led him to estimate the value of mechanical equivalent of heat. He spent lot of money while working on the verification of the mechanical equivalent of heat and became poor. But a pension was provided by the Royal Society and the queen to help him. He published his last scientific paper in 1878.

FUN TIME

CROSSWORD

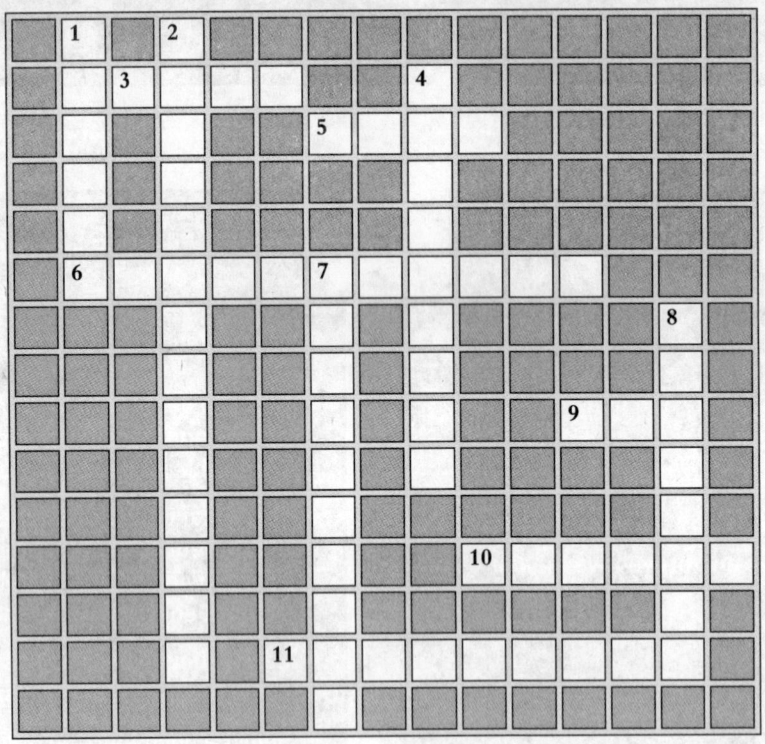

Across

3. The substance which gives out energy by burning.
5. The power plant in which the temperature difference of water on the surface and below in ocean is used.
6. A cooking device in which a renewable source of energy is used.
9. Ultimate source of energy.
10. Petroleum and natural gases are formed from this.
11. A device which is the source of electricity and works as the principle of photoelectric effect.

Down

1. A renewable source of energy which is the mixture of methane, CO_2, H_2 and H_2S.
2. The reaction which is taking place in the sun.
4. A fossil fuel which is also known as crude oil.
7. This process of a fuel is an oxidation and exothermic reaction.
8. Device that convert wind energy to electrical energy.

INTRODUCTION

Law of conservation of energy states that energy can be neither created nor destroyed. From work-energy theorem we understand how energy spent and work done are related. Whenever certain work is done, some form of energy is always involved, that is, to do some work, energy is required. For example, if water is to be brought to a height, electrical energy supplied to a pump motor gets transformed to mechanical energy which lifts the water. But what is the source of electrical energy? It could be either hydel energy, thermal energy or nuclear energy. Again the source of hydel energy is the water stored in a reservoir, those of thermal energy and nuclear energy are coal and fissionable uranium, respectively. Thus, we find that energy is stored in nature in some substances (coal, petrol, etc.) or in some forms (winds, tides, etc.). An indepth study of these sources of energy has become an important branch of science, as we need to replenish continuously those substances or sources, which are used up during conversion to other forms. The current chapter deals with different categories of sources of energy and the related topics.

Sources of Energy

Energy is the capacity of a physical system to perform work. Energy exists in several forms such as heat, kinetic or mechanical energy, light, potential energy, electrical, or other forms. Energy is the ability to do work. We are dependent upon various sources of energy in one way or the other for our energy requirements.

Characteristics of Sources of Energy

Energy can mean various things: Mostly it is used in science to describe how much potential a physical system has to change. In physics, energy is a property of matter and space, objects and fields. It can be transferred between objects and can also be converted in form. It cannot, however, be created or destroyed. Fuels can be classified based on the following:

1. **Net Energy Output:** The difference between the output energy and the input energy is termed as net energy output. For example, when we use a fuel, say coal or wood, we have to provide some initial heat to ignite it. This will be the input. The heat energy given by the fuel will be the output. Now, the net energy will be the difference between the two. A good fuel should have high net energy output.
2. **Availability:** The energy source should be able to provide energy over a long period of time. Sun, wind, etc., are the best examples for this.

   A good fuel should be capable of providing desired quantity of energy at a steady rate over a long period of time.
3. **Safe and Convenient to Use:** This is one of the important characteristics of a fuel; a fuel has to be safe and convenient to use.

   For example, nuclear energy cannot be used for cooking. Correct fuel has to be selected for the required purpose.
4. **Easy for Storage and Transportation:** Most of the sources of energy like petroleum, LPG, etc., are not found in all the places. So, they have to be transported over long distances.

   Moreover, these fuels have to be safely stored so that they can be helpful during crisis of energy sources. A good fuel should be safe to store and transport.
5. **Economical:** A fuel has to be economical. A common household or an industry should not feel burdened because they have to use it.

   A good fuel is one which has all the given characteristics.

Types of Sources of Energy

Sources of energy are mainly classified into two types. They are:

Non-renewable Sources of Energy

Energy sources which, when once used up, cannot be replenished are called **non-renewable sources of energy.**

Some non-renewable sources of energy are coal, petroleum and natural gas. These sources are related to solar energy, either directly or indirectly. The formation of these fuels have occurred over millions of years due to slow compression of plant bodies under high pressures inside the Earth.

Renewable Sources of Energy

The energy sources that can be replenished, once they are used up, are called **renewable sources of energy.** Some examples of renewable sources of energy are the Sun, water, wind, Earth, wood and biomass.

Info Bytes!

- Fossil fuels like coal, oil and natural gas still account for about 80% of the world's energy consumption!
- Renewable energy sources like solar, wind, and hydropower generate electricity without emitting greenhouse gases!

Solar Energy

Sunlight consists of waves called electromagnetic waves. Visible light has a wavelength between 400 nm and 700 nm. Our eyes are insensitive to radiations having wavelength beyond these values. Nearly one-third of sunlight consists of infrared rays. These rays heat up the objects that lie in their path. The heat that we feel in the sunlight is due to infrared radiation present in it. All bodies that are hot radiate energy in the form of infrared rays.

Nuclear fusion reactions in the interior of the Sun continuously release enormous amounts of energy. It is estimated that the Earth directly receives only 0.000000045792% of the Sun's total energy output. The Sun is the ultimate source of all the energy here on Earth. All forms of energy which are available on Earth owe their origin to the sun. The Solar energy reaching the periphery of the Earth's atmosphere is considered to be constant for all practical purposes, and is known as the solar constant.

Solar constant = $1.366 \text{ kJ m}^{-2} \text{ s}^{-1}$ or 1.366 kW m^{-2}

Only 47% of the solar energy that strikes the periphery of the Earth reaches the surface. The remaining part of the solar energy gets reflected to space and some portion of solar energy is absorbed by the atmosphere. During this process, UV rays get eliminated and only visible light and infrared radiation reaches the Earth's surface.

One third of sunlight consists of infrared radiation. Infrared radiation heats the substance through which they pass. Hot bodies transmit or radiate heat in the form of infrared radiation. The infrared radiation emitted by hot bodies have longer wavelength than the infrared radiation emitted by the Sun.

The landmass and water bodies absorb a part of the solar energy that reaches the surface of the Earth. This energy, then, manifests itself in a variety of forms through many natural processes, both biological and physical.

The various functions performed by solar energy on Earth are illustrated by a flow chart as shown in Fig. 3.1.

1. Solar energy provides wind energy, tidal energy and the energy of sea waves.
2. Solar energy causes large-scale evaporation of water. Water vapours condense to form clouds, cause rain and ultimately change to flowing water. The energy of flowing water is utilized in water-mills and in the generation of hydroelectric power.
3. Light energy present in the form of solar energy is stored in plants during photosynthesis in the form of chemical energy. The chemical energy of plants remains intact when they form fossil fuels such as coal. The chemical energy of coal is, then, used as a source of heat energy from domestic fuels to thermal power plants.

If plants do not become fossil after death, they can be converted to biogas (gobar gas). In biogas, the chemical energy stored in plants changes into the heat energy on burning. Similarly, the remains of dead animals can be changed into biogas.

When animals consume plants, the chemical energy of plants changes into heat energy during respiration. It is the heat energy which helps to keep animals warm and perform various activities using their muscular energy.

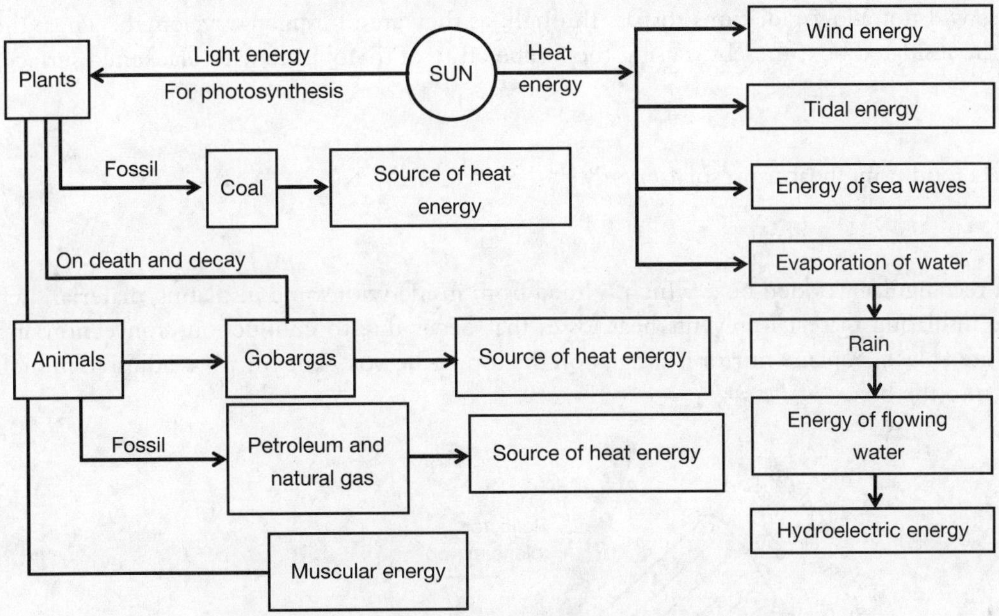

Figure 3.1 Functions performed by solar energy

> **Info Bytes!**
> - The Earth receives enough solar energy in one hour to power the world for a year!
> - Using mirrors or lenses can increase the amount of solar energy that can be collected!

If animals die in large numbers and get buried under the surface of the Earth, then their bodies under intense pressure and temperature for long durations change to petroleum and natural gas. These products are a source of heat energy for most of the industries.

Solar energy provides light energy which helps us to see the things around.

Direct Harnessing of Solar Energy

In this type, solar energy is directly converted into heat energy (as in the case of solar cookers, water heaters, solar concentrators, etc.) or electrical energy (as in case of solar cells).

Indirect Harnessing of Solar Energy

In nature, plants convert solar energy into chemical energy. The chemical energy of plants is used as food by animals or used as fuels to produce heat energy. Solar energy also changes into wind energy, the energy of flowing water, the energy of tides and the sea waves. This energy can be harnessed by water mills either in the form of mechanical energy or electrical energy.

Methods of Enhancing the Collection of Solar Energy

Devices working with solar energy as fuel need to enhance their solar energy collection so as to work quickly and effectively. The following are the methods to enhance the collection of solar energy.

Use of Black-painted Surface

Black bodies are good absorbers as well as good radiators of heat. Thus, the surfaces which are to collect radiant heat are painted black so that they can absorb (or radiate) more energy.

A perfect black body is one which absorbs (or radiates) all the energy (light, heat, etc.) incident on it.

Use of Insulated Box with Glass Cover

The wavelength of infrared radiation emitted by hot bodies is shorter than that of the radiation emitted by bodies of comparatively lower temperature.

It is observed that an insulated box with a glass cover prevents heat losses that occur due to conduction, convection and radiation. The glass cover allows solar energy to pass through it. It has the property of allowing radiation of shorter wavelength to pass through it. When the object with blackened surface gets hot within the box and radiates radiant heat with longer wavelength, the glass will not allow radiations to pass through, as they are of longer wavelength. Thus, the heat radiation is trapped within the insulated box, thereby, raising the temperature of the objects with blackened surface.

Solar Cooker

Solar cooker is a device that cooks food using heat from solar energy.

Box-type Solar Cooker

This type of cooker consists of a rectangular wooden box, which is lined from inside with some insulating material such as thermocol or glass wool. The insulating material prevents heat losses that occur due to conduction, convection and radiation. The inner walls are painted black. A plane mirror is hinged on the top of the box. The mirror is adjusted in such a manner that it reflects sunlight into the box.

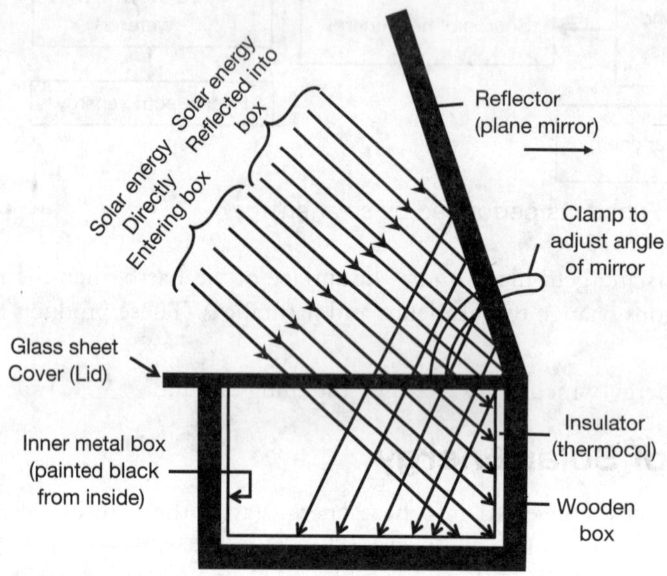

Figure 3.2 Solar cooker: A solar heating device for collecting maximum solar energy

Reflector Type Solar Cooker

In this type of cooker, the solar energy received over an area is concentrated at a particular point where the cooker is kept. The surface area of the disk-like structure is coated with a reflecting material. This type of cooker can generate temperatures upto 180 °C at the focus (point where it is concentrated). Thus, this is more effective than a box type cooker.

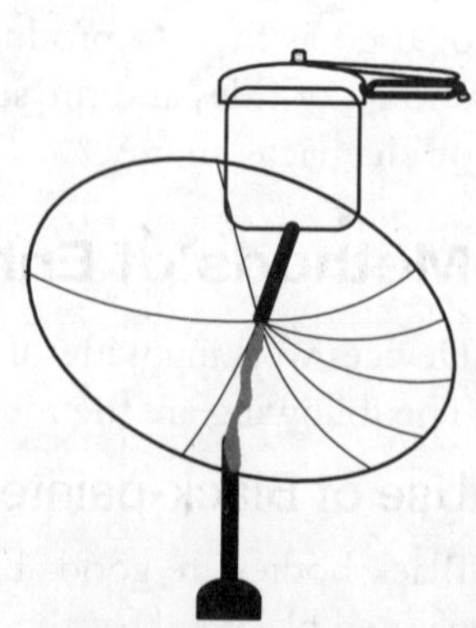

Figure 3.3 A reflector type solar cooker concentrates solar energy on a small area

Solar Concentrators

The principle behind reflector type solar cooker is concentration of all the received solar energy at a particular point. Thus, it can be called **solar concentrator.**

Solar furnace is of reflector type design where thousands of reflectors are arranged spherically so that each and every reflector reflects the incident light in a direction so that the reflected light focuses at a particular point. In this type of design, a temperature up to 3000°C can be produced.

Solar Water Heater

This is the most commonly used one among solar heating devices.

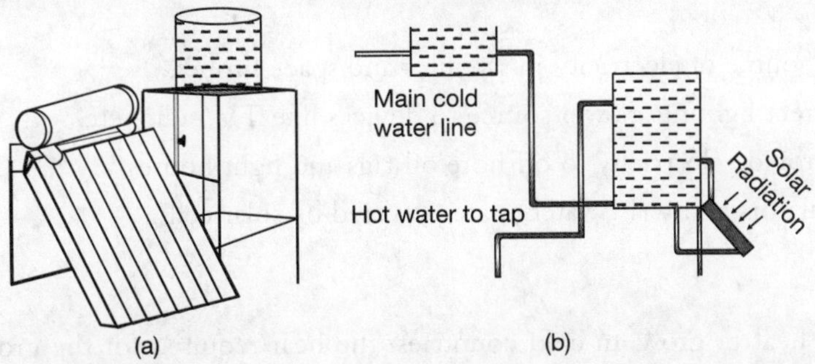

Figure 3.4 Schematic arrangement of a solar water heater

Here, a copper pipe with its outer surface painted in black, is fixed in the form of a coil in a box. Bending copper pipe as a coil helps to increase the surface area for heating. A reservoir kept at a higher level is used to store cold water, which is connected to a small tank kept slightly above the water heater. One end of the copper pipe is connected to the bottom of the small tank of water, while the other end is joined near its middle. Water in the tank continuously circulates through the copper pipe due to a small difference in pressure between its two ends.

As the water slowly moves through the pipe, it absorbs solar energy and gets heated up. The hot water again goes to the tank while the cooler water from the lower part of the tank replaces it.

Info Bytes!

- Solar water heaters can reduce your electricity bill by up to 50%!
- Solar cells have a theoretical efficiency limit of 33.7%!

Solar Cells

A device which can directly convert solar energy into electrical energy is called solar cell. Solar cell is also called **photovoltaic cell.**

Photoelectric Effect

The phenomenon due to which light energy directly changes into electrical energy, when light is incident on certain sensitive materials is called **photoelectric effect.**

First photovoltaic cell, that was invented in 1877, was only 0.6% efficient. It used selenium metal. In 1954, Bell laboratories of USA produced the first silicon solar cell, which had an efficiency of 5%.

Solar cells having multi layer silicon solar cells have been designed, which convert both visible and infrared radiation into electricity. This increases the efficiency of solar cells to a very great extent.

A large number of solar cells combined together produce large amount of current. The arrangement of large number of solar cells together is called solar panel.

Advantages of Solar Cells

1. It can be used as a source of electricity at any place.
2. It provides pollution free environment.

Disadvantages of Solar Cells

1. High cost of installation. This is due to the technology to obtain pure silicon is expensive and due to use of silver as conducting material which is used to connect solar cells. Silver is good conductor of electricity. If other metals are used in place of silver, a fraction of electricity generated by solar cells is used to overcome the resistance of the conductor or the connectors.

2. Electricity generated by solar cells is stored in batteries which can give DC. In order to operate devices working on AC, the DC has to be converted to AC. This decreases the efficiency and further adds up to the cost.

Uses of Solar Cells

1. Solar cells are the main source of electricity in satellites and space probes.
2. They can be used for street lighting, power source to devices like TV, radio, etc.
3. Solar cells are used to provide electricity to offshore oil rigs and light houses.
4. Certain electronic calculators and wrist watches are powered by solar cells.

Green House

Some crops require sufficient heat to grow. In cold countries, the heat required for the growth of plants is achieved by growing them in a green house.

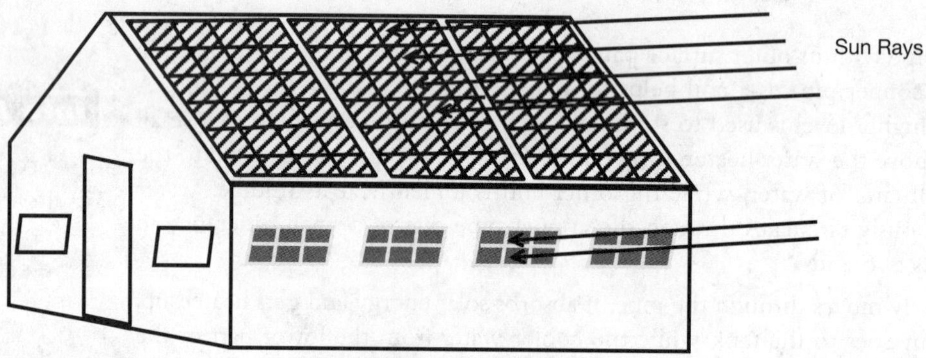

Figure 3.5 A green house

The principle used in this is the same as in box type solar cookers. The glass surface on the top receives light and heat from the Sun. The walls, which are coated in black, retain the heat inside the room, thus, maintaining a temperature higher than that outside of the house.

Wind Energy

Moving air is called wind. Sun's energy (solar energy) is one of the main factors responsible for the motion of air in the atmosphere. Picture are devices that convert wind energy into mechanical or electrical energy. They were used for grinding grains in many parts of the world, until a 100 years ago. Modern windmills are designed to convert wind energy into mechanical or electrical energy, on a large scale. A windmill essentially consists of a structure similar to that of a large electric fan that is erected at some height on a rigid support.

The principle of a windmill is that the blades of a windmill are designed to create a pressure difference between its different regions when wind strikes them. This pressure difference produces a turning effect to make the blades rotate.

In a water-lifting pump, the rotational motion of windmill is utilized to do mechanical work and draw underground water to the surface of the Earth.

Prȯduction of Electricity Wind Energy Farm

The rotatory motion of the windmills is utilized to rotate the armature of an electric generator. However, the electricity produced by a single windmill is quite small and cannot be used for commercial purposes.

A number of windmills are erected over a large area, which is known as wind energy farm. The energy output of each windmill in a farm is coupled together to generate electricity on a commercial scale.

Limitations in Harnessing of Wind Energy

Wind energy farms can be established only at those places where wind blows for large duration of the year. The wind should be strong, steady and should have a velocity of atleast 15 kmph.

Hydel Energy

Energy that comes from flowing of water is called **hydel energy.** Water flowing through rivers has both kinetic energy and potential energy. The energy of flowing water can be used to transport heavy logs of wood from inaccessible areas of forests in hilly regions.

Generation of Electricity: Hydroelectric Power Plant

The energy of flowing water is utilized to produce electricity on a large scale at hydroelectric power plants. The water stored in dams has potential energy. When this water is released, it possesses high-kinetic energy.

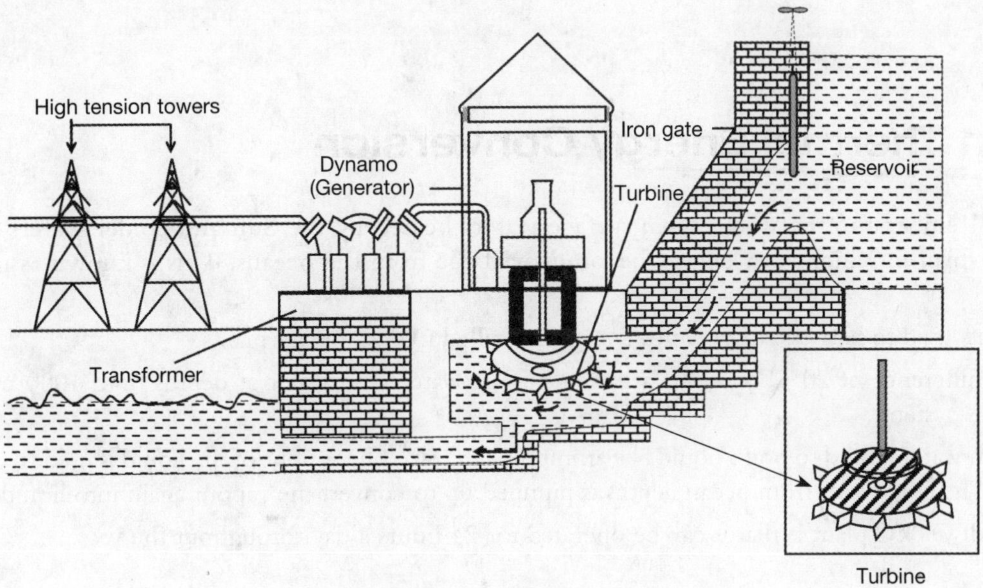

Figure 3.6 Hydel power plant

When the released water is made to fall on the blades of a turbine, they rotate and in turn rotate the armature of the electric generators to produce electricity.

Limitations of Hydroelectric Power Plant

1. The initial cost of the construction of a dam is very high.
2. For generation of electricity, abundant water should be available in the dam.
3. These hydroelectric power plants can be constructed only at certain places.

Advantage of Hydroelectric Power Plants

Water is a renewable source of energy and, further, these power plants do not pollute the environment.

Info Bytes!

- Hydel energy is one of the oldest forms of energy generation!
- A hydroelectric power plant can start generating electricity in just a few minutes!

Tidal Energy

Oceans are huge reservoirs of water and energy. The oceans store energy in many forms. Tidal energy caused by the ocean tides is a renewable source of energy. The daily rise and fall of the tides can be used to drive turbines for generating electricity.

A small dam is constructed across a narrow opening of the sea. During high tide, water flows to reservoir and during the low tide, water flows out from reservoir through a pipe and this flowing water is used to rotate a turbine which in the turn generates electric current.

However, these plants can be set up at certain places only where the amount of power released by waves striking the shoreline is at least 40 MW km^{-1}.

The three most common devices that are utilized for harnessing the energy of the ocean waves are:

1. Surface-followers, using floats or pitching devices
2. Oscillating water column
3. Surge or focusing devices

Since the rise and fall of water during tides is not so high, this is not likely to be a major source of energy.

The waves that continuously hit the ocean coast possess large amount of kinetic energy. The total amount of power released by the waves striking the short lines is about 2 to 3 million megawatts, and this energy can be harnessed only in limited sites.

Ocean Thermal Energy Conversion

The difference in temperature between warm surface waters heated by the Sun and colder waters found at ocean depths is another form in which solar energy becomes available from the oceans. This is known as **ocean thermal energy.**

The power plants used to harness this form of energy are called OTEC power plants.

A temperature difference of 20°C or more between surface waters and water at depths upto 1000 m is required for operating OTEC systems.

In this, the warm water is used to boil a liquid like ammonia or CFC. The vapour of the liquid is used to drive the turbine of a generator. The cold water from ocean depths is pumped up to convert the vapour again into liquid.

The advantage of OTEC plant is that it can be operated for 24 hours a day throughout the year.

Geothermal Energy

Geothermal energy is the energy stored as heat in the Earth. Geo means Earth and thermal means heat.

The temperature inside the Earth is high enough to liquify the rocks, etc. (called magma) and heat the substances in it. In certain areas below the surface of the Earth, hot magma swells up into the crust, but remains trapped below the surface of the Earth. Such areas in the Earth's crust are called hotspots. When these hotspots are nearer to the surface of the Earth, the water which seeps through gets converted to steam and comes out of the rocks in the upper layer (crust) of the Earth with great force. These are called geysers.

Generation of Electricity

This steam from geothermal sources can be directly utilized to turn turbines of the electrical generator to produce electricity. Such electricity is called **geothermal electricity.**

Advantages of Geothermal Energy

1. Geothermal power plants can operate round the clock.
2. It is pollution free.
3. Operating cost involved is less (but initial cost in setting up this plant will be high).
4. This type of source is free and renewable.

Info Bytes!

Geothermal power plants emit less than 1% of the carbon dioxide emitted by a fossil fuel plant!

Nuclear Energy

Huge amount of energy can be obtained from nuclear reactions. Nuclear reactions are of two types: **nuclear fission** and **nuclear fusion reactions.**

Nuclear fission is a process in which a heavy nucleus splits into lighter nuclei along with the release of huge amounts of energy. Nuclear fission reaction is the principle behind a nuclear power plant. Nuclear fusion is a reaction in which lighter nuclei (like hydrogen) combine to form a heavier nucleus at very high temperatures with evolution of enormous amounts of energy. The Sun's heat is due to the nuclear fusion reactions occurring in the interior of the Sun.

Nuclear fusion reactions occur generally in stars where very high temperatures (nearly 4 × 107 K) exist. However, the energy released in fusion reactions cannot be harnessed into productive applications as these reactions cannot be controlled.

Bioenergy

A small fraction of the solar energy radiation on Earth's surface is converted into chemical energy by green plants through the process of photosynthesis. This energy becomes available in the form of biomass stored in different parts of a plant. Animals, including humans, utilize a part of this energy for their food.

The excreta of living organisms and their bodies after death also contribute to biomass.

Biogas

Animal and plant wastes are easily degraded by anaerobic microorganisms in the presence of water, producing gases such as methane, CO_2, H_2 and H_2S. This mixture of gases is called **'biogas'.**

Fig. 3.7 (a) and (b) show the two designs of commonly used biogas plants.

Floating Gas-Holder Type Biogas Plant

Floating gas-holder type biogas plant consists of a dome-like structure, usually made of steel, that floats up as the pressure of biogas evolved increases. This type of biogas plant is more frequently used where cow dung is used to obtain biogas.

Fixed Dome Type Biogas Plant

This has an advantage that the dome can be constructed by laying bricks.

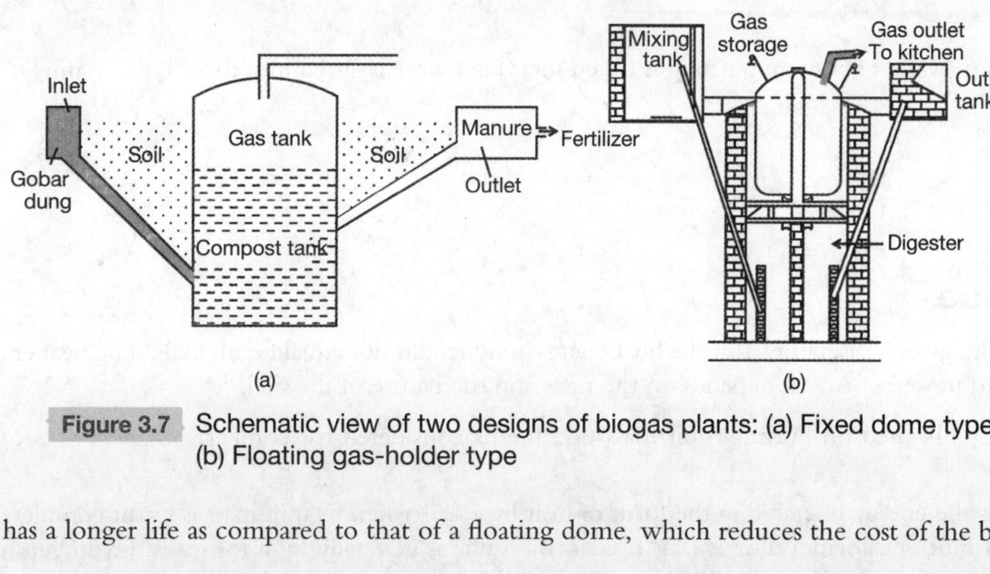

Figure 3.7 Schematic view of two designs of biogas plants: (a) Fixed dome type (b) Floating gas-holder type

Fixed dome has a longer life as compared to that of a floating dome, which reduces the cost of the biogas.

Formation of Biogas

Slurry of animal dung and water is made in the mixing tank from where it is fed into the digester tank. In the digester, the action of microorganisms breaks down or decomposes the complex compounds of the biomass in the slurry. Anaerobic microorganisms, in the presence of water, do the degradation of biomass in the digester.

Since anaerobic microorganisms do not require oxygen, the digesters are designed like a sealed chamber. This process takes a few days to complete during which gases like methane, CO_2, H_2 and H_2S are produced. Biogas, which is a mixture of these gases, is supplied to consumers through pipes.

Advantages of a Biogas Plant

Combustion of biogas produces no smoke but a large amount of heat as its calorific value is high. The use of biogas in villages improves the sanitary conditions and checks environmental pollution. It is convenient for domestic use. The slurry obtained as a byproduct, left in the plant after the gas is used, forms a good and enriched manure, containing compounds of nitrogen and phosphorous. The use of biogas reduces the dependence on the fossil fuels and wood.

Hydrogen and Alcohol as Fuels

The reaction between hydrogen and oxygen to form water is an exothermic reaction which evolves a lot of heat. Hydrogen is the substance that releases heat more than any fuel. Hydrogen is easily produced by the electrolysis of water and is also obtained as a by product in many industrial processes. Combustion of hydrogen does not pollute the environment.

Hydrogen is used in spaceships and high temperature flames as source of energy. However, it is difficult for the common man to work with hydrogen as the amount of heat emitted is very high. Moreover, storing and transportation of hydrogen is also a difficult task. The main reason for not using hydrogen as a fuel is due to its explosive nature.

Alcohol is another fuel that is gaining significance as a fuel. It reacts with oxygen and produces carbon dioxide and water, releasing heat energy. A mixture of alcohol and petrol is being used in some countries as a fuel for automobiles.

Example: Spirit lamp used in laboratories.

Fuels

Any substance that gives out energy on burning is called fuel. Fuels are classified into three types, namely:

1. Solid fuels
2. Liquid fuels
3. Gaseous fuels

Calorific Value

Any fuel, on burning, gives heat energy. But the heat energy produced is not equal for all fuels. The heat energy produced by a fuel is measured in joules. And it depends on the mass and the nature of the fuel.

Thus, heat energy liberated on burning unit mass of a fuel is considered for comparison and this is called **calorific value of the fuel.**

'Calorific value is the energy liberated in the form of heat by a fuel when its unit mass is burnt completely under ideal conditions'. The SI unit of calorific value is J kg^{-1}. Calorific value is generally high for gases. Hydrogen has the highest calorific value. Calorific values of some of the fuels are given below.

Table 3.1 Calorific values of fuels

Type of fuel	Fuel	Calorific value in kJ kg^{-1}
Solid fuel	Cow-dung cake	6000-8000
	Wood	17,000-22,000
	Coal	25,000-33,000
Liquid fuel	Ethanol	30,000
	Kerosene	45,000
	Petrol	47,000
Gaseous fuel	Biogas	35,000-40,000
	Butane (LPG)	55,000
	Methane	55,000

Fuels containing oxygen atoms have low calorific value than those of hydrocarbons but they burn readily.

Solid Fuels

Wood, charcoal, cow-dung cakes, coal, etc., are some examples of the solid fuels. Wood is the fuel that has been used over a very long time as the main source of fuel and it is becoming scarce due to uncontrolled felling of trees.

Wood is a source of heat. When wood is burnt in a limited supply of oxygen, water and other volatile substance are removed from it and the residue left is known charcoal. The process of burning wood in limited supply of oxygen is called destructive distillation. Hence, many nations have restricted felling of trees and have taken up afforestation as a major project.

In rural areas, cow-dung cakes, firewood and agricultural wastes are being used as a fuel for cooking. However, this increases pollution of atmosphere. Coal is another important fuel used in industries, cities and power stations. Coal can be called fossil fuel.

Fossil Fuels

Fossil fuels are the fuels formed by the decay of plants and marine animals that were buried in the Earth millions of years ago under extreme conditions of heat and pressure. Since these conditions do not exist any more, there is no chance of new reserves of these fuels. So, these fuels are termed as non-renewable sources of energy.

Coal is the fossiled remains of the plants that have been buried deep into the Earth's crust for millions of years while petroleum and natural gas are the fossiled remains of dead bodies of marine animals and plants.

Coal

Coal is a non-renewable source of energy. It is found below the surface of the Earth. The main constituent of coal is carbon. The other constituents are hydrogen and oxygen. The percentage of carbon and other constituents in a sample of coal varies from place to place. The quality of coal depends on the percentage of carbon present in it.

The following table gives the information of different types of coal and the percentage of carbon in them.

Table 3.2 Percentage of carbon in coal

Type of coal	% of carbon
Peat	27%
Lignite	28 - 30%
Bituminous	78 - 98%
Anthracite	94 – 98%

Anthracite is found to be the best quality of coal as the percentage of carbon in it is maximum. Coke is made from bituminous coal. High grade coke is a perfect fuel for blast furnaces.

Burning of coal creates serious air pollution. When coal is burnt, the carbon present in it reacts with oxygen to produce carbondioxide. This is an exothermic reaction which yields a lot of heat energy. Coal, on destructive distillation, gives coke. It is used as reducing agent in the extraction of some metals from their ores and in making steel.

Liquid Fuels

Fuels like petrol, diesel, kerosene, fuel oil, etc., come under the category of liquid fuels. All these fuels are liquids under normal state. They are obtained from petroleum, also called crude oil. Petroleum and coal are fossil fuels which have been formed under the Earth over thousands of years. Since these fuels are formed by natural evolutionary process of Earth, their replenishment is not in our control.

Petroleum products are mixtures of hydrogen and carbon and are called **hydrocarbons.**

Petroleum

The word 'petroleum' is derived from the Greek words '*Petra*' which means 'rock' and '*oleum*' which means 'oil' because it is an oil derived from rocks.

Petroleum is a complex mixture of many compounds of hydrogen and carbon known as hydrocarbons. It also contains small amounts of other compounds of oxygen, nitrogen and sulphur.

Formation of Petroleum

Petroleum was formed from the dead remains of marine plants and animals, which settled in muddy sediments at the bottom of the sea millions of years ago. Due to prolonged sedimentation and accumulation of organic debris, these got buried deep below the surface of the Earth. In intense heat and high pressure conditions underneath and in the presence of natural catalysts, the remains were ultimately converted into petroleum. For this reason, petroleum is also a fossil fuel. It is a dark oily liquid, which does not burn, and is insoluble in water and floats on it.

Extraction of Petroleum

Large reservoirs of petroleum have been formed in nature for millions of years between porous rocks beneath the Earth. It is pumped out by drilling holes and by digging wells. Petroleum in its natural form is a thick black liquid.

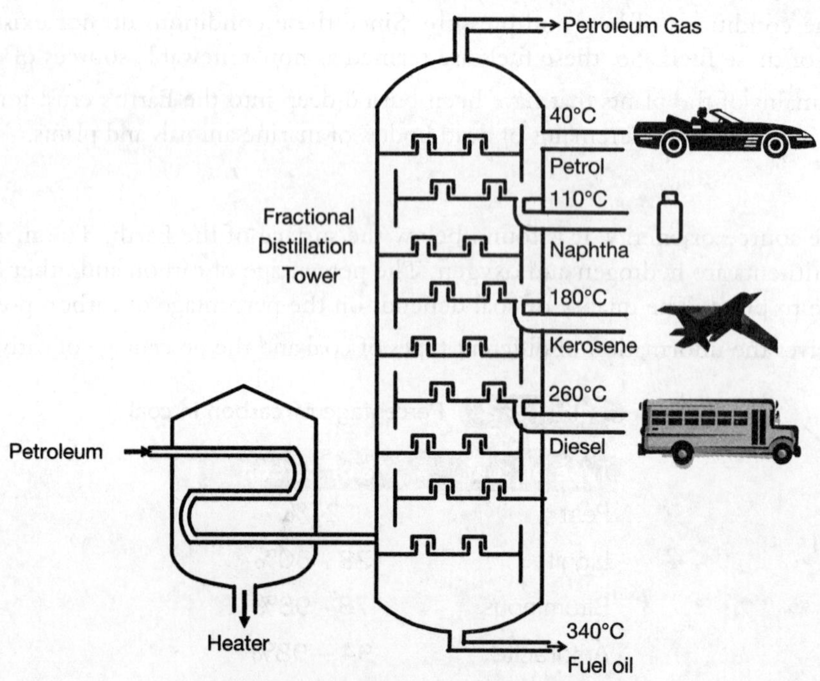

Figure 3.8 Distillation of petroleum

Refining of Petroleum

The crude oil extracted from deep Earth is separated into its constituents by a process called 'fractional distillation'. It is based on the principle that different fractions of petroleum boil at different temperature ranges.

In refining of petroleum, the crude oil is fed into the base of the fractionating column and heated to 650°C. The mixture of vapours of different liquid components so formed rise in the fractionating column also called distillation column. The vapours of higher boiling fraction cool first, get liquefied and finally get collected from the lower outlet of the chamber.

Table 3.3 Composition and uses of products formed during refining of petroleum

Fraction	Composition	Temperature Range (K)	Uses
Gaseous	$C_1 - C_4$	Below 298	As a fuel
Petroleum ether	$C_5 - C_7$	298 – 333	As solvent in dry cleaning
Petrol/gasoline	C_7-C_{10}	333 – 473	Motor fuel
Kerosene	$C_{12} - C_{16}$	448 – 550	Fuel in jet engines and for domestic purposes
Fuel oil or diesel oil	$C_{15} - C_{18}$	525 – 670	In diesel engines, in industries
Lubricating oil	$C_{16} - C_{20}$	Above 623	Lubrication, vaseline, greases
Petroleum wax	C_{20} and above	Above 623	Candles, waterproofers, fabrics, fuel, electrodes
Petroleum coke			Fuel

Gaseous Fuels

Petroleum gas and natural gas are two common gaseous fuels.

Petroleum gas is obtained as a by-product in the process of refining of petroleum. It consists mainly of butane and small fractions of ethane and propane. Butane can be liquefied easily under high pressure. Cooking gas cylinders contain liquefied petroleum gas LPG. The main constituent of LPG is butane. Small quantities of ethane and propane are also present.

Biogas is another example of gaseous fuel. Natural gas is an important fossil fuel that is found on the top of petroleum under the Earth. However, some oil wells yield only natural gas. Its main component is methane.

It is compressed under high pressure to form compressed natural gas (CNG). CNG is easier for transportation than natural gas and is being used as a fuel in automobiles. Since burning of CNG evolves CO_2 and water, it is environment friendly.

Ignition Temperature

Substances begin to burn only after it has attained certain minimum temperature. This minimum temperature at which the substance begins to burn is called **ignition temperature.** Ignition temperature is a characteristic of a substance. Hence, a substance does not catch fire until it attains the ignition temperature.

Condition for Combustion of Fuels

Combustion is a process of burning of a fuel. During combustion, fuel combines with oxygen of the air to produce heat and light. Combustion is an oxidation and an exothermic reaction.

The conditions required for combustion of fuels are:

1. Attainment of ignition temperature of the fuel.
2. Presence of oxygen and the combustible material or the fuel.
3. Adequate supply of oxygen is necessary to maintain combustion.

Examples: Burners of cooking gas and kerosene stove are designed such that to maintain adequate supply of oxygen. If stove burns with a blue flame, it indicates proper burning of the fuel. A yellow or smoky flame indicates inadequate supply of oxygen and this results in an incomplete combustion, i.e., the fuel is not completely burnt or unburnt. The partial burnt particles begins to glow due to heat which gives yellow colours to flame. For example, flame of the candle.

When fuel is burnt completely,

1. fuel is not wasted.
2. smoke will be less.
3. carbon dioxide is produced instead of carbon monoxide.
4. charcoal is not produced.

When fuel is partially burnt,

1. fuel is wasted.
2. large quantity of smoke is produced.
3. poisonous gas, carbon monoxide is produced.
4. carbon particles are expelled with smoke.

Choice of a Good Fuel

It is very important to have a knowledge of the chemical properties of different fuels so that it can be of a great help in choosing the best suitable fuel. For example, we cannot use nuclear energy for cooking or burning leaves or use of wood for producing electricity.

Some of the qualities that we should consider while choosing the most suitable fuel are:

1. easy availability, low cost,
2. no problems in storage and transport,
3. a high calorific value,
4. an ignition temperature that is well above the normal room temperature,
5. a controllable rate of combustion for different purposes,
6. low rate of evaporation at room temperature,
7. low content of non-combustibles, and
8. no combustion products that are poisonous or environmental pollutants.

POINTS TO REMEMBER

- ✔ Energy sources which, when once used up, cannot be replenished are called non-renewable sources of energy.
- ✔ The energy sources that can be replenished, once they are used up, are called renewable sources of energy
- ✔ Combustion is a process of burning of a fuel.
- ✔ Minimum temperature at which the substance begins to burn is called ignition temperature.
- ✔ Moving air is called wind. Sun's energy (solar energy) is one of the main factors responsible for the motion of air in the atmosphere.
- ✔ Tidal energy caused by the ocean tides is a renewable source of energy.
- ✔ Geothermal energy is the energy stored as heat in the earth. Geo means earth and thermal means heat.
- ✔ Nuclear reactions are of two types: nuclear fission and nuclear fusion reactions.
- ✔ The reaction between hydrogen and oxygen to form water is an exothermic reaction which evolves a lot of heat.
- ✔ Nuclear fission is a process in which a heavy nucleus splits into lighter nuclei along with the release of huge amounts of energy.
- ✔ Nuclear fusion reactions occur generally in stars where very high temperatures (nearly 4×10^7 K) exist.
- ✔ Calorific value is the energy liberated in the form of heat by a fuel when its unit mass is burnt completely under ideal conditions
- ✔ Petroleum is a complex mixture of many compounds of hydrogen and carbon known as hydrocarbons.
- ✔ A substance begin to burn only after it has attained certain minimum temperature. This minimum temperature at which the substance begins to burn is called ignition temperature.

DW

PRACTICE QUESTIONS CLASSROOM WING

Very Short Answer Type Questions

Direction for questions from 1 to 9:
Fill in the blanks.

1. Energy sources like coal and petroleum, once used up, cannot be replenished and are thus called ________ sources of energy.

2. Solar and wind energy are examples of ________ sources of energy.

3. The ________ is the temperature at which a substance starts to burn.

4. ________ energy, derived from the heat of the earth, is a renewable source.

5. In stars, where temperatures reach nearly 4×10^7 K, ________ reactions predominantly occur.

6. The energy released when a unit mass of a fuel burns completely is termed its ________ value.

7. The compounds found in petroleum, primarily made up of hydrogen and carbon, are known as ________.

8. The type of coal containing the lowest percentage of carbon is ______.

9. The heat that we feel in the sunlight is due to ________.

Direction for questions from 10 to 14:
For each of the questions, four choices have been provided. Select the correct alternative.

10. Which process involves the splitting of a heavy nucleus into lighter nuclei?
    (a) Combustion
    (b) Nuclear fusion
    (c) Nuclear fission
    (d) Calorific combustion

11. What is primarily responsible for the motion of air in the atmosphere, leading to wind energy?
    (a) Tidal energy
    (b) Geothermal energy
    (c) Nuclear energy
    (d) Sun's energy (solar energy)

12. Which reaction is exothermic and results in the formation of water?
    (a) Hydrogen combining with nitrogen
    (b) Hydrogen combining with oxygen
    (c) Oxygen combining with carbon
    (d) Nitrogen combining with carbon

13. The term 'calorific value' relates to:
    (a) Ignition temperature
    (b) Amount of water in a substance
    (c) Energy released by a unit mass of fuel when burnt
    (d) Energy required to split an atom

14. Which among the following energy sources is caused by ocean tides?
    (a) Solar energy (b) Wind energy
    (c) Tidal energy (d) Geothermal energy

Direction for questions from 15 to 24:
Answer the following questions briefly:

15. What is nuclear fission?

16. What is combustion?

17. What is petroleum? What is natural gas?

18. What is destructive distillation?

19. What are fossil fuels?

20. What are the types of fuels?

21. What is a hydroelectric power plant?

22. Between petrol and kerosene, which has a high calorific value?

23. What is a windmill?

24. What is a solar cell?

Short Answer Type Questions

25. How can wind energy be converted to electrical energy?
26. Write a short note on various types of fuels (with reference to their physical presence).
27. Give the characteristics of sources of energy.
28. Explain the production of geothermal electricity.
29. Write a short note on natural gas.
30. What are the different types of sources of energy? Give two examples for each.
31. What is a calorific value? Which gaseous substance has the highest calorific value?
32. Explain the construction of a fixed dome type biogas plant.
33. What are the types of fuels? Give two examples for each.
34. Give the differences between box type and reflector type solar cookers.
35. What are the limitations of a hydroelectric power plant?
36. How is petroleum formed? How is it extracted?
37. What are the various factors to be considered in choosing a fuel?
38. What are the limitations of harnessing wind energy?
39. Explain the construction of reflector type solar cooker.
40. What is a biogas plant? Explain the construction and working of a biogas plant.

Essay Answer Type Questions

41. Explain how various petroleum products are obtained from crude oil.
42. 'Solar energy is the chief source for all other forms of energy'. Explain.
43. How is coal formed? What are the different types of it?
44. Explain the principle, construction and working of a windmill.

PRACTICE QUESTIONS COMPETITION WING

Level 1: Apply Your Concepts

Direction for questions from 1 to 5:
Answer the following questions briefly:

1. What value represents the energy released by a unit mass of fuel when burnt?
2. What are the primary compounds in petroleum called?
3. At what temperature does a substance start combustion without external flame?
4. What is the chief source of energy for all natural activities?
5. Define ignition temperature.

Direction for questions from 6 to 12:
State whether the following statements are true or false.

6. Ignition temperature is the maximum temperature at which a substance melts.
7. Solar energy is a major factor responsible for the movement of air in the atmosphere.
8. Tidal energy, derived from ocean tides, is a non-renewable source of energy.
9. Geothermal energy is derived from the heat stored in the Earth.
10. Nuclear fission involves the combination of two light nuclei to form a heavier nucleus.
11. The process of burning wood in limited supply of oxygen to obtain charcoal as a resultant product is called destructive distillation.
12. Coal is the fossiled remains of dead bodies of marine animals that are buried in the Earth's crust for millions of years.

Direction for questions from 13 to 19:
Fill in the blanks.

13. The process where two lighter nuclei combine to form a heavier nucleus, typically seen in stars, is called ________.
14. ________ is a type of energy that utilizes the internal heat of the Earth, derived from its underground reservoirs.
15. Energy sources like wind and tidal are replenished naturally and are thus termed as ________ energy sources.
16. The splitting of a uranium nucleus in a reactor to produce a tremendous amount of heat energy is an example of ________.
17. The energy contained within chemical bonds, which when broken during combustion, releases heat, is often quantified as the ________ of the substance.
18. Although hydrogen has a high calorific value, its widespread use as fuel is limited because of its ________ ignition temperature.
19. The predominant compounds found in natural gas and petroleum, which can vary in length and structure, are termed ________.

Direction for question 20:
Match the entries in Column A with appropriate ones from Column B.

20.

Column A	Column B
A. Peat	a. liquid fuel
B. Alcohol	b. 27% of carbon
C. Decay of biomass	c. difference in temperature between warm surface waters and colder waters.
D. Rise and fall of water levels in oceans	d. biogas
E. OTEC	e. solar cell
F. Ultimate source of energy	f. tidal energy
G. Solar energy into electrical energy	g. Sun
H. Stored in food grains	h. wind
I. Moving air	i. bioenergy

Direction for questions from 21 to 39:
For each of the questions, four choices have been provided. Select the correct alternative.

21. Which factor primarily differentiates nuclear fission from nuclear fusion?
    (a) The amount of energy released
    (b) The type of nuclei involved
    (c) The location where they predominantly occur
    (d) The byproducts produced

22. Why is solar energy instrumental in the creation of wind?
    (a) It directly pushes the air creating wind.
    (b) It evaporates water, leading to wind currents.
    (c) It causes differential heating of the Earth's surface.
    (d) It ionizes the air, causing wind.

23. Which energy source primarily relies on the Earth's internal heat reservoirs?
    (a) Tidal energy (b) Wind energy
    (c) Geothermal energy (d) Solar energy

24. The reaction of hydrogen and oxygen to form water is exothermic. What does this imply?
    (a) The reaction requires a constant supply of heat.
    (b) The reaction cools the surroundings.
    (c) The reaction generates heat in the surrounding environment.
    (d) The reaction neither absorbs nor emits heat.

25. For a substance to begin combustion without an external flame, it must first reach its:
    (a) Calorific value
    (b) Fusion temperature
    (c) Ignition temperature
    (d) Melting point

26. What primarily differentiates geothermal energy sources from fossil fuel reserves in terms of origin?
    (a) Geothermal energy comes from the Earth's core while fossil fuels are derived from the mantle.
    (b) Geothermal energy is derived from ancient plant matter while fossil fuels are derived from the Earth's heat.
    (c) Both geothermal energy and fossil fuels are derived from ancient plant matter.
    (d) Geothermal energy is derived from the Earth's internal heat while fossil fuels are from ancient plant and animal matter.

27. Which of the following best describes why tidal energy has a limited influence on global climate change compared to solar energy?
    (a) Tidal energy influences the gravitational pull of the Earth, while solar energy affects temperature.
    (b) Tidal energy only affects oceans, while solar energy impacts both land and water.
    (c) Tidal energy directly determines the Earth's rotation speed, whereas solar energy drives weather patterns and ocean currents.
    (d) Tidal energy affects localized coastal climates, while solar energy plays a broader role in global climate patterns.

28. What is the value of solar constant if the energy received by 12 m2 area in 2 minutes is 2016 kJ?
    (a) $1{\cdot}4 \times 10^2$ J s^{-1} m^{-2}
    (b) 1400 J s^{-1} m^{-2}
    (c) 84 kJ s^{-1} m^{-2}
    (d) 84 J s^{-1} m^{-2}

29. A good fuel should ______.
    (a) be safe to store and transport
    (b) be able to provide desired quantity of energy at a steady rate over a long period of time
    (c) have low content of non-combustibles and no combustion products that are poisonous or environmental pollutants
    (d) All the above

30. Find the false statement from the statements given below.
    (a) Geothermal power plants cannot operate round the clock.
    (b) The initial cost in setting up this plant will be high.
    (c) This type of source is free and renewable.
    (d) Operating cost involved in a geothermal plant is less.

31. Which of the following metals is used as connecting wires that connect solar cells in a solar panel?
    (a) Copper (b) Iron
    (c) Aluminium (d) Silver

32. Quality that is not suitable for a fuel is ______.
    (a) high calorifgic value with ignition temperature that is well above the normal room temperature
    (b) low rate of evaporation at room temperature
    (c) carbon particles are expelled with smoke
    (d) low content of non-combustibles

33. Solar energy provides
    (a) wind energy

(b) light energy
(c) heat energy
(d) All the above

34. Which one of the following can be used as a box type solar cooker?
(a) A double walled cooker made of plastic and its inner wall is painted white.
(b) A double walled cooker made of copper and its inner wall is painted black.
(c) A double walled cooker made of plastic and its inner wall is painted black.
(d) A single walled cooker made of copper and its both sides are painted white.

35. If the output energy is 1000 J and input energy is 200 J, the net output is ______ J.
(a) 800 (b) 1200
(c) 10 (d) 500

36. A source of energy having an input energy ______ J and an output energy ______ J.
(a) 1000, 2000
(b) 2000, 2500
(c) 100, 12500
(d) 5000, 5250

37. The output of a given windmill
(a) increases with an increase in wind velocity.
(b) decreases with an increase in wind velocity
(c) is independent of wind velocity.
(d) Cannot be determined.

38. Arrange the following steps of conversion of ocean thermal energy into electricity in a proper sequence.
(A) The vapour of ammonia or CFC is passed over the turbines of generators.
(B) The hot water from the ocean is used to vapourize the liquid like ammonia or CFC.
(C) Cold water from the ocean depths is used to cool the vapour again into liquid.
(D) This cold liquid is again vapourized and the process continues.
(a) BACD
(b) CABD
(c) CBAD
(d) ABCD

39. Arrange the following steps in the conversion of hydel energy to electricity in a proper sequence.
(A) Released water is made to fall on the blades of the turbines.
(B) Water in the dam is released.
(C) Water is collected in the dam.
(D) Potential energy is converted to kinetic energy.
(E) The armature of the electric generator rotates to produce electricity.
(a) BCDEA
(b) ADBCE
(c) ECDBA
(d) CBDAE

Level 2: Review Your Concepts

40. Given the consistent motion of air (wind) and its renewable nature, why isn't wind energy capable of replacing all other energy sources?

41. Why might geothermal energy be abundant in some regions and scarce in others, even if the Earth's core is uniformly hot?

42. If combustion releases energy, why do we need to provide an initial spark or heat (achieving ignition temperature) to initiate the process?

43. How can tidal energy be renewable when the Moon is slowly moving away from the Earth, and its gravitational effects will change over time?

44. Nuclear fusion powers stars and offers a vast energy potential. However, why is it challenging to replicate and control this process on Earth for our energy needs?

45. How much time would it take for 1 litre of water to boil, initially at 0°C, if a concentrator type solar heater of area 5 m^2 is used, which can reflect 90% of energy incident on it? (Take solar constant as 1.4 kWm^{-2}).

46. Why is wood not preferred as a source of energy?

47. A power plant uses 100 tonnes of coal to produce a certain amount of electric energy. To produce the same amount of electric energy, find how much nuclear fuel U^{235} would

be required by a nuclear power plant. The calorific value of coal is 30 kJ g^{-1} and a nucleus of U^{235} on fission releases about 200 MeV energy per fission. (1eV = 1.6×10^{-19} J). Assume that the energy conversion efficiency is 50% for coal and 25% for fission of U-235 nucleus.

48. Find the electrical power generated in 1s by a windmill that is erected in a location when air flows with an average speed of 54 km h^{-1}. Assume that the moving air is completely stopped by the blades of the wind turbine of area 10 m^2, over which air flows normally and the energy conversion from wind energy to electrical energy is only 50%. (Take density of air = 1.3 kg/m^{-3})

49. The solar energy incident normal to the surface of the water in a container raises its temperature from 10°C to 20°C, in one minute. If the mass of water in the container is 1400 g, then find the surface area of the water in the container (solar constant = 1.4 kW m^{-2}) [Neglect the heat absorbed by the container].

50. What is the source of energy in artificial satellites? Why is this source of energy not used for meeting all our domestic electricity needs?

51. A nucleus of U-235 on fission releases about 200 MeV energy per fission. (1 MeV = 1.602×10^{-13} J). Estimate how much coal (calorific value = 33 kJ g^{-1}) has to be burnt to obtain energy equivalent to that released in the fission of 1g of U-235 assuming that energy conversion efficiency of 30% for charcoal and 25% for fission of U-235 nucleus.

52. An engine motor of 1 Hp power consumes 74.6 kg of a variety of biofuel to operate for one hour. If the efficiency is 100%, then find the calorific value of the fuel.

53. 1 kg of water at 0°C is taken in a vessel of water equivalent 100 g. This vessel is kept at the focal plane of a concentrator type solar heater of area 10 m^2, which can reflect 90% of energy incident on it. Find the time taken to raise the temperature of water by 100°C. (Take solar constant as 1.4 kW m^{-2}, specific heat capacity of water as 4.2 kJ kg^{-1} °C^{-1}).

54. Why is it not feasible to produce hydroelectricity by spending energy in lifting a huge amount of water? Explain.

55. What is the value of solar constant if the energy received by a portion of the outer edge of Earth's atmosphere of area 12 m^2 in 2 minutes is 2016 kJ?

56. Name any two materials that are used for making solar cells.

57. Why is geothermal energy preferable over wind energy for power generation?

58. Which of the following is the best approximation of a black body?

(a) A polished metal surface

(b) A black velvet cloth

(c) Pinhole in a blackened box. Justify your answer.

59. The wind is blowing at a speed of 36 km h^{-1} is falling on the blade of a windmill of area 0.375 m^2 and creating a pressure difference across blades of windmill. Then find the volume of air incident on the blade of windmill in a duration of 5 second.

Level 3: Assess Your Concepts

60. While both nuclear fission and nuclear fusion release enormous amounts of energy, they're not used equally in current energy production methods. Why is nuclear fission predominantly used in power plants, while fusion is not, even though fusion reactions power stars like our Sun?

61. Tidal energy and solar energy both originate from astronomical bodies (the Moon and the Sun, respectively). However, their impacts on Earth's energy balance differ. How do these energy sources differ in their direct impact on Earth's climatic conditions, and why might one be more influential than the other in terms of climate?

62. Combustion reactions, like the burning of fossil fuels, release carbon dioxide, which is a greenhouse gas. Why might the calorific value of a fuel not necessarily indicate its environmental impact, especially in the context of global warming?

63. Calculate the energy emitted by the Sun in one second. Also estimate the mass of the Sun that is converted to energy in one second.

(Take solar constant as 1.4×10^3 W m^{-2}, distance between the Earth and the Sun as 1.5×10^{11} m and the velocity of light as 3×10^8 m s^{-1}).

64. Why is hydrogen not used as a fuel for domestic purposes, even though it has a high calorific value?

65. Amount of solar energy received per unit area on the surface of Earth at a location is less than the value of solar constant. (i.e., the solar energy reaching unit area at outer edge of the Earth's atmosphere exposed perpendicularly to the rays of the Sun at the average distance between the Sun and the Earth). Discuss the reasons for this variation. Also, discuss the reasons for the variation in the amount of solar energy received per unit area at different locations on the surface of the Earth.

66. On combustion, 250 g of cow dung cake can raise the temperature of 60 g of water through 2°C. Assuming that all the heat generated was used to heat the water, calculate the calorific value of the cow dung cake. (Take specific heat of water as 4.2 J g^{-1} K^{-1}).

67. The solar energy incident on the surface of solar concentrator with an efficiency of 50% is 600 J s^{-1}. A bowl containing 1 kg of water is placed at the focal point of the concentrator. How long would it take to raise the temperature of water from 5°C to 35°C?

68. When 2 kg of coal is used to boil 2000 kg amount of water in a boiler which is at 30° and if the boiler uses 20% of the heat given by the coal and remaining is used by water, then find the final temperature of water. (The calorific value of coal is 30,000 kJ kg^{-1}).

69. We know that 47% of the solar energy that strikes the periphery of the earth reaches the surface. Of that energy only 10% is converted into electrical energy by a 1 m^2 area of a solar heater to increase the temperature of water by 10°C. If the total area of solar heater is 103 m^2, then find the mass of water taken in the solar heater.(Solar constant = 1.4 kJ m^{-2} s^{-1}(or) 1.4 kW m^{-2}; specific heat capacity of water = 1 cal g^{-1} °C^{-1}.)

70. It is observed that 2% of solar energy absorbed by 1000 km^2 area on the periphery of atmosphere in 2 hours reaches the earth surface in Hyderabad in each day per square metre. Then find the total solar energy absorbed by Hyderabad within the same interval. (Surface area of Hyderabad = 650 km^2 (approximately), solar constant = 1.4 kW m^{-2})

AT

PRACTICE QUESTIONS JEE-NEET SPECIAL WING

Multiple-Answer Type Questions

Directions for Questions 1 to 5: **Each question has FOUR options (a), (b), (c), and (d). ONE OR MORE THAN ONE of these four option(s) is/are the correct answer(s).**

1. The constituents of biogas are ________.
   (a) Methane (b) Carbon dioxide
   (c) Hydrogen (d) Nitrogen
2. The value of solar constant is ________.
   (a) 1.4 kJ m^{-2} s^{-1} (b) 4.1 kJ m^{-2} s^{-1}
   (c) 1.4 kW m^{-2} (d) 1.4 kW m^{-2} s^{-1}
3. Which of the following sources of energy can provide energy over a long period of time?
   (a) Sun (b) Wind
   (c) Coal (d) Petrol
4. Which of the following types of coal contains the highest percentage of carbon?
   (a) Peat (b) Lignite
   (c) Bituminous (d) Anthracite
5. The energy received on the periphery of the atmosphere of an area of 75 m^2 in one hour is ____.
   (a) 378 MJ (b) 378 kJ
   (c) 6.3 MJ (d) 6.3 kJ

Comprehension-Based Questions

Direction for Questions 6 to 11: **Read the paragraph given below and answer the questions.**

India mainly uses three types of thermal power plants. They are coal-based, gas-based, and liquid fuel-based. These plants contribute a major part of the total power generation in the country. It is about 70%. A coal-based thermal power plant burns an average of 14000 tons of coal every day. We know that coal is a non-renewable source of energy. i.e., it cannot be replenished once it is used up. The main constituent of coal is carbon, and the other constituents are hydrogen and oxygen. The quality of coal depends on the percentage of carbon present in it. Anthracite is one of the types of coal which is the best quality of coal as the percentage of carbon (about 95%) in it is maximum. Coal, on destructive distillation, gives coke. It is used as a reducing agent in the extraction of some metals from their ores and in making steel. Burning of coal creates serious air pollution. When coal is burnt, the carbon present in it reacts with oxygen to produce carbon dioxide. This is an exothermic reaction which yields a lot of heat energy.

6. Which of the following is the main constituent of coal?
   (a) Oxygen (b) Hydrogen
   (c) Carbon (d) All of these
7. What is the major type of power plant in India?
   (a) Thermal power plant
   (b) Nuclear power plant
   (c) Hydroelectric power plant
   (d) All of these
8. Coal on destructive distillation, gives ________.
   (a) Carbon (b) Oxygen
   (c) Carbon monoxide (d) Coke
9. The percentage of carbon in the best quality of coal is about ________.
   (a) 60 (b) 50
   (c) 80 (d) 95
10. In an exothermic reaction, ____________.
    (a) heat energy is absorbed
    (b) heat energy is released
    (c) carbon dioxide is released
    (d) oxygen is released

11. Using the data given in the above paragraph, match the following.

Column – A	Column – B
A. The percentage of contribution of thermal power plants in India	a. Reducing agent
B. coke	b. 70
C. coal	c. Renewable source of energy
D. Burning coal	d. Non-renewable source of energy
E. Solar energy	e. Air pollution

ANSWER KEYS

Crossword

Across

3. Fuel 5. OTEC 6. Solar cooker 9. Sun
10. Fossil 11. Solar cell

Down

1. Biogas 2. Nuclear Fusion 4. Petroleum 7. Combustion
8. Windmill

Classroom Wing

Very Short Answer Type Questions

1. non-renewable 2. renewable 3. ignition temperature 4. Geothermal
5. nuclear fusion 6. Calorific 7. hydrocarbons 8. Peat 9. Infrared radiations

Competition Wing

Level 1: Apply Your Concepts

1. Calorific value 2. Hydrocarbons 3. Ignition temperature 6. False
7. True 8. False 9. True 10. False 11. True
12. False 13. nuclear fusion 14. Geothermal energy 15. renewable
16. nuclear fission 17. calorific value 18. low 19. hydrocarbons
20. A : b, B : a, C : d, D : f, E : c, F : g, G : e, H : i, I : h
21. (b) 22. (c) 23. (c) 24. (c) 25. (c)
26. (d) 27. (d) 28. (b) 29. (d) 30. (a)
31. (d) 32. (c) 33. (d) 34. (c) 35. (a)
36. (c) 37. (a) 38. (a) 39. (d)

JEE-NEET SPECIAL WING

Multiple-Answer Type Questions

1. (a, b and c) 2. (a, c) 3. (a, b) 4. (d) 5. (a)

Comprehension-Based Questions

6. (c) 7. (a) 8. (d) 9. (d) 10. (b, c)
11. A-b, B-a, C-d, D-e, E-c

For answer key of Classroom wing and Competition wing, refer to Hints and Solutions

Hints and Explanations

CLASSROOM WING

Very Short Answer Type Questions

1. Non-renewable
2. Renewable
3. Ignition temperature
4. Geothermal
5. Nuclear fusion
6. Calorific
7. Hydrocarbons
8. Peat
9. Infrared radiations
10. (c). Nuclear fission is the process in which a heavy nucleus splits into lighter nuclei releasing a large amount of energy.
11. (d). The Sun's energy is the main factor causing differences in temperature, leading to air movements and winds.
12. (b). When hydrogen reacts with oxygen, it forms water and releases a lot of heat, making it an exothermic reaction.
13. (c). Calorific value represents the energy liberated as heat by a fuel when its unit mass is burnt completely.
14. (c). Tidal energy is a renewable source of energy derived from the gravitational effects of the moon and sun on Earth's oceans, causing tides.
15. A process in which a heavier nucleus splits into lighter nuclei with release of huge amounts of energy.
16. Burning a substance in presence of air or oxygen or a supporter of combustion.
17. (i) An oil derived from rocks. A complex mixture of hydrocarbons.
    (ii) Natural gas is a fossil fuel that is found on the top of petroleum under the Earth.
18. Process of burning wood in limited supply of oxygen.
19. Fuels obtained from the decay of plants and marine animals.
20. Solid, liquid and gaseous fuels.
21. Energy of flowing water is utilized to produce electricity on a large scale.
22. Petrol – presence of hydrogen.
23. A device that converts wind energy to mechanical or electrical energy.
24. A device which directly converts solar energy into electrical energy.

Short Answer Type Questions

Note: This is how you should frame your answer covering.

25. Wind mill, turbine.
26. (i) Solid fuels
    (ii) Liquid fuels
    (iii) Gaseous fuels
27. (i) Net energy output.
    (ii) Easy availability.
    (iii) Safe and convenient to use.
    (iv) Easy for storage and transportation.
    (v) Economical.
28. Steam from water, turbine runs with the help of steam.
29. (i) Main component is methane.
    (ii) Compressed under high pressure to form CNG.
    (iii) Used as fuel in automobiles.
30. (i) Renewable sources of energy – solar energy, wind energy.
    (ii) Non-renewable sources of energy – coal, petrol.
31. (i) Energy liberated when a unit mass of a fuel is burnt completely.
    (ii) Hydrogen.
32. Digester tank, raw material, inlet tank, outlet tank.
33. (i) Solid fuels – Wood, coal
    (ii) Liquid fuels – Petrol, kerosene
    (iii) Gaseous fuels – Natural gas, biogas
34. Box type solar cooker:
    (i) Rectangular wooden box, lined from inside with insulating material which prevents heat losses.
    (ii) Inner walls painted black.
    (iii) A plane mirror hinged at the top, which can be adjusted such that it reflects sunlight into the box.

    Reflector type solar cooker:

(i) In this the solar energy received over an area is concentrated at a particular point where the cooker is kept.
(ii) The surface area of the disc-like structure is coated with a reflecting material.
(iii) It can generate temperatures upto 180°.

35. (i) More economical to construct.
(ii) Need of abundant water in the dam.
(iii) Can be constructed only at certain places.

36. Formation:
(i) Dead remains of plants and animals that settled in muddy sediments at the bottom of the sea millions of years ago.
(ii) Got buried deep below the surface of the Earth.
(iii) Due to intense heat and high pressure, the remains were ultimately converted into petroleum.

Extraction:
(i) Large reservoirs.
(ii) Pumped out by drilling holes and digging wells.

37. (i) Easy availability, low cost.
(ii) High calorific value.
(iii) Easy storage and transport.
(iv) Ignition temperature above the room temperature.
(v) Low rate of evaporation at room temperature.

38. Minimum speed of air, cost of construction and erection.

39. Concave reflection surface, cooking items at focus.

40. (i) A plant designed to produce biogas.
(ii) Types of biogas plants—Its construction and working.

Essay Answer Type Questions

Note: This is how you should frame your answer covering.

41. (i) Fractional distillation.
(ii) Principle:-Different fractions of petroleum boil at different temperature ranges.

42. (i) Every source of energy either directly or indirectly is manifested from solar energy.
(ii) Flow chart for the various functions performed by solar energy.

43. (i) Fossiled remains of the plants.
(ii) Peat, lignite, bituminous, anthracite.

44. Huge stem like body, impellors, connecting levers and turbine.

Competition Wing

Level 1: Apply Your Concepts

Explanation for questions from 1 to 5:

1. Calorific value.
2. Hydrocarbons
3. Ignition temperature
4. Solar energy.
5. The minimum temperature at which the substance begins to burn.

Explanation for questions from 6 to 10:

6. False. Ignition temperature is the minimum temperature at which a substance begins to burn, not melt.
7. True.
8. False. Tidal energy is renewable as it relies on the gravitational effects of the moon and sun, which are repetitive and consistent.
9. True.
10. False. This description is for nuclear fusion.

Explanation for questions from 21 to 27:

21. (b). Nuclear fission involves the splitting of a heavy nucleus, while nuclear fusion involves the combination of lighter nuclei.
22. (c). The sun's energy causes differences in temperature, leading to pressure differences, which in turn cause air to move, forming winds.
23. (c). Geothermal energy utilizes the heat stored inside the Earth, often harnessed from underground reservoirs or volcanic areas.
24. (c). Exothermic reactions release heat, resulting in an increase in temperature of the surroundings.
25. (c). Ignition temperature is the minimum temperature at which a substance begins to burn without the need for an external flame.
26. (d). Geothermal energy taps into the Earth's internal heat reservoirs, often from volcanic regions or hot springs. Fossil fuels, on the other hand, are formed from the decomposition of ancient plant and animal matter over millions of years under specific conditions.
27. (d). While tidal energy can influence local coastal climates through its effects on ocean currents and tides, solar energy is the primary driver for global weather patterns, ocean currents, and overall climate. It affects both land and water, leading to a more profound impact on global climate change.

Explanation for questions from 31–39:

31. Silver is the metal which is used for connecting wires that connect solar cells in a solar panel, due to its large conductivity.
32. The most suitable fuel burns completely and does not release (expel) any carbon particles with smoke.
33. Solar energy provides wind energy, light energy and heat energy.
34. In case of box-type solar cooker, more energy will be trapped by using a box, whose inner surfaces are painted black and which cannot conduct more energy to the surroundings. Now from the given options, if we choose a double wall plastic box, whose inner surfaces are painted black, then the efficiency will be more.
35. The net output = output – input = 1000 – 200 = 800 J.
36. A good source of energy should have large, net energy output. Among the given options, a source of energy which has input energy of 100 J and an output energy of 12,500 J is the best source of energy, because the net energy output is (12,500–100) J = 12,400 J.
37. More is the velocity of wind, more will be the kinetic energy of blades of a windmill due to which more amount of electrical energy can be produced. That is, the output of a windmill increases with increase in the velocity of wind.
38. The hot water in the ocean is used to evaporate liquids like ammonia or CFC. This vapour is used to rotate the turbines of the generator and the vapour is again cooled down to a liquid by using the cold water from the ocean depth. This cooled liquid ammonia or CFC is again vapourized and the above process continues.
39. Initially water is collected in the dam. When it is released, the potential energy is converted to kinetic energy. The released water is made to fall on the blades of turbines. The armature of the electric generator rotates to produce electricity.

Level 2: Review Your Concepts

Note: This is how you should frame your answer covering.

40. Wind energy, while renewable and abundant, is intermittent and unpredictable. The strength and presence of wind vary, making it essential to have backup energy sources or storage solutions. Additionally, the infrastructure and land requirements for wind farms can be significant, making it challenging to implement universally.

41. The availability of geothermal energy depends on tectonic activity and the Earth's crust's thickness. Regions near tectonic plate boundaries or with volcanic activity have easier access to this internal heat, making geothermal energy more viable.

42. Combustion requires an initial activation energy to break chemical bonds before the energy-releasing process can occur. Achieving the ignition temperature provides this necessary activation energy to start the combustion reaction.

43. While the Moon is drifting away, the timescale for significant tidal energy changes spans millions of years. In human-relevant timeframes, the tides are consistent and predictable, making tidal energy effectively renewable for our purposes.

44. Nuclear fusion on Earth requires conditions similar to a star's core, meaning extremely high temperatures and pressures. Creating and maintaining these conditions, and containing the fusion reaction in a controlled environment, presents significant technological and material challenges.

45. (i) Find the change in temperature of 1 litre water. Then, find the amount of heat energy absorbed by water to raise its temperature, using the formula,

$Q = ms\,\Delta t$. (1)

Convert (1) in S.I. system by taking s= 4200 J $kg^{-1}°C^{-1}$

Find the percentage of incident solar energy that causes rise in temperature of water.

Then, the heat absorbed by water is equal to the heat produced in solar cooker.

Then, find the heat produced in solar heater by using formula,

$Q = \text{(Solar constant) (Area) (Time)} \times \frac{90}{100}$ (2)

Substitute the appropriate values in (1) and (2).

Equate (1) and (2), and find the value of time.

(ii) 1.11 minute

46. Find the calorific value of wood with respect to the other sources of energy.

47. (i) Heat released by combustion of 100 tonnes of coal is, $Q = mS$

$\Rightarrow Q = 100 \times 1000\ kg \times 30\ kJ\ kg^{-1} \rightarrow (1)$

(ii) Find 50% of the 'Q'.

(iii) Let above value be Q^1.

(iv) The amount of heat released by fission process should be equal to $= \frac{100 \times Q^1}{25}$ J

(v) 1 fission produces $\rightarrow 200 \times 10^6 \times 1.6 \times 10^{-19}$ J

(vi) Find the number of fissions to produce $\frac{100 \times Q^1}{25}$ J

(vii) 235 grams of U^{235} produces 6.023×10^{23} fissions.

(viii) Find the amount of U^{235} that produces $\frac{100 \times Q^1}{25}$ J

(ix) 0.07 g

48. (i) The volume of air that makes blades to rotate = V $= \ell \times$ area of the blade

(ii) Velocity $(v) = \frac{\ell}{t}$

(iii) Mass of the air = m = Volume × Density of air

(iv) Kinetic Energy (KE) of air $= \frac{1}{2}mv^2$

(v) 50% of kinetic energy of air is converted into Electrical Energy (EE)

(vi) The power of electrical generation is, $P = \frac{EE}{1s}$

(vii) 2.53 kW

49. (i) By using formula, $Q = ms\,\Delta t$, find the amount of heat energy absorbed by the water. (1)

Is this heat energy absorbed by the water equal to the solar energy that is incident on the water?

Then, find the solar constant and time for which solar energy is incident on water surface.

Find the amount of solar energy incident on water by using formula,

Q = (Solar constant) (Area) (Time) (2)

Then, substitute appropriate values and obtain the value of the area.

(ii) 0.7 m^2

50. What is the source of energy (Renewable) in outerspace?

Is it economical to harness solar energy?

Is there steady availability of the source of energy?

Then, find the efficiency of energy conversion into electrical energy.

51. (i) Find the Avogadro number.

How many atoms are contained in 235 g of uranium?

Then, find the number of atoms present in 1 g of uranium.

How many fissions are produced by 1 atom of uranium?

Find the energy of 1 eV in terms of joules.

Convert 200 MeV into joules by multiplying 200 with ($10^6 \times 1.6 \times 10^{-19}$).

Find the heat liberated by fission of 1 g of U – 235. (1)

The amount of heat liberated by burning coal is = (m as of coal) × (its calorific value) (10.2)

Find the energy conversion efficiencies of coal and uranium.

Then, equate the heat energies liberated by fission of uranium and combustion of coal.

From this, find mass of coal.

(ii) 2000 kg.

52. (i) The power of the engine = 1 Hp = 746 J s^{-1}

$= \frac{Q}{3600s}$ (1)

(ii) Find the value of Q from (10.1)

(iii) We know, Q = mS (2)

(iv) Equate (1) and (2) and find the value of 'S'.

(v) S = 36,000 J kg^{-1}

53. (i) Solar energy incident in time 't' is = Q = 1.4 $\times 10^3 \times t$ J → (1)

(ii) Q = $m_w s_w$ (Δt) + (water equivalent of vessel) $s_w(\Delta t)$

$_{w;}$ Δt = 100°C

(iii) $\frac{90}{100}$Q = 1 kg × 4200 J kg^{-1} °C^{-1} × 100°C + $\frac{1}{10}$ kg × 4200 J kg^{-1} °C^{-1} × 100°C → (2)

(iv) From (10.1) and (10.2), find the value of 't'.

(v) 36.6 s

54. How much energy is needed in lifting water to a certain height?

Then, this energy stored in the water is converted to produce electricity.

What is the efficiency of conversion to electrical energy?

Is it economical, if electricity produced is less than the energy spent in lifting water?

Explanation for questions from 55 to 59:

55. Area of the surface which receives energy = 12 m^2.

Time of reception (t) = 2 minute = 2 x 60 s = 120 s

The amount of energy received (E) = 2016 kJ = 2016 × 10^3J

As solar constant is the amount of energy received by a surface of unit area, per unit time from the rays which are falling normally on it. $K = \frac{2016 \text{ kJ}}{12m^2 \times 120s} = 1.4 \text{ kJ } m^{-2}s^{-1}$.

56. Silicon and Selenium are used for making solar cells.

57. Geothermal energy can be harnessed for 24 hours, throughout the year. The cost of production of electricity by geothermal energy is very less than that produced by wind energy.

58. Pinhole in a blackened box, practically all radiant energy entering the pinhole is absorbed by the walls of the blackened box.

59. The speed of the wind = 36 km h^{-1} = 36 × 5/18 m s^{-1}

u = 10 ms^{-1}

Area of cross section of the blade of the windmill A = 0.375 m^2

Time taken to create pressure difference (t) = 5 s

Volume of wind falling on the blade (V) = ?

Length of air column falling on surface of windmill in 1 second = 10 m

∴ Volume of air falling per second

= 10 m × 0.375 m^2 = 3.75 m^3

∴ Volume of air falling on wing in 5 second = 5 × 3.75 = 18.75 m^3.

Level 3: Assess Your Concepts

Note: This is how you should frame your answer covering.

60. Nuclear fission is predominantly used in power plants because the technology to control fission reactions is more mature and easier to manage. Fission reactions involve the splitting of heavy atoms like uranium, which can be controlled using current technology. On the other hand, nuclear fusion requires extremely high temperatures (akin to those in stars) to fuse lighter nuclei, making it challenging to achieve and maintain on Earth. While fusion offers vast energy potential and cleaner by-products, the technological challenges of containing and controlling such reactions have made its widespread use in power generation elusive.

61. While both tidal and solar energies are influenced by astronomical bodies, their impacts on Earth's climate vary. Solar energy directly influences the Earth's temperature by providing the primary energy that drives weather systems, ocean currents, and supports life. The differential heating due to solar energy results in wind patterns and plays a pivotal role in determining climate

zones. Tidal energy, on the other hand, impacts ocean currents and can influence localized coastal climates, but its broader climatic effect is minimal compared to solar energy. Thus, in terms of overarching climatic influence, solar energy has a more profound impact on Earth's climate than tidal energy.

62. The calorific value of a fuel measures the amount of heat energy released when a unit mass of the fuel is burnt completely. While a higher calorific value suggests more energy output, it doesn't provide insights into the composition or amount of by-products, especially greenhouse gases like CO_2. A fuel might have a high calorific value but could also release a significant amount of CO_2 and other pollutants when burned. Thus, considering global warming and environmental impact, it's essential to evaluate not just the calorific value but also the nature and quantity of emissions from the fuel.

63 . (i) Is the energy emitted by the Sun in one second equal to the energy reaching an imaginary sphere of radius equal to the distance between the Sun and the Earth?

Take the distance between the Sun and the Earth as radius of the sphere.

Then, the total surface area (T.S.A) of the sphere is $4\pi r^2$.

Then, energy received in one second (E) = (solar constant) (T.S.A).

Find the velocity of light (c) from given data.
Find the mass of the Sun that is converted into energy in one second by using the formula, $E = mc^2$.

Then, $m = \dfrac{E}{c^2}$.

(ii) 4.14×10^9 kg s^{-1}.

64. Is it more difficult to store, handle and transport the hydrogen fuel?

Explanation for questions 65 to 70:

65. Due to the nearly spherical shape of the Earth, the Sun's radiations are not normal at every location on the surface of the Earth. Furthermore, due to the rotation of Earth on its axis, the angle of incidence of the incident radiation from the Sun is changing constantly.

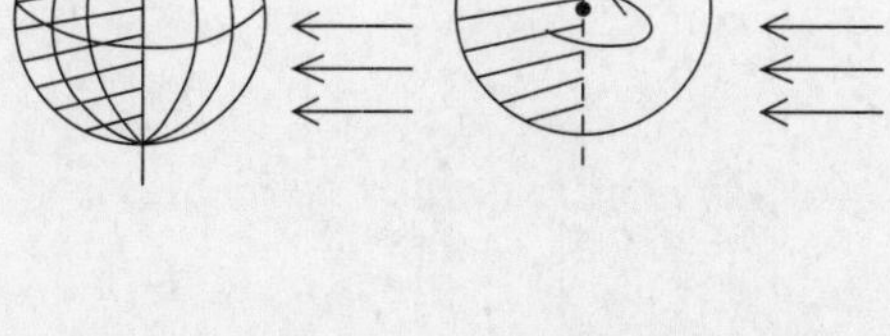

In addition, on an average there are only 250 – 300 days of Sun shine in most of the places in India. Nearly 50% of the Sun's energy entering the atmosphere is either absorbed by the atmosphere or it is reflected into space. Only infrared radiations and visible range of electromagnetic radiations reach the surface of the Earth.

66. The energy required to raise the temperature of 60 g water

= Mass × Specific heat × Rise in temp.
$= 60 \times 4.2 \times 2 = 12 \times 42$ J

The above energy is supplied by 250 g of cow dung cake. Hence, its calorific value is $\dfrac{12 \times 42}{250} \approx 2\text{ J g}^{-1}$.

67. Efficiency = 50%
The power of concentration = 50% of 600 J s^{-1}
= 300 J s^{-1}.
Heat required to rise temp of water in bowl is $mc\Delta\theta$
$= 4200 \times 30$ J

$$\text{Time taken} = \frac{4200 \times 30}{300} = 420s = 7 \text{ minute}$$

68. Mass of coal = 2 kg = 2000 g
Initial temperature of water = T_1 = 30°
Mass of water = 2 10^6 g
Calorific value of coal = C = 30,000 kJ kg^{-1}

$$= 30{,}000 \quad \frac{1}{4.2} \text{ cal g}^{-1}$$

The amount of heat used by boiler = Q_B = 20% (Q_{coal})
= 20% (M_{coal} C_{coal})
Final temperature of water = T_2 =?
(Specific heat of water) = 1 cal g^{-1}°C^{-1}

$$Q_{coal} = Q_{water} + Q_B$$

$$M_{coal} C_{coal} = M_{water} S_{water} (T_2 - T_1) + 20\% (M_{coal} C_{coal})$$

$$2000 \times \frac{30{,}000}{4.2} = 2000 \times 10^3 \times 1\ (T_2 - 30)$$

$$+ \frac{20}{100} \times 2000 \times \frac{30{,}000}{4.2}$$

$$\frac{3}{42} \times 10^5 - 0.2 \times \frac{3}{42} \times 10^5 = (T_2 - 30) \times 10^3$$

$$\frac{3}{42} \times 10^2 \times 0.8 = T_2 - 30$$

$$\frac{24}{42} \times 10^1 = T_2 - 30$$

$$T_2 = \frac{240}{42} + 30 = 5.7 + 30 = 35.7\ °C$$

69. Solar constant = 1.4 kJ m^{-2} s^{-1} (or) 1.4 kW m^{-2},

specific heat capacity of water = S_w = 4200 J kg^{-1} K^{-1}

ΔT = 10 °C; Area of solar heater = 1000 m^2

Solar energy at the periphery of the earth's atmosphere = 1.4 kW m^{-2}

Solar energy that strikes the surface of the earth (E)= 47% × 1.4 kW m^{-2}

E = 0.658 kW m^{-2} = 6580 Wm^{-2}

10% of E × t × Area = $m_w s_w \Delta T \times t$ (∵ where "t" is time)

10% × 6580 × 10^3 = m_w × 4200 × 10

0.1 × 6580 × 10^3 = m_w x 42 × 103

$$M_w = \frac{658}{42} = 15.6 \text{kg}$$

70. time, t = 2 h = 2 × 60 × 60 s

Area of periphery is 1000 km^2 = 1000 × 10^6 m^2

Area of Hyderabad is 650 km^2 = 650 × 10^6 m^2

Solar energy absorbed by Hyderabad in a day = 2% (Solar energy received by the periphery of the earth of area 1000 km^2) × area of Hyderabad × time

$$= \frac{2}{100}(10^3 \times 10^6 \times 1.4 \times 10^3 \text{ W}) \times 650 \times 10^6 \times (2 \times 60 \times 60 \text{ s})$$

= 13104000 × 10^{16} J = 1.3104 × 10^{23} J

JEE-NEET SPECIAL WING

Multiple-Answer Type Questions

1. The constituents of biogas are Methane, Carbon dioxide, and Hydrogen.
Hence, the correct option is (a, b and c)

2. The value of solar constant is 1.4 kJ m^{-2} s^{-1} or 1.4 kW m^{-2}
Hence, the correct option is (a, c)

3. Sun and wind are the sources of energy that can provide energy over a long period of time.
Hence, the correct option is (a, b)

4. Anthracite is a type of coal that contains the highest percentage of carbon.
Hence, the correct option is (d)

5. We have, solar constant = 1.4 kJ m^{-2} s^{-1}
This is the solar energy received on the periphery of the atmosphere per m^2 per second.
For an area of 75 m^2 in one hour,
solar energy received = 1.4 kJ × 75 × 3600 = 378 MJ
Hence, the correct option is (a)

Comprehension-Based Questions

6. Carbon is the main constituent of coal.
Hence, the correct option is (c)

7. Thermal power plant is the major type of power plant in India.
Hence, the correct option is (a)

8. Coal on destructive distillation, gives coke.
Hence, the correct option is (d)

9. The percentage of carbon in the best-quality of coal is about 95%.
Hence, the correct option is (d)

10. In an exothermic reaction, carbon dioxide and heat energy are released.
Hence, the correct option is (b, c)

11. **A → b**
B → a
C → d
D → e
E → c

Unit III

Waves and Sound

In this Unit

* **Chapter 4** Wave Motion and Sound

CHAPTER 4

Wave Motion and Sound

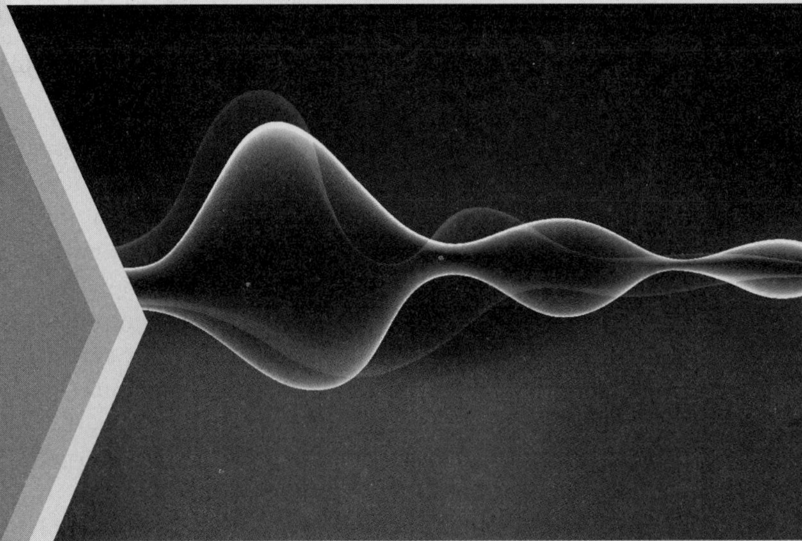

Remember

Before beginning this chapter, you should be able to:

- Learn about the different types of wave motion and to represent simple harmonic motion graphically.
- Learn how a sound is produced and the classification of sound based on its frequency.
- Understand the formula of velocity of sound and the factors that affect the velocity.
- Learn about natural and forced oscillations and resonance.

Key Ideas

After completing this chapter, you should be able to:

- Understand the classification of waves, sound as a mechanical wave.
- Learn different types of vibrations, vibrations of stretched string, etc.
- Study about simple harmonic motion.
- Find relation between velocity, wavelength and frequency of sound.
- Study the phenomenon of resonance.
- Understand terms and concepts related to sound like pitch, intensity, quality, noise pollution, recording and reproduction of sound, etc.

Scientific Crypt

A Tribute to Heinrich Rudolf Hertz (1857 – 1894)

Heinrich Hertz was born on 22nd February 1857, in Hamburg, Germany. His father Gustav Hertz, was head of the judiciary in the city of Hamburg and his mother's name was Elizabeth Pfefferkorn Hertz. From his childhood days itself, he started showing unusual talent in science, mathematics, manual skills and languages. As a teenager, he constructed a spectrometer and a galvanometer which he used during his university studies also. Hertz did his graduation from the gymnasium in Hamburg in 1875 and completed his regular engineering studies from the University of Munich in 1877. During this time he developed a preference for physics to engineering. This lead to the remarkable combination of theoretical and experimental work, and he received the degree of Magna Cum Laude for "Induction in Rotating Spheres".

This German physicist also discovered the photoelectric effect and gave the first experimental proof of the existence of radio waves. With his acumenship, he experimentally produced and studied electromagnetic waves (also known as Hertzian waves). He studied electric charge in rarefied gases and also produced the great works "Electric Waves" and "Principles of Mechanics". In his honour, the unit of frequency is named "hertz". This great physicist left the world on January 1st, 1894 but not before leaving a huge impact in the field of science.

FUN TIME

CROSSWORD

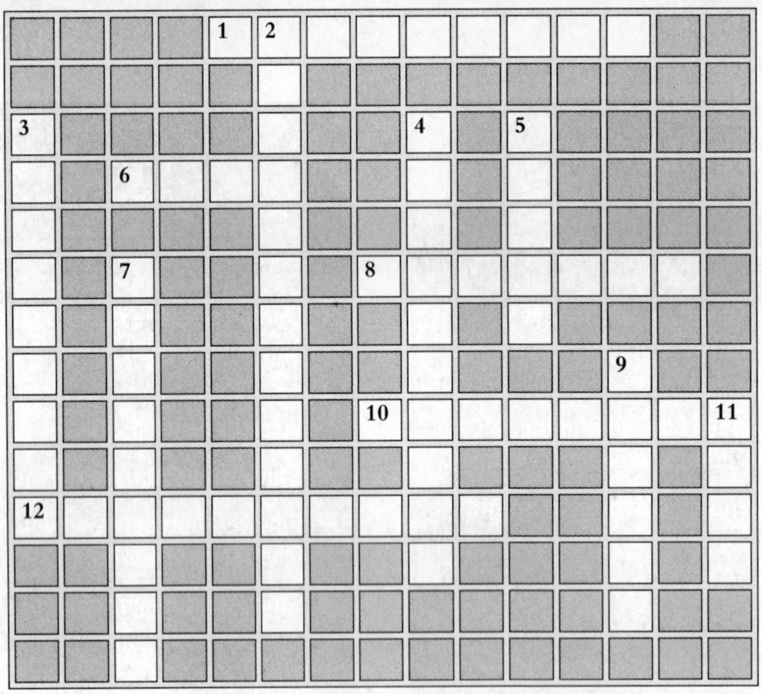

Across

1. The pitch of sound depends upon ______.
6. In a stationary wave, the displacement of particle is zero at this point.
8. The velocity of sound through a medium is inversely proportional to the square root of ______.
10. The particles at these points in a stationary wave have maximum displacement.
12. The velocity of a mechanical wave is directly proportional to the square root of ______.

Down

2. This is caused due to the multiple reflection of sound.
3. This physical quantity of a wave depends upon the energy spent to produce the wave.
4. If the distance between adjacent nodes of a stationary wave is 40 cm, then 80 cm is ______ of the wave.
5. At this point in a transverse wave, the particle will have the maximum displacement.
7. A special case of forced vibration.
9. The velocity of sound is maximum in ______.
11. Reflection of sound from a rigid boundary.

INTRODUCTION

Sensation of hearing through the vibrating ear drum IS caused by Sound which is a form of energy. A loud thunder or high-intensity sound produced by a low-flying jet plane results in the rattling of window panes and doors. We know that work is done at the expense of energy and the rattling of doors and windows is caused by the sound, thus, indicating that sound is a form of energy.

Sound

The source of sound energy is the mechanical energy possessed by vibrating bodies. In other words, sound is produced by vibrating bodies. This can be demonstrated by a simple experiment as described below.

A tuning fork is clamped to a wooden base and the prongs are gently struck with a leather or rubber hammer. As the sound is produced from the tuning fork, a pith ball suspended from a string is brought into contact with the tuning fork. It is found that as soon the pith ball comes in contact with the tuning fork, it instantaneously moves away. On the other hand, the pith ball does not jump away when it comes in contact with a tuning fork that does not produce sound. The jumping away of the pith ball is indicative of the vibrations of the tuning fork and this experiment illustrates that a tuning fork produces sound only when it vibrates.

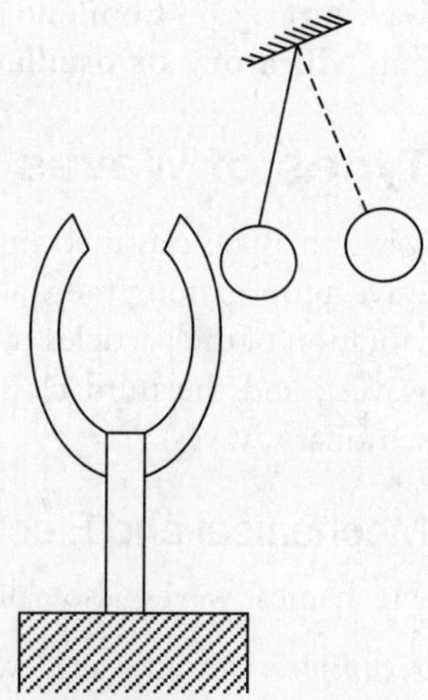

Figure 4.1 A tuning fork and a pith ball producing sound on collision

Do all the vibrating bodies produce audible sound? It has been found that bodies vibrating with a frequency in the range from 20 Hz to 20 kHz only can cause a sensation of hearing in humans, and this range is called audible range of frequencies. Animals, birds and insects in general are sensitive to sound with a frequency outside this range also. If the frequency of the vibrations is less than 20 Hz, it is called **infrasonic sound** and the sound produced by bodies vibrating with a frequency greater than 20 kHz, is called **ultrasonic sound**.

Propagation of Sound

A little earlier, we had mentioned that sound is a sensation produced in the brain through the vibrations of the ear drum—a thin membrane in the ear. For the vibrations of the tuning fork to be transmitted to the ear, the intervening material medium plays an important role. In other words, material medium is required for the propagation of sound energy. This is demonstrated in the bell-jar experiment. The sound produced by the electric bell located inside the bell-jar can be heard from the outside, only when there is air inside the jar. It is observed that the sound produced by the electric bell is not heard when the jar is completely evacuated. No wonder we can only see the sun but not hear the roaring solar flames!

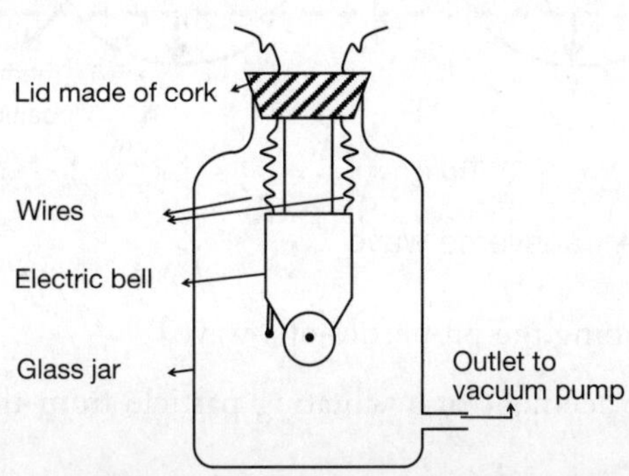

Figure 4.2 Bell-jar experiment

Konnect

Sound can't travel through a vacuum; it needs a medium like air, water, or solids to propagate.

The important properties of a material medium that help in the proportion of sound energy are the elasticity and inertia of the medium.

Wave Motion

Consider the row of bicycles parked in a cycle-stand. If the bicycle at one end is pushed, progressively all the bicycles would fall and within a few seconds the bicycle at the other end also would fall. Without physically going to it, the last bicycle is successfully pushed down. This is the principle of wave motion, in which the vibrations of the particles of the intervening material medium are utilized to transmit the energy without the actual translatory motion of the source causing the disturbance, just as the intermediate bicycles help in pushing the last bicycle in the row.

A wave is a disturbance created at a place in a medium and travels in all possible directions in the medium. When a wave propagates from one place to another, the particles of the medium do not undergo any translatory motion but have only **vibratory or oscillatory motion**.

Types of Waves

Waves may be classified in three different ways. The first classification is based on the requirement of a medium for the wave propagation (mechanical and electromagnetic waves); the second classification is based on the direction of the vibration of the particles of the medium with respect to the direction of the wave propagation (transverse and longitudinal waves); and the third classification is based on the limitation of the propagation of the waves (progressive waves and stationary waves).

Mechanical and Electromagnetic Waves

Mechanical waves, also called elastic waves, require a material (an elastic) medium for their propagation.

Examples: Sound waves, water waves, etc.

Electromagnetic waves are the waves which do not require any material medium for their propagation. They can propagate even through vacuum.

Examples: Light waves, X-rays, radio waves, etc.

Transverse and Longitudinal Waves

If the direction of the vibration of the particles of the medium is perpendicular to the direction of the propagation of the wave, the wave is called **transverse wave**.

Examples: Ripples on water surface; a wave pattern set in a stretched string.

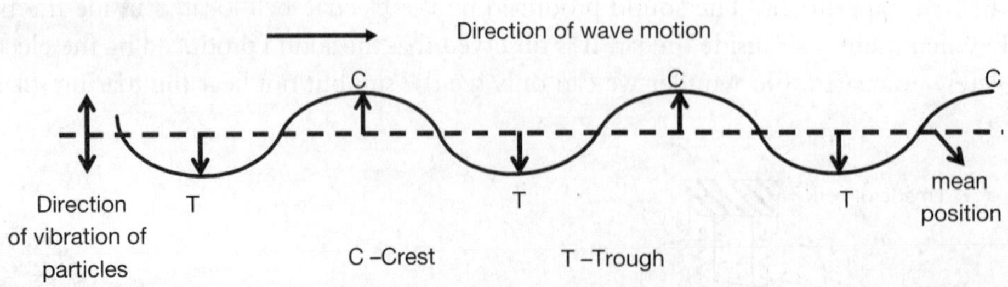

Figure 4.3 A transverse wave

Given below are the definitions of standard terms describing the properties of a wave.

1. **Crest:** The position of the maximum upward displacement of a vibrating particle from the mean position in a transverse wave is called **crest**.
2. **Trough:** The position of the maximum downward displacement of a vibrating particle from the mean position in a transverse wave is called **trough**.

3. **Amplitude:** The maximum displacement of a vibrating particle from the mean position (either upward or downward) in the wave is called **amplitude** and is measured in metres or centimetres.
4. **Phase:** The state of a vibrating particle in the wave with regard to its displacement from the mean position and the direction of vibration is called phase and is measured in radians. If the phase of any two particles in a wave is equal, i.e., they have a phase difference of 2π radians, they are said to be in phase else they are said to be out of **phase**.
5. **Wavelength:** The distance between any two successive particles of the wave which are in phase is known as **wavelength (λ)** and is measured in metres or centimetres.
6. **Time Period:** The time taken by a vibrating particle to complete one full vibration or the time taken to produce one complete wave pulse is known as **time period (T)** and is measured in seconds.
7. **Frequency:** The number of vibrations made by a vibrating particle in one second or the number of waves produced per second is known as **frequency** and is measured in hertz (*Hz*). It is denoted by ν(*nu*) or *n* or *f*.

If the direction of the vibration of particles of the medium is parallel to the direction of the wave propagation, the wave is called **'longitudinal' wave**.

Example: Sound waves in air or in a gas; waves set in a long spring.

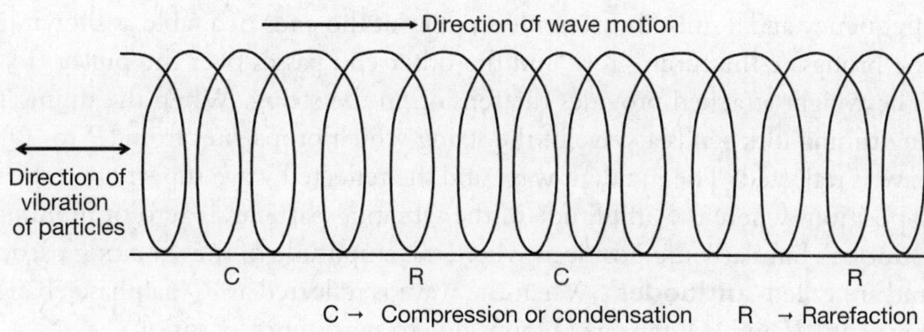

Figure 4.4 A longitudinal wave set in a spring

When a long spring is placed horizontally on a table and one end is vibrated as shown in Fig. 4.4, there are certain regions formed in the spring where the rings of the spring are much closer to each other than they would be when they are at rest position. Such regions are called **compressions** or **condensations**. Similarly, there are certain regions formed in the spring where the distance between the rings is more than the distance when they are at rest position. These regions are known as **rarefactions**.

Progressive and Stationary Waves

When a wave starts from a point in a medium and propagates in all the possible directions and never returns, the wave is called **progressive wave**. When a progressive wave strikes a hard surface and is reflected, the incident wave and the reflected wave superpose forming a standing wave, also called stationary wave. In such a wave, the amplitude of vibration of different particles.

Phase difference between waves (1) and (3) is π, i.e., if the shape of the wave in (1) is described by $y = \sin x$, the shape of the wave in (3) is given by, $y = \sin (x + \pi) = -\sin x$.

$\therefore$ When wave in (1) reaches a maximum, wave in (3) reaches a minimum and vice-versa.

Phase difference between (1) and (2) is $(\pi/2)$, i.e., if the wave in (1) is given by, y = sin x, the wave in (2) is given by,

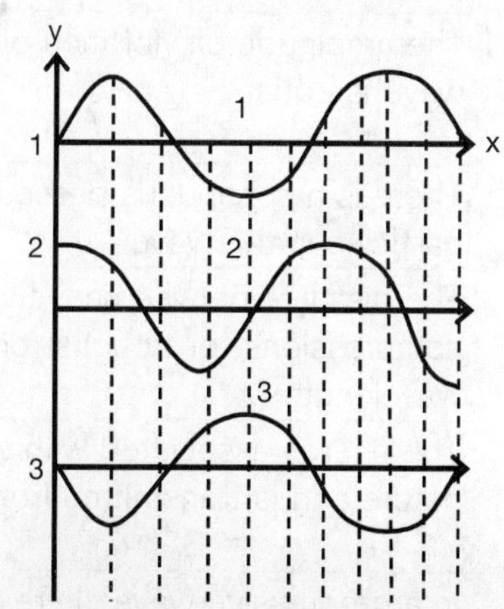

Figure 4.5 Progressive waves

$$y = \sin (x + \pi) = -\sin x.$$

Therefore, if a wave on reflection undergoes a phase change π, the shape of the wave before and after reflection at the wall would appear as below.

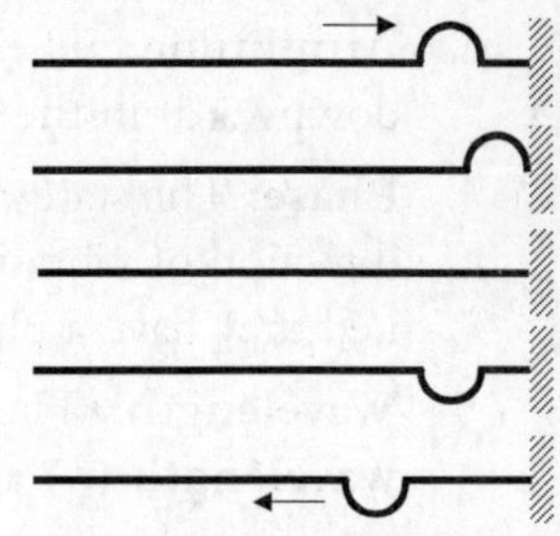

Figure 4.6 The shape of the wave before and after reflection at the wall

Stationary Wave Formation in a Stretched String

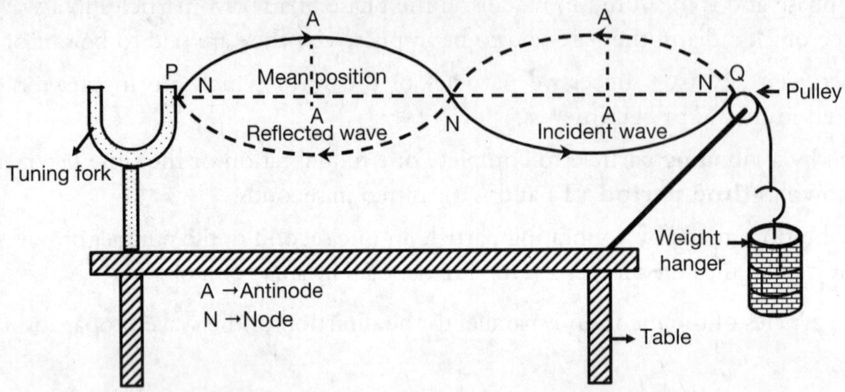

Figure 4.7 Formation of stationary waves in a string

Fix a tuning fork of some frequency and a smooth frictionless pulley at the ends of a table as shown in Fig. 4.7. One end of a string is tied to one of the prongs of the tuning fork and the other end passes over the pulley. To this free end of the string, a weight is attached. The weight attached provides the tension in the string. When the tuning fork is excited with a rubber hammer, the vibrating tuning fork sends a wave in the string which propagates from '*P*' to '*Q*' It is called incident wave. At the pulley '*Q*' the wave is reflected. The incident wave and the reflected wave superpose to form a stationary wave as shown in the Fig. 4.7. The positions where the amplitude of the vibrating particles is zero or minimum are shown as 'N' in the Fig. 4.7 and are called '**nodes**'. Similarly the positions where the amplitude of the vibrating particles is maximum are shown as '*A*' in the Fig. 4.7 and are called '**antinodes**'. When the wave is reflected at '*Q*', a phase change of π radians takes place. The string between the points '*P*' and '*Q*' appears as loops due to persistence of vision.

Table 4.1 Differences Between Progressive and Stationary Waves

Progressive waves	Stationary waves
These waves are produced at a point and progress in all the possible directions till they die out due to damping.	These waves are limited between two positions and appear to be standing.
These waves cause crests and troughs or compressions and rarefactions.	These waves cause nodes and antinodes.
The amplitude of vibration of all the particles in the wave is equal.	The amplitude of vibration of different particles in the wave is different. It is maximum at antinodes and minimum or zero at nodes.
There is a continuous phase difference between particles in the wave.	All the particles between two successive nodes in the wave are in phase.
The distance between any two adjacent crests (or compressions) or troughs (or rarefactions) is one wavelength (λ).	The distance between any two successive nodes or two successive antinodes is one half of the wavelength (λ/2).
The energy associated with these waves is kinetic in nature and is transmitted from one place to another.	The energy associated with these waves is potential in nature and it is stored in the medium between two fixed points.
In a progressive wave, there is no instant when all the particles cross the mean position together.	In a standing wave, all the particles cross their mean positions together.
In a traveling wave, there is no particle which is always at rest.	In a standing wave, the particles at nodes are always at rest.

Sound Waves

Sound waves are longitudinal waves formed due to the compressions and rarefactions produced in the material medium surrounding the source.

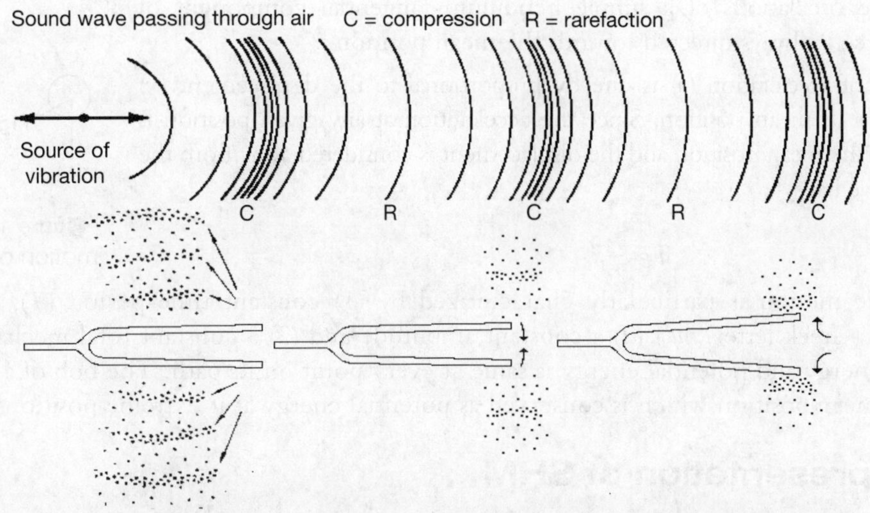

Figure 4.8 Sound waves produced by a tuning fork

Sound waves can propagate in solids, liquids as well as gases. Put your ear to one end of a long pipe, say 100 m, long and ask your friend to gently tap the other end. Almost immediately, you would be able to hear the sound at your end.

Propagation of Sound Through Liquids

Place a trough of water on a hollow wooden box (sound box) open at one end. Fix the stem of a tuning fork to a metallic disc. The prongs of the tuning fork are set to vibrate and the disc is gently made to come in contact with the water surface as shown in the Fig. 4.9. It is found that immediately the sound of the tuning fork with greater intensity is heard from the sound box.

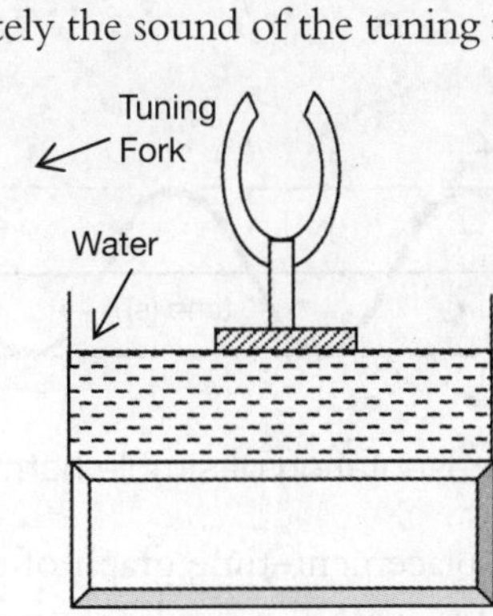

Figure 4.9 Propagation of sounds through liquids

Konnect

Sound travels faster in liquids than in gases but slower than in solids. Water can transmit sound up to four times faster than air!

Simple Harmonic Motion

The transmission of sound is by longitudinal wave propagation caused by the vibration of the particles of the medium resulting in compressions and rarefactions. These vibrations are periodic and oscillatory in nature, i.e., the motion of each particle repeats itself along the same path at regular intervals of time (periodic motion) and at the same time, the motion is to and fro along the path (oscillatory). The oscillations of the bob of a simple pendulum, the vibrations of a body suspended from a spring, to and fro motion of the air molecules during the propagation of sound are all examples of harmonic motion.

A harmonic motion is categorized as a simple harmonic motion (S.H.M.) if it satisfies the following conditions.

1. The acceleration of the body is always directed towards its mean position. In other words a restoring force acts on the body directed always towards the mean position. In the oscillations of a simple pendulum tangential component of gravitational force is always directed towards the mean position.
2. The magnitude of acceleration (a) is directly proportional to the displacement (x) of the body from its mean position. Since the acceleration at any given position is directed towards the mean position and the displacement is considered away from the mean position, we have

$$\vec{a} \propto -\vec{x}$$

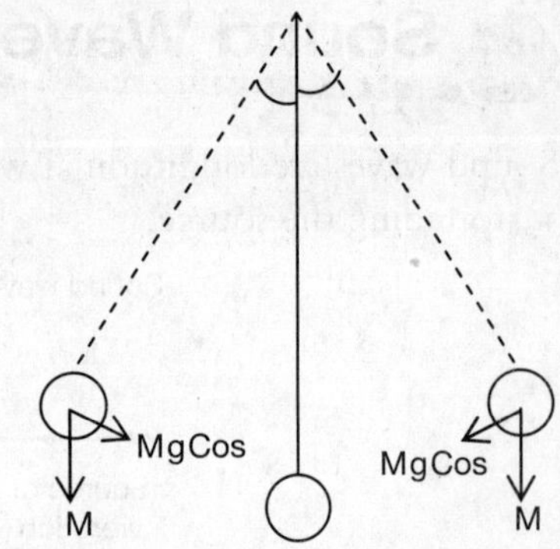

Figure 4.10 Simple harmonic motion of a pendulum

A simple harmonic motion is particularly characterized by (1) constant time-period (T), which also implies a constant frequency ν (Greek letter '*nu*') (2) a constant amplitude and (3) a constant total mechanical energy, i.e., the sum total of kinetic energy and potential energy is same at every point on its path. The bob of a simple pendulum has kinetic energy at its mean position which is conserved as potential energy at it extreme positions.

Graphical Representation of SHM

When we plot displacement time graph of a body suspended freely from a spring executing free oscillations, we get a curve as shown in the Fig. 4.11.

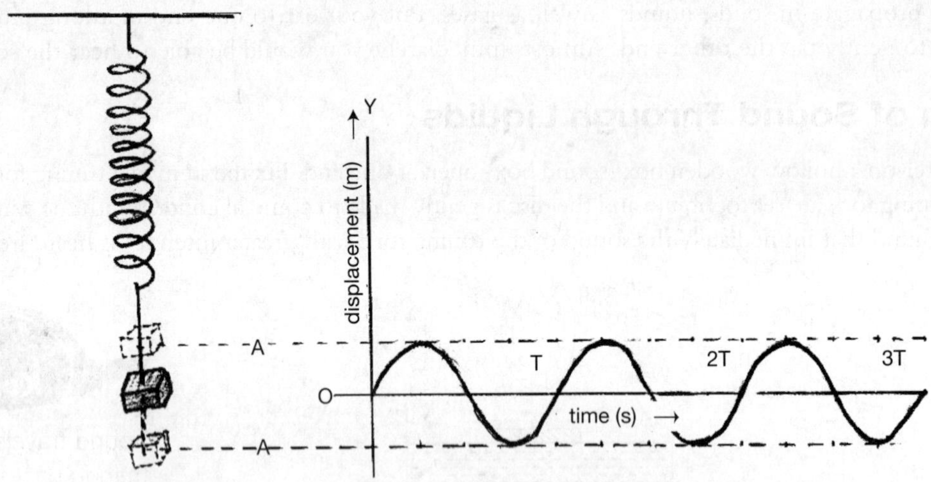

Figure 4.11 Graphical representation of simple harmonic motion

We find that the curve is in the form of a wave. Displacement–time graph of the particles in a transverse wave (water surface) and the pressure–time graph of a longitudinal wave are also similar to this graph.

1. **Displacement–time graph for a longitudinal wave propagation.**

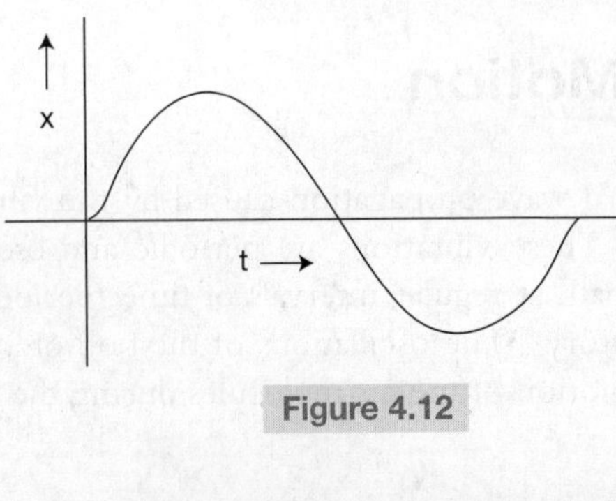

Figure 4.12

2. Pressure–time graph for a sound wave.

The crest in a transverse wave corresponds to a compression in a longitudinal wave, and the trough corresponds to the rarefaction.

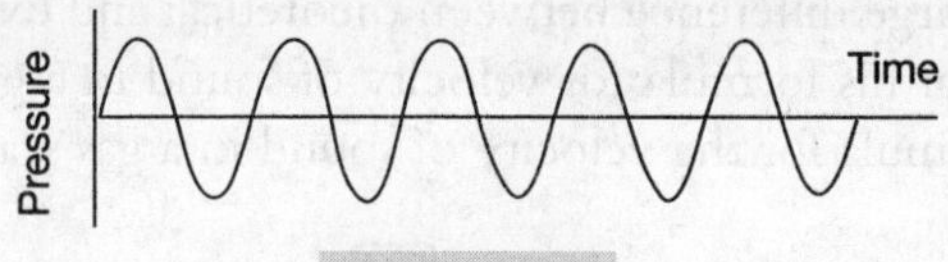

Figure 4.13

If T is the time-period of oscillations and λ is the wavelength of the wave propagating, then the velocity (v) of the wave propagation is given by,

$$V = \frac{\lambda}{T}$$

Since

$$\frac{1}{T} = n$$

$$V = \lambda n$$

Velocity of Sound

Expression for the velocity of sound waves in a medium was given by Sir Isaac Newton as $V = \sqrt{\frac{E}{d}}$, where 'V' is the velocity of the waves, 'E' and 'd' are the elasticity and the density of the medium, respectively. The elasticity factor changes with the state of matter, i.e., solids, liquids or gases and we get the expression for the velocity of sound in the corresponding medium accordingly.

Velocity of Sound in Solids

The elasticity factor in solids is given by Young's modulus (Y), and so, the expression for the velocity of sound in solids is given as

$$V = \sqrt{\frac{E}{d}},$$

where 'Y' and 'd' are Young's modulus of elasticity and density of the given solid medium, respectively.

Velocity of Sound in Liquids

The elasticity factor in liquids is taken as its bulk modulus of elasticity (K), and so, the expression for the velocity of sound in liquids is given as

$$V = \sqrt{\frac{K}{d}},$$

where, 'K' and 'd' are the bulk modulus of elasticity and the density of the liquid, respectively.

Velocity of Sound in Gases

The elasticity factor in a gas is, also bulk modulus which is equal to its pressure. Thus, the Newton's formula for the velocity of sound in a gas changes to

$$V = \sqrt{\frac{P}{d}},$$

Info Bytes!

- The fastest speed of sound recorded in a solid is 12,000 meters per second in diamond!
- Sound travels at about 1,500 meters per second in seawater, much faster than in air.
- Helium can speed up the velocity of sound, making your voice sound funny when you inhale it.

where, 'P' and 'd' are pressure and density of the given gas. On theoretical calculation, at normal temperature, velocity of sound in air (a mixture of gases) using Newton's formula was obtained as 280 m s^{-1} whereas experimental value was found to be nearly 330 m s^{-1}. Owing to the large difference between theoretical and experimental values of velocity of sound in air, Newton's assumptions in arriving at his formula for velocity of sound in a given gas were reviewed and a correction was made by Laplace. Thereby, the formula for the velocity of sound in a gas was given as

$$V = \sqrt{\frac{\gamma P}{d}},$$

where, 'γ' is a constant for a given gas and is defined as the ratio of the specific heat capacity of the given gas at constant pressure (C_p) to its specific heat capacity at constant volume (C_v).

Factors Affecting the Velocity of Sound in a Gas

1. **Absolute Temperature of Gas:** The velocity of sound in a gas is directly proportional to the square root of its absolute temperature. Mathematically, $V \propto \sqrt{T}$ where 'V' is the velocity of sound in a gas and 'T' is its absolute temperature. If 'V_1' and 'V_2' are the velocities of sound in a gas at absolute temperatures 'T_1' and 'T_2', respectively, then

$$V_2 = K\sqrt{T_1} \qquad (4.1)$$

$$\text{and } V_2 = K\sqrt{T_2}. \qquad (4.2)$$

On Dividing (4.1) by (4.2),

we get $$\frac{V_1}{V_2} = \sqrt{\frac{T_1}{T_2}}$$

2. **Density of a Gas:** The velocity of sound in a gas is inversely proportional to the square root of its density. Mathematically,

$$V \propto \frac{1}{\sqrt{d}}$$

where, 'V' is the velocity of sound in a gas and 'd' is its density. If 'V_1' and 'V_2' are the velocities of sound in two gases having densities 'd_1' and 'd_2', respectively, other parameters of the gases being constant, then $\frac{V_1}{V_2} \propto \sqrt{\frac{d_2}{d_1}}$.

3. **Molecular Weight of a Gas:** The velocity of sound in a gas is inversely proportional to the square root of its molecular weight. Mathematically,

$$V \propto \frac{1}{\sqrt{M}},$$

where, 'V' and 'M' are the velocity of sound in a gas and the molecular weight of the given gas, respectively. If 'V_1' and 'V_2' are the velocities of sound in two gases whose molecular weights are 'M_1' and 'M_2', respectively, the other parameters of gases being constant, then

$$\frac{V_1}{V_2} = \sqrt{\frac{M_2}{M_1}}.$$

Factors that do not Affect Velocity of Sound in a Gas

1. **Pressure of a Gas:** When the pressure of a gas is changed at a constant temperature, its density also changes accordingly such that the ratio 'P/d' is always a constant. For a given gas, the value of 'γ' is also constant. So, the variation in the pressure of a gas does not affect the velocity of sound in it, provided its temperature is kept constant.
2. **Amplitude:** Amplitude is the maximum displacement of a vibrating particle from its mean position. The amplitude of a sound wave in a medium does not affect its velocity.
3. **Frequency:** Frequency is the number of waves produced per second. The velocity of sound in a gas or any medium does not depend on its frequency.
4. **Wavelength:** Wavelength is the distance between two successive particles of a medium which are vibrating in phase. The velocity of a wave in a medium does not depend on the wavelength of the wave.

The Velocity of Sound in Air

Air is a mixture of gases. So, the factors that affect the velocity of sound in gases also affect the velocity of sound in air. If V_0 and V_t are the velocities of sound in air at 0°C and t°C, respectively, then they are related as

$$V_t = V_0\left(1+\frac{t}{546}\right).$$

Another factor (to be considered) which affects the velocity of sound in air is humidity. Humidity is the amount of water vapour present in air. The presence of humidity decreases the density of air. So, higher the humidity, less is the density of air and more is the velocity of sound in it. Thus, the velocity of sound in air increases as the humidity in air increases.

Relation among Velocity, Wavelength and Frequency of Sound

In one time period (T), a sound wave advances in a medium by one wavelength (λ). So, the velocity of sound in the given medium is given by,

$$V = \frac{S(\text{distance})}{t(\text{time})} = \frac{\lambda}{T}$$

But as $\frac{1}{T} = n$, the frequency of sound, we have, $V = n\lambda$.

Reflection of Sound

Echo

Like the light waves, sound waves also undergo reflection on striking a hard surface. The reflected sound is known as an echo.

When a person makes a sound in front of a big wall, he hears two sounds, one produced by him and the other is the reflected sound. The person can hear the two sounds distinctly if they reach his ear with a time gap of at least 0.1 s. This is known as **persistence of hearing**. Consider a person standing at 'P' at a distance 'd' from a wall (reflector of sound) as shown in Fig. 4.14.

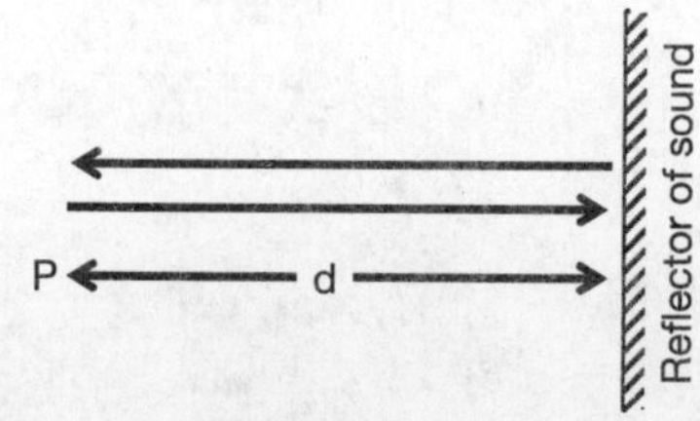

Figure 4.14 Echo

The person produces a sound and hears an echo after 't' seconds. Then the velocity of sound in air is given by the expression, $V = \frac{2d}{t}$. If the velocity of sound is known, the distance between the person and the reflector is given by, $d = \frac{Vt}{2}$. Since the persistence of hearing (the minimum time gap between two sounds reaching the ear) is 0.1 second, the minimum distance required to hear an echo $= \frac{V(0.1)}{2} = \frac{V}{20}\text{m.} \simeq \frac{340\text{m}}{20} \simeq 17\text{m.}$

Applications of Reflection of Sound (Echo)

1. Echo can be used to find out the velocity of sound in air.
2. The reflection of sound can be used in instruments like megaphone and in hearing aids.
3. The reflection of sound is used in sound boards and whispering galleries.
4. The reflection of sound is an important phenomenon used in SONAR, which is a special technique to find the depth of ocean beds.
5. Bats produce ultrasonics and can even sense their reflections from objects. With the help of this phenomenon, they can move even in darkness.

Determination of Velocity of Sound in Air by Echo Method

Consider a person standing at position 'P' in the front of a wall (reflector of sound) (R). He produces a sound and hears the echo after 't_1' seconds. He then moves to a new position 'Q' towards the reflector by a distance 'd' in a direction normal to it. Now, he produces the sound again and hears the echo after 't_2' seconds.

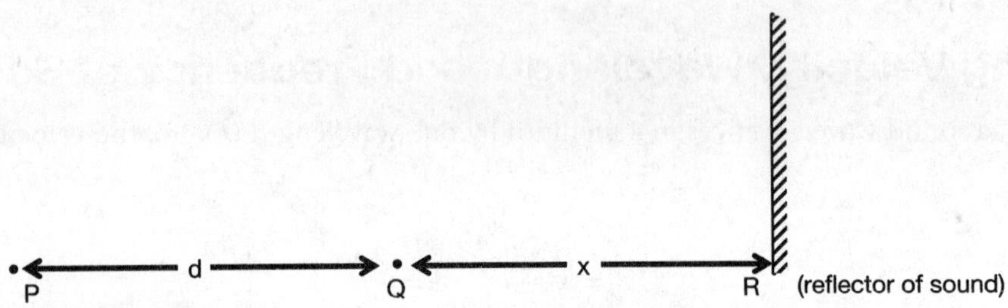

Figure 4.15 Determining the velocity of sound in air by echo method

If the velocity of sound in air is 'V', then $V = \frac{2(d+x)}{t_1}$ and also $V = \frac{2(x)}{t_2}$

$$\therefore\ Vt_1 = 2d + 2x \text{ and } Vt_2 = 2x$$

$$\therefore\ Vt_1 = 2d + Vt_2$$

$$\therefore\ V(t_1 - t_2) = 2d$$

or

$$V = \frac{2d}{t_1 - t_2}$$

Reverberation

Consider a source and an observer of sound placed in a closed room as shown in Fig. 4.16. The observer hears the sound that travels not only directly from the source, but also indirectly from a series of reflections taking place at the walls of the room. So, the observer can hear the sound even after the source has stopped producing it due to multiple reflections taking place at the walls of the enclosure. This phenomenon is known as '**reverberation**'. Reverberations are often heard in empty halls, theatres and auditoriums.

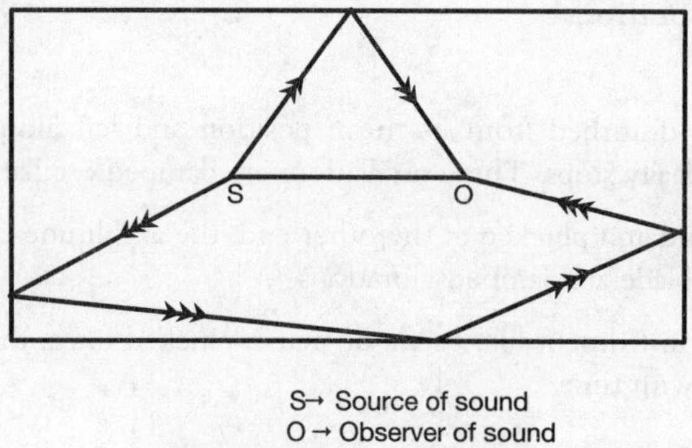

Figure 4.16 Reverberation

Acoustics

Taking the effects of echo and reverberation into consideration in designing an auditorium and the interior of buildings is called acoustics. The time required to reduce the intensity of sound to one millionth of its initial value is called reverberation time. This time plays an important role in designing an auditorium. Generally a reverberation time of 0.5 is considered as optimum value for speeches whereas for good acoustic effect in a music hall, a reverberation time of 2 to 2.5 is taken into consideration. Reflecting surfaces like walls and ceiling are covered with good sound absorbing materials and the floor is carpeted. Curtains and sound-absorbing hangings are also used for better acoustic effect.

Natural Vibrations

If a body is set into vibrations and allowed to vibrate on its own, the vibrations of the body are known as '**natural**' or '**free vibrations**'. The frequency with which the body vibrates is known as natural frequency and the corresponding time period is known as natural time period.

Examples:

1. The strings of musical instruments that vibrate freely when plucked.
2. Oscillating pendulum that is suspended freely.
3. A blade clamped at one end and plucked at the other end.
4. A tuning fork when hit by a rubber hammer.

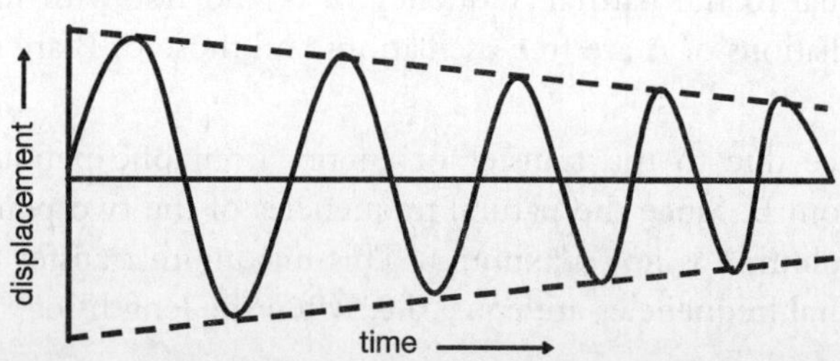

Figure 4.17 Displacement versus time graph for damped vibration

Damped Vibrations

When a pebble is thrown on the surface of still water, ripples are formed and these ripples travel in all possible directions. As the ripples move away from the source of disturbance, we observe that the amplitude of the waves decreases continuously and finally the wave vanishes. This 'damping' of the wave takes place because the medium itself absorbs the energy of the wave that is propagated in the medium.

The vibrations whose amplitude progressively decreases with time or with position or with both as the wave is propagated in a medium are called '**damped vibrations**'.

Examples:

1. When a simple pendulum is disturbed from its mean position and left alone, the amplitude of the pendulum decreases with time and eventually stops. These oscillations are damped oscillations.
2. If a blade is clamped at one end and plucked at the other end, the amplitude of the vibrating blade decreases with time. These vibrations of the blade are damped vibrations.
3. When the string of a musical instrument like veena or sitar is plucked once, the amplitude of the vibrations in the string progressively decreases with time.

Forced Vibrations

If a body is set into vibrations by the influence of another vibrating body or an external periodic force, the vibrations executed by the former are known as **forced vibrations**.

Examples:

1. The vibrations executed by the pendulum of a clock are forced vibrations as they are caused under the influence of a main spring which is wound.
2. Musical instruments with strings contain hollow sound boxes. When a string of an instrument like veena is plucked, the sound produced by the vibrating string causes the air in the sound box to vibrate at the same frequency as the string and a loud sound is heard. The vibrations of air in the sound box are forced vibrations.

Resonance

Consider two simple pendula A and B of different lengths ($\ell_A > \ell_B$) suspended from an elastic, rigid support like a thin rod as shown in Fig. 4.18. Since the natural frequency of a simple pendulum is inversely proportional to the square root of its length, the natural frequency of A (n_A) is less than that of B (n_B). When only pendulum B is made to oscillate, we observe that after some time, pendulum A also begins to oscillate under the influence of B. So, vibrations of A are forced vibrations. Now since A is oscilliating under the influence of B, it will oscillate with the frequency of B and not with its own natural frequency.

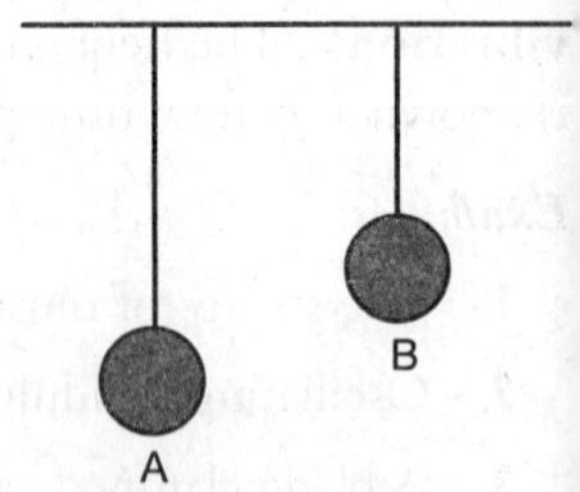

Figure 4.18 Two simple pendula of different lengths

Similarly, if B is at rest and A is set into oscillations, after some time, we observe that B also oscillates with a frequency equal to the natural frequency of A and not with its own natural frequency. So, here the oscillations of A are free oscillations and those of B are forced oscillations.

The forced oscillations take place due to the transfer of energy from one pendulum to another. If A has forced oscillations, it will derive energy from B. Since the natural frequencies of the two pendula are not equal, the transfer of energy from pendulum B to pendulum A is not maximum. This maximum transfer of energy from one pendulum to another takes place when their natural frequencies are equal, i.e.,when the lengths of the two pendula are equal.

Consider two pendula C and D of equal length suspended from an elastic rigid support as shown in Fig. 4.19. As they have equal length, their natural frequencies are also equal. If one of them, say C is set into oscillations, the other being at rest; the second pendulum D too oscillates after sometime. The pendulum D oscillates with the maximum possible amplitude because both C and D have the same natural frequency and so, energy transmitted from C to D is the maximum. This phenomenon is known as '**resonance**'.

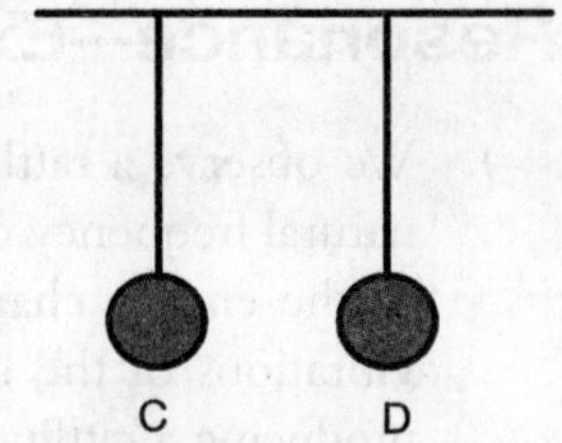

Figure 4.19 Two simple pendula of same length

Thus, resonance can be defined as "the phenomenon in which when one of the two bodies having confusing natural frequencies is set into vibration, then under its influence the other body also vibrates with increased amplitude".

Resonance in Sound Boxes

Consider two hollow boxes P and Q with one end open placed adjacent to each other, such that their open ends face each other. Two tuning forks A and B having equal frequencies are fixed on boxes P and Q, respectively. A pith ball suspended from a hook is in contact with the fork B as shown in Fig. 4.20.

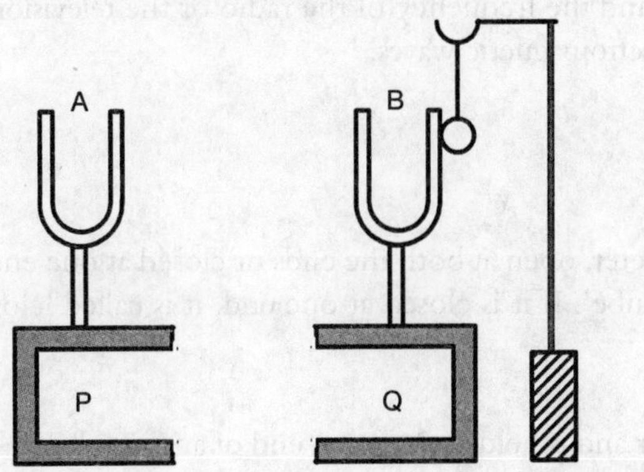

Figure 4.20 Apparatus to find resonance in sound boxes

Info Bytes!

The Tacoma Narrows Bridge collapse in 1940 is a famous example of the power of resonance.

When the fork A is struck gently with a rubber hammer, it vibrates and after some time, we observe that the pith ball which is in contact with fork B flies outward, indicating that fork B too vibrates with maximum amplitude. At the same time, a loud booming sound is heard. This is due to the resonance between the two forks A and B.

The vibrations of the fork A produce forced vibrations in the box P, which produce forced vibrations in the air in the box Q. These vibrations of air lead to vibrations in the box Q and through it to the fork B. Since the two forks, A and B are of equal frequency, maximum energy transfer takes place, and thus, B is in resonance with A. The vibrations of B which are forced vibrations and in resonance with those of A, are also known as '**sympathetic vibrations**'.

Condition for Resonance

1. The vibrations of a body causing resonance should be strong enough to set forced vibrations in the other body.

Examples: A single soldier marching on a rope bridge cannot cause sympathetic vibrations in the bridge, but a large group of soldiers marching to rhythmic steps on the bridge could cause the bridge to collapse.

2. The natural frequency of the given body (*A*) causing vibrations must be equal to either the natural frequency or an integral multiple of the natural frequency of the vibrating body (*B*).

Examples: The resonance in air columns takes place only at certain lengths of the air columns that correspond to the resonating lengths.

Resonance—Examples and Applications

1. We observe a rattling sound in a bus when the natural frequency of vibrations of the body of the bus equals the natural frequency of the vibrations of its engine. When the speed of the bus changes, the frequency of the vibrations of the engine changes. When this frequency of the vibrations of the engine equals the natural frequency of the vibrations of the body of the bus, both are in resonance and the body of the bus vibrates with larger amplitude producing a rattling sound.
2. When a group of soldiers march across a rope bridge, they are asked to march out of step. This is because, when they march in step across the bridge, the natural frequency of the rhythmic marching of soldiers may become equal to the natural frequency of the vibrations in the bridge. If this happens, resonance takes place between the marching soldiers and the bridge which then vibrates with maximum amplitude leading to its collapse.
3. A wine glass kept before a loudspeaker vibrates to the musical notes emitted by the speaker. When the frequency of the musical note is equal to the frequency of the vibrating wine glass, resonance takes place and the glass vibrates with larger amplitude. This may topple or even brake the glass.
4. The basic principle involved in the transmission of radio and television programmes is resonance between the frequency of signals emitted from the station and the frequency of the radio or the television set. The resonance that takes place here is not of sound waves but of electromagnetic waves.

Resonance in Air Columns

Air Column

A long tube about 40 cm in length and 6 cm in diameter, open at both the ends or closed at one end forms an 'air column'. If it is open at both the ends, it is called 'open end tube'. If it is closed at one end, it is called 'closed end tube'.

Resonating Air Column

When a tuning fork is excited with a rubber hammer and is held at the open end of an air column such that the vibrating prongs are perpendicular to the length of the air column, as shown in Fig. 4.21, the air in the tube vibrates (forced vibrations). If the natural frequency of the air column matches with that of the tuning fork, a loud sound is produced. This happens as the vibrating air column is in resonance with the given tuning fork. The air column in this condition is known as 'resonating air column'.

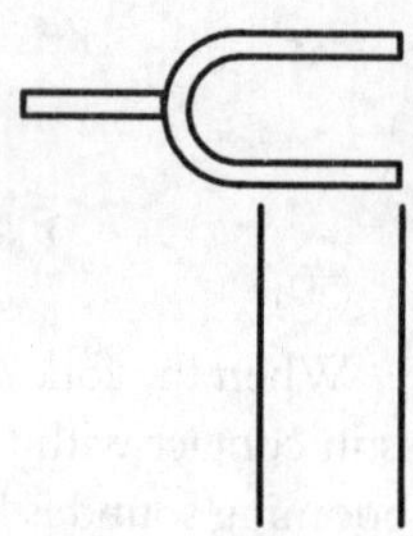

Figure 4.21 A tuning fork placed perpendicular to vibrating prongs

Closed End Resonating Air Column

Consider a long cylindrical glass jar of length of about 50 cm and 6 cm diameter, filled with water to more than (3/4) th of its height as shown in the Fig. 4.22. Let a glass tube of smaller diameter (say 2 cm) and length approximately about 40 cm and open at both ends be inserted into the jar as shown in the Fig. 4.22. The length of the smaller tube above the water level in the jar can be adjusted, thus, varying the length of the air column above the water surface in the smaller tube.

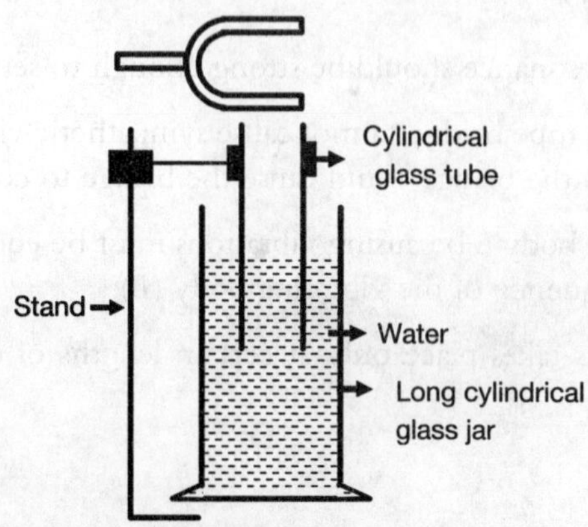

Figure 4.22 Closed end resonating air column

When a vibrating tuning fork is held horizontally above the open end of the smaller tube, it sets vibrations in the air in the tube, thus, producing forced vibrations in the air column. The other end of the smaller tube being immersed in water jar, the water surface acts as a reflecting surface to the waves set in the air column. Thus, the smaller tube acts as a closed-end tube.

The compressions and rarefactions formed at the open end by the vibrating tuning fork travel towards the water surface, get reflected and again travel back towards the open end. So, the incident and reflected waves superpose each other to form stationary longitudinal waves in the air column. At the open end of the air column, the particles are free to vibrate. So, this end corresponds to a rarefaction. The closed end (water surface) is rigid and the air particles at this location are not free enough to vibrate longitudinally (along the length of the tube). So, at the closed end, a compression is formed.

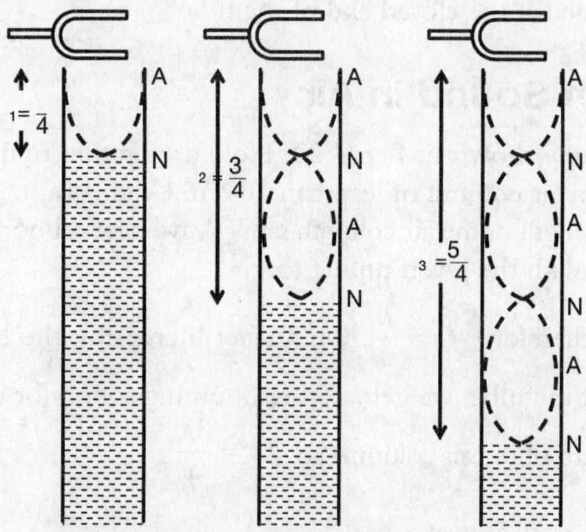

Figure 4.23 Resonating air columns

The length of the air column can be adjusted and when it is equal to ($\lambda/4$) where 'λ' is the wavelength of the sound wave, resonance occurs between the tuning fork and the air column. This can be confirmed by a loud (booming) sound heard. The length of the air column is the '**first resonating length**' of the air column. It is observed that resonance takes place whenever the length of the air column is an odd integral multiple of '($\pi/4$)'. The general expression for resonating length of an air column is given by,

$$\ell n = \frac{(2n-1)\lambda}{4}$$

where $n = 1, 2, 3, ---$. Thus, for a given tuning fork of a certain frequency, the resonating lengths of air column are

1st resonating length, $\ell_1 = \frac{(2\times 1-1)\lambda}{4} = \frac{\lambda}{4}$;

2nd resonating length, $\ell_2 = \frac{(2\times 2-1)\lambda}{4} = \frac{3\lambda}{4}$;

3rd resonating length, $\ell_3 = \frac{(2\times 3-1)\lambda}{4} = \frac{5\lambda}{4}$; and so on.

When the reflection of a sound wave takes place at the water surface in the closed tube, phase change does not take place at the instant of reflection. Thus, a compression is reflected as compression and a rarefaction is reflected as rarefaction. As these reflected compressions or rarefactions reach the open end of the tube, phase change occurs. The reflected compression becomes rarefaction and the reflected rarefaction becomes compression on reaching the open end. This occurs due to the volume changes of air taking place in the tube.

As a reflected rarefaction reaches the open end, due to low pressure, some of the air is pushed into the tube making a compression. Similarly, as a reflected compression reaches the open end, due to excess pressure, some of the air is pushed out of the tube creating a rarefaction. When such a rarefaction reaches the mouth of the tube, another rarefaction is produced by the tuning fork at the mouth, therefore, these two rarefactions superpose giving the maximum amplitude and an antinode is formed at the mouth of the tube.

Similarly, when a compression reaches the mouth of the tube, another compression is produced by the tuning fork at the mouth of the tube, therefore, these two compressions superpose giving the maximum amplitude, and so, an antinode is formed at the mouth of the tube.

Thus, "whenever resonance occurs between the vibrating air column and the tuning fork, an antinode is formed at the mouth of the tube and a node is formed at the closed end of the tube".

Resonance—Velocity of Sound in Air

Consider the glass jar and the glass tube shown in Fig. 4.22. Hold a vibrating tuning fork of frequency 'n' horizontally over the mouth of the tube, having an air column of less than 10 cm. Gradually, increase the length of the air column by raising the tube and at one particular length of the air column, say 'ℓ_1', we hear a booming sound indicating that the length 'ℓ_1' of the air column is in resonance with the given tuning fork.

This is the first resonating length, therefore, $\ell_1 = \frac{\lambda}{4}$. On further increasing the length of the air column, holding the vibrating tuning fork at the mouth of the tube, we get another booming sound for the air column of length, say 'ℓ_2' such that this is the second resonating length of the air column. So, $\ell_2 = \frac{3\lambda}{4}$.

Thus, $$\ell_2 - \ell_1 = \frac{3\lambda}{4} - \frac{\lambda}{4} = \frac{2\lambda}{4} = \frac{\lambda}{2} \therefore \lambda = 2(\ell_2 - \ell_1)$$

If 'n' is the frequency of the tuning fork, and 'v' is the velocity of sound in air, we have $v = n\lambda = n_2(\ell_2 - \ell_1)$ $\therefore v = 2n(\ell_2 - \ell_1)$. From the above expression, we can find out the velocity of sound in air at room temperature.

Resonance in Open Organ Pipe

Resonance of sound can take place in open organ pipes also. An open organ pipe is a tube with both ends open, and in this case both the ends correspond to antinodes. For fundamental frequency one node is formed at the centre of the pipe and the length of the tube (ℓ) corresponds to half the wavelength, being the distance between two consecutive antinodes.

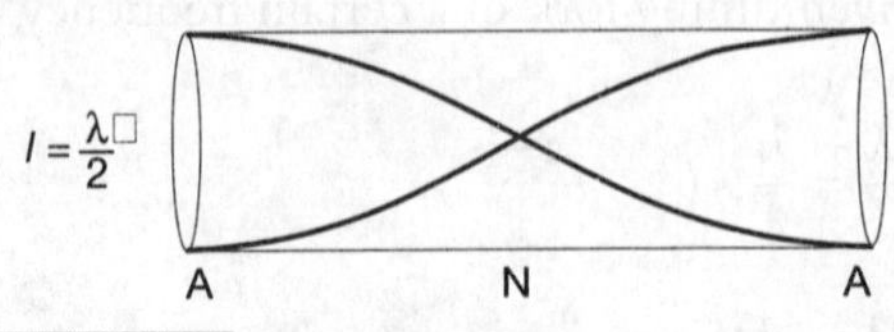

Figure 4.24 Resonance in open organ pipe

Thus, we have

$$\ell = \frac{\lambda}{2} \text{ or } \lambda = 2\ell$$

Since $v = \upsilon\lambda$,

$$\upsilon = \frac{\upsilon}{\lambda} = \frac{\upsilon}{2\ell}$$

This frequency is called 'fundamental' frequency and is denoted as $\upsilon_o = \frac{v}{2\ell}$.

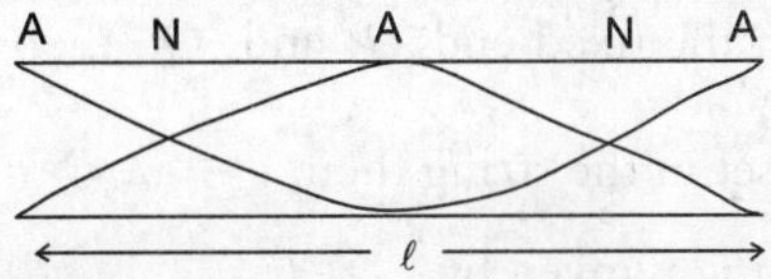

Figure 4.25 First overtone in open organ pipe

For the first overtone or second harmonic, two nodes are formed inside the tube. In this case the length of the tube corresponds to λ, the wavelength, as shown in the Fig. 4.25.

$\therefore \ell = \lambda$ and $$\upsilon_1 = \frac{v}{\ell} = 2\upsilon_o$$

Hence, υ_1, the frequency of the first overtone is twice the fundamental frequency, υ_0.

The second overtone or the third harmonic is produced when three nodes are formed inside the tube as shown. A total of four antinodes are formed such that ℓ, the length of the tube corresponds to $(3\lambda/2)$. Thus, we have

$$\ell = \frac{3\lambda}{2} \text{ or } \lambda = \frac{2\ell}{3}$$

and

$$\upsilon_2 = \frac{v}{\lambda} = \frac{3v}{2\ell} = 3\upsilon_o$$

Therefore, frequency of the second overtone is thrice the fundamental frequency.

Thus, the frequencies in an open organ pipe are in the ratio 1 : 2 : 3 indicating that all harmonics are present, whereas in a closed-end pipe the ratio of the frequencies is 1 : 3 : 5….. showing that only the odd harmonics are present.

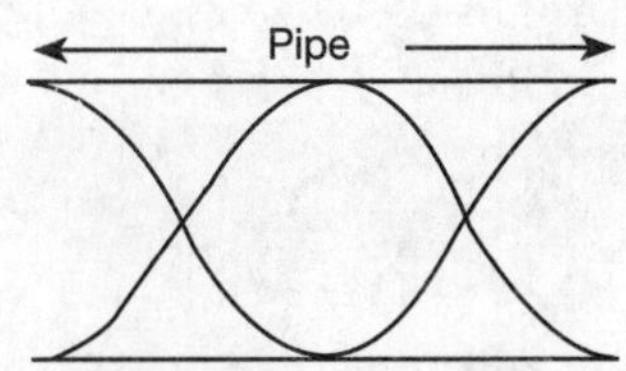

Figure 4.26 Second overtone in open organ pipe

Vibrations in Stretched Strings

A string is a thin wire or a thread which is inextensible. When such a string is stretched by applying a force that acts along the length of the wire, the force applied is known as 'tensile force' or 'tension'. When a stretched wire is plucked, stationary waves perpendicular to its length are produced.

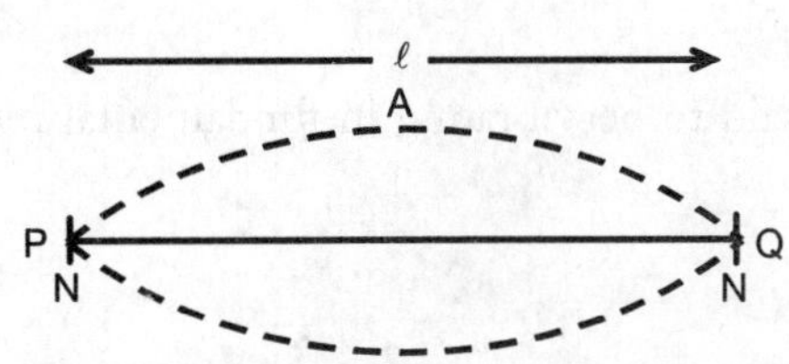

Figure 4.27 Stationary waves in strings; string vibrating in fundamental mode

Consider a string stretched between two points '*P*' and '*Q*'. When the string is plucked at the middle, a transverse stationary wave is set up in the string with nodes (*N*) at the fixed-end points '*P*' and '*Q*' and an antinode (*A*) at the middle of the string, as shown in the Fig. 4.27.

The distance between two successive nodes or antinodes in a stationary wave is equal to half the wavelength $\left(\frac{\lambda}{2}\right)$. If '$\ell$' is the length of the vibrating string between the fixed ends 'P' and 'Q', then $\ell = \frac{\lambda}{2}$ or $\lambda = 2\ \ell$. If 'n' is the frequency of vibration and 'v' is the velocity of the wave set in the string then, $v = n\lambda \Rightarrow v = n\ (2\ell)$.

But the velocity of the wave set in the string is given by,

$$v = \sqrt{\frac{T}{M}}$$

where 'T' is the tension in the string and 'm' is mass per unit length (linear density) of the string.

$$\therefore \sqrt{\frac{T}{m}} = n(2\ell)$$

or

$$n = \frac{1}{2\ell}\sqrt{\frac{T}{m}} \tag{4.3}$$

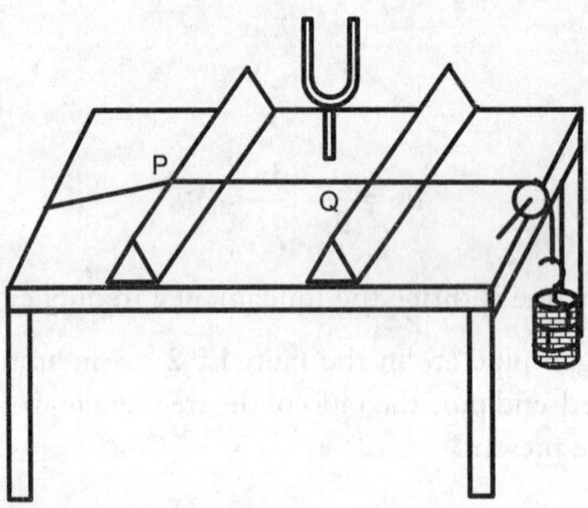

Figure 4.28 Vibrations in stretched strings by a tuning fork

If the string described above is considered to be placed on a table and stretched between two fixed points 'P' and 'Q' and a vibrating tuning fork of frequency 'n' is kept in between the fixed points 'P' and 'Q' as shown in Fig. 4.28, resonance takes place in the stretched string between 'P' and 'Q', and the tuning fork. A stationary wave is set up in the string as shown in Fig. 4.27. Then the length 'ℓ' of the string between the fixed points 'P' and 'Q' is called resonating length.

This resonating length of the string is said to be vibrating in fundamental mode and the corresponding frequency of the vibrating string, given by,

$$n = \frac{1}{2\ell}\sqrt{\frac{T}{m}},$$

is known as the fundamental frequency or first harmonic.

The length 'ℓ' of the stretched string is found to be in resonance with another higher frequency 'n_1' with the tension (T) and linear density (m) being constant. Then, the string is found to be vibrating in two segments, with two antinodes (A) and three nodes (N) as shown in Fig. 4.29. Then, the length of the vibrating stretched string is $\ell = \lambda$ and so frequency.

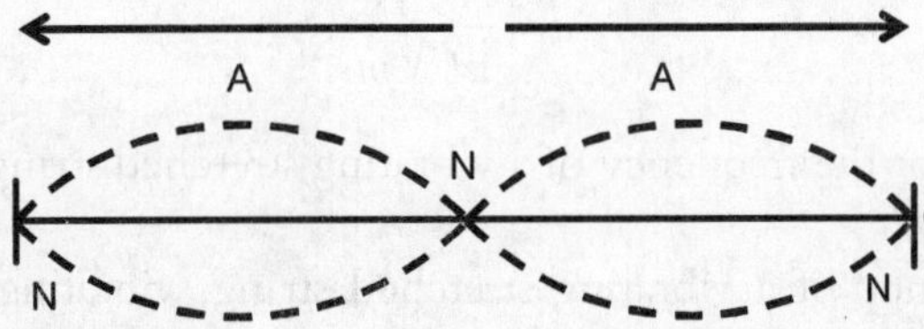

Figure 4.29 String vibrating in second harmonic

$$n_1 = \frac{1}{\ell}\sqrt{\frac{T}{m}} = \frac{2}{2\ell}\sqrt{\frac{T}{m}} = 2\left(\frac{1}{2\ell}\sqrt{\frac{T}{m}}\right) = 2n \tag{4.4}$$

So, this frequency '$n1$' is double the fundamental frequency and is called **'second harmonic' or 'first overtone'**. We get similar resonating lengths whenever length of the string

$$\ell = \frac{K\lambda}{2}$$

where $K = 1, 2, 3$ - - - -.

So, the corresponding frequencies obtained are tabulated as follows.

Table 4.2 Frequency and wavelength of vibrating string

Value of P	Length of string (ℓ)	Wavelength (λ)	Frequency	Number of loops	Description of frequency
1.	$\frac{\lambda}{2}$	$\frac{2\ell}{1}$	$n = \frac{1}{2\ell}\sqrt{\frac{T}{m}}$	One	Fundamental frequency or 1st harmonic
2.	$\frac{2\lambda}{2}$	$\frac{2\ell}{2}$	$n_1 = \frac{1}{\ell}\sqrt{\frac{T}{m}}$ $= \frac{2}{2\ell}\sqrt{\frac{T}{m}} = 2n$	Two	2nd harmonic or 1st overtone
3.	—	$\frac{2\ell}{3}$	$n_2 = \frac{1}{\left(\frac{2\ell}{3}\right)}\sqrt{\frac{T}{m}}$ $= \frac{3}{2\ell}\sqrt{\frac{T}{m}} = 3n$	Three	3rd harmonic or 2nd overtone
K	$\frac{K\lambda}{2}$	$\frac{2\ell}{K}$	$n_{k-1} = \frac{K}{2\ell}\sqrt{\frac{T}{m}}$ $= Kn$	K	Kth harmonic or $(K-1)$th overtone

Laws of Vibrating Stretched Strings

The expression for the fundamental frequency of a stretched vibrating string is given by,

$$n = \frac{1}{2\ell}\sqrt{\frac{T}{m}}.$$

From this, three laws are derived for the frequency of a vibrating stretched string and are as follows.

1. **Law of Length:** The frequency of a vibrating stretched string, vibrating in a fundamental mode, is inversely proportional to its length, when its tension and linear density are constant. Mathematically, $n \propto \frac{1}{\ell}$ when 'T' and 'm' are constant. $\Rightarrow n\ell$ = constant.

   If 'ℓ_1' and 'ℓ_2' are the lengths of two strings vibrating in the fundamental frequency having their linear density and tension constant and 'n_1' and 'n_2' are their fundamental frequencies, respectively, then $n_1 \ell_1 = n_2 \ell_2$

2. **Law of Tension:** The frequency of a vibrating stretched string, vibrating in a fundamental mode, is directly proportional to the square root of its tension, when length and linear density remain constant. Mathematically, $n \propto \sqrt{T}$, when 'ℓ' and 'm' are constant.

   $\Rightarrow \frac{n}{\sqrt{T}}$ = constant.

   If 'T_1' and 'T_2' are the tensions of two strings whose length and linear density are constant and vibrating in the fundamental mode and 'n_1' and 'n_2' are their fundamental frequencies, respectively, then $\frac{n_1}{\sqrt{T_1}} = \frac{n_2}{\sqrt{T_2}}$.

3. **Law of Linear Density:** The frequency of a vibrating stretched string, vibrating in a fundamental mode, is inversely proportional to the square root of its linear density, when its length and tension are constant. Mathematically, $n \propto \frac{1}{\sqrt{m}}$ when 'ℓ' and 'T' are constant.

   $\Rightarrow n\sqrt{m}$ = constant.

   If 'm_1' and 'm_2' are the linear densities of two strings vibrating in fundamental mode having equal length and tension and 'n_1' and 'n_2' are their fundamental frequencies, respectively, then $n_1\sqrt{m_1} = n_2\sqrt{m_2}$.

Sonometer

It is a hollow wooden box about one metre long on which a peg is fixed at one end and a smooth frictionless pulley is fixed at the other end on the top surface which is also called sonometer table as shown in the Fig. 4.30. Wedge-shaped wooden pieces known as bridges are placed on the table and they are movable. At one end of the Sonometer table, along its length, a metre scale is fixed. A string is tied at one end to the peg and other end is passed over the two bridges and the pulley, and attached to a weighted hanger. The weights attached to the hanger provide tension in the string. On the lateral walls of the sonometer box, holes are provided.

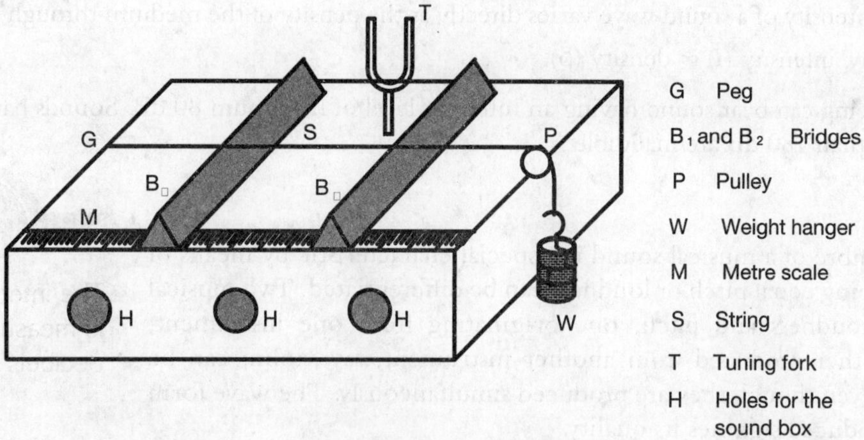

Figure 4.30 Sonometer

Sonometer is used to verify the laws of transverse vibrations in a stretched string. Excite a tuning fork of frequency 'n_1' and keep it on the sonometer table between the bridges as shown in Fig. 4.30. Adjust the distance between the bridges to change the length of the vibrating string between the bridges. At a particular length, say 'ℓ_1', the wire between the bridges vibrates with maximum amplitude and this can be confirmed by the flying away of a small paper rider of light weight and inverted *V*–shape (Λ) placed on the string between the bridges. Then, the length 'ℓ_1' of the wire is in resonance with the tuning fork. The procedure is repeated by taking another tuning fork of frequency 'n_2' and the resonating length 'ℓ_2' is obtained. The first law of vibrating stretched strings is verified by showing $n_1\ell_1 = n_2\ell_2$. Similarly, other two laws of vibrating stretched string can also be verified.

Music and Noise

Sound that causes a pleasing sensation to ears is called music. Sound that causes an unpleasant or irritating sensation to ears is called noise. A sound cannot be strictly classified into either music or noise, as a sound that causes a pleasing sensation to one person can cause an unpleasant sensation to another person. But based on certain characteristics, we can broadly classify any sound note into either music or noise.

Characteristics of Musical Sound

Pitch

It is a special characteristic of sound based on which we can differentiate between two sounds having equal loudness. The pitch of a given sound can be measured by its frequency.

Example: Female voices in general are high pitched compared to male voices though both the female voice and the male voice may have equal loudness.

Intensity

Intensity is a measure of loudness of sound. It is defined as the energy that passes through unit area per unit time.

The following are the factors on which the intensity of sound depends.

1. **Amplitude:** The intensity of a sound wave varies directly as the square of its amplitude. Mathematically, intensity (I) $\propto$ (amplitude)^2.
2. **Distance from Source:** The intensity of a sound wave varies inversely as the square of the distance of the point of observation from the source.

   Mathematically, intensity (I) $\propto \dfrac{1}{(\text{distance})^2}$

3. **Density:** The intensity of a sound wave varies directly as the density of the medium through which it is propagated.

   Mathematically, intensity (I) $\propto$ density (ρ).

A normal human being can bear sound having an intensity level of maximum 80 dB. Sounds having intensity level less than 10 dB and more than 180 dB are inaudible.

Quality or Timbre

The quality or the timbre of a musical sound is a special characteristic by means of which two sounds having equal pitch or loudness can be differentiated. Two musical notes having equal loudness and pitch, one originating from one instrument, say veena; and the other produced from another instrument, say violin; can be identified separately even though they are produced simultaneously. The wave form of the sound note produced signifies its quality.

Konnect

The intensity level of sound is measured in units of decibels (dB).

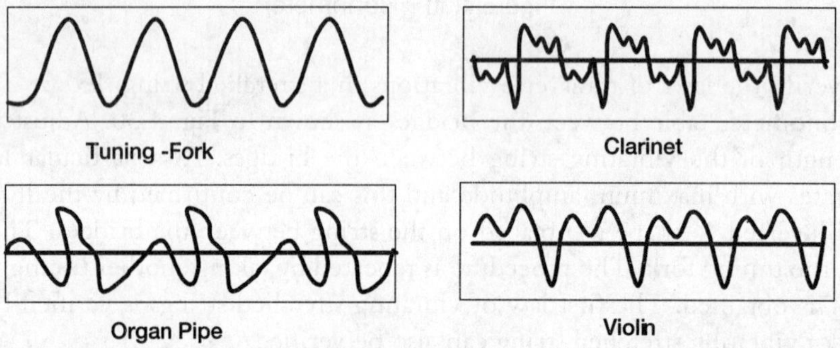

Figure 4.31 Quality of a sound by different musical instruments

Difference between Music and Noise

1. Music produces a pleasing effect whereas noise produces an irritating effect in our ears.
2. Music has variations in amplitude or frequency at regular intervals of time whereas in noise, the variations in amplitude or frequency are abrupt.
3. Musical sound has a definite waveform which repeats itself at regular intervals of time; whereas noise does not have any regular or definite waveform.

Drum

It is an instrument that produces sound by vibrating membrane. It is a hollow cylindrical box to which the processed skin of animals (leather) is attached at sides like a membrane. The membranes are stretched and then excited at any point on the membrane to produce sound.

Bell

A cone shaped metallic object, which produces sound when excited is known as a bell. It has a complex mode of vibration. When a bell is struck at its edge, it is divided into an even number of vibrating sectors and it produces transverse stationary waves.

Pollution Due to Noise

Noise, in general, disturbs the regular work. It causes strain, irritation, etc. Thus, noise is undesirable and uncomfortable and can be considered as a pollution.

The undesirable unaudible, harsh and irritating sound produced in the surroundings is called noise pollution. The noise which can be called pollution depends on its (1) loudness (2) duration.

Effects of Noise Pollution

1. It disturbs the normal work, conversations.
2. It produces irritation, strain, headache, etc.
3. Very loud noise may cause temporary or permanent deafness.
4. Noise may also create night blindness and colour blindness.

Sources of Noise Pollution

Grinders, mixers, vacuum cleaners using at home, loudspeakers, exploding crackers in various functions, hawkers in streets, various machines used in factories create a large amount of noise in our surroundings. Along with these, various transportation means such as trains, buses, air crafts, etc., also create noise pollution.

Controlling of Noise Pollution

Nowadays, in modern society, it is not easy to eliminate the noise pollution but by taking some measures and precautions, it can be decreased. Various means that can be followed are:

1. The volume levels of various audio-video systems should be lowered, as much as possible.
2. The factories and various industries should be established very far from residential areas.
3. It is better to ban the various musical entertainments in public places.
4. The vehicles that produce loud sound should not be allowed in residential areas.
5. All machines, automobiles, generators, motors should be designed in such a way that less noise is produced.

Recording and Reproduction of Sound

Sound can be recorded and can be reproduced, when it is desired. Microphone is an instrument which can convert sound vibrations into electrical signals. These electrical signals can be converted back to sound by using loudspeakers. The recording of sound can be done either on magnetic tapes or photosensitive films.

> **Info Bytes!**
>
> The first sound recording device, called the phonautograph, was invented in 1857.

Recording and Reproduction of Sound by Using Magnetic Tapes

The tape is very thin, flexible and usually made of polyvinyl chloride. One side of it is coated with ferric oxide (Fe_2O_3) paste. Before recording any sound, the molecules of magnetic paste align such that the net magnetic moment is zero.

Sound Recording

The major part of the sound recording equipment is the recording head. Recording head is a soft iron ring having a narrow gap. It is wound by an insulated conducting wire. The two ends of which are connected to an amplifier which in turn is connected to a microphone. The unrecorded magnetic tape is made to run in front of the narrow gap of recording. Microphone converts the sound vibrations created in front of it into electrical signals which are amplified by the amplifier.

When these signals are made to pass through the wire wound around the recording head, it acts as an electromagnet. Due to the varying electrical signals, the magnetic field created in the narrow gap also varies and accordingly the molecules of ferric oxide realign. The amount of realignment depends on the strength of magnetic field produced.

Sound Reproduction

In sound reproduction process equipment, the major part is playback head which is similar to the recording head used in the recording process. The ends of insulated conducting wire wound around the play back head is connected to loudspeaker through an amplifier. During the reproduction the recorded tape is made to run in front of the narrow gap of the playback head. The varying magnetic impressions recorded on the tape create a varying magnetic field in the gap of the head. This produces electrical signals in the wire wound around the head. These signals are amplified by amplifier and sent to a loudspeaker which converts electric signals into sound vibrations.

Recording and Reproduction of Sound by Using Films

The sound is recorded on the photosensitive film in the form of zigzag patches called sound track. In this method a phosphor-bronze loop is suspended between the concave poles a magnet. The loop is attached by a small mirror. The mirror reflects the light coming from an intense source towards a narrow slit behind which the photosensitive film is made to run at constant speed.

The sound to be recorded is converted into electrical signals by a microphone and is passed through a phosphor-bronze loop. Due to these signals, the loop and the mirror deflect in different orientations. Depending on the amount of deflection of the mirror a zigzag patch of different widths are formed on the film.

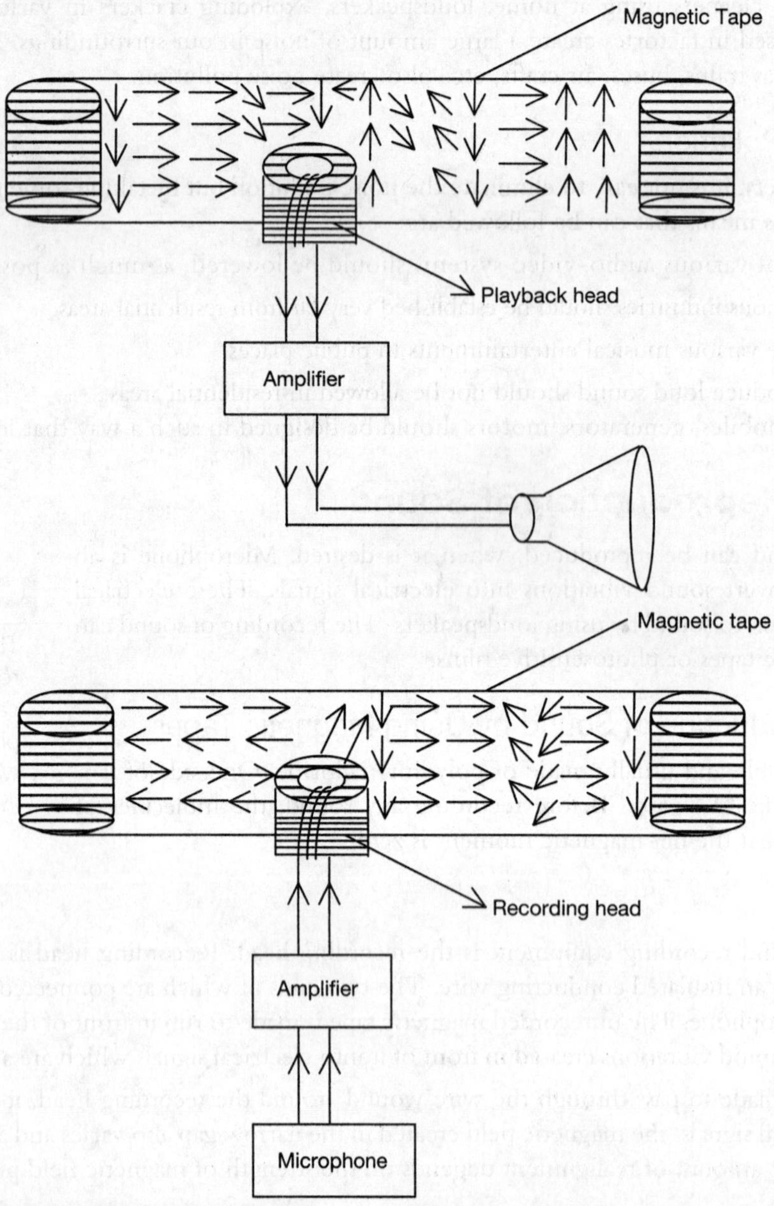

Figure 4.32 Recording and reproduction of sound by using films

Sound Reproduction

The sound track is exposed to the light coming from an intense source after passing through a converging lens system. The emergent light is allowed to fall on a photo cell, which works on the principle of photo electric effect. Due to variations in the intensity of light emerging from film, photo cell produces varying electric signals. These are converted into sound by using a loudspeaker.

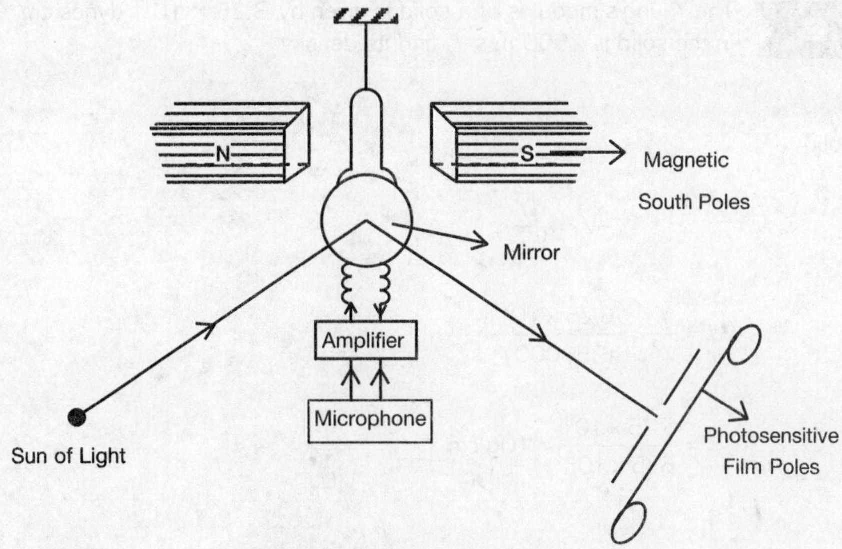

Figure 4.33 Sound reproduction

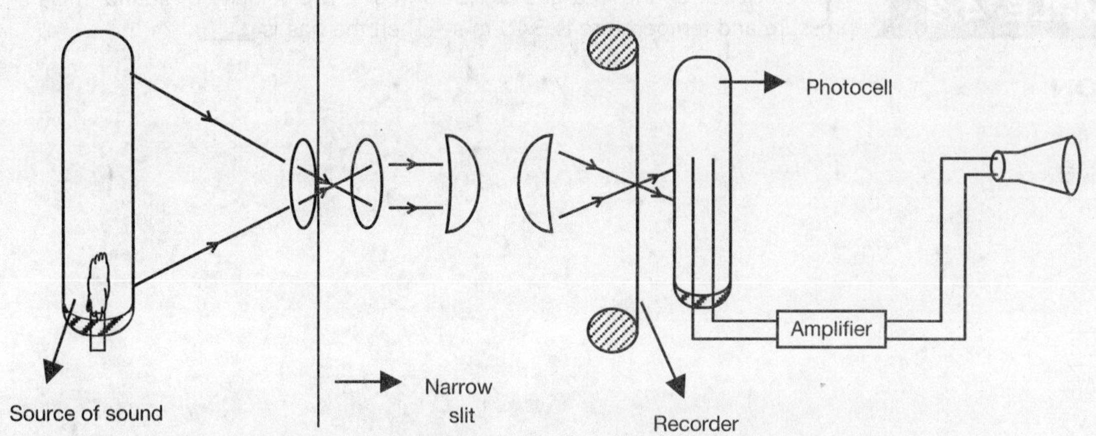

Figure 4.34 Sound reproduction in a loudspeaker

EXAMPLE 4.1

At a distance of 5 m from a source, the intensity of a sound wave is found to be I. The distance from the source at which the intensity is 4I is _______.

SOLUTION

$I_1 = I,\ I_2 = 4I$

$d_1 = 5$ m, $d_2 = ?$

$$\frac{I_1}{I_2} = \left(\frac{d_2}{d_1}\right)^2$$

$$d_2 = \sqrt{\frac{I_1}{I_2}} \times d_1$$

$$\sqrt{\frac{I}{4I}} \times 5 = 2.5 \text{ m}$$

EXAMPLE 4.2

The Young's modulus of a solid is given by, 3.25×10^{11} dynes cm^{-2}. If the velocity of sound in the solid is 2500 m s^{-1}, find its density.

SOLUTION

Velocity of sound in a solid

$$V = \sqrt{\frac{Y}{d}}$$

⇒ Density,

$$d = \frac{Y}{V^2} = \frac{6.25 \times 10^{11}}{(250000)^2}$$

$$= \frac{6.25 \times 10^9}{625 \times 10^8} = 10\text{g cm}^{-3}$$

EXAMPLE 4.3

The velocity of sound in a gas is 1,360 m s^{-1}. The velocity of sound in O_2 under the same pressure and temperature is 340 m s^{-1}.Then the gas is ____.

SOLUTION

$V_2 = 1360$ m s^{-1}

$V_2 = 340$ m s^{-1}

$$\frac{V_1}{V_2} = \sqrt{\frac{M_2}{M_1}}$$

$$\frac{1360}{340} = \sqrt{\frac{32}{M_1}}$$

$$\frac{136}{34} = \frac{4\sqrt{2}}{\sqrt{M_1}}, \sqrt{M_1} = \frac{34 \times 4\sqrt{2}}{136}$$

$$M_1 = \frac{4^2 \times 34^2 \times 2}{(136)^2} = 2$$

EXAMPLE 4.4

A car is moving at a speed of 108 km h^{-1} away from a wall. When it is at a distance of 100 m, the driver blows horn in the car. If he hears the echo of the horn after 2/3 s, determine the speed of the sound in air.

SOLUTION

$$V = 108\text{ k m h}^{-1} = \frac{108 \times 5}{18} = 30\text{ ms}^{-1}$$

$$V = \frac{100 + 100 + 30 \times \frac{2}{3}}{\frac{2}{3}} = \frac{220 \times 3}{2} = 110 \times 3 = 330\text{ ms}^{-1}$$

EXAMPLE 4.5 A person, trying to determine the velocity of sound in air by the echo method, produces a sound at a certain time and hears the echo after 10 seconds. If the reflector is at a distance of 1700 m, find the velocity of sound in air.

SOLUTION

Velocity of sound, $V = \dfrac{2d}{t} = \dfrac{2\times1700}{10}$

$= \dfrac{3400}{10} = 340\,\text{m s}^{-1}$

EXAMPLE 4.6 In a resonating air column method, the first and second resonating lengths are recorded as 25 cm and 75 cm, respectively. If the velocity of the sound in air is 300 m s^{-1}, find the frequency of the tuning fork used.

SOLUTION

$v = 300$ m s^{-1}

$\ell_1 = 25$ cm $= 0.25$ m

$\ell_2 = 75$ cm $= 0.75$ m

$v = 2n(\ell_2 - \ell_1)$

$n = \dfrac{v}{2(\ell_2 - \ell_1)} = \dfrac{300}{2(0.75 - 0.25)} = \dfrac{300}{2\times0.5}$

$= \dfrac{300}{1} = 300$ Hz.

EXAMPLE 4.7 The velocity of wave through a string is 15 m s^{-1}. If the string is held with a tension of 200 N, and the mass of the string is 50 g, determine the length of the string.

SOLUTION

T = 200 N

M = 0.05 kg, ℓ = ?, v = 15 m s^{-1}

$V = \sqrt{\dfrac{T}{\mu}} = \sqrt{\dfrac{200}{\frac{0.05}{\ell}}}$

$15 = \sqrt{\dfrac{200}{1} \times \dfrac{\ell}{0.05}}$

$225 = 4000\,\ell$

$\ell = \dfrac{225}{4000}\,m = \dfrac{225}{4000} = 0.056\,m = 5.6$ cm

POINTS TO REMEMBER

- ✔ If the frequency of the vibrations is less than 20 Hz, it is called infrasonic sound and the sound produced by bodies vibrating with a frequency greater than 20 kHz, is called ultrasonic sound.
- ✔ When a wave propagates from one place to another, the particles of the medium do not undergo any translatory motion but have only vibratory or oscillatory motion.
- ✔ Mechanical waves, also called elastic waves, require a material (an elastic) medium for their propagation
- ✔ If the direction of the vibration of the particles of the medium is perpendicular to the direction of the propagation of the wave, the wave is called transverse wave.
- ✔ If the direction of the vibration of particles of the medium is parallel to the direction of the wave propagation, the wave is called 'longitudinal' wave.
- ✔ When a wave starts from a point in a medium and propagates in all the possible directions and never returns, the wave is called progressive wave.
- ✔ The transmission of sound is by longitudinal wave propagation caused by the vibration of the particles of the medium resulting in compressions and rarefactions. These vibrations are periodic and oscillatory in nature
- ✔ The vibrations whose amplitude progressively decreases with time or with position or with both as the wave is propagated in a medium are called 'damped vibrations'.
- ✔ If a body is set into vibrations by the influence of another vibrating body or an external periodic force, the vibrations executed by the former are known as forced vibrations
- ✔ The elasticity factor in solids is given by Young's modulus (Y).
- ✔ The elasticity factor in liquids is taken as its bulk modulus of elasticity (K).
- ✔ The phenomenon in which when one of the two bodies having confusing natural frequencies is set into vibration, then under its influence the other body also vibrates with increased amplitude.
- ✔ Sonometer is used to verify the laws of transverse vibrations in a stretched string.
- ✔ The elasticity factor in a gas is, also bulk modulus which is equal to its pressure.
- ✔ The reflected sound is known as an echo.
- ✔ If a body is set into vibrations and allowed to vibrate on its own, the vibrations of the body are known as 'natural' or 'free vibrations'.
- ✔ The vibrations whose amplitude progressively decreases with time or with position or with both as the wave is propagated in a medium are called 'damped vibrations.
- ✔ If a body is set into vibrations by the influence of another vibrating body or an external periodic force, the vibrations executed by the former are known as forced vibrations.

PRACTICE QUESTIONS CLASSROOM WING

Very Short Answer Type Questions

Directions for questions from 1 to 3:
Fill in the blanks

1. The energy carried by a progressive wave is the sum of ____ and ___ of the vibrating particles of the medium.
2. Out of the following: Amplitude, Pitch, Frequency and Time period, ____ has no unit?
3. The SI unit of frequency is______.

Directions for questions from 4 to 25:
Answer the following questions

4. What is the expression for the velocity of sound in air using resonating air column method?
5. How does the intensity of sound vary with its amplitude and density of a medium?
6. Is the following statement true or false?
   "The velocity of sound is not affected by the pressure when temperature is kept constant."
7. What are damped vibrations? Give an example.
8. Write the following steps to determine the velocity of sound in air by resonating air column experiment in proper sequence.
   (A) Note the first resonating length of the air column (ℓ_1).
   (B) Note the second resonating length of the air column (ℓ_2).
   (C) Determine the velocity of sound in air by using the expression, $v = f(\ell_2 - \ell_1)$
   (D) Find the difference in the length of the resonating air columns.
9. When a tuning fork of 512 Hz is used, the first and the second resonating lengths of closed air column are obtained as 16 cm and 48 cm, respectively. What is the velocity of sound in air in metre per second?
10. What is the characteristic of sound that distinguishes between two sounds of equal amplitude and frequency?
11. What is the expression for the velocity of a stationary wave set in a stretched string?
12. Define progressive and stationary waves?
13. What are infrasonics and ultrasonics?
14. What is resonating air column?
15. Mention Newton's formula for the velocity of sound in a medium, and Laplace correction to Newton's formula.
16. What is the pitch of a sound?
17. How does the intensity of sound vary with the distance of the point of observation from the source of sound?
18. What is the principle used in a megaphone?
19. How does the velocity of sound in a gas vary with its absolute temperature?
20. Match the statements of Column A with those of Column B.

Column A	Column B
A. Reverberation	a. Apparent change in frequency
B. Doppler effect	b. Changes with temperature
C. Velocity of sound in air	c. Reflection of sound

21. How many antinodes are obtained when a closed end resonating air column vibrates in the fundamental mode?
22. How does the velocity of sound in a gas vary with its molecular weight, and pressure?
23. If the fundamental frequency of a vibrating stretched string is 200 Hz, what are frequencies of its 1st and 2nd overtones?
24. Match the statements of Column A with those of Column B.

Column A	Column B
A. Velocity of sound in air	a. $\sqrt{\frac{Y}{d}}$
B. Velocity of sound in solids	b. $\frac{1}{2l}\sqrt{\frac{T}{\mu}}$
C. Fundamental frequency of a string	c. $\sqrt{\frac{\gamma P}{\rho}}$

25. By changing either the wavelength or the frequency of a sound wave, is it possible to change the velocity of sound in a medium?

Short Answer Type Questions

26. The intensity of sound wave at a distance of 40 m from the source is *I*. What will be the intensity at a distance of 90 m from the source?

27. Determine the value of velocity of sound in CO_2 if the velocity of sound in O_2 is 340 m s^{-1} under the same pressure and temperature.

28. A scooterist moves away from a wall with a speed of 54 km h^{-1}. He blows horn when he is at a distance of 100 m from the wall. Determine the time after which he hears the echo of the horn. The velocity of sound in air is 340 m s^{-1}.

29. One end of a string of length 2 m and mass 50 g is fixed and a 2 kg mass is suspended from the other end. Determine the velocity of the wave travelling through the string.

30. The first resonating length of a closed end air column is 30 cm. At approximately, what length of the air column, do we obtain the second resonance?

31. A string is in its first overtone when vibrated with a tuning fork of frequency 50 Hz. If the length of the string is 20 cm, determine the velocity of the wave travelling through the string.

32. The fundamental frequency of an air column in a closed end tube is 30 Hz. Find the frequency of the third harmonic.

33. If the velocity of sound in air is 300 m s^{-1}, express the audible range in terms of wavelength.

34. Explain the factors on which the velocity of sound in a given gas depends.

35. The velocity of the sound in a gas is 300 m s^{-1}. The density of gas and the ratio of specific heats of gas are given by, 0.002 g cm^{-2} and 2, respectively. Find the pressure of the gas.

36. If the velocity of sound in air is 330 m s^{-1}, what is the minimum distance between the source or the observer of sound and the reflector to hear an echo?

37. What are the factors which do not affect the velocity of sound in a gas?

38. The molecular weights of two gases A and B are given as 36 units and 16 units, respectively. If the velocity of sound in gas A is 300 m s^{-1}, find the velocity of sound in B.

39. The velocity of sound in a gas at 0°C is x m s^{-1}. At what temperature of the gas, does the velocity of sound become $2x$ m s^{-1}?

40. How do you determine the velocity of sound in air using an echo?

Essay Answer Type Questions

41. Explain the formation of transverse stationary waves in stretched strings and their different modes of vibrations.

42. The first and second resonances take place in a resonating air column at 21 cm and 61 cm, respectively. If the frequency of vibration is 400 Hz, determine the velocity of sound.

43. Apparent frequency felt by the observer is changed from 250 Hz to 280 Hz, when source of sound moving towards the observer changes its speed from 10 m s^{-1} to x m s^{-1}. Calculate the value of x. (take velocity of sound in air = 350 m s^{-1})

44. A string of length 8 m is fixed between two ends in resonance with a tuning fork of frequency 420 Hz in 7th overtone. What would be the ratio of distances of the third antinode and the 5th antinodes?

45. Describe an experiment to find out the velocity of sound in air using resonating air columns.

PRACTICE QUESTIONS COMPETITION WING

Level 1: Apply Your Concepts

Direction for questions from 1 to 5:
Answer the following questions briefly:

1. Define echo.
2. What are forced vibrations? Give an example.
3. Define pitch.
4. What is meant by the fundamental frequency of a vibrating stretched string?
5. How does humidity in air affect the velocity of sound in it?

Direction for questions from 6 to 12:
State whether the following statements are true or false.

6. The frequency of a note produced by a stretched string is directly proportional to the square root of linear mass density of the string.
7. The phenomenon of resonance is used in receiving the radio and television programmes.
8. In order to transmit sound waves, the medium should possess elasticity and inertia.
9. In simple harmonic motion, the acceleration is inversely proportional to the displacement of the body from its mean position.
10. The frequency of damped vibrations remains same but the amplitude decreases gradually.
11. Motion of a particle in the atmosphere is periodic.
12. Velocity of sound is least in solids.

Direction for questions from 13 to 19:
Fill in the blanks.

13. The motion of the needle of a sewing machine is an example of ______ motion.
14. γ is the ratio of molar specific heat capacity of the given gas at constant ____ to its specific heat capacity at constant ____.
15. The pitch of a given sound can be measured by its ______.
16. The pitch of the sound produced by a stretched string gets higher as the tension______________.
17. In a standing wave, the distance between two successive antinodes is 15 cm. The distance covered by it in producing 4 waves is ___ m.
18. A rope is vibrating with a frequency 20 Hz. If the velocity of the wave in the rope is 20 m s^{-1}, then the distance between a crest and the successive trough is ______.
19. If d is the distance between the source of sound and reflector, t_1, t_2 are times at which first two echoes are heard, the expression for determination of velocity of sound in air by echo method is ________.

Direction for question 20:
Match the entries in Column A with appropriate ones from Column B.

20.

Column A	Column B
A. Elastic waves	a. nodes and antinodes
B. Infrasonic sound waves	b. reflection of sound
C. Phase	c. laws of transverse vibrations in a stretched string
D. Stationary waves	d. water waves
E. SHM	e. Sound track
F. Newton's formula	f. frequency less than 20 Hz
G. Whispering galleries	g. measured in radians
H. Damped vibrations	h. isothermal change
I. Sonometer	i. constant time period
J. Photosensitive films	j. decrease in amplitude

Direction for questions from 21 to 40:

For each of the questions, four choices have been provided. Select the correct alternative.

21. A man moving towards a vertical cliff at a constant velocity of u m s^{-1}, fires a gun and hears the echo after t s. If he was at a distance of d m from the cliff when he fired the gun, the velocity of sound in air is __________ m s^{-1}.

(a) $\frac{2d}{t}$ (b) $\frac{2d}{t}+u$

(c) $\frac{2d}{t}-u$ (d) $\frac{d}{t}$

22. **Assertion (A):** Velocity of sound in iron is greater than that of in water.

Reason (R): Velocity of sound in solids is greater than that of in liquids.

(a) A and R are true and R is the correct explanation of A.

(b) A and R are true, but R is not the correct explanation of A.

(c) A is true but R is false.

(d) Both A and R are false.

23. **Assertion(A):** Velocity of sound in solid substance A is less than that of solid substance B, if Young's modulus of A is less than that of B and density of A and B are equal.

Reason (R): Velocity of sound in solids is directly proportional to square root of Young's modulus and inversely proportional to square root of density of solid.

(a) A and R are true and R is the correct explanation of A.

(b) A and R are true, but R is not the correct explanation of A.

(c) A is true but R is false.

(d) Both A and R are false.

24. The general expression for the resonating length of an air column in organ pipes with one end closed is given by, ______.

(a) $\frac{(2n-1)\lambda}{2}$ (b) $\frac{n\lambda}{4}$

(c) $\frac{(2n-1)\lambda}{4}$ (d) $\frac{(n+1)\lambda}{2}$

25. If the amplitude of a sound is doubled, then its

(a) velocity is doubled.

(b) frequency is doubled.

(c) wavelength is doubled.

(d) None of the above.

26. In a resonating air column, the second resonating length is 60 cm. The first resonance occurs when the length of the air column is ______ cm.

(a) 30 (b) 10

(c) 20 (d) 60

27. In a closed end organ pipe, if ℓ_1 and ℓ_2 are two successive resonating lengths, then $2(\ell_2 - \ell_1)$ is ______.

(a) $\frac{\lambda}{2}$ (b) λ

(c) 2λ (d) None of these

28. In a stationary wave,

(a) energy is carried away throughout the infinite medium.

(b) energy is confined to a limited region of the medium.

(c) different particles in a loop have different amplitudes.

(d) Both (b) and (c).

29. The energy of the wave that passes through unit area per unit time is called ______.

(a) pitch (b) quality

(c) intensity (d) amplitude

30. If the velocity of sound in a gas is 200 m s^{-1} when the temperature is 127°C, then the velocity of sound in the same gas when temperature is increased by 900 K is ______ m s^{-1}.

(a) $200\sqrt{3}$ (b) 300

(c) $100\sqrt{5}$ (d) 450

31. Hertz is the unit of

(a) wavelength. (b) amplitude.

(c) frequency. (d) None of these

32. The velocity of sound in air depends upon

(a) its density and pressure only.

(b) its ratio of specific heat capacities and pressure only.

(c) its ratio of specific heats capacities and density only.

(d) its ratio of specific heat capacities, density and pressure.

33. The audible range of frequency of sound waves for human beings is ______.

(a) 10 Hz to 10,000 Hz

(b) 20 Hz to 20,000 Hz

(c) 5 Hz to 50,000 Hz

(d) 50 Hz to 20,000 Hz

34. Which of the following quantity decrease as sound wave travels through a medium?

(a) Amplitude (b) frequency

(c) velocity (d) wavelength

35. The ratio of intensities of two sound waves is 16 : 25. The ratio of their amplitudes is

(a) 1 : 2 (b) 5 : 4

(c) 2 : 1 (d) 4 : 5

36. The frequency of sound waves is 11 kHz and its wavelength is 20 cm, then the velocity of sound waves is______.

(a) 220 m s^{-1} (b) 220 cm s^{-1}
(c) 2200 cm s^{-1} (d) 2200 m s^{-1}

37. The ratio of frequencies of 1st and 2nd overtones produced in the vibrating stretched strings is ______.
(a) 1 : 3 (b) 3 : 2
(c) 2 : 3 (d) 1 : 2

38. The length of a stretched string is 2 m. The tension in it and its mass are 10 N and 0.80 kg, respectively. Arrange the following steps in a sequence to find the third harmonic of transverse wave that can be created in the string.
(A) Find the linear mass density (m) using the formula, $m = \frac{\text{Mass (M) of the string}}{\text{Length } (\ell) \text{ of the string}}$
(B) Collect the data from the problem and find the length (ℓ) tension (T) and mass (M) of the stretched string.
(C) The fundamental frequency of a stretched vibrating string is given by, $n = \frac{1}{2\ell}\sqrt{\frac{T}{m}}$.
(D) The frequency of 2nd overtone or 3rd harmonic is given by, $n_2 = \frac{3}{2\ell}\sqrt{\frac{T}{m}} = 3n$.
(a) ABCD (b) DBCA
(c) BACD (d) BDCA

39. In a resonating air column method, the first and second resonating lengths of the air columns are 16 cm and 48 cm, respectively. If the frequency of a tuning fork used is 500 Hz, arrange the following steps in a sequential order to find the velocity of sound in air.
(A) Find the first and second resonating lengths of the air columns and frequency of the tuning fork from the given problem.
(B) The difference of lengths of two resonating air columns is, $\ell_2 - \ell_1 = \lambda/2$ and $\lambda = 2(\ell_2 - \ell_1)$.
(C) Find the first and second resonating lengths 'ℓ_1' and 'ℓ_2' in terms of 'λ', i.e., $\ell_1 = \frac{\lambda}{4}$ and $\ell_2 = 3\lambda/4$.
(D) The velocity of sound, $V = n\lambda = 2n(\ell_2 - \ell_1)$. Substitute the corresponding values and obtain the value of 'V'.
(a) ACBD (b) ABCD
(c) DCBA (d) CDBA

40. Arrange the following steps to determine the velocity of wave through a string:
(A) Use the formula $V = \sqrt{\frac{T}{\mu}}$ to determine the velocity of wave.
(B) Determine the linear density of the string.
(C) Fix a string to a rigid support and hang a known weight from the other end.
(D) Set the string into vibration.
(a) CDBA (b) CBDA
(c) DBCA (d) DACB

Level 2: Review Your Concepts

41. At a distance of 5 m from a source, the intensity of a sound wave is found to be *I*. What would be the distance from the source at which the intensity is *4I*?

42. A person speaks at one end of a metal pipe 200 m long and a person at other end hears two sounds at an interval of 0.5 seconds. If the velocity of sound in air is 300 m s^{-1}, answer the following questions.
(a) In which of the two media, air or pipe, does sound travel faster?
(b) Why are two sound notes heard at two different instants?
(c) Find the speed of sound in the metal pipe.

43. For a certain organ pipe, three successive resonant frequencies are observed at 225 Hz, 375 Hz, and 525 Hz, respectively. If the velocity of sound in air is 330 m s^{-1}, find whether the pipe is closed at one end or open at both the ends. Also, find the length of the pipe.

44. The velocity of sound in a gas is 1,360 m s^{-1}. The velocity of sound in O_2 under the same pressure and temperature is 340 m s^{-1}. Which gases is it?

45. A sonar fixed to a stationary submarine is used to detect a shoal of fish. It sends waves in east direction and the reflected waves from the shoal of fish are observed at the end of 8 seconds. After 20 minutes, again the waves are sent in east direction and the reflection is observed at the end of 2.0 seconds. Find the speed and direction of motion of the shoal of fish.

Take the velocity of sound in water as 1500 m s^{-1}.

46. A car is moving at a speed of 108 km h^{-1} away from a wall. When it is at a distance of 100 m, the driver blows horn in the car. If he hears the echo of the horn after 2/3 s, determine the speed of the sound in air.

47. A person drops a stone in a well of depth 80 m and hears the sound of the splash after 4.25 seconds. If the acceleration due to gravity is 10 m s^{-2}, find the velocity of sound in air.

48. The velocity of sound in a gas at 0°C is 335 m s^{-1}. If its γ value is 1.4, find the molecular weight of the gas. (Take R = 8.3 J K^{-1} $mole^{-1}$).

49. Find the temperature in °C at which sound travels in hydrogen with the same velocity as in oxygen at 1007°C.

50. A man stands in front of a cliff and finds that when he claps at regular time interval of 1.2 seconds, he does not hear the echo distinctly. Then he moves closer to the cliff by 32 m and finds that he cannot hear the echo distinctly when he claps at an interval of 1 second. Find the velocity of sound waves.

51. A sonometer wire of length '*l*' under tension '*T*' is vibrating with its fundamental frequency. If its length is decreased by 45% and tension is increased by 21%, find the percentage change in its frequency.

52. Explain why the pitch of sound increases gradually when a vessel is being filled by a water tap.

53. Empty vessels make more vibrations than the vessels filled with a liquid when they are disturbed. Explain.

54. A vibrating tuning fork is held between an open organ pipe P_1 and a closed organ pipe P_2 of lengths ℓ_1 and ℓ_2, respectively as shown in the figure.

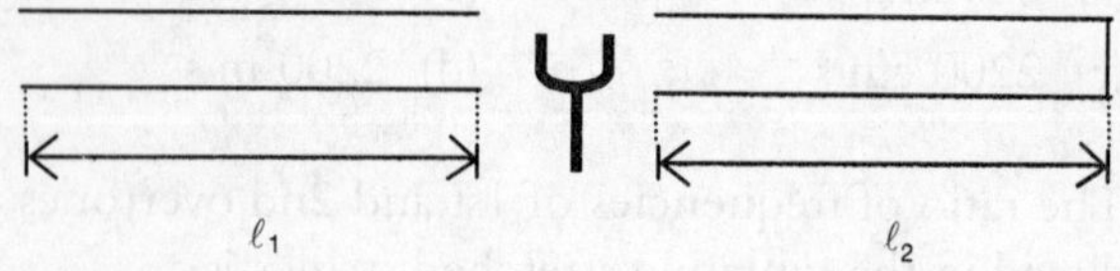

If the first overtones are produced in each organ pipe, find the ratio of the lengths of the two organ pipes.

55. The velocity of wave through a string is 15 m s^{-1}. If the string is held with a tension of 200 N, and the mass of the string is 50 g, determine the length of the string.

56. A block of mass 3 kg is suspended from the ceiling of a lift through a string having a linear density of 32.4 × 10^{-3} kg m^{-1}. Find the speed with which a wave can move on the string, if the lift accelerates upward at a rate of 2 m s^{-2}. (Take g = 10 m s^{-2})

57. An open pipe of length 12 cm in its fundamental mode vibrates in resonance with the first overtone of a closed organ pipe of length 13.5 cm, which is filled with some gas. If the velocity of sound in air is 320 m s^{-1}, find the velocity of sound in the unknown gas.

58. A straight wire is made up of two copper wires welded in the middle. This wire is used as a sonometer wire. Stationary waves are set up in the wire with tension '*T*' and welded joint as a node. If one-half of the wire vibrates with 3 loops and the other half with 6 loops, find the ratio of velocities of the waves in one half to that in the other half of the wire. Is the thicknesses of each half of wire same? If no, find the ratio of the radii of the two halves.

59. A string is in its first harmonic motion, when vibrated with a tuning fork of frequency 10 Hz. If the velocity of the wave through the string is 10 m s^{-1}, find out the length (in m) of the string.

Level 3: Assess Your Concepts

60. A straight wire is made up of two copper wires welded in the middle. This wire is used as a sonometer wire. Stationary waves are set up in the wire with tension '*T*' and welded joint as node. If one-half of the wire vibrates with 3 loops and the other half with 6 loops, find the ratio of the velocities of the waves in one half to that in the other half of the wire. Is the thicknesses of each half of wire same? If no, find the ratio of the radii of each half of the wires.

61. Would the following, be in resonance with tuning fork of frequency 110 Hz?

Open pipe of length 3 m when velocity of sound in air is 330 m s^{-1}

62. The 3rd and 5th resonance take place in a resonating air column experiment at the lengths of 82 cm and at 122 cm of the air column. If the velocity of the sound

in the air is 320 m s^{-1}, calculate the frequency (in Hz) of vibration.

63. An observer is moving towards a stationary source of sound and frequency felt by him is 200 Hz. If the observer changes his speed from 5 m s^{-1} to 10 m s^{-1}, then (take velocity of sound in air = 330 m s^{-1}) what would be:

(i) change in apparent frequency?

(ii) apparent frequency when he moves with 10 m s^{-1}?

(iii) frequency of source of sound?

64. A source of sound at rest produces sound waves, which move with velocity v. Wind blows with velocity 0.2v towards an observer standing at a distance from the source. Find the percentage change in the wavelength and frequency of the sound as heard by the observer.

65. A scooterist is at a distance of 150 m from a wall. He blows a horn after 1 s when he starts moving away from the wall with a velocity of 12 m s^{-1}. If he hears the echo after 1 s, find the velocity of sound in air.

66. A simple pendulum which has a bob made of metal oscillates with a time period *T*. The bob of the pendulum is immersed in a non-viscous liquid and then oscillated. If the density of the metal bob is 5 times the density of the liquid, then find the time period of the oscillation of pendulum.

67. A pointer is attached to the prong of a tuning fork of frequency 56 Hz mounted on a stand such that the pointer strikes the vertical plate as the tuning fork vibrates. If the vertical plate falls freely from rest through 10 cm, find how many times the pointer strikes the plate during the descent of the plates?

68. A string is in resonance with a tuning fork of frequency 500 Hz in its 6th harmonic. If the distance between 1st node and 3rd antinode is 2.5 m, then what will be the length of the string?

69. An open pipe of length 2 m and a closed pipe of length 2.5 m are in resonance with the tuning fork of frequency 150 Hz. Find the number of harmonics in open pipe and closed pipe. (velocity of sound in air 300 m s^{-1})

70. 'Hyderabad A' radio station does its transmission at frequency of 738 kHz, wavelength of 406.5 m. What will be the length of the wave produced by 'Hyderabad Commercial Broadcasting' station, if it operates at 102.8 MHz?

71. The velocity of sound produced in a liquid is 1500 m s^{-1}. If the density of the liquid is 8×10^3 kg m^{-3}, find the bulk modulus of the liquid.

72. A person standing at a distance 495 m from a hill blows a horn. After what time can he hear the echo? (Given that the velocity of sound in air is 330 m s^{-1}).

73. In a resonating air column method, the first and second resonating lengths are recorded as 25 cm and 75 cm, respectively. If the velocity of the sound in air is 330 m s^{-1}, find the frequency of the tuning fork used.

74. In a sonometer experiment, the mass suspended from the string is 1 kg. The resonating length for a given tuning fork is noted as 25 cm. If the mass suspended is increased to 9 kg, find the resonating length of the string for the same frequency.

AT

PRACTICE QUESTIONS JEE-NEET SPECIAL WING

Multiple-Answer Type Questions

Direction for Questions 1 to 5: **Each question has FOUR options (a), (b), (c), and (d). ONE OR MORE THAN ONE of these four option(s) is/are the correct answer(s).**

1. Factors that do not affect the velocity of sound in air are ________
   (a) Frequency of sound wave
   (b) Pressure
   (c) Humidity
   (d) Temperature

2. Two sound waves S_1 and S_2 of frequencies 110 Hz and 120 Hz respectively travel in a gas. If the wavelength of the wave S_1 is 3 *m*, then the wavelength of S_2 and the velocity of S_1 and S_2 in the gas respectively are ________.
   (a) 2.75 m, 320 m/s
   (b) 3.25 m, 320 m/s
   (c) 2.75 m, 330 m/s
   (d) 3.25 m, 330 m/s

3. A car approaches a hill at a constant speed. When the car is at 1 km from the hill, it sounds a horn, whose echo is heard by the driver after 4.5 *s*. If the speed of the sound in air is 330 ms^{-1}, then the speed of the car is ________.
   (a) 114.4 m/s (b) 411.9 km/h
   (c) 114.4 km/h (d) 411.9 m/s

4. A sonometer has a wire of constant length. If the weight attached to the wire is increased by 21%, then the fundamental frequency of the sonometer increases by 5 Hz. By keeping the tension on the string constant, if the length of the sonometer wire increased by 10%, then the change in the fundamental frequency of the sonometer is ________.
   (a) 4.55 Hz, decreases
   (b) 4.55 Hz, increases
   (c) 10 Hz, increases
   (d) 10 Hz, decreases

5. The air column in a pipe closed at one end is made to vibrate in its second overtone by a tuning fork of frequency 250 Hz. (The speed of sound in air is 320 m s^{-1})
   (a) The fundamental frequency is $\frac{v}{4L}$.
   (b) Odd harmonics are present in the vibration of a closed organ pipe.
   (c) The length of the air column is 1.6 *m*
   (d) Only even harmonics are present in the vibration of the second overtone.

Comprehension-Based Questions

Direction for Questions 6 to 11: **Read the paragraph given below and answer the questions.**

Mechanical waves, also called elastic waves, require a material (an elastic) medium for their propagation. Sound waves are longitudinal mechanical waves. In the case of a longitudinal wave, the direction of the vibration of particles of the medium is parallel to the direction of the wave propagation. A longitudinal wave propagates as compressions and rarefactions. The Pressure–time graph for a sound wave is as follows.

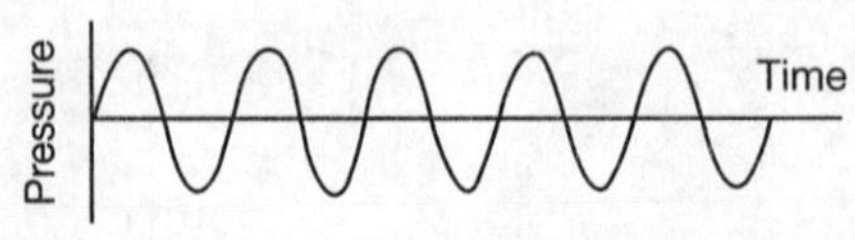

The velocity of sound wave in a gas is given by $v = \sqrt{\frac{\gamma P}{d}}$

where, 'P' and 'd' are the pressure and density of the given gas and 'γ' is a constant for a given gas and is defined as the ratio of the specific heat capacity of the given gas at constant pressure (C_p) to its specific heat capacity at constant volume (C_v).

The factors that affect the velocity of sound in a gas are as follows:

(i) Absolute Temperature of Gas: The velocity of sound in a gas is directly proportional to the square root of its absolute temperature.

(ii) Density of a Gas: The velocity of sound in a gas is inversely proportional to the square root of its density.

(iii) Molecular Weight of a Gas: The velocity of sound in a gas is inversely proportional to the square root of its molecular weight.

Factors that do not affect the velocity of sound in a gas are pressure of gas, amplitude, frequency, and wavelength of sound wave.

The reflected sound is known as an echo. If a person produces a sound and hears an echo after '*t*' seconds from an object that is at a distance '*d*', then the velocity of sound in air is given by $v = \frac{2d}{t}$.

6. The following waves require a medium for their propagation:
(a) Sound waves
(b) waves on the surface of water
(c) Light waves
(d) Both (a) and (b)

7. During the propagation of a sound wave, the regions of compressions of the medium have ________.
(a) High pressure
(b) High density
(c) High frequency
(d) Both (a) and (b)

8. If the absolute temperature of the gas increases by 3 times, then the velocity of sound in the gas ________.
(a) increases to 4 times
(b) decreases to 4 times
(c) increases to 2 times
(d) decreases to 2 times

9. When a sound wave propagates through a gas medium, ________.
(a) the particles of the medium vibrate parallel to the direction of propagation
(b) the particles of the medium vibrate perpendicular to the direction of propagation
(c) the particles of the medium do not move
(d) the particles of the medium move randomly

10. If the pressure of the gas increases, the velocity of sound in the gas ________.
(a) increases
(b) decreases
(c) does not change
(d) first increases and then decreases

11. Using the data given in the previous paragraph, match the following.

Column – A	Column – B
A. The ratio of molecular weight of two gases are in the ratio 1:4, then the ratio of the velocity of sound in them is	a. 1:1
B. The ratio of the velocity of sound in two gases is in the ratio 1:2, then the ratio of their densities is in the ratio of	b. 16.5 m
C. If the frequency of a sound wave is doubled, then the speed of sound in the given gas is	c. 4:1
D. If the ratio of wavelengths of two sound waves is in the ratio of 1:16, then the ratio of velocity of the two sound waves in a given gas is	d. 2:1
E. If the persistence of hearing is 0.1 s and the speed of sound is 330 m/s, then the minimum distance required to hear an echo is	e. 1:2

ANSWER KEYS

Crossword

Across

1. Frequency 6. Node 8. Density 10. Antinode
12. Elasticity

Down

2. Reverberation 3. Amplitude 4. Wavelength 5. Crest
7. Resonance 9. Solids 11. Echo

Classroom Wing

Very Short Answer Type Questions

1. Potential energy, kinetic energy 2. pitch 3. Hertz (Hz) 6. True
8. A, B, D, C 20. A-c, B-a, C-b 24. A-c, B-a, C-b

Competition Wing

Level 1: Apply Your Concepts

6. False 7. True 8. True 9. False 10. True
11. False 12. False 13. Oscillatory motion 14. constant pressure, constant volume
15. frequency 16. increases 17. 1.2 18. 0.5 m 19. $\dfrac{2d}{t_1 - t_2}$
20. A : d, B : f, C : g, D : a, E : i, F : h, G : b, H : j, I : c, J : e
21. (c) 22. (a) 23. (a) 24. (c) 25. (d)
26. (a) 27. (b) 28. (d) 29. (c) 30. (b)
31. (c) 32. (d) 33. (b) 34. (a) 35. (d)
36. (d) 37. (c) 38. (c) 39. (a) 40. (b)

JEE-NEET SPECIAL WING

Multiple-Answer Type Questions

1. (a, b) 2. (c) 3. (a, b) 4. (a) 5. (a, b, c)

Comprehension-Based Questions

6. (d) 7. (d) 8. (c) 9. (a) 10. (c)
11. A-d, B-c, C-a , D-a , E-b

For answer key of Classroom wing and Competition wing, refer to Hints and Solutions

Hints and Explanations

CLASSROOM WING

Very Short Answer Type Questions

1. Potential energy, kinetic energy
2. Units of amplitude, frequency and time period are m, Hz and second, respectively but pitch has no unit.
3. Hertz (Hz)
4. $V = n\lambda$

   $\therefore V = 2n(l_2 - l_1)$
5. Intensity $(I) \propto (\text{amplitude})^2$
   Intensity $(I) \propto$ density (ρ)
6. Velocity of sound is not affected by pressure at constant temperature.

   Hence, the statement is true.
7. The vibrations whose amplitude progressively decreases with time or with position or with both as the wave is propagated in a medium are called 'damped vibrations'.

   Example: The oscillations of a disturbed simple pendulum.
8. (A) Note the first resonating length of the air column.

   (B) Note the second resonating length of the air column.

   (D) Find the difference in the length of the resonating air columns.

   (C) Determine the velocity of sound in air by using the expression, $v = f(l_2 - l_1)$

   A B D C is the required sequential order.
9. Frequency of the tuning fork, $n = 512$ Hz
   First resonating length, $l_1 = 16$ cm
   Second resonating length, $l_2 = 48$ cm
   $(l_2 - l_1) = 32$ cm

   $$V = 2n(l_2 - l_1) = \frac{2 \times 512 \times 32}{100} = 327.68\text{m s}^{-1}$$
10. Timbre or quality
11. $V = \sqrt{\dfrac{T}{m}}$
12. When a wave starts from point in a medium and propagates in all the possible directions and never returns, the wave is called a progressive wave. When a progressive we strikes a hard surface and is reflected, the incident wave and the reflected wave superpose forming a standing wave, also called a stationary wave.
13. If the frequency of the vibrations is less than 20 Hz, it is called infrasonic and if greater than 20,000 Hz it is called ultrasonic.
14. If the natural frequency of the air column matches with that of the tuning fork, a loud sound is produced due to resonance. The air column in this condition is known as 'resonating air column'.
15. Velocity of sound in air is given by:

   $$V = \sqrt{\frac{P}{d}} \text{ (By Newton)}$$

   $$V = \sqrt{\frac{\gamma P}{d}} \text{(By Laplace)}$$
16. Pitch is a special characteristic of sound based on which we can differentiate between two sounds having equal loudness. It is measured by sound frequency.
17. Intensity (I) $\propto \dfrac{1}{(\text{density})^2}$
18. Multiple reflections of sound.
19. $V \propto \sqrt{T}$

   $$\frac{v_1}{v_2} = \sqrt{\frac{T_1}{T_2}}$$
20. Reverberation—Reflection of sound

   Doppler effect—Apparent change in frequency.

   Velocity of sound in air changes with the temperature

   A-c, B-a, C-b
21. One
22. $V \propto \dfrac{1}{\sqrt{M}}$

   $$\frac{V_1}{V_2} = \sqrt{\frac{M_2}{M_1}}$$

The variation of the pressure of a gas does not affect the velocity of the sound in it.

$$V = \sqrt{\frac{\gamma P}{d}};$$

$\frac{p}{d}$ is always constant.

23. $n_0 = 200$ Hz
First overtone, $n_1 = 2n_0 = 2 \times 200 = 400$ Hz
Second overtone, $n_2 = 3n_0 = 3 \times 200 = 600$ Hz

24. Velocity of sound in air $= \sqrt{\frac{\gamma P}{\rho}}$ A-c

Velocity of sound in solid $= \sqrt{\frac{Y}{d}}$ B-a

Fundamental frequency $= \frac{1}{2l}\sqrt{\frac{T}{\mu}}$ C-b

25. Velocity of sound depends only on the nature of the medium.

Short Answer Type Questions

Note: This is how you should frame your answer covering.

26. $I \propto \frac{1}{d^2}$

$$\frac{I_2}{I_1} = \left(\frac{d_1}{d_2}\right)^2$$

$$I_2 = \left(\frac{40}{90}\right)^2 I$$

$$I_2 = \frac{16I}{81} = \frac{I}{5}$$

27. $V \propto \frac{1}{\sqrt{M}}$

$$\frac{V_1}{V_2} = \sqrt{\frac{M_2}{M_1}}$$

$$\frac{340}{V_2} = \sqrt{\frac{44}{32}} = \sqrt{\frac{11}{8}}$$

$$\frac{340}{V_2} = \sqrt{\frac{11}{8}}$$

$$V_2 = 340\sqrt{\frac{8}{11}}$$

28. $V = 54 \text{ km h}^{-1} = \frac{54 \times 5}{18} = 15 \text{ m s}^{-1}$.

$$\frac{(100 + 100 + 15 \times t)}{t} = 340$$

$200 + 15t = 340t$

$340t - 15t = 200$

$325t = 200$

$$t = \frac{200}{325} = 0.6 \text{ s}$$

29. Length = 2 m, mass = 0.05 kg

Load = 2 × 10 = 20 N

$$V = \sqrt{\frac{T}{\mu}} = \sqrt{\frac{20}{\frac{0.05}{2}}}$$

$$= \sqrt{\frac{40}{0.05}} = \sqrt{\frac{3000}{5}} = \sqrt{800} \text{ ms}^{-1}$$

$$= 20\sqrt{2} \text{ ms}^{-1}$$

30. $L_2 = 3L_1 = 3 \times 30 = 90$ cm

31. $f = 50$ Hz

first overtone frequency = 50 Hz

$$\frac{2}{2\ell}\sqrt{\frac{T}{\mu}} = 50$$

$$\sqrt{\frac{T}{\mu}} = 50 \times 0.2 = 10 \text{ m s}^{-1}$$

$$v = 10 \text{ m s}^{-1}.$$

32. $n_p = (2p - 1)n_0$

Ans: 150 Hz

33. $V = n\lambda$

If $n = 20$ Hz,

$$\lambda = \frac{300 \text{ m s}^{-1}}{20 Hz} = 15 \text{m}$$

If $n = 20{,}000$ Hz,

$$\lambda = \frac{300 \text{ m s}^{-1}}{20{,}000 Hz} = 15 \times 10^{-3} \text{m}.$$

Audible Range in terms of wave length is 15×10^{-3} m to 15 m.

34. (i) Absolute temperature of gas

(ii) Density of a gas

(iii) Molecular weight of a gas

35. $V = \sqrt{\frac{\gamma P}{\rho}}$

Ans: 9×10^5 Pa

36. $d = \frac{v}{20} = \frac{330}{20} = 16.5$ m

37. (i) Pressure of a gas
(ii) Amplitude
(iii) Frequency
(iv) Wave length

38. $\frac{V_1}{V_2} = \sqrt{\frac{M_2}{M_1}}$

Ans: 450 m s^{-1}

39. $\frac{X}{2X} = \sqrt{\frac{273}{T_2}}$

$T_2 = 273 \times 4 = 1092\text{K} = 819°\text{C}$

40. (i) A person makes a sound in front of a big wall at a distance '*d*'.
(ii) hears two sounds distinctly with a time interval of seconds.
(iii) Velocity of sound, $V = \frac{2d}{t}$

Essay Answer Type Questions

Note: This is how you should frame your answer covering.

41. (i) Stretched string with both ends tied to fixed ends.
(ii) Formation of standing waves when exited.
(iii) Fundamental frequency and overtones.

42. $\frac{\lambda}{4} + e = 21$ cm

$\frac{3\lambda}{4} + e = 61$ cm

$\frac{3\lambda}{4} + e - \left(\frac{\lambda}{4} + e\right) = 61 - 21 = 40 = \frac{\lambda}{2}$

$\lambda = 80$ cm

$V = n\lambda$

$= 400 \times 0.8 = 320$ m s^{-1}.

43. $f' = f\left[\frac{C}{C - Vs}\right]$

I case

$250 = f\left[\frac{350}{350 - 10}\right]$

$\therefore f = 242.9$

$= 243$ Hz.

II case

$280 = 242\left[\frac{350}{350 - x}\right]$

$\frac{280}{243} = \frac{350}{350 - x}$

$350 - x = \frac{350 \times 243}{280}$

$\therefore \quad x = 350 - 303.75$

$= 46.25$

$\therefore \quad = 46$ m s^{-1}

44. 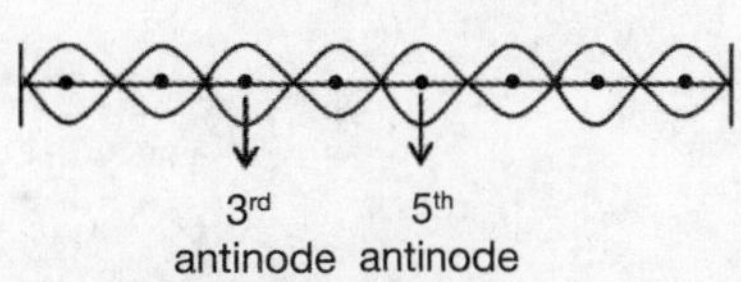

$\frac{8\lambda}{2} = \ell$

$\frac{3\lambda}{2} = 8$

$\lambda = 2$ m

Distance of the third antinode $= \frac{5\lambda}{4} = \frac{5 \times 2}{4} = 2.5$ m

Distance of the 5th antinode $= \frac{9\lambda}{4} = \frac{9 \times 2}{4} = 4.5$ m

Distance between them = 4.5 − 2.5 = 2 m.

45. (i) Two boys standing on two distant hills at night.
(ii) Sound and flash being produced when a boy shoots a gun.
(iii) Determination of time taken by sound to travel from the source (to the other boy).
(iv) Calculation of the velocity of sound.
(v) Repetition of the same procedure after the boys interchange their places.
(vi) Calculating velocity of sound in opposite direction.
(vii) Taking the average of two values.
(viii) Producing a stationary wave by using a tuning fork.
(ix) Determination of the first resonating length, and the second resonating length of the air columns for the given frequency.
(x) Expression for velocity of sound in terms of resonating air column.

Competition Wing

Level 1: Apply Your Concepts

1. The reflected sound is known as echo.
2. If a body is set into vibrations by the influence of another vibrating body or an external periodic force, the vibrations executed by the former are known forced vibrations.
   Example: The vibrations executed by the pendulum of a clock are forced vibrations as they are caused under the influence of a main spring which is wound.
3. Pitch is a special characteristic of sound based on which we can differentiate between two sounds having equal loudness. The pitch of a given sound can be measured by its frequency.
4. $n = \frac{1}{2\ell}\sqrt{\frac{T}{M}}$
5. If humidity in air increases then the velocity of sound also increases.

11. False. Motion of particles in the atmosphere is not periodic.
12. False. Velocity is sound is high in solids. So, the statement is false.
13. Motion of the needle of a sewing machine is an example for oscillatory motion.
22. Velocity of sound in solids is greater than that of in liquids.
    Hence, the correct option is (a).
23. Velocity of sound in solids is given by

    $$Vs = \sqrt{\frac{Y}{d}}$$

    Y = Young's modulus of solid
    d = density of solid medium.
    Hence, the correct option is (a).
31. Hertz is the SI unit of frequency.
32. Velocity of sound in air is given by, $V = \sqrt{\frac{\gamma P}{\rho}}$,
    where, $\gamma = \frac{C_P}{C_v}$, where C_p, C_v are specific heat capacities of gas at constant pressure and volume, respectively.
    $\rho \rightarrow$ density of gas.
33. The audible range of frequency of sound waves for human beings is 20 Hz to 20 kHz.
34. When sound wave propagates through a medium, the amplitude of vibration decreases.
35. Since the intensity (I) varies directly as the square of the amplitude A, we can write:

    $$\frac{I_1}{I_2} = \frac{A_1^2}{A_2^2} \Rightarrow \frac{16}{25} = \frac{A_1^2}{A_2^2}$$

    Taking the square root, we get $\frac{A_1}{A_2} = \frac{4}{5}$
36. The frequency of sound wave (n) = 11 kHz
    $n = 11 \times 10^3$Hz
    Wavelength of sound wave (λ) = 20 cm = 20×10^{-2} m.
    $\therefore$ Velocity of sound wave (V) = $n\,\lambda$
    = $(11 \times 10^3 \times 20 \times 10^{-2})$ m s^{-1}
    = $11 \times 2 \times 10^2$ m s^{-1} = 2200 m s^{-1}
37. The ratio of frequencies produced, by a vibrating stretched string is 1 : 2 : 3 : 4 ......etc. The fore, the ratio of frequencies of 1st overtone (second harmonic) and 2nd overtone (3rd harmonic) is = 2 : 3.
38. Collect the data from the problem and find the length (ℓ), tension (T) and mass (M) of the stretched string (b). Find the linear mass density (m) using the formula, $m = M/\ell$ (a). The fundamental frequency of a stretched vibrating string is given by, $n = \frac{1}{2\ell}\sqrt{\frac{T}{m}}$(c). The frequency of 2nd overtone or 3rd harmonic is given by,

    $$n_2 = \frac{3}{2\ell}\sqrt{\frac{T}{m}} = 3n(d).$$
39. Find the first and second resonating lengths of air columns and frequency of the tuning fork from the given problem (a). Find the first and second resonating lengths 'ℓ_1' and 'ℓ_2' in terms of 'λ'. $\ell_1 = \lambda/4$ and $\ell_2 = 3\lambda/4$ (c). The velocity of sound $V = n\lambda = 2n(\ell_2 - \ell_1)$ (b) Substitute values and get value of 'V' (d).
40. (b)

    (C) Fix a string to a rigid support and hang a known weight from the other end.

    (B) Determine the linear mass density of the string.

    (D) Set the string into vibration.

    (A) Use the formula $V = \sqrt{\frac{T}{\mu}}$ to determine the velocity of wave.

    Hence, the correction option is (b), i.e., C B D A is the required sequential order.

Level 2: Review Your Concepts

Note: This is how you should frame your answer covering.

41. $I_1 = I$, $I_2 = 4I$

$d_1 = 5$ m, $d_2 = ?$

$$\frac{I_1}{I_2} = \left(\frac{d_2}{d_1}\right)^2$$

$$d_2 = \sqrt{\frac{I_1}{I_2}} \times d_1$$

$$\sqrt{\frac{I}{4I}} \times 5 = 2.5 \text{ m}$$

42. (i) Find the distance the sound travels to reach the observer from source of sound.

Find the interval of time heard between the two sounds that passes through the pipe and air x.

Find the velocity of sound in air from the given information.

Find time taken by sound to reach from source to observer through air, by using formula time,

$$t_1 = \frac{\text{Distance}}{\text{Velocity}}$$

since u the velocity of sound in solids more than that of the air then, the time taken by sound to travel in solids is less than that in air.

Time taken by sound to travel in metallic pipe,

$$t_2 = \left(t_1 - \frac{1}{2}\right)\text{s.}$$

Find the time taken by sound to reach the observer through the metallic pipe.

Find the velocity of sound in metallic pipe by dividing distance by 't_2'.

(ii) Sound travels faster in pipe.

(iii) Speed of sound is different in the two media.

(iv) 1200 m s^{-1}

43. (i) Fundamental frequency for a closed pipe, $n = \frac{v}{4\ell}$

(ii) Closed pipe, 110 cm

44. $V_2 = 1360$ m s^{-1}

$V_2 = 340$ m s^{-1}

$$\frac{V_1}{V_2} = \sqrt{\frac{M_2}{M_1}}$$

$$\frac{1360}{340} = \sqrt{\frac{32}{M_1}}$$

$$\frac{136}{34} = \frac{4\sqrt{2}}{\sqrt{M_1}},\ \sqrt{M_1} = \frac{34 \times 4\sqrt{2}}{136}$$

$$M_1 = \frac{4^2 \times 34^2 \times 2}{(136)^2} = 2$$

Hence, it is H_2 gas.

45. (i) Find the time taken by the reflected waves from the shoal of fish to reach the stationary submarine two times in an interval of 20 minutes form the given data.

Take them as t_1 and t_2.

Find the velocity of sound in water using given information.

Here, $$v = \frac{2d}{t} \qquad (1)$$

By using the formula, (1) for echo, find the distance of the shoal of fish from the submarine. (Take it as d_1 and d_2).

Now, the speed of the shoal of fish, v is equal to the distance moved by the shoal of fish in one second.

Consider, $v = \frac{d_1 \sim d_2}{t}$

What is the direction in which sonar sends waves?

Find the direction of the motion of the fish.

(ii) 3.75 m s^{-1} (west)

46. $V = 108$ km h^{-1} $= \frac{108 \times 5}{18} = 30$ m s^{-1}.

$$V = \frac{100 + 100 + 30 \times \frac{2}{3}}{\frac{2}{3}}$$

$$= \frac{220 \times 3}{2} = 110 \times 3 = 330 \text{ m s}^{-1}$$

47. (i) What is the depth of the well?

What is the initial velocity of the stone?

What is the time (t_1) taken by the stone to reach the bottom of the well?

Find the value of "t_1" by using the formula, $s = ut + \frac{1}{2}gt^2$.

Take the time taken by the person to hear sound of splash as 't_2'.
Find the time interval between t_2 and t_1 by using the formula, $\Delta t = (t_2 - t_1)$s.
Then, find the velocity of sound in air by dividing the depth of the well by Δt.

(ii) 320 m s^{-1}

48. (i) Find $\frac{P}{\rho}$ from $V = \sqrt{\frac{\gamma p}{\rho}}$

(ii) Substitute it in $\frac{P}{\rho} = \frac{RT}{M}$

(iii) 28

49. (i) $v \propto \sqrt{T}$, $v \propto \frac{1}{\sqrt{M}}$

(ii) −193 °C

50. (i) **Case 1:**

When a man claps at regular time interval of 1.2 seconds, he does not hear the echo distinctly.
Now, find the time taken to produce echo (t_1).
Consider the distance between man and cliff as 'd_1'.

Case 2:
The man moves closer to the cliff by 32 m and claps at regular interval of time of 1 second. He doesn't hear the echo distinctly.
Find the time taken for producing an echo (t_2).
Now, consider the distance between man and cliff as "d_2".
Find the relation between d_1 and d_2.

$d_2 = d_1 - 32$ (1)

The formula for velocity of sound using echo method is:

$$V = \frac{2d_1}{t_1} = \frac{2d_2}{t_2} \quad (2)$$

Substitute the value of 'd_2' interms of 'd_1'.

Calculate the value of 'v' from 2nd equation.

(ii) 320 m s^{-1}

51. (i) $n \propto \frac{\sqrt{T}}{\ell}$

(ii) Percentage change in frequency $= \frac{n_2 - n_1}{n_1} \times 100$

(iii) 100%

52. Which physical quantity is a measure of pitch? How does it vary in the case of vibrating air columns?
When a vessel is filled by a water tap, will the length of the vibrating air column decreases?
Will this decrease in the length affect the frequency of the vibrations?
Find the relation between the frequency and the length of the resonating column.
Now, find the relation between the pitch and frequency.

53. (i) How the frequency depends on length of the air column?

(ii) How the presence of water influences the frequency of vibrations.

54. (i) Take the velocity of sound in air as 'v'.
Take the frequency of the tuning fork as 'n'.

When the first overtone (or) second harmonic is considered, then, $\ell_1 = \lambda$ and $\ell_2 = 3\frac{\lambda}{4}$ (1)
Obtain the value of 'λ' in terms of ℓ_1 and ℓ_2 and substitute it in the formula $v = n\lambda$.
Find the ratio of 'ℓ_1' to 'ℓ_2'.

(ii) 4 : 3

55. $T = 200$ N
$M = 0.05$ kg, $\ell = ?$ $V = 15$ m s^{-1}

$$V = \sqrt{\frac{T}{\mu}}$$

$$= \sqrt{\frac{200}{\frac{0.05}{\ell}}}$$

$$15 = \sqrt{\frac{200}{1} \times \frac{\ell}{0.05}}$$

$$225 = 4000\,\ell$$

$$\ell = \frac{225}{4000} \text{ m}$$

$$= \frac{225}{4000}$$
$= 0.056$ m.
$= 5.6$ cm.

56. Velocity of a wave in a string, $v = \sqrt{\frac{T}{m}}$

$T = M(a + g) = 3(2 + 10)$

$T = 3 \times 12 = 36$N

$m = 32.4 \times 10^3$ kg m^{-1}

$$v = \sqrt{\frac{T}{m}} = \sqrt{\frac{36}{32.4 \times 10^{-3}}} = \sqrt{\frac{1}{9 \times 10^{-4}}}$$

$$= \sqrt{\frac{10^4}{9}} = \frac{100}{3} = 33.3\,\text{ms}^{-1}$$

57. Fundamental frequency of an open pipe,

$$n_1 = \frac{v_{air}}{2\ell}$$

$v_{air} = 320$ m s^{-1}

$l = 12$ cm $= 0.12$ m

Fundamental frequency of closed pipe,

$$n_1 = \frac{v_{gas}}{4\ell}$$

$v_{gas} = ?$

$\ell = 13.5$ cm $= 0.135$ m

Frequency of first overtone,

$$n_2 = 3\left(\frac{v_g}{4\ell}\right)$$

$$n_1 = n_2$$

$$\frac{320}{2 \times 0.12} = 3\left(\frac{v_g}{4 \times 0.135}\right)$$

$$v_g = \frac{320 \times 4 \times 0.135}{2 \times 0.12 \times 3} \Rightarrow v_g = 240\text{ms}^{-1}$$

58. Let the length of each half of the wire be L.

Let the wavelength of each half be λ_1 and λ_2 as the number of loops are different in each half.

$$\lambda_1 = \frac{V_1}{v} \text{ and } \lambda_2 = \frac{V_2}{n} \Rightarrow \frac{V_1}{V_2} = \frac{n\lambda_1}{n\lambda_2} = \frac{\lambda_1}{\lambda_2} \quad (1)$$

$$3\frac{\lambda_1}{2} = L \Rightarrow \lambda_1 = \frac{2L}{3} \Rightarrow 6\frac{\lambda_2}{2} = L \Rightarrow \lambda_2 = \frac{2L}{6} = \frac{L}{3}$$

Substituting in (1) $\frac{V_1}{V_2} = \frac{2L}{3} \times \frac{3}{L} = 2 \quad (2)$

Each half of the wire consists of copper wire of different thickness because the wavelength of waves is different in each half of the wire.

Now,

$$V_1 = \sqrt{\frac{T}{M}} \text{ and } V_2 = \sqrt{\frac{T}{M_2}}\ \frac{V_1}{V_2} = \sqrt{\frac{M_2}{M_1}} = \sqrt{\frac{A_2 \times d}{A_1 \times d}}$$

where, d is the density which is the same $\frac{V_1}{V_2}$

$$= \sqrt{\frac{A_2}{A_1}} = \sqrt{\left(\frac{r_2}{r_1}\right)^2} = \frac{r_2}{r_1}$$

From (2) $\frac{r_2}{r_1} = 2 \Rightarrow \frac{r_1}{r_2} = 1:2$

59. Fundamental frequency = 10 Hz

$V = 10$ m s^{-1}

$\ell = ?$

$$\upsilon = \sqrt{\frac{T}{\mu}}$$

$$n = \frac{1}{2\ell}\sqrt{\frac{T}{\mu}}$$

$\ell = 0.5$ m or $\ell = 50$ cm

Level 3: Assess Your Concepts

Note: This is how you should frame your answer covering.

60. (i) Take the length of one half of the wire as 'ℓ'.
Take tuning fork of frequency 'n', to excite the sonometer wire.
How are the velocities (v), frequency (n) and wavelengths (λ) in each half related?
Find the values of λ in terms of 'ℓ' for both the sides (halves).

Find the ratio of velocities of both the halves, using the formula,

$$v = n\lambda \quad (1)$$

Does the tension (T) in two halves of the wire remain same?

Find the formula that shows the relation between v, T and linear density (m).

Is it, $$V = \sqrt{\frac{T}{m}} \quad (2)$$

Now, take linear densities of first and second half as M_1 and M_2.

$$\text{Linear density, } M = \frac{\text{Mass of wire (m)}}{\text{Length of the wire } (\ell)}$$

Then, $$\frac{v_1}{v_2} = \sqrt{\frac{M_2}{M_1}} = \sqrt{\frac{m_2}{m_1}}$$

Is the metal of the two halves of the wire same?

Will the density (d) of the two halves be equal?

Then, find the value of 'm' in terms of volume and density.

Here, volume (V) of the wire = (Area of cross – section) (length of the wire)

Then, $V = \pi r^2 \ell$.

Take the radii of two halves of the sonometer wire as 'r_1' and 'r_2'

Now, find the ratio of v_1 and v_2 interms of r_1 and r_2.

(ii) 1 : 2 or 2 : 1 (ratio of velocity)

(iii) 2 : 1 or 1 : 2 (ratio of radii)

61. $f_2 = \frac{2V}{2\ell} = \frac{2 \times 330}{2 \times 3} = 110 \text{ Hz}$

Yes, it would be in resonance with tuning fork of frequency 110 Hz.

62. $\frac{5\lambda}{4} + e = 82$

$\frac{7\lambda}{4} - e = 122$

$\frac{\lambda}{2} = 122 - 82 = 40$

$\lambda = 80$ cm

$v = 320 = f \times 0.8$

$f = \frac{320}{0.8} = \frac{3200}{8} = 400 \text{ Hz}$

63. $f' = f\left[\frac{C + V_0}{C}\right]$

I case

$$200 = f\left[\frac{330 + 5}{330}\right]$$

$$f = \frac{200 + 330}{335}$$

$\therefore f = 197$ Hz = Frequency of source of sound

II case

$$f'' = f\left[\frac{C + V_0}{C}\right]$$

$$f'' = 197\left[\frac{330 + 10}{330}\right]$$

$\therefore \quad f'' = 203$ Hz = Apparent frequency

$f'' - f' = 203 - 200$

= 3 Hz = Change in apparent frequency.

64. (i) When the source of sound and observer are at rest, is there any apparent change in the frequency of the sound?

Will it result in Doppler effect?

Find the relation between the velocity of the sound (v_1) and its wavelength (λ_1), when frequency of the sound remains constant.

Find λ_1 in terms of v_1 and f.

Is the direction of the wind and sound same?

Does the velocity of the sound increase? (Take it as v_2)

Find the value of 'v_2' interms of 'v_1.'

$V_2 = v + 0.2v$, Find λ_2.

Ratio of frequency is the ratio of velocity of sound with respect to the observer to that with respect to the source.

(ii) 20% change in wavelength, zero per cent change in frequency.

65. Initially the person is at 'P' at a distance of 150 m from the wall.

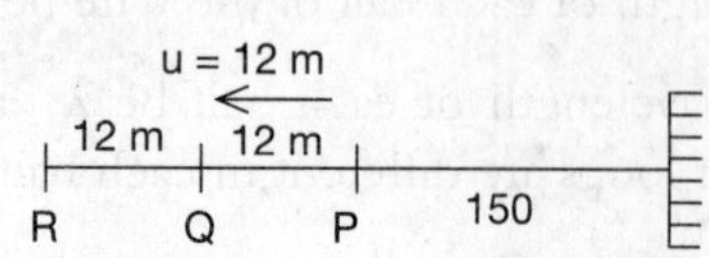

In 1s he moves a distance of 12 m.

When he is at a distance of 162 m from the wall, he blows the horn.

Time taken to hear an echo = 1 s

Total distance traveled by the sound

= (162 × 2) + 12

= 324 + 12 = 336 m

Velocity of sound = 336/1 = 336 m s^{-1}

66. $T = 2\pi\sqrt{\frac{\ell}{g}} = 2\pi\sqrt{\frac{m\ell}{mg}}$

When the bob is immersed in a liquid, net downward force = weight of bob – upthrust

$$ma = mg - m\frac{\rho_\ell}{\rho_m}g = mg\left(1 - \frac{\rho_\ell}{\rho_m}\right)$$

Given, $\rho_m = 5\rho_\ell$

$$ma = mg\left(1 - \frac{1}{5}\right) = mg\left(\frac{4}{5}\right)$$

$$T^1 = 2\pi\sqrt{\frac{m\ell}{mg\left(\frac{4}{5}\right)}} = T\sqrt{\frac{4}{5}}T^1 = \sqrt{\frac{5}{4}}T$$

67. The time taken by the plate to fall through 10 cm can be found by the equation of motion for a freely falling body.

$$s = ut + \frac{1}{2}at^2$$

In this case, u = 0 and a = g. So,

$$s = \frac{1}{2}gt^2 \Rightarrow t = \sqrt{\frac{2s}{g}}$$

Substitute s = 10 cm = 0.1 m

$$T = \sqrt{\frac{2s}{g}} = \sqrt{\frac{2 \times 0.1}{9.8}} = \sqrt{\frac{2}{98}} = \frac{1}{7}\text{ second.}$$

The number of oscillations of the tuning fork in 1/7 second

$$= 56 \times \frac{1}{7} = 8 \text{ oscillations}$$

The pointer strikes the plate 8 times during the fall of the plate.

68.

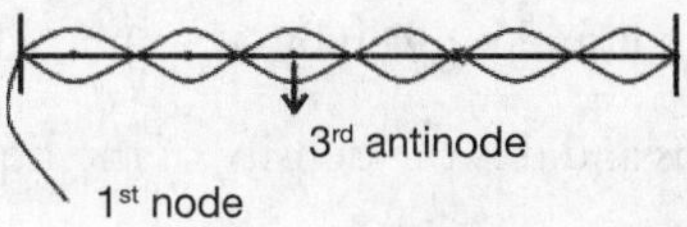

Distance between 1st node and 3rd antinode is $\frac{5\lambda}{4} - 0 =$ 2.5 m

λ = 2 m

In 6th harmonic

$$\frac{6\lambda}{2} = \ell$$

$$\frac{6 \times 2}{2} = \ell$$

$\therefore \ell = 6$ m.

69. Open pipe

$$\frac{PV}{2l} = 150$$

$$P = \frac{150 \times 2\ell}{V}$$

$$= \frac{150 \times 2 \times 2}{300}$$

= 2

Closed pipe

$$\frac{V(2P-1)}{4\ell} = 150$$

$$2P - 1 = \frac{150 \times 4\ell}{V}$$

$$= \frac{150 \times 4 \times 2.5}{300}$$

$\Rightarrow$ 2P – 1 = 5

2P = 6

$\therefore$ P = 3

(2P – 1) = (2 × 3 – 1) = 5

Harmonic in open pipe is 2nd

Harmonic in closed pipe is 5th.

70. The speed of the waves is the same for whatever the frequency used.

Hence, we have $n_1\lambda_1 = n_2\lambda_2 \Rightarrow \lambda_2 = \frac{n_1\lambda_1}{n_2}$

$$= \frac{738 \times 10^3 \text{Hz} \times 406.5\text{m}}{102.8 \times 10^6 \, Hz} = 2918.258 \times 10^{-3} m \approx 2.92 m$$

71. Velocity of sound in a liquid is given by, $v = \sqrt{\frac{k}{d}}$, where k is the bulk modulus and d is the density of the liquid.

Given velocity of sound, v = 1500 m/s,

Density, d = 8×10^3 kg m^{-3}

$$\therefore 1500 = \sqrt{\frac{k}{8 \times 10^3}} \Rightarrow 1500^2 = \frac{k}{8 \times 10^3}$$

$$\Rightarrow k = 8 \times 10^3 \times 1500^2 = 18 \times 10^9\, Pa$$

72. Let t be the time after the production of sound, for which the person hears the echo.

The distance travelled by sound, in the time,

$$d = \frac{v \times t}{2} \Leftarrow t = \frac{2d}{v} = \frac{2 \times 495}{330} = \frac{990}{330} = 3\, s$$

73. Given, l_1 = 25 cm and l_2 = 75 cm; velocity v = 330 m/s

If 'v' is the velocity of sound, then we have $v = 2n\,(l_2 - l_1)$

$$\Rightarrow n = \frac{v}{2(l_2 - l_1)} = \frac{330m/s}{2(75cm - 25cm)}$$

$$= \frac{33000cm/s}{2(50)\,cm} = 330Hz$$

74. The frequency of the vibrating stretched string in a sonometer is given by the expression

$$n = \frac{1}{2l}\sqrt{\frac{T}{m}}$$

Where l is the length of the string, T is the tension in the string and m is the linear density or mass per unit volume of the string.

When the frequency is the same, the resonating square root of tension in the string is directly proportional to the length of the string.

$$\Rightarrow \frac{\sqrt{T_1}}{l_1} = \frac{\sqrt{T_2}}{l_2} \Rightarrow l_2 = l_1\sqrt{\frac{T_2}{T_1}}$$

$$= 25\, cm \times \sqrt{\frac{9kg\ wt}{1kg\ wt}} = 25\, cm \times 3 = 75\, cm$$

JEE-NEET SPECIAL WING

Multiple-Answer Type Questions

1. The frequency of sound waves and the pressure of the gas do not affect the velocity of sound in the air.
Hence, the correct option is (a, b)

2. Given,
Frequencies, $n_1 = 110$ Hz and $n_2 = 120$ Hz
Wavelength, $\lambda_1 = 3\ m$
We have, the velocity of a sound wave, $v = n\lambda$
Then $n_1 \times \lambda_1 = n_2 \times \lambda_2$ (since the velocity of sound is constant in a given gas)
$\Rightarrow 110 \times 3 = 120 \times \lambda_2$
$\Rightarrow \lambda_2 = 330/120 = 2.75$ m
Now, the velocity of the waves, $v = n_1 \times \lambda_1$
$= 110 \times 3 = 330$ m/s
Hence, the correct option is (c)

3. Given, Initial distance between the car and the hill, $s = 1$ km $= 1000\ m$
Velocity of sound, $v = 330\ \text{ms}^{-1}$
Let 'x' be the distance travelled by the car by the time the driver heard the sound of an echo.
Therefore, the total distance travelled by the sound $= 1000 + (1000 - x) = 2000 - x$
Let 'u' be the velocity of the car.
Then the distance travelled 'x' in 4.5 *s* can be taken as, $x = 4.5\ u$
Then the total distance travelled by the sound $= 2000 - 4.5\ u$ (a)
In the same time, 4.5 *s*, the distance travelled by the sound = 4.5 × velocity of sound
$= 4.5 \times 330$ (*b*)
From (a) and (*b*), $2000 - 4.5\ u = 4.5 \times 330$
$\Rightarrow 4.5\ u = 2000 - 1485 = 515$
$\Rightarrow u = 515/4.5 = 114.4$ m/s $= 114.4 \times 18/5$
$= 411.9$ km/h
Hence, the correct option is (a, b)

4. Given,
Increase in the weight = 21%
i.e., an increase in the tension (*T*) is 21%
Therefore, the increase in the fundamental frequency is 5 Hz
We have, the fundamental frequency is given by
$$f = \frac{1}{2l}\sqrt{\frac{T}{m}}$$
Since the length of the wire is constant, the linear mass density (*m*) also remains constant.
Then $\dfrac{f_1}{f_2} = \sqrt{\dfrac{T_1}{T_2}}$ (a)
Let the initial tension in the string, $T_1 = T$
Then the final tension in the string, $T_2 = T + 0.21T = 1.21T$
Let the initial frequency, $f_1 = f$
Then the final frequency, $f_2 = f + 5$
Using the equation (a), $\dfrac{f}{f+5} = \sqrt{\dfrac{T}{1.21T}}$
$$\Rightarrow \frac{f}{f+5} = \frac{1}{1.1} \Rightarrow 1.1f = f + 5$$
$\Rightarrow 0.1f = 5 \Rightarrow f = 50\text{ Hz} = f_1$
Now, keeping the original tension constant and increasing the length of the sonometer wire by 10%,
i.e., Let the initial length, $L_1 = L$
then the final length, $L_2 = L + 0.1L = 1.1L$
Now, from the fundamental frequency, $f = \dfrac{1}{2l}\sqrt{\dfrac{T}{m}}$
We have, $\dfrac{f_1}{f_2} = \dfrac{L_2}{L_1}$
$$\Rightarrow \frac{50}{f_2} = \frac{1.1L}{L} \Rightarrow f_2 = \frac{50}{1.1} = 45.45\text{ Hz}$$
Therefore, the change in fundamental frequency $= f_1 - f_2 = 50 - 45.45 = 4.55$ Hz
Therefore, the fundamental frequency will decrease by 4.55 Hz.
Hence, the correct option is (a)

5. Given, frequency of the tuning fork, $f = 250$ Hz
Speed of sound in air, $v = 320\ \text{m s}^{-1}$
In case of a closed organ pipe, the fundamental frequency is $\dfrac{v}{4L}$ and only odd harmonics are present.
Therefore, the second overtone will mean fifth harmonic.
i.e., $f = \dfrac{5v}{4L}$
$$\Rightarrow L = \frac{5v}{4f} = \frac{5 \times 320}{4 \times 250} = \frac{1600}{1000} = 1.6\ m$$
Hence, the correct option is (a, b, c)

Comprehension-Based Questions

6. Sound waves and the waves on the surface of water require medium
Hence, the correct option is (d)

7. During the propagation of a sound wave, the regions of compressions of the medium have high pressure and high density.
Hence, the correct option is (d)

8. We have, the velocity of sound in a gas is directly proportional to the square root of its absolute temperature.

i.e., velocity of sound, $v \propto \sqrt{T} \Rightarrow \frac{v_1}{v_2} = \sqrt{\frac{T_1}{T_2}}$

Let $T_1 = T$ then $T_2 = T + 3T = 4T$

Now, $\frac{v_1}{v_2} = \sqrt{\frac{T}{4T}} = \frac{1}{2} \Rightarrow v_2 = 2v_1$

Hence, the correct option is (c)

9. When a sound wave propagates through a gas medium, the particles of the medium vibrate parallel to the direction of propagation.
Hence, the correct option is (a)

10. If the pressure of the gas increases, the velocity of sound in the gas does not change as it does not depend on the pressure of the gas.
Hence, the correct option is (c)

11. A. The velocity of sound in a gas is inversely proportional to the square root of its molecular weight (M). i.e., $v \propto \frac{1}{\sqrt{M}} \Rightarrow \frac{v_1}{v_2} = \sqrt{\frac{M_2}{M_1}}$

Given, $\frac{M_1}{M_2} = \frac{1}{4}$

Then $\frac{v_1}{v_2} = \sqrt{\frac{4}{1}} = \frac{2}{1}$ **A → d**

B. The velocity of sound in a gas is inversely proportional to the square root of its density (d).

i.e., $v \propto \frac{1}{\sqrt{d}} \Rightarrow \frac{v_1}{v_2} = \sqrt{\frac{d_2}{d_1}} \Rightarrow \frac{d_1}{d_2} = \left(\frac{v_2}{v_1}\right)^2$

Given, $\frac{v_1}{v_2} = \frac{1}{2}$

Then $\frac{d_1}{d_2} = \left(\frac{v_2}{v_1}\right)^2 = \left(\frac{2}{1}\right)^2 = \frac{4}{1}$ **B → c**

C. The velocity of sound in a gas does not depend on the frequency of the sound wave.
Therefore, the ratio of velocities will be 1:1.
C → a

D. The velocity of sound in a gas does not depend on the wavelength of the sound wave.
Therefore, the ratio of velocities will be 1:1.
D → a

E. Given, persistence of hearing, $t = 0.1\ s$
Speed of sound, $v = 330$ m/s
The minimum distance required to hear an echo,

$$d = \frac{vt}{2} = \frac{330 \times 0.1}{2} = 16.5\ m$$

E → b

Unit IV

Thermodynamics

In this Unit

CHAPTER

5

Thermodynamics-II

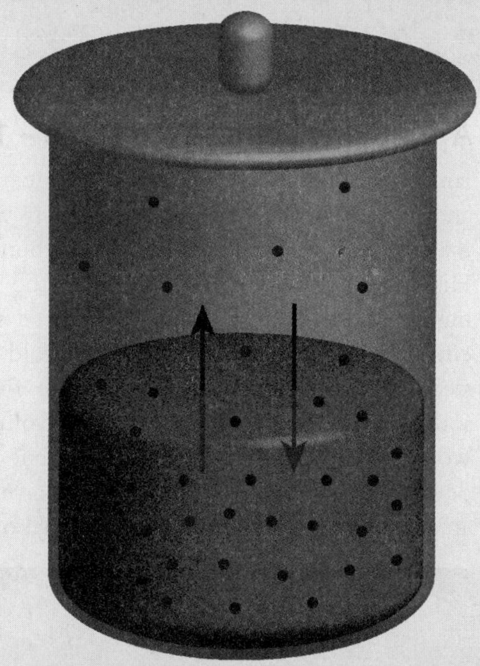

Remember

Before beginning this chapter, you should be able to:

- Make clear distinction between heat and temperature, understand measurement of temperature with the help of thermometers.
- Know good and bad conductors of heat, different modes of heat transfer and their applications.
- Understand the change of states of matter on supplying heat, factors affecting heat absorbed and lost by a substance and measurement of heat energy.
- State certain laws such as Boyle's Law, Charles' Law, etc.

Key Ideas

After completing this chapter, you should be able to:

- Understand the various factors affecting the heat absorbed by a body and to deduce an expression for heat energy.
- Study the different factors affecting the thermal expansion of substance and to understand how this is used in different practical applications.
- Understand why there is no change in temperature during the change of state and to deduce an expression for the calculations of latent heat.
- Recognize heat as a form of energy and to understand that heat energy can also be converted into mechanical energy.
- Understand how the conversion of heat energy into mechanical energy is used in heat engines.

Scientific Crypt

A Tribute to James Watt (1736 – 1819)

James Watt, was a mechanical engineer by profession and a famous Scottish inventor. He is well known for making improvement to the Newcomen steam engine. His improvements not only made the steam engines highly cost-effective but also enhanced the power and efficiency of the steam engines manifold. The modified steam engine eventually became the foremost energy source which led to the industrial revolution across the world. The cost-effective and efficient steam engines developed by Watt helped transforming the world from an agricultural society into an industrial one.

Because of his ill health, his initial part of schooling was done at home and it was only when he was fourteen that he started his formal schooling. His experience with the tools from his father's carpenter bench provided him the basics of engineering and tooling. His experience with his mother's tea kettle provided him an insight into the fundamental nature of steam, which ultimately led to his greatest contribution to mankind. The concept of horsepower was developed by Watt and the SI unit of power, the watt, was named in his honor.

FUN TIME

CROSSWORD

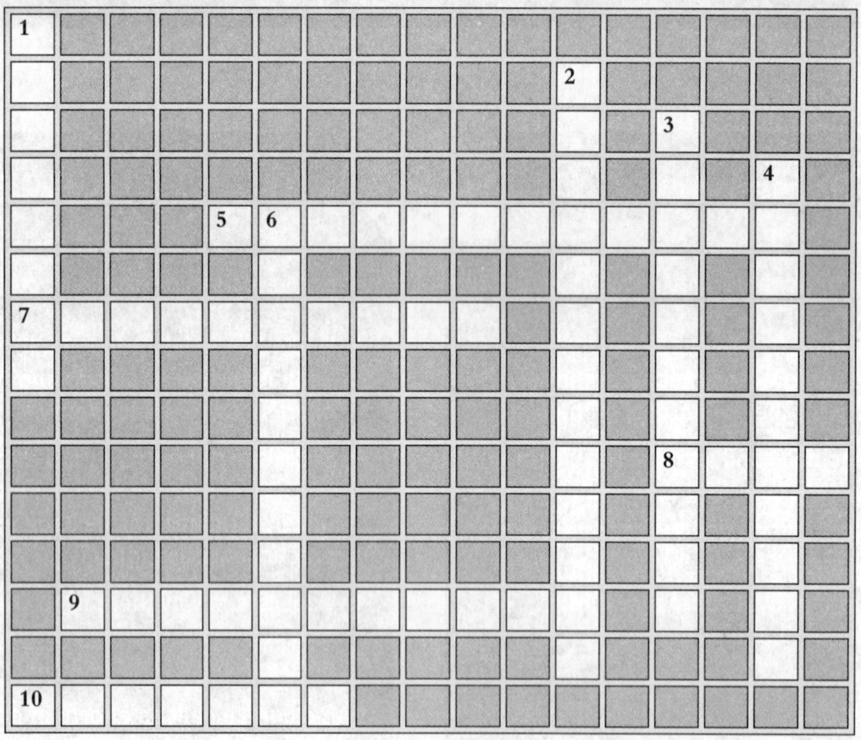

Across

5. Absolute scale of temperature.
7. This is a process in which ice is melted by applying pressure.
8. This is the unit of water equivalent.
9. The process in which substance is directly converted from solid state to gaseous state.
10. This process of conversion of a substance from liquid state to gaseous state at a particular temperature.

Down

1. This is a physical quantity increase of which will lead to the increase in boiling point of water.
2. The engine which has the efficiency of 40%.
3. In this the conversion of heat energy to mechanical energy takes place.
4. This is proportional to the average kinetic energy of molecules.
6. This process of conversion of a substance from one state to another can takes place at different temperatures.

INTRODUCTION

In the previous classes, we have understood that heat is a form of energy, also, some of the other forms of energy can be converted to heat and vice versa. Similarly, by the work-energy theorem, we understand that work done on a body can appear in the form of heat. For example, when we rub our palms, the biochemical energy is expended to do the 'work' which results in warmth in the palms.

Thus, we see that when some form of energy is converted to heat energy, it makes a substance or a body 'hotter'. This degree of hotness (or coldness) is called 'temperature'.

Furthermore, we have also seen that when hot lead shots are dropped into cold water, the temperature of the lead shots decreases while the temperature of the water increases, indicating that heat energy always flows from hot bodies to cold bodies, and this flow of heat stops when the temperatures of the two bodies are equal—a condition known as thermal equilibrium.

To elaborate on this, let us take another example. If an ice-cube at 0°C is dropped into a vessel containing water at 0°C, the ice cube does not melt, since the two substances are at the same temperature and heat does not flow from water to ice even though water has more heat content (336 J g^{-1}) than ice.

Thus, while heat is a form of energy, rise (or fall) of temperature is one of its effects. Another important effect of heat is that, on supply of heat, matter changes its state—ice melts to become water, a liquid boils to vaporize. Similarly, when heat is taken away from a hot substance, it can also result in change of state–water freezing to form ice, steam condensing into water.

We have also studied that the thermal expansion is another effect of heat, and solids as well as liquids and gases expand on heating. We shall now study calorimetry (measurement of heat energy) in greater detail. We will also direct our attention to working principle of heat engines, an important application of thermal energy.

Heat

Every body contains some amount of heat. This is equal to sum total of kinetic energy and potential energy of all the molecules present in the body. When heat is supplied to a body, average kinetic energy of its molecules increases, thus, increasing its temperature. We say that the body has become hot. The opposite happens if heat is removed from a body. Then, we say that the body has cooled. Thus, heat is a form of energy which gives us sensation of hotness or coldness.

Units of Heat

Since heat is a form of energy, its units are same as that of other forms of energy.

S.I. unit of heat is joule (J).

Calorie (cal) is another unit which is specially used for heat.

One calorie is the amount of heat required to raise the temperature of 1 g of water by one degree celsius.

The two units of heat are related as below:

1 cal = 4.1863 J ≅ 4.2 J

1 kcal = 4186.3 J ≅ 4200 J

where, 1 kcal = 1000 cal.

Heat Capacity

To increase the temperature of a body, we have to supply heat to it. But the rise in temperature is not the same for all bodies for the same amount of heat supplied.

If we supply the same amount of heat to 400 g and 700 g of water, we find that rise in temperature is more in the former than in the latter case. If equal masses of water and milk are supplied with the same amount of heat, the rise in temperature of milk is more than that of water.

Thus, rise in temperature and heat supplied to a body are related by a term called 'heat capacity' or 'thermal capacity' of a body. It is denoted by '*C*'. It is defined as the amount of heat needed to raise the temperature of a given mass of a body by 1 K or 1°C.

It is equal to the ratio of total heat '*Q*' supplied to the rise in temperature '$\Delta\theta$' of a body. Let *Q* joule of heat be supplied to a body so that its temperature rises by $\Delta\theta$ K. Then heat capacity (*C*) of the body $= \dfrac{Q}{\Delta\theta}$

$$\therefore C = \frac{Q}{\Delta\theta}$$

Thus, unit of heat capacity $= \dfrac{\text{Unit of heat}}{\text{Unit of temperature}}$

Hence, S.I. unit of heat capacity is $\dfrac{\text{joule}}{\text{kelvin}}$ ($J\,K^{-1}$).

Other common units of heat capacity (*C*) are

$J\,°C^{-1}$, $cal\,°C^{-1}$ or $kcal\,°C^{-1}$

$1\,cal\,°C^{-1} = 4.2\,J\,K^{-1} = 4.2\,J\,°C^{-1}$

$1\,kcal\,°C^{-1} = 4200\,J\,K^{-1} = 4200\,J\,°C^{-1}$

It can be seen that here °C and K are interchangeable since we consider only the change in temperature.

Konnect

The heat capacity of an object is directly proportional to its mass. That's why larger objects take longer to heat up or cool down.

Factors Affecting Heat Absorbed or Given Out by a Body

Consider two similar containers *A* and *B* containing half a litre and one litre of water, respectively. The initial temperature of water in both the containers (which is equal to room temperature, say θ_1) is noted with the help of a thermometer. Both these containers are placed on two similar burners that supply heat at a constant rate; and heated. To attain an equal higher temperature, say θ_2, it is observed that the container *B* takes more time compared to the time taken by the water in the container *A*. Thus, heat absorbed by *B* is greater than that absorbed by *A*. This implies that larger the mass of a body, greater is the heat absorbed or given out by it.

Now consider two similar containers *P* and *Q* having equal volumes of water. Thus, the mass of water in both the containers is equal. Now both the containers are placed on burners that supply heat at a constant rate and heated. If the required rise in temperature of *P* is more than that of Q, it is observed that *P* has to be heated for more time compared to Q. Thus, the heat absorbed by *P* is greater than that absorbed by Q. This implies that the amount of heat absorbed or given out by a body depends on the change in its temperature.

The experimental results show that,

1. Heat absorbed or given out by a body is directly proportional to the mass of the body.

$$Q \propto m \tag{5.1}$$

2. Heat absorbed or given out by a body is directly proportional to the rise or fall in temperature of the body.

$$Q \propto \Delta\theta \tag{5.2}$$

Combining equations (5.1) and (5.2), we get $Q \propto m\,\Delta\theta$ $\;Q = m\,s\,\Delta\theta$, where, *s* is a constant of proportionality, which we shall discuss later.

EXAMPLE 5.1 Suppose 2 g of a metal requires 10 J of heat energy to raise its temperature by 2°C, and 50 g of the same metal requires 250 J of heat energy for the same temperature rise. Calculate the heat capacity of the metal in both cases.

SOLUTION

$$\text{Heat Capacity} = \frac{\text{Heat}}{\text{Rise in temperature}}$$

1st case:

For 2 g of metal:

Given heat = 10 J and temperature rise = 2°C,

$$C = \frac{10J}{2°C} = 5J°C^{-1}$$

2nd case:

For 50 g of metal:

Given heat = 250 J and temperature rise = 2°C,

$$C = \frac{250J}{2°C} = 125J°C^{-1}$$

Thus, in the first case, the heat capacity of the metal is 5 $J°C^{-1}$, and in the second case, it's 125 $J°C^{-1}$.

Specific Heat Capacity

From the above example, it is seen that water has different heat capacities for different masses. This is observed in all the substances. As the mass changes, heat capacity also changes. But for a given mass of a given substance, it is constant. Therefore, heat capacity of a unit mass of substance is taken as reference and is called specific heat capacity. It is denoted by '*c*' or '*s*'

Specific heat capacity is defined as the amount of heat required to raise the temperature of unit mass of substance (1 kg or 1 g) by one kelvin or one degree celsius. Heat absorbed or given out by a body is given by,

$$Q = ms\,\Delta\,\theta$$

Thus, the constant of proportionality in the above equation is the specific heat capacity of the given body.

Units of Specific Heat Capacity

Info Bytes!

Water has one of the highest specific heat capacities among common substances, which is why it is often used as a coolant in car engines.

From the above equation, we get $s = \dfrac{Q}{m\Delta\theta}$.

$$\text{Thus, unit of } s = \frac{\text{Unit of Q}}{(\text{Unit of } m)\ (\text{Unit of } \Delta\theta)}$$

S.I. unit of specific heat capacity is $\dfrac{\text{joule}}{\text{kilogram} \times \text{kelvin}} = \text{J kg}^{-1}\,\text{K}^{-1}$.

As change in temperature in kelvin and celsius scales is equal, it can be written as $\text{J kg}^{-1}\ °\text{C}^{-1}$ also.

Other common units of specific heat capacity are $\text{cal g}^{-1}\,°\text{C}^{-1}$ or $\text{kcal kg}^{-1}\ °\text{C}^{-1}$.

$1\text{cal g}^{-1}\,°\text{C}^{-1} = 4.2\ \text{J g}^{-1}\ °\text{C}^{-1}$ and $1\ \text{kcal kg}^{-1}\ °\text{C}^{-1} = 4200\ \text{J kg}^{-1}\ °\text{C}^{-1}$

The specific heat capacity of a substance is independent of its mass. It is a characteristic property of a substance. Its value is different for different substances.

Table 5.1 Specific heat capacity of substances

Substance	Specific heat capacity cal g^{-1} °C^{-1}	J g^{-1} °C^{-1}	J kg^{-1} K^{-1}
Water	1.00	4.20	4200
Alcohol	0.52	2.18	2180
Kerosene Oil	0.50	2.10	2100
Turpentine Oil	0.42	1.76	1760
Aluminium	0.21	0.882	882
Flint glass	0.12	0.504	504
Iron	0.115	0.483	483
Copper	0.095	0.399	399
Zinc	0.093	0.391	391
Brass	0.092	0.386	386
Silver	0.056	0.235	235
Tin	0.055	0.231	231
Mercury	0.033	0.139	139
Gold	0.032	0.134	134
Lead	0.031	0.130	130

★Note that specific heat capacity of water is maximum

$$Q = mc\Delta\theta \quad c = \frac{Q}{m\Delta\theta}$$

$$\Rightarrow \frac{Q}{\Delta\theta} = mc = C \text{ (heat capacity)}$$

Heat capacity = Mass × Specific heat capacity

EXAMPLE 5.2 10 g of kerosene oil absorbs 210 J of heat and its temperature rises by 10°C. Find its specific heat capacity.

SOLUTION

Given mass (m) of the kerosene oil = 10 g

Heat absorbed (Q) = 210 J

Rise in temperature $(\Delta\theta)$ = 10°C

Specific heat capacity (s) = ?

$$Q = ms\Delta\theta$$

$$\Rightarrow 210\text{ J} = 10\text{ g} \times s \times 10°\text{C}$$

$$\therefore s = \frac{210\text{J}}{10\text{g} \times 10°\text{C}} = 2.1\text{ J g}^{-1}\,°\text{C}^{-1}$$

EXAMPLE 5.3 The number of metal balls each of mass 50 g of specific heat capacity of 0.1 cal $g^{-1}\,°C^{-1}$ at temperature of 90°C to be added to 300 g of water at 25°C, so that the resultant temperature is equal to 60°C is _______.

SOLUTION

$M \times 0.1 \times (90 - 60) = 300 \times 1 \times (60 - 25)$

$M = \dfrac{300 \times 35}{0.1 \times 30} = 3500$ g

Mass of one ball = 50 g

$\therefore n \times 50 = 3500$

n = 70.

Thus, one gram of water needs 1 cal or 4.2 J of heat to raise its temperature by 1°C. Specific heat capacity of water is maximum, amongst all solids, liquids and gases. It means the temperature of water doesn't rise or fall quickly as compared to that of other substances. Hence, we find water bodies to be comparatively cool even in sweltering heat of summer.

The high specific heat capacity of water gives rise to some natural phenomena and has many advantages in our day-to-day life. Let us discuss some consequences of it.

1. *Land breeze and sea breeze:* The specific heat capacity of water is nearly five times that of land. This means, water needs nearly five times more heat than land to raise its temperature by 1°C. Similarly, water has to lose five times more heat for 1°C fall in temperature. Thus, land heats up and cools five times quicker than water. In coastal areas, this gives rise to cool sea breeze from sea to land during day time and land breeze from land to sea during night. This keeps the temperature in coastal areas moderate.
2. We apply hot water bag to the swollen parts of our body when sprained to get relief from pain. This is called fomentation as water contains very high amount of heat energy at comparatively low temperature.
3. Water is used as a coolant in number of applications. It can absorb large amount of heat without its temperature increasing appreciably. Hence, it is used as a coolant in car radiators, nuclear plants and in industries.
4. In cold countries, during winter, farmers water their fields in the evening. Owing to its high specific heat capacity, temperature of water doesn't fall quickly. In the absence of external water, due to drop in atmospheric temperature, water in fine capillaries and veins of plants freezes and capillaries burst due to increase in volume, destroying the crop.

EXAMPLE 5.4 A 450 W electric kettle is used to heat 750 g of water. The kettle is on for 2 minutes and the initial temperature of the water is 25°C. Calculate the final temperature of the water. (Specific heat capacity of water = 4.18 J g−1°C−1)

SOLUTION

Given,

Power of the kettle, P = 450 W

Total heat produced in 2 minutes = $P \times t$

Heat = 450 W × 120 s = 54000 L

Now, we have $Q = m \times c = D_q$

Where, m = 750g

C = 4.18 J/g°C

Initial temperature = 25 °C

Let x be the final temperature of water, so $D_q = x - 25$

Plugging in values:

$54000 = 750 \times 4.18 \times (x - 25)$

$54000 = 3135(x - 25)$

$\Rightarrow x = 42.22°C$

So, the final temperature is 42.22 °C.

Principle of Mixtures

Take few lead shots whose temperature is 70°C and add them to water at 30°C contained in an insulating container and stir well. The temperature of lead shots decreases and that of water rises. This means lead shots lose heat and water gains heat. If no heat is lost to surroundings, then heat lost by lead shots is equal to the heat gained by water. This is the principle of mixtures which states that when a hot body is mixed with a cold body, the hot body loses heat and the cold body gains heat till they are in thermal equilibrium and the heat lost by the hot body is equal to the heat gained by the cold body, provided heat is not lost to the surroundings. This principle is in accordance with the principle of conservation of energy and is used to determine specific heat capacity of solids and liquids.

According to the principle of calorimetry or method of mixtures,

Heat lost by the hot body = Heat gained by the cold body.

Let

m_1 = Mass of hot body

m_2 = Mass of cold body

θ_1 = Temperature of hot body

θ_2 = Temperature of cold body

θ = Temperature of both bodies under thermal equilibrium

s_1 = Specific heat capacity of hot body

s_2 = Specific heat capacity of cold body

Fall in temperature of hot body = $\theta_1 - \theta$

Rise in temperature of cold body = $\theta - \theta_2$

Heat lost by hot body = $m_1 s_1(\theta_1 - \theta)$

Heat gained by cold body = $m_2 s_2 (\theta - \theta_2)$

$\therefore m_1 s_1(\theta_1 - \theta) = m_2 s_2 (\theta - \theta_2)$

Calorimeter

Heat is a form of energy. Like other forms of energy, it can be measured. The branch of physics which deals with the measurement of heat is called 'calorimetry'.

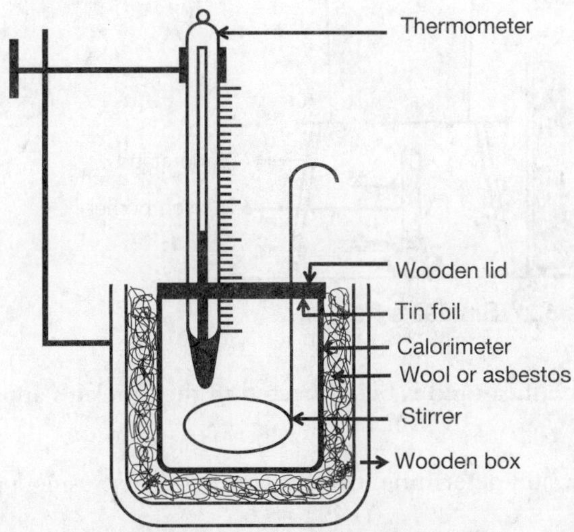

Figure 5.1 Calorimeter

Info Bytes!

The calorimeter was invented by Antoine Lavoisier in 1782.

The device which is used to measure quantity of heat is called calorimeter. It uses the principle of mixtures to find the specific heat capacity of different bodies. Hence, the method is also called method of mixtures.

Calorimeter consists of a thin cylindrical copper vessel. Its outer and inner surfaces are highly polished to prevent heat loss by radiation. The copper vessel is kept in rectangular wooden box and space between them is filled with materials like asbestos or cotton wool which are good insulators of heat. This prevents heat loss by conduction.

At its top, the box has a wooden lid with two holes, one for inserting a thermometer and the other for a stirrer which is also made of copper. The lid is coated with tin or aluminum foil.

Experiment to Determine Specific Heat Capacity of a Given Solid by Method of Mixtures

A solid whose specific heat capacity is to be measured is taken in the form of small pieces. It is first heated separately and then added to calorimeter which contains cold water. Devices like Sinclair's heater and hypsometer are suitable for this purpose.

Sinclair's Heater

It consists of a cylindrical double-walled copper vessel fitted with an outlet tube as shown in Fig. 5.2. Water is heated at the lower portion and steam is passed out through steam outlet. Through an opening at the top, a tube is introduced in the outlet tube. This tube is open at both ends. The bottom open end of the tube is tappered so that it fits well at the slope of the outlet tube. The solid which is to be heated is introduced in the tube in the form of small pieces. To measure its temperature, a thermometer is inserted in the tube through a rubber cork. Care should be taken that the bulb of the thermometer is completely immersed in the solid pieces. The cylindrical vessel is now heated by bunsen burner and temperature of solid pieces is noted. The solid gets heated as it is surrounded by steam formed by boiling water. This ensures uniform heating. A wooden partition (not shown in the Fig. 5.2) is kept on the side of this arrangement to prevent heat radiations from reaching the calorimeter into which the hot solid pieces have to be transferred. Once the temperature of solid is sufficiently high and steady, heating is stopped and calorimeter is brought below the outlet tube. The open-ended tube along with thermometer is lifted and heated solid pieces are allowed to fall into calorimeter and calorimeter is then closed quickly.

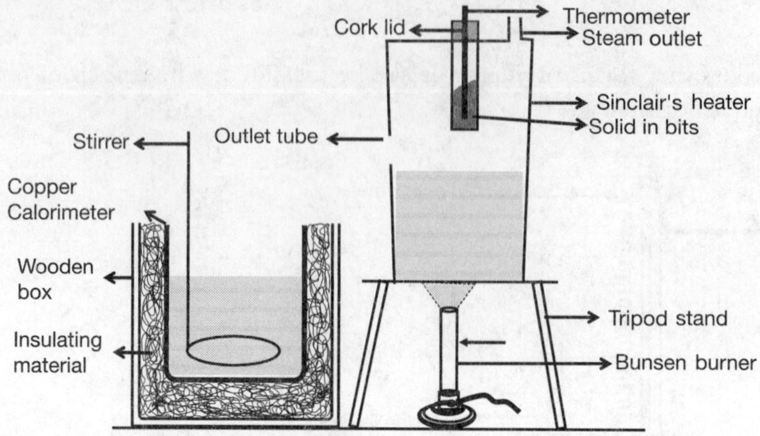

Figure 5.2 Sinclair's heater

While the solid whose specific heat capacity is to be measured is being heated in the Sinclair's apparatus, the following procedure can be completed.

1. Take dry, clean and highly polished calorimeter and determine its mass with its stirrer, using a physical balance. Let it be m_1 g.
2. Now pour water into it at room temperature till it is half-full and determine its mass again. Let it be m_2 g.
3. Put calorimeter in wooden box and note the temperature of water. Let it be θ_1°C.
4. Note the temperature of hot solid pieces. Let it be θ_2°C. Introduce them into the water in the calorimeter and close the wooden lid quickly to prevent heat loss.
5. Stir the mixture well with stirrer and note the steady temperature of mixture. Let it be θ°C.
6. Remove calorimeter from the wooden box and determine its mass along with solid pieces. Let it be m_3 g.

Calculations

When the hot solid pieces are added to water, they lose heat which is absorbed by water and calorimeter. This transfer of heat continues till they are all at same temperature, i.e., they are in thermal equilibrium.

Fall in temperature of solid = $\theta_2 - \theta$

Rise in temperature of water = $\theta - \theta_1$

Rise in temperature of calorimeter = $\theta - \theta_1$

Mass of solid = $(m_3 - m_2)$g

Mass of water = $(m_2 - m_1)$g

Heat lost by solid = $(m_3 - m_2)\, s\, (\theta_2 - \theta)$

where, s = specific heat capacity of the solid, which is to be determined.

Heat gained by water = $(m_2 - m_1)s_w\,(\theta - \theta_1)$

Heat gained by calorimeter = $m_1 s_C(\theta - \theta_1)$

Heat lost by the solid = Heat gained by the water + Heat gained by the calorimeter

$(m_3 - m_2)s\,(\theta_2 - \theta) = (m_2 - m_1)_W\,(\theta - \theta_1) + m_{1C}\,(\theta - \theta_1)$

$$\therefore s = \frac{[m_1 s_c + (m_2 - m_1)s_w](\theta - \theta_1)}{(m_3 - m_2)(\theta_2 - \theta)}$$

While determining specific heat capacity by the above method, certain precautions need to be taken to ensure the accuracy of measurements. They are as follows.

1. The calorimeter should be clean, dry and highly polished.
2. Good heat insulators should be used in the wooden box of the calorimeter.
3. The thermometer should be highly sensitive.
4. The final temperature of the mixture should be noted one minute after the temperature has stabilized.
5. Calorimeter should not be kept near a source of heat.
6. Water must be stirred continuously, taking care that it doesn't it spill over.

EXAMPLE 5.5 A solid of mass 70 g at 80°C is dropped into 100 g of water at 20°C contained in a copper calorimeter of mass 60 g and specific heat capacity 0.40 J g^{-1} $°C^{-1}$. The final steady state temperature of the mixture is 30°C. Find the specific heat of solid. (Specific heat of water = 4.2 J g^{-1} $°C^{-1}$).

SOLUTION

Compile the given information in tabular form as shown below:

Substance	Mass (gram)	Specific heat capacity J g^{-1} $°C^{-1}$	Initial temperature	Final temperature = 30°C	
				Rise in temperature (°C)	Fall in temperature
Solid	70	X	80°C	-	80°C – 30°C $\Delta\theta_F$ = 50°C
Water	100	4.2	20°C	$\Delta\theta_R$ = 30°C – 20°C = 10°C	–
Calorimeter	60	0.40	20°C	$\Delta\theta_R$ = 30°C – 20°C = 10°C	–

Heat lost by solid = $ms\,\Delta\theta_F$ = 70 g × x × 50 °C = 3500 x J

Heat gained by water = $ms\,\Delta\theta_R$ = 100 g × 4.2 J g^{-1} $°C^{-1}$ × 10 °C = 4200 J

Heat gained by calorimeter = $ms\,\Delta\theta_R$ = 60 g × 0.4 J g^{-1} $°C^{-1}$ × 10 °C = 240 J

Applying principle of calorimetry, we get

$$3500x = 4200\text{ J} + 240\text{ J}$$

$$\therefore x = \frac{4440}{3500} = 1.268\text{ J g}^{-1}\,°\text{C}^{-1}$$

Measurement of Specific Heat Capacity of a Liquid by Method of Mixtures

The procedure for measurement of specific heat capacity of a liquid by method of mixtures is same as that for a solid. Liquid whose specific heat capacity is to be determined is taken in calorimeter instead of water. A solid whose specific heat capacity is known is heated and introduced into it.

According to the principle of calorimetry,

Heat lost by solid = Heat gained by the liquid + Heat gained by the calorimeter.

$$(m_3 - m_2)\ s\ (\theta_2 - \theta) = (m_2 - m_1)\ s_\ell\ (\theta - \theta_1) + m_1 s_C\ (\theta - \theta_1)$$

$$\therefore (m_2 - m_1)\ s_\ell\ (\theta - \theta_1) = (m_3 - m_2)\ s\ (\theta_2 - \theta) - m_1 s_C\ (\theta - \theta_1)$$

$$\therefore s_\ell = \frac{(m_3 - m_2)s(\theta_2 - \theta) - m_1 s_c(\theta - \theta_1)}{(m_1 - m_2)(\theta - \theta_1)}$$

where, m_1, m_2 and m_3 are masses of empty calorimeter, calorimeter with liquid, calorimeter with liquid and solid, respectively; θ_1, θ_2 and θ are initial temperature of calorimeter and liquid, initial temperature of the hot solid and final steady temperature of the mixture, respectively and s_ℓ, s_C and s are the specific heats of liquid, calorimeter and solid, respectively. In the above procedure, the solid is selected such that it does not dissolve or react with the given liquid.

Change of State

Matter can exist in three states or phases namely solids, liquids and gases. The state of matter can be changed by changing the temperature or pressure. For example, when ice is heated, it converts to water which converts to vapour or steam on further heating. When ice and water are heated, their temperatures rise. But, when ice changes into water or water changes into steam, there is no rise in temperature although heat is supplied continuously. Reverse of this is also true, i.e., when steam on cooling converts to ice, there is no fall in temperature during change of state. Thus, change of state always takes place at constant temperature. When a solid on heating changes to liquid at a constant temperature, the change of state is called melting or fusion. The constant temperature at which the solid melts is called its 'melting point'. Melting point of ice is 0°C. The conversion of liquid into solid on cooling at constant temperature is called freezing. The constant temperature at which liquid freezes to solid is called freezing point. Freezing point of water is 0°C. The melting point of a substance when it is converted from solid to liquid state has the same value as its 'freezing point' when it is converted from liquid to solid state. Change of a liquid to gas on heating at a constant temperature is called its boiling or vaporization. The constant temperature at which a liquid changes to gas is called boiling point or ebullition point. The change from gaseous to liquid state on cooling at a constant temperature is called condensation. The constant temperature at which condensation occurs is called liquefaction point.

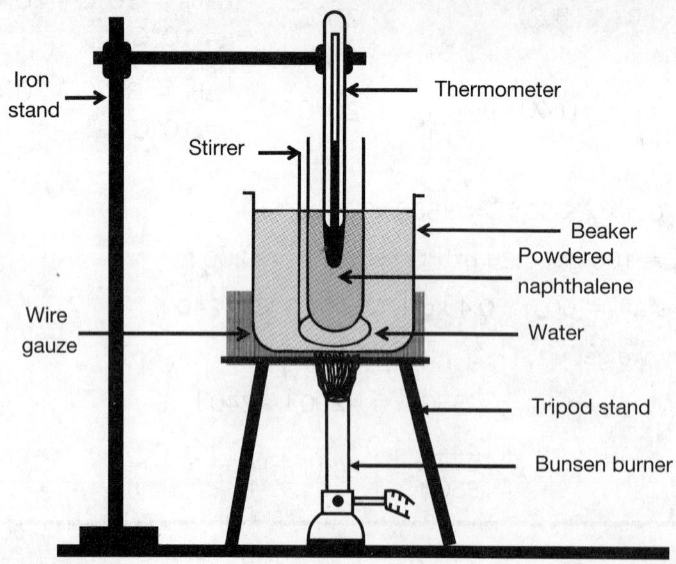

Figure 5.3 Apparatus to determine melting point of a substance

Let us perform a simple experiment to determine the melting point of a solid. This method is suitable for solids which have their melting point between 30°C and 100°C. Take some powdered naphthalene in a thin glass test tube fitted with a thermometer. Arrange the apparatus as shown in Fig 5.3.

Turn on the bunsen burner and take thermometer reading after every 1 minute. Plot a graph of temperature versus time, taking temperature on *Y*-axis and time on *X*-axis.

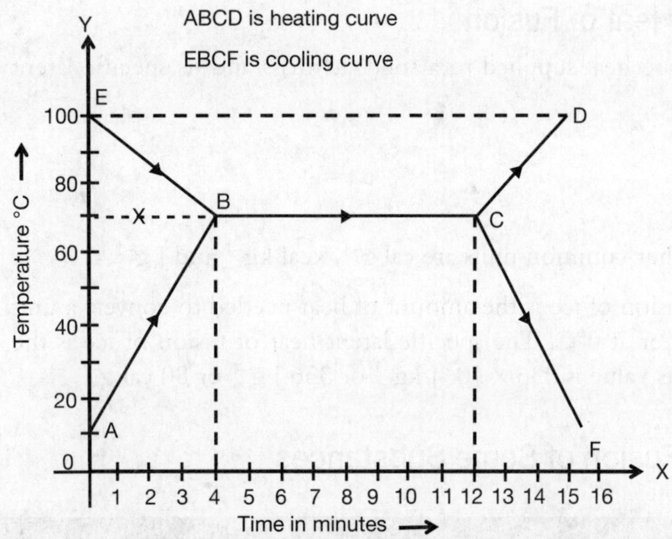

Figure 5.4 Temperature vs time graph to obtain melting point of a substance

Initially, we get a straight line inclined to *X*-axis (*AB* of graph) indicating that as naphthalene is heated, its temperature rises proportionately. After some time, we get a line parallel to *X*-axis (*BC* of graph) indicating that there is no rise in temperature, though naphthalene is being heated continuously. By definition, we know that a change of phase from solid to liquid is taking place during *BC*. This represents melting of naphthalene. After some time, we again get a straight line graph (*CD*) inclined to *X*-axis. This indicates that the temperature of the liquid naphthalene rises on heating. *ABCD* represents the heating curve of naphthalene.

AB $\rightarrow$ rise in temperature of solid naphthalene on heating.

BC $\rightarrow$ melting of naphthalene on heating at constant temperature.

CD $\rightarrow$ rise in temperature of liquid naphthalene on heating.

The heating is stopped and naphthalene is allowed to cool. Temperature of liquid naphthalene is recorded at an interval of one minute and again temperature versus time graph is plotted, giving us cooling curve *EBCF*.

EB $\rightarrow$ fall in temperature of liquid naphthalene on cooling.

BC $\rightarrow$ freezing of naphthalene at constant temperature.

CF $\rightarrow$ fall in temperature of solid naphthalene on cooling.

The temperature on *Y*-axis corresponding to *BC* is the melting point of the solid naphthalene or freezing point of the liquid naphthalene.

Latent Heat of Fusion

We have seen that during melting or vaporization, the temperature of a substance remains constant although heat is continuously being supplied to it. Why doesn't its temperature rise? What happens to heat supplied during change of state?

The heat supplied to a body during its change of state does not result in rise of temperature as it is used for changing its state. The intermolecular space increases when a solid melts overcoming the intermolecular force of attraction.

Thus, the heat supplied to a solid during its change of state is stored as potential energy of liquid molecules. The heat energy that is used to change its state without any rise in temperature is called latent heat or hidden heat. The heat required to change a solid into liquid at its melting point without any rise in temperature is called latent heat of fusion. Thus, heat needed to melt ice into water at 0°C is called latent heat of fusion of ice. The latent heat of fusion depends on the mass of substance. The higher the mass of a solid, the larger is its latent heat of fusion. The latent heat required to convert a unit mass of a solid to liquid at constant temperature is called its specific latent heat of fusion.

Units of Specific Latent Heat of Fusion

$Q = mL$, where, Q, m and L are heat supplied to a solid, its mass and its specific latent heat of fusion, respectively.

$$\text{Thus, unit of } L = \frac{\text{Unit of Q}}{\text{Unit of } m}$$

S.I. unit of 'L' is J kg^{-1}. Other common units are cal g^{-1}, kcal kg^{-1} and J g^{-1}.

The specific latent heat of fusion of ice is the amount of heat needed to convert a unit mass of ice (1 kg or 1g) to water at 0°C. The specific latent heat of fusion of ice is the highest among all substances. Its value is 336×10^3 J kg^{-1} or 336 J g^{-1} or 80 cal g^{-1}.

Info Bytes!

The specific latent heat of fusion of helium is much lower than that of other substances, which is why it remains a liquid even at extremely low temperatures.

Specific Latent Heat of Fusion of Some Substances

Substance→ Latent heat ↓	Ice	Copper	Paraffin wax	Silver	Sulphur	Lead	Mercury
J g^{-1}	336	180	146	88	37.7	27	12.5
J kg^{-1}	336000	180000	146000	88000	37700	27000	12500
cal g^{-1}	80	43	35	21	9	6.42	3

Application and Consequences of High Specific Latent Heat of Fusion of Ice

The specific latent heat of fusion of ice is 336000 J kg^{-1}. Thus, 1kg of ice absorbs 336×10^3 J of heat when it melts without any rise in its temperature. Conversely, 1kg of water releases 336×10^3 J of heat when it freezes.

Few natural consequences of this are discussed below:

1. Water bodies such as lakes, ponds and rivers do not freeze suddenly in cold countries with the onset of winter. Also when they do freeze, they give 336 J g^{-1} of heat to the surroundings making the weather moderate.
2. During snow storm, snow is formed due to freezing of water vapour in the atmosphere. It gives out large amount of heat to the surroundings which makes the surrounding weather moderate.
3. During summer, snow melts slowly on mountains as it needs large amount of heat. Hence, there are no flash floods in rivers and they contain water for the whole year.

General Applications

1. Soft drinks and fruit juices are cooled with ice rather than with cold water as ice can absorb 336 J g^{-1} of heat. So, cooling with ice additionally is more effective.
2. Ice cream at 0°C is felt cooler than water at 0°C as ice can absorb 336 J g^{-1}, while water absorbs 4.2 J g^{-1}.

Determination of Latent Heat of Fusion of Ice

To determine latent heat of fusion of ice by the method of mixtures, the following procedure is followed.

1. Take a clean, dry and highly polished calorimeter with stirrer and measure its mass using an accurate physical balance. Let it be m_1 g.
2. Fill in the calorimeter with water at room temperature till it is half filled. Measure the mass of the calorimeter with water. Let it be m_2 g.

3. Place the calorimeter in the wooden box having good heat insulating material like cotton wool or asbestos. With the help of a highly sensitive thermometer, note the temperature of water. Let it be θ_1°C.
4. Now take ice pieces made of pure distilled water and crush them into small pieces. Wipe them dry with the help of filter paper and drop them gently and carefully in the calorimeter. Allow the ice pieces to melt by gently stirring the water. Repeat the process till the temperature of mixture falls by about 15°C. Note the stabilized steady temperature of the mixture. Let it be θ°C.
5. Remove the calorimeter from the wooden box and record its mass with the mixture. Let it be m_3 g.

Calculations

1. Mass of water at room temperature = $(m_2 - m_1)$ g.
2. Mass of ice = $(m_3 - m_2)$ g.
3. Rise in temperature of water formed from ice = $\theta - 0° = \theta$°C
4. Fall in temperature of water and calorimeter at room temperature = $(\theta_1 - \theta)$°C

   Heat gained by ice to change its state to water at 0°C

   = Mass of ice × Specific latent heat of fusion of ice = $(m_3 - m_2)\,L_{ice}$

   Heat gained by water formed from ice = (mass of ice) (specific heat capacity of water) (rise in temperature of water formed from ice)

   $$= (m_3 - m_2)\text{ g} \times 4.2\text{ J g}^{-1}\,°\text{C}^{-1} \times \theta\,°\text{C}$$

   $$= 4.2(m_3 - m_2) \times \theta\text{J}$$

   Heat lost by calorimeter = $m_1 \times 0.40\text{ J g}^{-1}\,°\text{C}^{-1} \times (\theta_1 - \theta)°\text{C} = 0.4m_1(\theta_1 - \theta)$ J.

   Heat lost by water = $(m_2 - m_1) \times 4.2\text{ J g}^{-1}\,°\text{C}^{-1} \times (\theta_1 - \theta)°\text{C} = 4.2\,(m_2 - m_1)\,(\theta_1 - \theta)$ J

   According to principle of mixtures,

   Heat gained by ice = Heat lost by calorimeter + Heat lost by water at room temperature + Resulting water

   $$(m_3 - m_2)\,L_{ice} + 4.2(m_3 - m_2)\theta = 0.4m_1(\theta_1 - \theta) + 4.2(m_2 - m_1)\,(\theta_1 - \theta)$$

   $$\therefore (m_3 - m_2)L_{ice} = [\{0.4m_1 + 4.2(m_2 - m_1)\}\,(\theta_1 - \theta) - 4.2(m_3 - m_2)\theta]$$

   $$\therefore L_{ice} = \left[\frac{\{0.4m_1 + 4.2(m_2 - m_2)\}(\theta_1 - \theta) - 4.2(m_3 - m_2)\theta}{(m_3 - m_2)}\right]$$

Precautions

In addition to precautions already discussed, following precautions need to be taken while finding specific latent heat of fusion of ice.

1. Ice should be prepared using distilled water and should be dried thoroughly before adding to water in the calorimeter.
2. Water in the calorimeter should be stirred gently.
3. Final temperature should be recorded only when all the ice has melted and one minute after the temperature has stabilized.

EXAMPLE 5.6 A calorimeter of mass 50 g and specific heat capacity 0.40 J g^{-1} °C^{-1} contains 200 g of water at 40°C. What amount of ice at 0°C should be added to it so that the final temperature is 10°C? (Specific heat capacity of water = 4.2 J g^{-1} °C^{-1} and specific latent heat of fusion of ice = 336 J g^{-1} °C^{-1})

SOLUTION

Substance	Mass (g)	Specific latent heat of fusion/ specific heat capacity	Initial Temp°C	Rise in temperature °C	Fall in temperature°C
Ice	m	336 J g^{-1} °C^{-1}	0	$\Delta\theta = 10 - 0 = 10$	-
Water	200	4.2 J g^{-1} °C^{-1}	40		$\Delta\theta = 40 - 10 = 30$
Calorimeter	50	0.40 J g^{-1} °C^{-1}	40		$\Delta\theta = 40 - 10 = 30$

Heat gained by ice to form water at 0°C = mL_{ice} = m × 336 J g^{-1} °C^{-1} = 336m J

Heat gained by water formed from ice = ms $\Delta\theta$ = m × 4.2 J g^{-1} °C^{-1} × 10°C = 42m J

Heat lost by water at 40°C = $ms\ \Delta\theta$ = 200 g × 4.2 J g^{-1} °C^{-1} × 30°C = 25200 J

Heat lost by calorimeter at 40°C = $ms\ \Delta\theta$ = 50 g × 0.40 J g^{-1} °C^{-1} × 30°C = 600 J

Heat gained by ice to form water + Heat gained by water formed from ice = Heat lost by water + Heat lost by calorimeter

$\Rightarrow 336\ m + 42\ m = 25200 + 600$

$\Rightarrow 378\ m = 25800 \Rightarrow m = \frac{25,800}{378} = 68.25$ g.

Factors Affecting Melting Point

Melting point of a solid is affected by pressure and impurities present in it.

Effect of Pressure

In general, melting point increases with increase in pressure. But for substances which expand on freezing like water, iron, etc., the melting point decreases with increase in pressure. Thus, pure ice which melts at 0°C under normal pressure will melt at temperature less than 0°C if pressure is increased.

Regelation

It is a phenomenon in which melting point of ice is lowered with increasing pressure and it is restored to normal value when external pressure is removed. This can be illustrated as under. Take a string and attach weights, to its two ends place the string over an ice block. You will find that string passes through the ice block without breaking it and falls down. This is due to regelation.

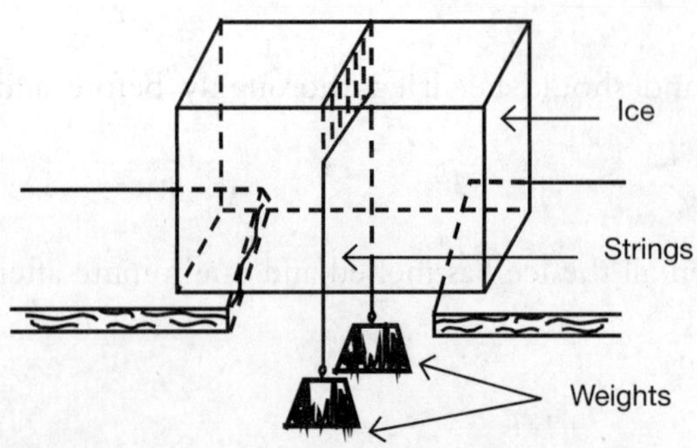

Figure 5.5 Apparatus to show regelation

Info Bytes!

The melting point of tungsten is the highest among all pure elements, at 3422°C.

When the string is kept on the top surface of the ice block, it exerts pressure on the block due to which its melting point decreases. So, it melts and the string goes down. The water above the string again freezes as the external pressure is removed. In this way, the string slips down the whole of the ice block. It is also due to regelation that an ice skater is able to slide over ice. The ice below the skates melts due to increase in pressure forming a thin layer of water which allows the skater to move ahead smoothly. As soon as skater goes ahead, the water freezes again.

Effect of Impurities on Melting Point

Addition of impurities decreases the melting point of ice.

Freezing Mixture

A mixture of ice and an impurity like common salt (which is soluble in water) in proper ratio is called freezing mixture. The melting point of freezing mixture is lower than 0°C. For example, the melting point of the mixture of ice and common salt mixed in the ratio 3 : 1 is −22°C. The melting point of mixture of ice and calcium chloride mixed in the ratio 3 : 4 is –55°C. Freezing mixtures are used in preparing ice creams and in laboratories for preserving biological specimens.

Latent Heat of Vaporization

Temperature of a liquid increases when it is heated, till it reaches the boiling point. At boiling point, while liquid vaporizes, its temperature remains constant. During vaporization, the heat supplied is used to overcome intermolecular forces of attraction to increase intermolecular space is stored in vapour molecules in the form of potential energy. This heat is called latent heat of vaporization. The latent heat of vaporization of a given liquid increases with mass. In order to have a unique or specific value, we define latent heat of vaporization for unit mass of a given liquid. The latent heat of vaporization of a unit mass of a liquid is called its specific latent heat of vaporization.

Units of Specific Latent Heat of Vaporization

$Q = m L$; where Q, m and L are heat supplied to a liquid, mass of a liquid and its specific latent heat of vaporization, respectively.

$$\text{Thus, unit of } L = \frac{\text{unit of Q}}{\text{unit of } m}$$

Hence, S.I. unit of 'L' is joule per kilogram (J kg^{-1}). Other common units are cal g^{-1}, kcal g^{-1} and J g^{-1}.

Specific Latent Heat of Vaporization of Steam

Amount of heat required to convert unit mass of water (1 kg or 1 g) at 100 °C to steam at 100 °C is called specific latent heat of vaporization of steam. Steam has the highest specific latent heat of vaporization. Its value is 2268 J g^{-1} or 226.8 × 10^4 J kg^{-1} or 540 cal g^{-1}.

Table 5.2 Specific latent heat of vaporization of substances

Substance	Boiling point	Specific latent heat of vaporization J g^{-1}	Specific latent heat of vaporization J kg^{-1}
Methyl alcohol	64 °C	1120	112 × 10^4
Acetone	57 °C	520	52 × 10^4
Benzene	80 °C	400	40 × 10^4
Carbon disulphide	46 °C	360	36 × 10^4
Carbon tetrachloride	77 °C	190	19 × 10^4
Ethyl alcohol	79 °C	850	85 × 10^4
Mercury	357 °C	290	29 × 10^4
Turpentine oil	156 °C	290	29 × 10^4
Water	100 °C	2268	226.8 × 10^4

Advantages and Natural Consequences of High Specific Latent Heat of Vaporization of Steam

1. For water in soil to evaporate, a very large amount of heat, i.e., $226.8 \times 10^4 \text{ J kg}^{-1}$ is needed which slows down vaporization. Therefore, plants do not wilt easily even in summer.
2. One gram of water at 100°C contains 100 cal of heat. If the same water is to be converted into steam at the same temperature, it needs 540 cal of additional heat. Thus, 1 g of steam at 100°C contains 640 cal of heat. Therefore, burns caused by steam at 100°C are more severe than these caused by water at 100°C.
3. Steam can carry large amount of heat. Therefore, it is used in thermal power stations where heat energy from coals is carried by steam and converted to electric energy.

Determination of Specific Latent Heat of Vaporization by Method of Mixtures

Follow first three steps mentioned in determination of latent heat of fusion of ice by calorimeter on page 3.9. The subsequent steps are as follows:

4. In this case the wooden lid of the calorimeter box has a third hole for introducing steam into the calorimeter. Steam is generated in a boiling flask and passed through steam trap which removes condensed water vapours. The steam coming out of steam trap is introduced in the calorimeter till the temperature of the mixture rises by about 20°C. The mixture is stirred gently for uniform distribution of temperature. The final steady temperature of mixture is recorded. Let it be θ°C. The temperature of steam is 100°C.
5. Remove the calorimeter and record its mass. Let it be m_3.

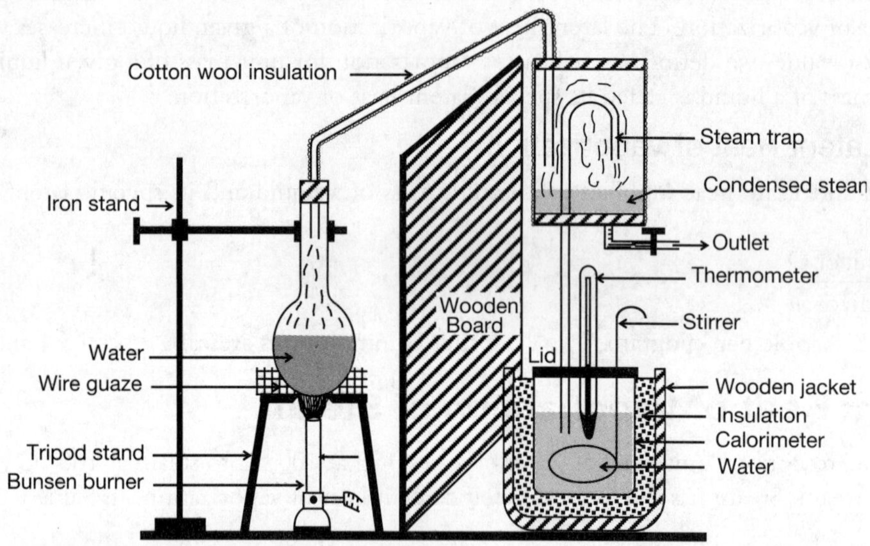

Figure 5.6 Apparatus to determine specific latent heat of vaporization

Calculations

Mass of water at room temperature = $(m_2 - m_1)$g, Mass of steam condensed and mixed with water = $(m_3 - m_2)$ g

Fall in temperature of water formed from steam = $\Delta\theta = (100 - \theta)$°C

Rise in temperature of calorimeter and water at room temperature $\Delta\theta = (\theta - \theta_1)$°C

Heat lost by steam to form water at 100°C

$= (m_3 - m_2) \times L_{steam}$

$= (m_3 = m_2)x,$

where, $L_{steam} = x$, the latent heat of vaporization of water, which is to be determined.

Heat lost by water at 100°C formed from steam

$= (m_3 - m_2) \text{ g} \times 4.2 \text{ J g}^{-1} \text{°C}^{-1} \times (100 - \theta)\text{°C}$

$= 4.2(m_3 - m_2)\ (100 - \theta)\text{J}$

Heat gained by calorimeter = $m_1 \times 0.40$ J g^{-1}°C^{-1} × $(\theta - \theta_1)$°C

Heat gained by water at room temperature = $(m_2 - m_1) \times 4.2$ J g^{-1} °C^{-1} × $(\theta - \theta_1)$°C

$= 4.2(m_2 - m_1)(\theta - \theta_1)$ J

By principle of mixtures,

Heat lost by steam = Heat gained by calorimeter + Heat gained by water at room temperature and resulting water

$$= (m_3 - m_2)x + 4.2(m_3 - m_2)(100 - \theta) = 0.40m_1(\theta - \theta_1) + 4.2(m_2 - m_1)(\theta - \theta_1)$$

$$\therefore x = \left[\frac{\{0.4m_1 + 4.2(m_2 - m_1)\}(\theta - \theta_1) - 4.2(m_3 - m_2)(100 - \theta)}{(m_3 - m_2)}\right] \text{Jg}^{-1}$$

Precautions

Other than customary precautions with calorimeter, observe the following precautions for steam.

1. Steam should be perfectly dry.
2. Steam should be passed only till temperature of mixtures rises by about 20°C.

EXAMPLE 5.7 100 g of water at 10°C is taken in a calorimeter of mass 50 g and specific heat capacity 0.40 Jg^{-1} °C^{-1}. Calculate the mass of steam which should be passed into the water in the calorimeter so that the temperature of mixture becomes 40°C. [Specific heat capacity of water = 4.2 J g^{-1} °C^{-1} and specific latent heat of vaporization of steam = 2260 J g^{-1}.]

SOLUTION

Substance	Mass (g)	L/S	Initial temperature	Rise in temperature	Fall in temperature
Steam	x	2260 J g^{-1}°C^{-1}	100 °C	–	$\Delta\theta$ = 100 °C – 40 °C = 60°C
Water	100	4.2 J g^{-1} °C^{-1}	10 °C	$\Delta\theta$ = 40°C – 10 °C = 30°C	–
Calorimeter	50	0.4 J g^{-1} °C^{-1}	10 °C	30 °C	–

Heat given by steam to form water at 100°C = $m L$ = 2260x J

Heat lost by water formed from steam at 100°C = $m\,s\,\Delta\theta$

= $m \times 4.2$ J g^{-1} °C^{-1} × 30°C = 126x J

Total heat lost by steam and the water formed from steam = 2260x + 126x = 2386x J.

Heat gained by water at 10°C = 100 g × 4.2 J g^{-1} °C^{-1} × 30°C = 12600 J

Heat gained by calorimeter at 10°C = 50 g × 0.4 J g^{-1} °C^{-1} × 30°C = 600 J

By the principle of calorimetry,

2386x J = 12600 J + 600 J

∴ x = 5.53 g (approx).

Experiment to Determine Boiling Point of a Liquid

Take water in a closed vessel fitted with a thermometer. Heat it with bunsen burner and note the temperature every minute. Plot temperature versus time graph, taking temperature on *Y*-axis and time on *X*-axis.

ABCD represents heating curve of water.

AB represents rise in temperature of water on heating.

BC represents change of state of water to steam at constant temperature.

CD represents rise in temperature of steam on heating.

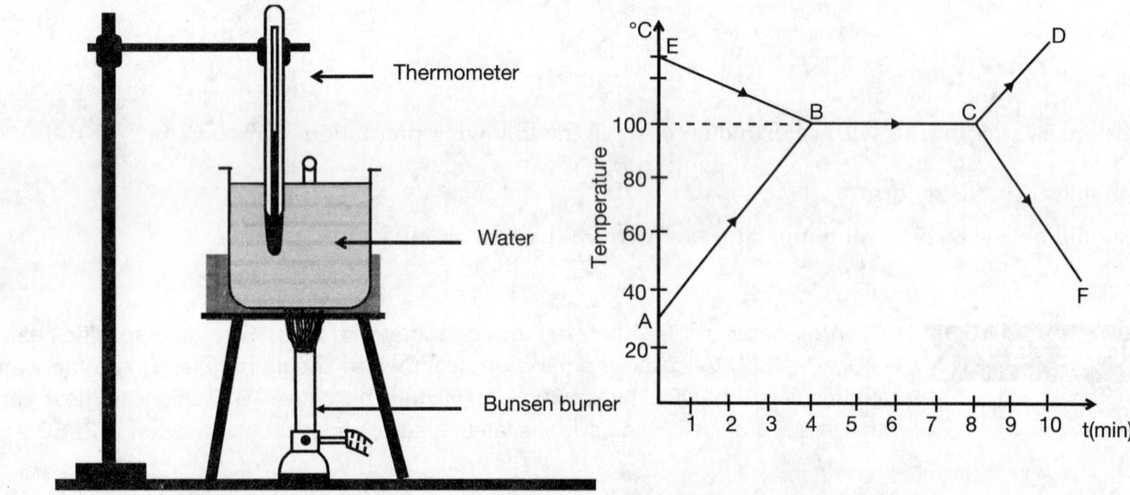

Figure 5.7 Apparatus to determine boiling point of a liquid and its graph

Heating is stopped and vessel is allowed to cool and cooling curve *EBCF* is plotted.

EB represents fall in temperature of steam on cooling.

BC represents change in state of steam to water at a constant temperature.

CF represents fall in temperature of water on cooling.

Effects of Pressure and Impurities on Boiling Point

Pressure

Increase in pressure increases the boiling point of a liquid and decrease in pressure decreases its boiling point.

Let us discuss an activity to understand the above fact.

Take some water in a flask. Close the mouth of flask with two holed rubber cork fitted with a delivery tube and a thermometer. Heat the flask and note the temperature of water. It begins to boil at 100°C and steam begins to form. Now partly close the delivery tube so that pressure due to steam increases inside. Check the flask for the temperature at which water boils. You will find that it has increased. Stop heating and allow the water to cool. Close the flask completely. On cooling the steam inside the flask condenses, thereby, decreasing the pressure. You will find water boils at lower temperature. Some examples of effect of pressure on boiling point are:

1. Pressure cooker is used to cook food quickly.
2. Water boils at a temperature much lower than 100°C at higher altitudes.

Impurities Addition of impurities increases the boiling point. When 100 g of common salt is added to 100 g of water, the boiling point increases by 1°C.

Evaporation

Wet clothes, when hung on a rope, dry. The water in the wet clothes vaporizes without boiling. If you drop some spirit on your hand, it vaporizes leaving cooling sensation on your hand. The process by which water vaporizes without boiling is called evaporation. The molecules on the surface of water are attracted to water molecules below the surface by cohesive forces and by the surrounding air molecules by adhesive force. If the energy of some molecules on the surface is high, they escape to the surrounding air. Since this process takes place continuously at all temperatures, we find that wet clothes dry after some time. This is due to continuous evaporation. Since the energetic molecules leave water, the average kinetic energy of molecules decreases causing fall in temperature and gives cooling effect. Evaporation is purely a surface phenomenon. Therefore, water stored in an earthern porous container cools faster than that in a metallic container. Since evaporation involves escaping of surface molecules to surroundings, the rate of evaporation depends on the following factors:

1. Surrounding temperature
2. Wind velocity
3. Surface area of the liquid

Boiling is different from evaporation, as boiling takes place rapidly at a fixed temperature only and throughout the liquid.

Refrigeration

When a liquid evaporates, it extracts heat energy required for phase change from the surroundings. Therefore, evaporation has a cooling effect. Refrigerator is a device which is used to store food, vegetables and other perishable items at low temperature. It works on the principle that evaporation of a liquid gives cooling effect. Basically, it consi ts of the following main parts connected to the main frame.

1. Pump
2. Cooling chamber
3. Evaporation tube
4. Condensation tube
5. Copper fins

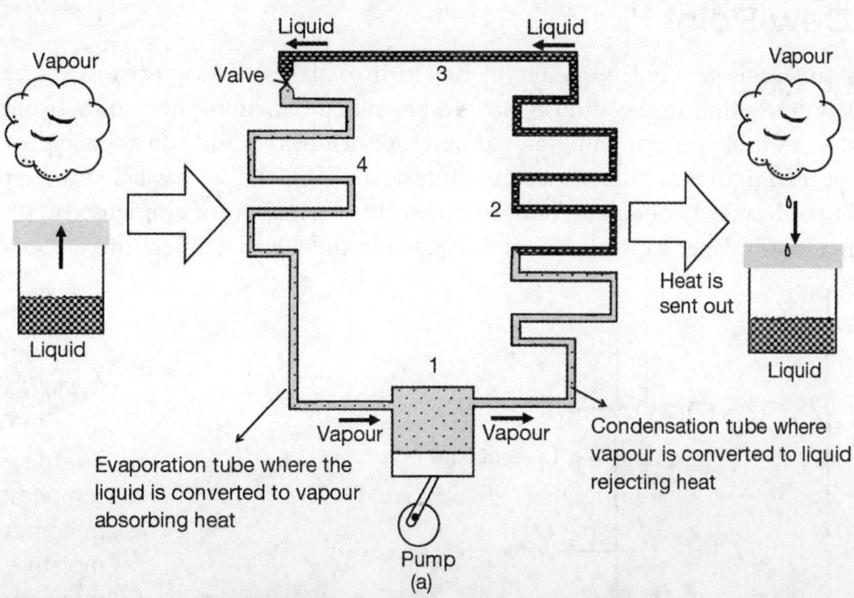

Figure 5.8 Pump of the refrigerator

A pump situated behind the main structure of a refrigerator at the bottom, circulates volatile liquid like liquid freon through the evaporation tube. Evaporation tube passes through cooling chamber. When freon reaches cooling chamber, it evaporates, extracting the required heat from the cooling chamber. The temperature of cooling chamber decreases considerably. The vapours then reach condensation tube and pump exerts pressure which condenses them to liquid which is again circulated through evaporation tube. The condensation tube is connected to copper fins which radiate the heat released during condensation. This process is repeated continuously and temperature in cooling chamber is brought down to desired level.

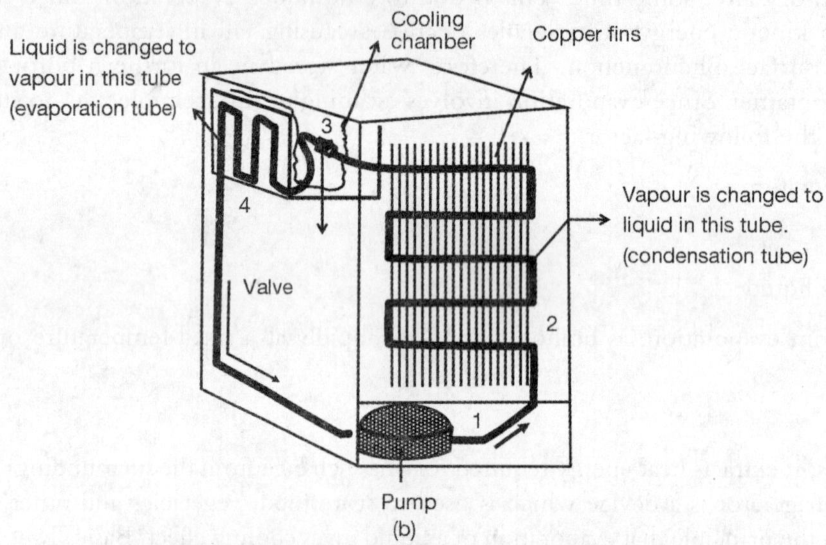

Figure 5.9 Main structure of the refrigerator

Sublimation

A solid when heated converts to liquid at melting point and liquid on further heating changes to gas at boiling point. There are few substances which convert to gas from solid state without changing to liquid state. This process is called sublimation.

Examples: naphthalene balls, camphor, etc., are some solids that undergo sublimation.

Humidity and Dew Point

Almost 70% of Earth's surface is covered by water in the form of lakes, rivers, oceans, etc. Thus, water evaporates continuously and forms water vapour in the atmosphere. To prove that the atmosphere always contains certain amount of water vapor, let us discuss a simple experiment. Take some water in a beaker and add a few pieces of ice to it. Melting of ice causes temperature of the mixture to fall. After some time as the temperature has fallen to certain value you will find that the outer surface of the beaker has become blurred due to the formation of condensed water film. This water film develops due to condensation of water vapour present in air due to the fall in temperature.

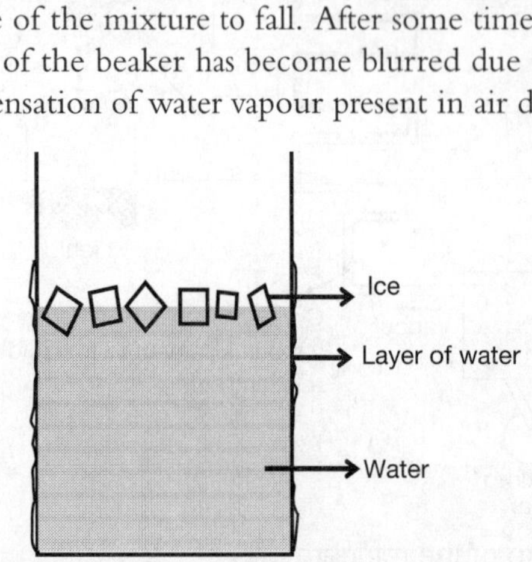

Figure 5.10 Mixture of ice and water to observe evaporation

Konnect

The dew point is the temperature at which air becomes saturated with moisture and water vapor begins to condense.

The presence of vapour makes the air moist or damp. This moisture or dampness of air due to water vapour is called humidity. The higher the vapour content present in air, the higher is the humidity of air. Humidity is high in coastal areas. The amount of water vapour present in one cubic metre of air is called its absolute humidity. There is a limit to the mass of water vapour which can be present in a given volume of air. When the mass of water vapour present in air is equal to this limit, i.e., maximum possible value, the air is said to be saturated with water vapour and if it is less than air, it is said to be unsaturated. Sometimes we feel air to be dry and at other times, damp. This feeling not only depends on the exact amount of vapour present in air but also on the difference between this amount and the quantity of water vapour required to saturate the air. If this difference is less, air is felt more damp and if this difference is more, air is felt dry. It is because of this factor that even though the actual amount of water vapour in air is more on a dry summer day than on a moist winter day, the air still is felt drier on summer day. This means that the quantity of water vapour required to saturate given volume of air increases with an increase in temperature. The extent of moistness of air felt by us is determined by a quantity called relative humidity.

Relative Humidity

It is defined as ratio of amount of water vapour actually present in a given volume of air to the amount of water vapour required to saturate the same volume of air at the same temperature.

$$\text{Relative humidity} = \frac{\text{Amount of vapour in a given volume of air}}{\text{Amount of vapour needed to saturate same volume of air at the same temperature}} \times 100$$

Thus, relative humidity of completely saturated air is 100%. The air is felt damp if relative humidity is greater than 60%, otherwise it is felt dry. As already discussed, the amount of vapour required to saturate a given mass of air depends on temperature. Keeping the amount of unsaturated air and the vapour content in it constant, if its temperature is continuously decreased, the air will get saturated. Now it cannot hold any more amount of vapour for the given temperature. If the temperature is decreased slightly, the vapour in the given volume of air condenses. This is how a thin film of water was formed on the outer surface of the beaker discussed earlier. The water droplets so formed are also called dew. The temperature at which the given volume of air becomes saturated with water vapour without actually increasing the vapour content in it is called dew point. At this temperature, the water vapour in air just begins to condense. During day time you rarely find dew, but during night when the temperature falls below dew point, dew is formed on cold bodies. Sometimes dew is formed on dust particles in the atmosphere forming fog or mist.

Anomalous behaviour of Water

Liquids expand on heating and contract on cooling. Water shows exception to this rule below 4°C. If water at room temperature is cooled, it contracts till its temperature reaches 4°C. On further cooling, as its temperature falls below 4°C, it begins to expand instead of contracting. Conversely if water is heated from 0°C to 4°C, it contracts instead of expanding. This behaviour of water is known as anomalous behaviour of water and the expansion of water on cooling below 4°C is called anomalous expansion of water. The anomalous behaviour of water can be demonstrated with the help of Hope's apparatus.

Hope's Apparatus

It consists of a cylindrical vessel A surrounded by a cylindrical trough B at its centre. Two thermometers can be inserted in the vessel at the top and the bottom as shown in Fig. 5.11.

The vessel is filled with water at 10°C and the trough with a freezing mixture of ice and salt. The changes in temperature of water are recorded by the thermometers.

Following observations are made.

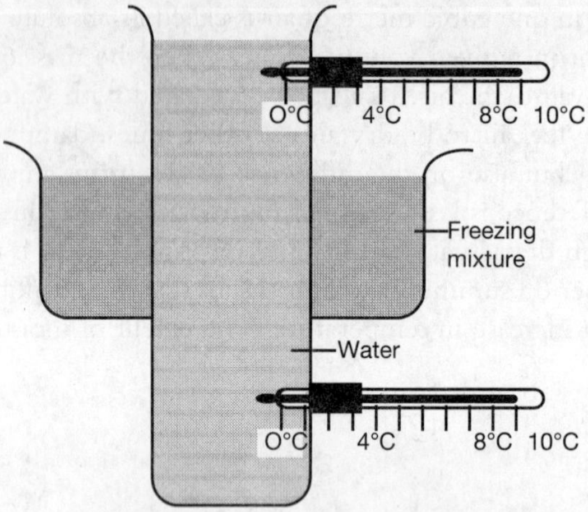

Figure 5.11 Hope's apparatus

1. Initially, the temperature shown by both thermometers is same, i.e., 10°C. As time elapses, the lower thermometer records lower temperatures while temperature shown by the upper thermometer is almost constant. The temperature shown by the lower thermometer decreases gradually till 4°C and then remains constant at 4°C.
2. The temperature shown by the upper thermometer begins to fall till it is 0°C. But the temperature recorded by the lower thermometer remains constant at 4°C.
3. After the upper thermometer shows 0°C, thin layer of ice is formed at the top surface of water.

The above observation can be explained as follows:

Initially, the temperature of water is 10°C. Due to the freezing mixture, the temperature of water at central portion begins to fall and it contracts. As its density increases, the cold water goes to the bottom. Therefore, the lower thermometer records fall in temperatures. This continues till temperature of water at the central portion reaches 4°C. Now as temperature falls further, water expands instead of contracting and its density decreases. Therefore, cold water below 4°C goes up instead of going down. Therefore, temperature of water at the top of the vessel begins to fall till it reaches 0°C as shown by the upper thermometer. At 0°C, water freezes into ice. As density of ice is less than that of water, layer of ice is formed on the top surface. The temperature of water at the bottom of the vessel remains constant at 4°C as ice being a bad conductor of heat, prevents loss of heat from water below it to the surrounding.

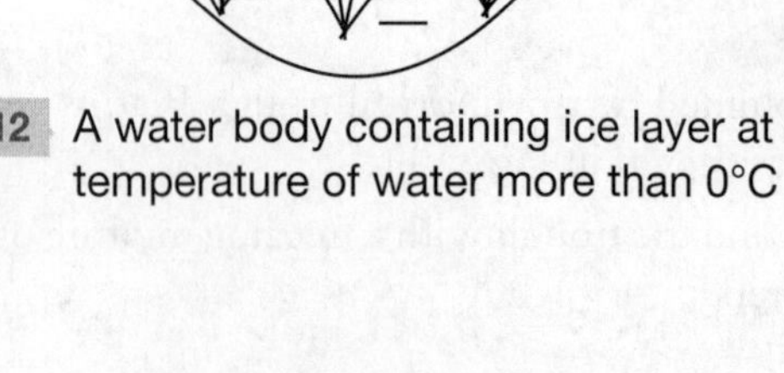

Figure 5.12 A water body containing ice layer at surface and temperature of water more than 0°C

Consequences of Anomalous Behaviour of Water

1. The anomalous behaviour of water plays very significant role in the survival of aquatic flora and fauna in cold countries. As explained in Hope's apparatus, the water surface of lakes, ponds or rivers may get frozen in winter, but the temperature of water at bottom remains constant at 4°C.
2. Water pipes in cold countries burst when temperature falls below 4°C as water expands.
3. Fruits and vegetables also get damaged if temperature falls below 4°C as water contained in their capillaries expands.

Heat Engine

Heat is a form of energy. It can be converted to other forms of energy and vice versa. Energy is ability to do work. Thus, heat can also be used to do useful work.

Some examples of work done by heat are:

1. The weight of a pressure cooker is raised when sufficient amount of steam is accumulated in it.
2. James Watt, a Scotish scientist, observed that while making tea, the lid of the tea kettle flew up as steam was generated due to heating of water. James Watt later developed modern steam engine which could transport marine loads over large distances rapidly. Heat energy cannot be used directly to do useful work. The device which converts heat into useful mechanical work is called heat engine.

Heat engines are classified into two types namely, external combustion engine and internal combustion engine.

External Combustion Engine

It consists of a cylinder C fitted with an air tight piston (Fig 5.13). The piston is connected to a crank shaft. The cylinder is connected to a boiler through an inlet valve and to a condensor through an outlet valve. The boiler and condensor are connected to each other through a pump.

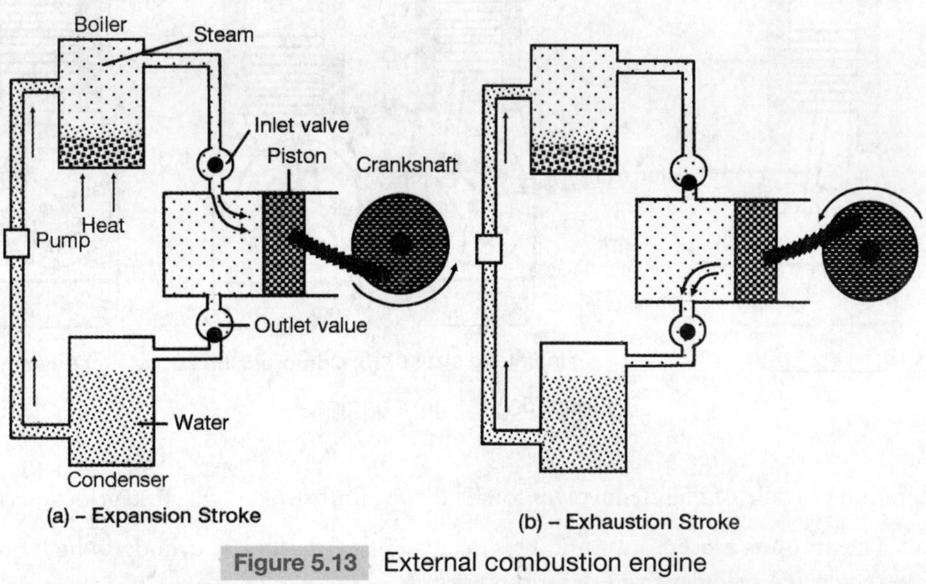

Figure 5.13 External combustion engine

Water is heated in the boiler and steam is generated. The pressure of accumulated steam opens the inlet valve and forces the piston outwards. This is called expansion stroke. The outward or inward movement of the piston is called 'stroke'. At the end of expansion stroke, the inlet valve is closed and the piston begins to move inwards.

The outlet valve is opened and used steam is passed on to the condensor, where it condenses. The water is then pumped back to the boiler.

This action is repeated. In external combustion engine, steam is used to do useful work Therefore, it is also called steam engine.

Steam engine is not used extensively as it has certain disadvantages.

1. Steam engines are bulky and cannot be used to run smaller machines.
2. Steam engines can be dangerous as due to high pressure of steam, the boiler may burst.
3. Steam engine cannot be started instantly. To obtain steam at high temperature, some time is needed.

Internal Combustion Engine

Due to these drawbacks, a steam engine cannot be used in many applications. To overcome the drawbacks of a steam engine, a new heat engine was devised. In this heat engine, combustion of fuel and conversion of heat energy to mechanical energy is done inside the cylinder itself. Therefore, it is called internal combustion engine. Depending on the fuel used, internal combustion engines are classified into petrol engines and diesel engines.

Petrol Engine

It consists of a cylinder and an airtight piston which is connected to a crankshaft. Inlet and outlet valves and a spark plug are provided at the head of the cylinder. Petrol engine is connected to carburettor. It mixes petrol and air in proper proportion and supplies it to the cylinder through the inlet valve.

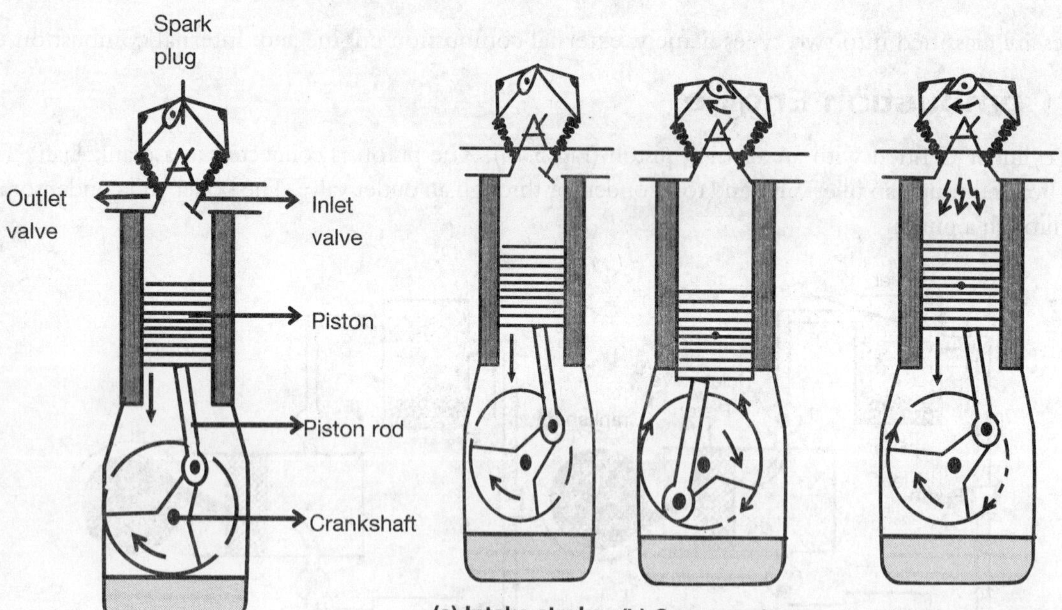

Figure 5.14 Petrol engine

One complete operation or cycle of engine involves four stages or four strokes. Each stage is described below:

1. **Intake Stroke:** The piston is moved outward. This decreases the pressure in cylinder which opens the inlet valve. The fuel mixture enters the cylinder from the carburettor.
2. **Compression Stroke:** The piston is moved inwards towards the cylinder head which compresses the fuel mixture. Both the inlet and the outlet valves are closed.
3. **Power Stroke:** The compressed fuel is burnt by the sparks from spark plug. The by-products of combustion like water vapour and carbon dioxide expand rapidly pushing the piston outwards with great force.

4. **Exhaust Stroke:** The gases released during combustion are expelled through outlet valve as the piston is moved back and the outlet valve is opened. These four strokes constitute one work cycle. As the cycles are repeated piston moves to and fro rapidly which rotates the crankshaft. The internal combustion engine has to be started with the help of self starter, kick starter or push starter. The internal combustion engine is used in almost all vehicles like scooters, motorcycles, cars, etc.

Diesel Engine

Diesel engine is similar to a petrol engine with few changes in construction. The spark plug is replaced by fuel injection pump. Carburettor is not used in a diesel engine. One work cycle of diesel engine consists of four strokes as in petrol engine.

Intake stroke: Pistons move out and filtered air is taken into the cylinder.

Compression stroke: The air is compressed to $\frac{1}{16}$th of its volume as piston moves in. The compressed air becomes hot enough to ignite the fuel. Hence, there is no need of spark plug.

Power stroke: At the end of compression stroke, required amount of diesel is injected into the cylinder by fuel injection pump. Diesel bursts into flame instantly. Due to the high pressure generated by combustion and expansion of gases, the piston is pushed out with large force.

Exhaust stroke: The spent gases are expelled in the exhaust stroke. Although internal combustion engine has many advantages over steam engine, its biggest drawback is that it is a single largest source of air pollution. Some of the pollutants released like carbon monoxide, sulphur dioxide and lead compounds are highly toxic and harmful.

Efficiency of Heat Engine

It is defined as ratio of useful work done by heat engine to the total amount of heat supplied to it. It is generally expressed as a percentage.

$$\text{Efficiency} = \frac{\text{Work done (useful)}}{\text{Total heat supplied}} \times 100$$

No heat engine is 100% efficient. Efficiency of few types of heat engines are given below:

Table below lists efficiencies of some commonly used engines.

Table 5.3 Efficiency of engines

S.No.	Type of engine	Efficiency
1	Steam engine	15
2	Jet engine	15
3	Petrol engine	30
4	Steam turbine	35
5	Diesel engine	40

Advantages of an internal combustion engine over a steam engine:

1. An internal combustion engine is more efficient and safer than a steam engine.
2. It can be started instantaneously.
3. Internal combustion engines are less bulky, and can be manufactured in a range of different sizes. They are suitable for small machines also.

POINTS TO REMEMBER

- ✔ Specific heat capacity is defined as the amount of heat required to raise the temperature of unit mass of substance (1 kg or 1 g) by one kelvin or one degree celsius.
- ✔ Principle of mixtures states that when a hot body is mixed with a cold body, the hot body loses heat and the cold body gains heat till they are in thermal equilibrium and the heat lost by the hot body is equal to the heat gained by the cold body, provided heat is not lost to the surroundings.
- ✔ The state of matter can be changed by changing the temperature or pressure.
- ✔ When a solid on heating changes to liquid at a constant temperature, the change of state is called melting or fusion. The constant temperature at which the solid melts is called its 'melting point'.
- ✔ The conversion of liquid into solid on cooling at constant temperature is called freezing. The constant temperature at which liquid freezes to solid is called freezing point.
- ✔ The branch of physics which deals with the measurement of heat is called 'calorimetry'.
- ✔ The heat required to change a solid into liquid at its melting point without any rise in temperature is called latent heat of fusion.
- ✔ Increase in pressure increases the boiling point of a liquid and decrease in pressure decreases its boiling point.
- ✔ Addition of impurities increases the boiling point. When 100 g of common salt is added to 100 g of water, the boiling point increases by 1°C.
- ✔ There are few substances which convert to gas from solid state without changing to liquid state. This process is called sublimation.
- ✔ Relative humidity is defined as ratio of amount of water vapour actually present in a given volume of air to the amount of water vapour required to saturate the same volume of air at the same temperature.
- ✔ Efficiency of heat engine is defined as ratio of useful work done by heat engine to the total amount of heat supplied to it. It is generally expressed in percentage.

DW

PRACTICE QUESTIONS CLASSROOM WING

Very Short Answer Type Questions

Directions for questions 1 to 11:
Fill in the blanks.

1. In diesel as well as in petrol engines, one complete cycle of operation involves ____, ____, ____ and ____ strokes.
2. Density of water is maximum at ____ °C.
3. In diesel engines, carburetor is replaced by ____.
4. The expansion of water on cooling below 4°C is called ____.
5. Calorimeter works on the principle of ____.
6. The specific latent heat of fusion of ice is ____ J kg^{-1} K^{-1} or ____ cal g^{-1}.
7. The latent heat of vaporization of a unit mass of a liquid is called its ____.
8. 1 g of steam at 100°C cools to form water at 80°C. The amount of heat liberated is ____.

   (Total heat released = Q + H)
9. The amount of heat required to raise the temperature of unit mass of a substance by one kelvin is called ____.
10. The direction of heat flow between two bodies is determined by____.
11. The temperature at which the given volume of air becomes saturated with water vapour without actually increasing the vapour content in it is called ____.

Directions for questions 12 to 30:
Answer the following questions.

12. Define heat in terms of internal energy.
13. A metal plate, with a hole in it, is heated. What will happen to the size of the hole?
14. Three metal rods of initial lengths ℓ_1, ℓ_2 and ℓ_3 made of different materials are heated to the same temperature. If $\ell_1 > \ell_2 > \ell_3$, then what would be the relation between the final lengths ℓ_1', ℓ_2', ℓ_3'?
15. Define heat capacity and specific heat capacity.
16. An object is dropped into water at 20°C and water at 40°C. If the upthrust acting on it is F_1 and F_2 at 20°C and 40°C, respectively, then what will be the relation between them?
17. State the principle of mixtures.
18. Define temperature in term of kinetic energy.
19. Define the following.
    (i) Melting or fusion
    (ii) Freezing
    (iii) Boiling
    (iv) Condensation
20. A hollow metal sphere is heated. What will happen to its internal volume and external volume, respectively?
21. How much heat is absorbed when 10 g of ice at 0°C is completely converted to water at 0°C?
22. Define latent heat.
23. State the principle on which a refrigerator works.
24. Define latent heat of fusion and specific latent heat of fusion of ice.
25. What is a heat engine and name two types of heat engines?
26. Define latent heat of vaporization and specific latent heat of vaporization of water.
27. What is sublimation?
28. State two factors which affect the melting point of a solid.
29. Match the statements of Column A with those of Column B.

Column A	Column B
A. Heat	P. Average kinetic energy
B. Temperature	Q. Internal energy flowing
C. Specific heat capacity	R. Depends on the nature of the material

30. Match the statements of Column A with those of Column B.

Column A	Column B
A. Specific heat capacity	P. gram
B. Latent heat of fusion	Q. cal g^{-1}°C^{-1}
C. Water equivalent	c. cal g^{-1}

Short Answer Type Questions

31. Water equivalent of a substance of mass 200 g is 400 g. What is the specific heat capacity (in cal g^{-1} °C^{-1}) of the substance?

32. A liquid of mass *m* at a temperature of 20°C is mixed with a similar liquid of mass m at 30°C. What will be the temperature of the mixture?

33. Water falls from a height of 300 m. If 80% of the mechanical energy is used to increase the temperature of the water, then what would be the change in temperature (in °C) of the water?

34. 5 kg of water is at a temperature of 70°C. How much amount (in kg) of water at 20°C is to be added, so that the resultant temperature is 40°C?

35. Give some natural consequences and a few practical applications of high specific heat capacity of water.

36. 1kg of ice at 0°C is converted into steam at 100°C. Calculate the heat required.

    Specific heat of fusion of ice = 336×10^3 J kg^{-1}

    Specific heat of vaporization of water = 2260×10^3 J kg^{-1}

    Specific heat capacity of water = 4200 J kg^{-1} °C^{-1}

37. Differentiate between evaporation and boiling.

38. Explain the working of a refrigerator.

39. Describe a calorimeter.

40. An electric heater of power 500 W is used to raise the temperature of a liquid from 30°C to 40°C in 2 minutes. Find the heat capacity of the liquid.

41. Explain the formation of dew.

42. 10000 J heat is required to raise the temperature of a metal ball by 20 K. Calculate its heat capacity.

43. Mention few natural consequences and some practical applications of high specific latent heat of fusion of ice.

44. State a few advantages of an internal combustion engine.

45. The temperature of the atmosphere is 20°C and the amount of water vapour in the atmosphere is 12.78 g m^{-3}. Using the table below, find the dew point.

Temperature of air (°C)	Mass of Water Vapour at Saturation
10	9.38 g m^{-3}
15	12.78 g m^{-3}
20	17.18 g m^{-3}
25	22.88 g m^{-3}

Essay Answer Type Questions

46. A substance of mass 400 g with an initial temperature of 30°C and specific heat capacity of 1 cal g^{-1}°C^{-1} is dropped into a calorimeter filled with liquid of mass 50 g at a temperature of 10°C. If the specific heat capacity of the liquid is 2 cal g^{-1}°C^{-1}, and the resultant temperature is 20°C then what will be the water equivalent (in g) of the calorimeter?

47. Explain the experiment to find the boiling point of water. Also, explain its heating and cooling curves.

48. Describe an experiment to determine the specific heat capacity of a given solid by the method of mixtures.

49. Describe the method to determine specific latent heat of vaporization of water using a calorimeter.

50. The time period of a pendulum clock is 1 s at 0°C. If the temperature of the pendulum is increased to 50°C, and the material of the pendulum clock is made of brass with the coefficient of linear expansion 2×10^{-5}°C^{-1}, then determine the new time period of the pendulum.

PRACTICE QUESTIONS COMPETITION WING

Level 1: Apply Your Concepts

Directions for questions from 1 to 7:
Select whether the following statements are true or false.

1. Due to anomalous behaviour of water, volume of ice is more than that of the same mass of water.
2. When common salt is added to water, the boiling point of water increases.
3. Heat required to change the state of substance at constant temperature is called latent heat.
4. Refrigerator is a device which works on the principle that evaporation of a liquid gives cooling effect.
5. The specific heat capacity of water is 4200 J kg^{-1} K^{-1}.
6. The rate of evaporation of a given liquid depends only on the surface area of the liquid exposed to air.
7. Equal volume of three different liquids A, B and C are heated through the same temperature change. If ΔV_A, ΔV_B, ΔV_C are the changes in the volumes of the liquids, then, it depends on each other.

Directions for questions from 8 to 14:
Fill in the blanks.

8. A body P is in thermal equilibrium with Q and Q is not in thermal equilibrium with R, then the P and R _______ be in thermal equilibrium.
9. An object, half immersed, is floating in water. The volume immersed in the liquid will __________, when only the temperature of the water is increased.
10. The dimensional formula of heat is _____.
11. Heat absorbed or lost by a substance is proportional to _____ and _____.
12. Arrange the following steps to determine the latent heat of fusion of ice in a proper sequence.
    (A) Measure the final temperature of the mixture.
    (B) Take a known quantity of ice at 0°C into a calorimeter.
    (C) Drop a piece of metal ball of known mass, specific heat capacity and temperature into the calorimeter.
    (D) Use the law of mixture and find latent heat of fusion of the substance.
    (a) BACD (b) BDAC
    (c) CABD (d) BCAD
13. The device which is used to measure specific heat capacity of solids and liquids is ______.
14. Calorimeter is highly polished from inside and outside to prevent heat loss by _____.

Direction for question 15:
Match the entries in Column A with appropriate ones from Column B.

15.

	Column A		Column B
A.	Water equivalent	a.	Conversion from solid state to gaseous state directly
B.	High specific heat capacity	b.	Heat lost by hot body = Heat gained by the cold body.
C.	Bomb calorimeter	c.	$\frac{\text{Work output (or) heat utilized}}{\text{Heat produced}}$
D.	Principle of calorimeter	d.	Liquid converts to gas
E.	Evaporation	e.	226 × 10^4 J kg^{-1}.
F.	Latent heat of Vaporization of pure water	f.	Burns caused by steam
G.	Sublimation	g.	Petrol engine
H.	Thermal efficiency	h.	Water
I.	Scalding	i.	Calorific values
J.	Carburettor	j.	gram (or) kilogram

Direction for questions from 16 to 35:

For each of the questions, four choices have been provided. Select the correct alternative.

16. In a device, the complete conversion of heat energy into mechanical work ______.
(a) is not possible at any cost
(b) depends on type of device in use
(c) depends on the atmospheric temperature, pressure, etc.
(d) depends on the type of fuel used

17. If water is converted into ice and maintained at 0°C, which of the following statements is true for the molecules of the substance?
(a) Only kinetic energy decreases
(b) Only potential energy decreases
(c) Both the energies increase
(d) Potential energy increases and kinetic energy decreases

18. Steam engine is not extensively used because
(a) it is bulky.
(b) it takes long time to generate the steam.
(c) high pressure of steam may burst the boiler which is dangerous.
(d) All of the above.

19. The specific heat capacity of a substance depends on its
(a) nature (b) mass
(c) rise in temperature (d) Both (b) and (c)

20. Study the adjacent graph drawn between the amount of heat energy supplied to 500 g of a substance and its rise in temperature. Identify the correct option.

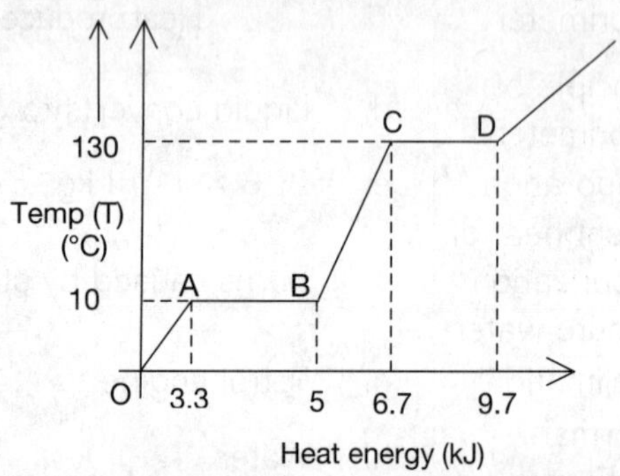

(a) The melting point of the given substance is 10°C.
(b) The latent heat of fusion of the given substance is 2300 J.
(c) The boiling point of the substance 130°C.
(d) All the above.

21. A hot body at temperature θ_1 is mixed with a cold body at temprature θ_2 both having the same heat capacity, such that the rise in temperature of the cold body is equal to the fall in temperature of the hot body. The resultant temperature θ is
(a) $\frac{\theta_1 - \theta_2}{2}$ (b) $\theta_1 + \theta_2$
(c) $\frac{\theta_1 - \theta_2}{2}$ (d) $\theta_1 - \theta_2$

22. Snow balls are formed due to
(a) melting of ice
(b) freezing of atmospheric moisture
(c) regelation
(d) sublimation

23. A substance of mass m_1 with specific heat capacity s_1 and initial temperature θ_1 is mixed with another substance of mass m_2, specific heat capacity s_2 and initial temperature θ_2, respectively. Then, their equilibrium temperature is ______ (take $\theta_1 > \theta_2$).
(a) $\frac{m_1 s_1 \theta_1 + m_2 s_2 \theta_2}{m_1 s_1 - m_2 s_2}$ (b) $\frac{m_1 s_1 \theta_1 + m_2 s_2 \theta_2}{m_1 s_1 + m_2 s_2}$
(c) $\frac{m_2 s_2 \theta_2 + m_1 s_1 \theta_1}{m_1 + m_2}$ (d) $\frac{m_1 s_1 \theta_1 + m_2 s_2 \theta_2}{m_1 s_1 + m_2 s_2}$

24. Heat gained by 1 g of water when heated from 0°C to 100°C is
(Specific heat capacity of water = 1 cal g^{-1} °C^{-1})
(a) 4200 cal. (b) 4.2 cal.
(c) 100 cal. (d) 1 cal.

25. Two bodies of masses 50 g and 100 g, have their water equivalents as 10 g and 20 g, respectively. The values of their specific heat capacities are ______ cal g^{-1} °C^{-1} and ______ cal g^{-1} °C^{-1}.
(a) $\frac{1}{5}$ and $\frac{1}{5}$ (b) $\frac{1}{3}$ and $\frac{1}{3}$
(c) $\frac{11}{5}$ and $\frac{11}{5}$ (d) $\frac{1}{2}$ and $\frac{1}{2}$

26. Arrange the following steps in the proper order to explain how a sea breeze occurs, near coastal regions.
(A) The temperature of land rises rapidly as compared to sea, because the specific heat capacity of land is five times less than that of water.
(B) Due to the low pressure over the land mass, the cool air over the sea starts blowing towards the land.

(C) The sun shines equally on the land mass and sea, giving equal amount of heat energy to both.

(D) The air above the land becomes hot and light, rises up, and hence, creates the low pressure over the land.

(a) ADCB (b) CDAB
(c) CABD (d) CADB

27. Linear expansion of a substance depends upon its
(a) initial length.
(b) change in temperature.
(c) nature of the material.
(d) All of the above.

28. The area of cross-sections of three metal rods of the equal length and made of the same materials are A_1, A_2 and A_3, respectively. When heated through the same change in temperature, their linear expansions are found to be l_1, l_2 and l_3, respectively Which among the following is the correct relation between l_1, l_2 and l_3?
(a) $l_1 = l_2 = l_3$
(b) $l_1 > l_2 > l_3$
(c) $l_1 < l_2 < l_3$
(d) $l_1 = l_2 < l_3$

29. The coefficient of linear expansion α of steel is $11 \times 10^{-6}\ °C^{-1}$ = Then α = ______ $\times 10^{-6}\ °F^{-1}$
(a) 6.11 (b) 19.8
(c) 11 (d) 43.

30. A copper wire is bent as shown in the figure. When its temperature is increased, the distance between A and B ______.

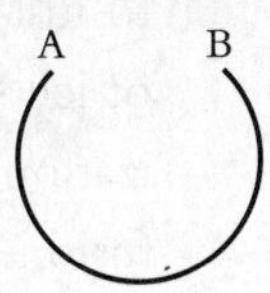

(a) decreases
(b) increases
(c) remains same
(d) increases or decreases depending up on its initial temperature.

31. The coefficient of linear expansion α is ______ that of the coefficient of areal expansion.
(a) double of (b) triple of
(c) half of (d) equal to

32. The coefficient of linear and areal expansion cannot be defined for liquids, as liquids do not have a definite ______.
(a) volume (b) shape
(c) density (d) specific heat capacity

33. Anomalous behaviour of water can be demonstrated with the help of Hope's apparatus. Arrange the following steps of changes taking place in Hopes apparatus in the proper sequence.

(A) The temperature shown by the lower thermometer reaches to 4°C and remains constant at 4°C.

(B) Water freezes into ice at 0 °C, and the layer of ice is formed at the top surface because the density of ice is less than that of water.

(C) The initial temperature of water is maintained at 10 °C. The temperature of water begins to fall due to the freezing mixture at the centre and it contracts.

(D) As temperature of water falls below 4°C, water expands instead of contracting and its density decreases. So, water goes up from the centre portion.

(E) As density increases, the cold water goes to the bottom. The temperature shown by the lower thermometer falls.

(F) The temperature of water at the top of the vessel begins to fall till 0 °C as shown by the upper thermometer.

(G) Being a bad conductor of heat, ice prevents the loss of heat from water below it into the surroundings.

(a) CEBFAGD (b) CEADFBG
(c) CEAFDGB (d) CBEGDAF

34. Arrange the following steps to determine the specific heat capacity of a substance in a sequential order.
(A) Note the initial temperature of water.
(B) Use the law of mixture.
(C) Take a known mass of water in calorimeter.
(D) Determine the specific heat capacity of the material.
(E) Drop the material taken from hot water into the colorimeter.
(F) Find the temperature of the mixture.

(a) CAEFBD (b) CABFD
(c) ACFBD (d) CBEAFD

35. Steam is used in external combustion engine as working medium because of its
(a) high specific heat capacity.
(b) high thermal capacity.
(c) high latent heat of vaporization.
(d) low liquefaction point (B.P).

Level 2: Review Your Concepts

36. A copper calorimeter of mass 100 g contains 200 g of ice at a temperature of −10°C. Heat is supplied to the system containing calorimeter and ice at a constant rate of 50 cal s^{-1}. Find the time required to raise the temperature of the system to 50°C. [Neglect the loss of heat to the surroundings.] Take specific heat capacity of copper and ice as 0.2 cal g^{-1} °C^{-1} and 0.5 cal g^{-1} °C^{-1}. Take latent heat of fusion of ice as 80 cal g^{-1} and specific heat capacity of water as 1 cal g^{-1} °C^{-1}.

37. The water equivalent of a substance is 40 g. How much is the heat energy (in cal) required to raise the temperature of the substance by 20°C?

38. When a liquid at 50°C is mixed with a similar liquid of the same mass, the resultant temperature of the mixture is found to be 30°C. How much is the initial temperature of the second liquid?

39. The graph below shows the rise in temperature of a solid of specific heat capacity 0.5 cal g^{-1} °C^{-1} and the heat supplied to it. Find its mass and specific latent heat of fusion.

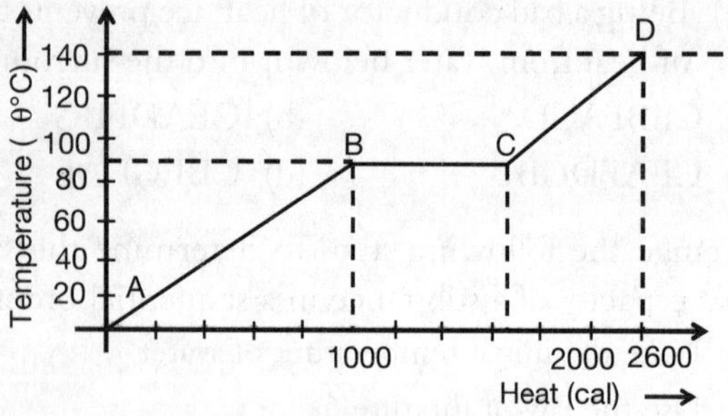

Also find the specific heat capacity of the body in its liquid state.

40. A bullet of 50 g is fired from a revolver with a velocity of 100 m s^{-1} into an ice block at 0 °C. The bullet stops after it gets embedded into ice. Assuming that all the kinetic energy of the bullet is converted into heat energy which is absorbed by the melting ice, find the quantity of the ice that just melts.

41. The temperature of water is 20°C. If the water falls from a height of 500 m, and 90% of the potential energy is used to increase the temperature of water, then what is the final temperature (in °C) of the water?

42. How much energy in watt-hour is required for an electric heater to convert 2 kg of ice at 0 °C to water at 25°C. Assume the water equivalent of the given heater to be 10 g. (Assume that initially the heater and the ice are in thermal equilibrium).

43. When heat is supplied at constant rate, ice of mass 200 g at 0°C is converted to water at 0°C in 8 minutes. Calculate the time taken to raise the temperature of resulting water to 100°C. (Take latent heat of fusion of ice = 336 J g^{-1} °C^{-1} and specific heat capacity of water = 4.2 J g^{-1} °C^{-1}.)

44. The initial temperature of half a litre of water is 20°C. On supplying heat to it, its temperature rises to 72 °F. For every 1°C rise in temperature per gram of water, 4.2 J of heat is needed. Calculate the heat capacity of water.

45. What is the number of metal balls each of mass 50 g of specific heat capacity of 0.1 cal g^{-1}°C^{-1} at temperature of 90°C to be added to 300 g of water at 25°C so that the resultant temperature is equal to 60°C?

46. Two identical calorimeters X and Y, of water equivalent 10 g each, contain equal quantities of same liquid. The mass, initial temperature and specific heat capacity of the liquid present in the two calorimeters are 50 g, 25°C 0.5 cal g^{-1} °C^{-1}, respectively. A 10 g metal piece (say A) of specific heat capacity 0.4 cal g^{-1} °C^{-1} is dropped in calorimeter X and 25 g of metal piece (say B) of specific heat capacity 'S_B' is dropped into calorimeter Y. Due to this, the equilibrium temperature in X and Y rises to 30°C and 40°C, respectively. If the initial temperature of B is twice that of A, then find the value of S_B.

47. Calculate the mass of steam at 100°C which is needed to just melt 320 g of ice at −10°C. (Take specific heat of ice = 0.5 cal g^{-1} °C^{-1}, specific latent heat of vaporization of steam = 540 cal g^{-1}, specific latent heat of fusion of ice = 80 cal g^{-1}.)

48. A thermally insulated container has 500 g of mercury in liquid state at its freezing point. The container is connected to a vacuum pump and air above the liquid (mercury) is pumped out of the container. Due to this, some of the liquid evaporates and the remaining liquid solidifies. Then find the mass of the solid that is found by solidification of liquid. (Take specific latent heat of fusion, L_F = 12500 J kg^{-1} and specific Latent heat of vaporization, L_V = 290000 J kg^{-1}.)

49. 100 g of water at 70°C is added to 120 g of water at 30°C contained in a vessel. The final temperature of mixture is 40°C. Calculate the thermal capacity of the vessel.

50. A mercury thermometer whose markings are in centimeter scale, is used to measure the temperature. It shows 3 cm and 15 cm when kept in melting ice and boiling water, respectively. Find the equilibrium temperature, as recorded by the above thermometer when 10 g of iron ball at 229° C is dropped into 50 g of water at 25°C. Here, the water equivalent of the container is negligible and heat lost to the surroundings is almost zero. (Take specific heat capacity of iron and water as 0.1 cal g^{-1} $°C^{-1}$ and 1 cal g^{-1} $°C^{-1}$, respectively.)

51. If 1050 J of heat is required to increase the temperature of 15 kg of substance from 25°C to 35°C, find the thermal capacity and water equivalent of the substance.

52. Water falls from a height of 100 m. Find the rise in temperature of the water, when it reaches the bottom, assuming all its energy is converted to heat at the bottom of the water fall. (g = 10 m s^{-2}, sw = 4200 J kg^{-1} K^{-1})

53. Using the table given below, determine the relative humidity at 25°C if the amount of water vapour in the atmosphere is 11.48 g m^{-3}.

Temperature of air (°C)	Mass of Water Vapour at Saturation
10	9.38 g m^{-3}
15	12.78 g m^{-2}
20	17.18 m^{-3}
25	22.88 m^{-3}

54. Why is it that the RCC (cement) slabs on the houses are laid at one stretch?

55. A physicist took a circular metallic sheet of radius 4 cm at a temperature of 27°C. He heated metallic sheet up to 127°C and found that the diameter of the sheet increased to 8.2 cm, then what is the coefficient of a real expansion?

Level 3: Assess Your Concepts

56. 5 g of ice at 0°C is mixed with 5 g of water at 20°C what will be the resultant temperature (in °C) of the mixture?

57. Three liquids A, B and C of densities in the ratio of 1 : 2 : 3, respectively are taken. Their initial temperatures are 60°C, 50°C and 30°C, respectively. When equal parts (by volumes) of 'A' and 'B' are mixed, the resultant temperature of the mixture is 55°C. When equal parts (by weights) of A and C are mixed, then the equilibrium temperature of the mixture is 40°C. Find the ratio of specific heat capacity of the liquids.

58. The intensity of sunlight incident on a block of ice is 800 W m^{-2}. If ice absorbs 60% of the light, calculate the thickness of ice that would melt in 1 minute (Density of ice = 917 kg m^{-3}).

59. Why is that the hot water is preferred over cold water to put off the fire?

60. The water equivalent of a container filled with 300 g of water at 30°C is 200 g. How much heat energy (in cal) required to raise the temperature of the content to 70°C?

61. 10 g of ice at –20°C is mixed with 10 g of water at 10°C. What will be the resultant temperature (in °C) of the mixture?

62. If the length of a steel rod is 100 cm at 0°C, then what should be the original length of a copper rod at 0°C if the difference in their lengths is exactly equal to 5 cm at 100°C.

(α for copper = 1.7 × 10^{-5} $°C^{-1}$ and α for steel = 1.1 × 10^{-5} $°C^{-1}$)

63. A pendulum has a time period of 2 s at 10°C. What would be its time period if the temperature is increased to 110°C ($\alpha = 2 \times 10^{-5}°C^{-1}$).

64. An alloy (in liquid state) of mass 100 g and at 242 °C is transferred into a copper calorimeter of water equivalent 40 g containing 200 g of water. When the equilibrium is reached, the temperature of calorimeter and water rises from 12.1 °C to 22.1 °C. Now, when the experiment is repeated with the given alloy in the solid state, at the same temperature of 242 °C, by dropping it in the calorimeter, the equilibrium temperature was found to be 14 °C. Find the latent heat of fusion of the given alloy.

65. The graph below shows the different stages of conversion of given substance from its solid state to vapour state. Compare the specific heat capacities of the given substance in the solid (S_1), liquid (S_2) and gaseous(S_3) states. Here, $\theta_3 < \theta_2 < \theta_1$.

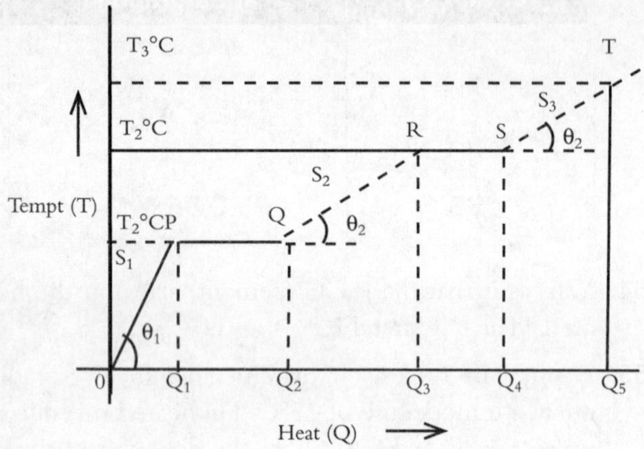

66. If 50 g of water at 30 °C is added to 150 g of water at 90 °C, and stirred well to obtain an equilibrium temperature, then find the equilibrium temperature.

67. Three liquids of different mass m_1, m_2, and m_3, with specific heat capacity s_1, s_2, and s_3 and initial temperature θ_1, θ_2, and θ_3 respectively are mixed to form a uniform mixture. What is the equilibrium temperature of the mixture?

68. If 500 g of castor oil absorbs 13.5 kJ heat to raise its temperature from a room temperature of 25°C to a lukewarm temperature of 40°C, then find the specific heat capacity of the oil in SI system.

69. When 100 g of silver is heated at atmospheric pressure, it begins to change its state at a steady temperature of 961.8°C. If it absorbs 10500 J to completely convert to its liquid form, then find the specific latent heat of fusion of silver.

70 . When 50 g of ice at 0°C is added to 150 g of water at 60°C, find the equilibrium temperature.

AT

PRACTICE QUESTIONS JEE-NEET SPECIAL WING

Multiple-Answer Type Questions

Directions for Questions 1 to 5: **Each question has FOUR options (a), (b), (c), and (d). ONE OR MORE THAN ONE of these four option(s) is/are the correct answer(s).**

1. The water in a glass flask is heated from 40 °C to 100 °C. The change in its temperature is equal to ________.

(a) 60 K (b) 40 *K*
(c) 60 °F (d) 108 °F

2. If the specific heat capacity of alcohol is 2180 *J* kg^{-1} K^{-1}, then ________.

(a) the heat capacity of alcohol of 100 *g* is 218 *J* K^{-1}
(b) the heat energy supplied to 100 *g* of alcohol to raise its temperature by 10 °C is 2180 *J*.
(c) The common temperature of the mixture of 10 *g* of alcohol at 20 °C and 20 *g* of alcohol at 10 °C is 286.33 *K*.
(d) its value is 0.52 cal g^{-1} $°C^{-1}$ in common units.

3. Choose the correct statement of the following.

(a) Calorimeter uses the principle of mixtures to find the specific heat capacity of different bodies.
(b) The specific heat capacity of water is nearly five times that of land. That means water needs less heat than land to raise its temperature by 1°C.
(c) Heat absorbed or given out by a body is directly proportional to the temperature of the body.
(d) In cold countries, during winter, farmers water their fields in the evening because the temperature of the water does not fall quickly and protect the crop.

4. The following is the temperature versus time graph plotted to find the melting point of naphthalene.

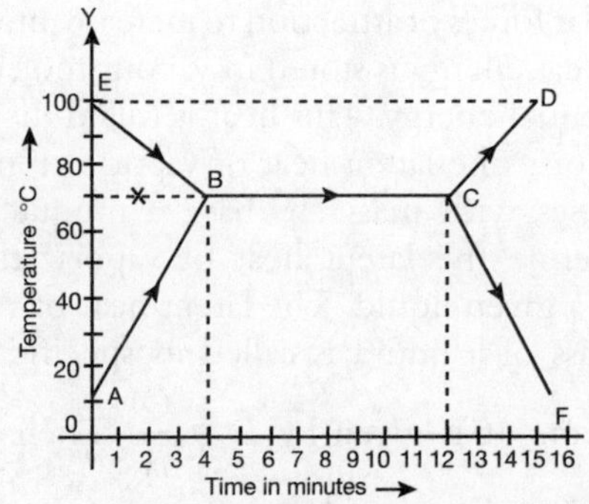

(a) The part BC of the graph shows the change in the state of naphthalene at constant temperature.
(b) For the part AB of the graph, the heat capacity of naphthalene is 3.4 *J* $°C^{-1}$ if the heat energy absorbed is 204 *J*.
(c) The part CD of the graph shows that the temperature of the solid naphthalene increases on heating.
(d) The part CF of the graph shows that the temperature of the solid naphthalene decreases on cooling.

5. A calorimeter of mass 70 *g* and specific heat capacity 0.40 *J* g^{-1} $°C^{-1}$ contains 310 *g* of water at 30°C. If an ice piece of 50 *g* is added to water, then ________.

(Specific heat capacity of water = 4.2 *J* g^{-1} $°C^{-1}$ and specific latent heat of fusion of ice = 336 *J* g^{-1} $°C^{-1}$)

(a) The heat gained by the ice piece to form water is 16.8 kJ.
(b) The heat energy gained by the water that formed from the ice (if the final temperature is 15 °C) is 3.15 kJ
(c) The heat lost by the water in the calorimeter is 3.6 kJ
(d) Heat lost by calorimeter + Heat lost by water (in the calorimeter) = Heat gained by the ice to form water + Heat gained by the water (formed from ice)

Comprehension-Based Questions

Direction for questions 6 to 11: **Read the paragraph given below and answer the questions.**

When a liquid is heated till it reaches the boiling point, the liquid vaporizes but its temperature remains constant. During vaporization, the heat supplied is used to overcome intermolecular forces of attraction to increase intermolecular space. This heat energy is stored in vapour molecules in the form of potential energy. This heat is called the latent heat of vaporization. The latent heat of vaporization of a given liquid increases with mass. To have a unique or specific value, we define the latent heat of vaporization for the unit mass of a given liquid. The latent heat of vaporization of a unit mass of a liquid is called its specific latent heat of vaporization. It is given by $L = \frac{Q}{m}$. There are several advantages of specific latent heat of vaporization such as plants do not wilt easily even in summer because the water in soil needs a very large amount of heat, i.e., 226.8×10^4 J kg^{-1}, one gram of water at 100 °C contains 100 cal of heat but 1 g of steam at 100 °C contains 640 cal of heat so it is used in thermal power stations to produce electrical energy. The experimental setup to determine the specific latent heat of vaporization consists of a calorimeter of mass m_1. The specific heat capacity of the calorimeter is s and it is at T_1 °C. When the calorimeter is filled with water, its mass becomes m_2. Then the mass of the water will be $(m_2 - m_1)$. The steam coming from the boiled water is made to pass through the water of the calorimeter until the temperature of the mixture becomes T °C. Let the final mass of the calorimeter be m_3. We know that the temperature of the steam is 100 °C.

Now, Initial mass of the calorimeter = m_1 g
Mass of the calorimeter with water = m_2 g
Then, Mass of the water = $(m_2 - m_1)$ g
Now, Mass of the calorimeter with water and condensed steam = m_3 g
Then, Mass of the condensed steam = $(m_3 - m_2)$ g
If L_{steam} be the specific latent heat of vaporization of water, then
Heat lost by the steam $Q_1 = (m_3 - m_2) \times L_{steam}$
Heat lost by water formed from steam (that is at 100°C), $Q_2 = (m_3 - m_2) \times 4.2$ J g$^{-1} \times (100 - T)$ Heat gained by the calorimeter, $Q_3 = m_1 \times s \times (T - T_1)$
Heat gained by the water of mass $(m_2 - m_1)$,
$Q_4 = (m_2 - m_1) \times 4.2$ J g$^{-1} \times (T - T_1)$
By the principle of mixtures,
Heat lost by the steam (Q_1) + Heat lost by water formed from steam (Q_2)
= Heat gained by the calorimeter (Q_3) + Heat gained by the water (Q_4)

$$\Rightarrow [(m_3 - m_2) \times L_{steam}] + [(m_3 - m_2) \times 4.2 \text{ J g}^{-1} \times (100 - T)] = [m_1 \times s \times (T - T_1)] + [(m_2 - m_1) \times 4.2 \text{ J g}^{-1} \times (T - T_1)]$$

$$\Rightarrow L_{steam} = \frac{[m_1 \times s \times (T - T_1)] + [(m_2 - m_1) \times 4.2 \times (T - T_1)] - [(m_3 - m_2) \times 4.2 \times (100 - T)]}{(m_3 - m_2)}$$

Using the above equation, the specific latent heat of vaporization can be determined.

6. The latent heat of vaporization is __________.
(a) used to overcome intermolecular forces of attraction
(b) stored in vapour molecules in the form of potential energy
(c) directly proportional to the mass of the substance
(d) All of these

7. During the change of state of a substance, __________.
(a) The heat energy absorbed by the substance remains constant
(b) The heat energy absorbed by the substance increases
(c) The temperature of the substance remains constant
(d) None of these

8. The specific latent heat of the fusion of wax is 146 J g^{-1}. If the mass of the wax is 0.5 kg, then the heat absorbed by the change of state from solid to liquid is __________.
(a) 73 J (b) 292 J
(c) 73 kJ (d) 292 kJ

9. One gram of water at 100 °C contains 100 cal of heat but 1 g of steam at 100 °C contains 640 cal of heat. The heat energy stored in vapour molecules in the form of potential energy is __________.
(a) 540 cal (b) 100 cal
(c) 640 cal (d) 640 *k* cal

10. According to the principle of method of mixtures, __________.
(a) The total energy of the system remains constant
(b) The heat lost by hot body is equal to the heat gained by cold body
(c) The total energy of the system increases.
(d) Both (a) and (b)

11. Using the data given in the previous paragraph, match the following.

Column – A	Column – B
A. If the mass of the calorimeter is 50 g and the mass of the calorimeter with water is 150 g, then the mass of the water is	a. 90 J
B. If the mass of the calorimeter is 45 g, its specific heat capacity is 0.4 J g^{-1} $°C^{-1}$, and the change in temperature is 5 °C, then the heat gained by it is	b. 4.2 kJ
C. If the mass of the condensed steam is 10 g, the specific latent heat of vaporization is 2260 J g^{-1} $°C^{-1}$, then the heat lost by the steam is	c. 100 g
D. The heat absorbed by 100 g of water of specific heat capacity 4.2 J g^{-1} $°C^{-1}$ to raise its temperature from 35 °C to 45 °C is	d. 15 g
E. If the mass of the calorimeter is 50 g and the mass of the calorimeter with water is 180 g. When the stem is made to pass through the water, the total mass of the calorimeter becomes 195 g. The mass of the condensed steam is	e. 22.6 k J

ANSWER KEYS

Crossword

Across

5. Kelvin 7. Regelation 8. Gram 9. Sublimation
10. Boiling

Down

1. Pressure 2. Diesel Engine 3. Heat Engine 4. Temperature
6. Evaporation

Classroom Wing

Very Short Answer Type Questions

1. intake, compression, power and exhaust 2. 4°C 3. Fuel injection pump
4. Anomalous expansion of water 5. Mixtures or calorimetry 6. 336 × 103 or 80
7. specific latent heat of vaporization 8. 2344 Jg 9. specific heat capacity of the body
10. temperature 11. dew point 12. The part of the internal energy transferred.
13. The entire size of the plate increases. 14. Expansion depends on nature of material.
29. $A \rightarrow Q, B \rightarrow P, C \rightarrow R$. 30. $A \rightarrow Q, B \rightarrow R, C \rightarrow P$

Competition Wing

Level 1: Apply Your Concepts

1. True 2. True 3. True 4. True 5. True
6. False 7. True 8. cannot 9. increases. 10. $[ML^2T^{-2}]$
11. Mass, Change in temperature 12. (d) 13. calorimeter 14. Radiation
15. A : j, B : h, C : i, D : b, E : d, F : e, G : a, H : c, I : f, J : g
16. (a) 17. (b) 18. (d) 19. (a) 20. (d)
21. (a) 22. (c) 23. (d) 24. (c) 25. (a)
26. (d) 27. (d) 28. (a) 29. (a) 30. (b)
31. (c) 32. (b) 33. (b) 34. (a) 35. (c)

JEE-NEET SPECIAL WING

Multiple-Answer Type Questions

1. (a, d) 2. (a, b, c, d) 3. (a, d) 4. (a, b, d) 5. (a, b, d)

Comprehension-Based Questions

6. (d) 7. (c) 8. (c) 9. (a) 10. (d)
11. A-c, B-a, C-e, D-b, E-d

For answer key of Classroom wing and Competition wing, refer to Hints and Solutions

Hints and Explanations

CLASSROOM WING

Very Short Answer Type Questions

1. intake, compression, power and exhaust
2. 4°C
3. Fuel injection pump
4. Anomalous expansion of water
5. Mixtures or calorimetry
6. 336×10^3 or 80
7. specific latent heat of vaporization
8. 2344 Jg
9. specific heat capacity of the body
10. temperature
11. dew point
12. The part of the internal energy transferred is known as heat.
13. When a metal plate is heated the entire size of the plate increases. Hence, the size of the hole also increases.
14. The expansion of the material also depends upon the nature of the material.
15. $C = \frac{Q}{\Delta\theta}, s = \frac{Q}{M\Delta\theta}$
16. When the temperature is increased the density decreases, and hence, the upthrust decreases.
17. Heat lost by the hotter body is equal to Heat gained by the colder body.
18. Temperature is the average kinetic energy.
19. (i) Conversion from solid to liquid
    (ii) Conversion from liquid to solid
    (iii) Conversion from liquid to gas
    (iv) Conversion from gas to liquid
20. When a metal is heated, the overall volume increases.
21. 3360 J
22. The heat supplied to overcome intermolecular forces of attraction during phase transition.
23. Evaporation leads to cooling
24. latent heat of fusion- The heat supplied to convert unit mass of a solid to liquid –
    Specific latent heat of fusion of ice is the amount of heat needed to convert a unit mass of ice (1 kg or 1g) to water at 0°C
25. A device in which heat is utilized to do some useful work, is called heat engine. Internal and external combustion engine.
26. Conversion from liquid to gas, conversion of unit mass of liquid to gas.
27. Solid converted to vapour directly.
28. Pressure, soluble impurities
29. A → Q, B → P, C → R.
30. A → Q, B → R, C → P.

Short Answer Type Questions

Note: This is how you should frame your answer covering.

31. Mass = 200 g

    Water equivalent = 400 g

    Water equivalent = ms

    $400 = 200 \times s$

    $S = 2 \text{ cal g}^{-1}{}^\circ\text{C}^{-1}$.

32. $t_1 = 20°C$, $t_2 = 30°C$

    $ms\,(t - 20) = ms\,(30 - t)$

    $2t = 50$

    $T = 25°C$.

33. $\frac{80}{100}(mgh) = ms\Delta t$

    $0.8 \times 300 \times 10 = 4200 \times \Delta t$

    $\Delta t = \frac{2400}{4200} = 0.57°C$.

34. $5 \times 1 \times (70 - 40) = m \times 1 \times (40 - 20)$

    $m = \frac{5 \times 30}{20} = 7.5$ kg.

35. Land and sea breezes

36. $Q = Q_1 + Q_2 + Q_3$

$Q = m\ L_{ice}$, $Q_2 = ms\ \Delta\theta$, $Q_3 = m\ L_{steam}$

3016×10^3 J

37. (i) Surface phenomenon

(ii) Rate of process

(iii) Temperature

(iv) Effect

(v) Factors affecting

38. (i) Refrigeration

(ii) Working principle

(iii) Construction

(iv) List of major parts

(v) Working of each part

(vi) Use

39. (i) Definition

(ii) Construction

(iii) Copper vessel and stove

(iv) Wooden box

(v) Working principle

(vi) Use

40. $Q = ms\ \Delta\theta$,

$Q = P\,t$

Ans: 6 kJ °C^{-1}

41. (i) Saturation

(ii) Effect of temperature on saturation

(iii) Dew point

(iv) Temperature below dew point

42. $C = Q/\Delta\theta$

Ans: 500 J K^{-1}

43. No flash floods, surrounding weather will become moderate, the cream preparation, etc.

44. (i) Efficiency

(ii) Starting time

(iii) Size

(iv) Safety

45. According to the table the dew point is 15 °C.

Essay Answer Type Questions

Note: This is how you should frame your answer covering.

46. Mass = 400 g

$s = 0.1$ cal g^{-1}°C^{-1}

Mass of liquid = 50 g

$t_1 = 10$°C

$S_n = 2$ cal g^{-1}°C^{-1}. $t_r = 20$°C

$W_e = ?$

Heat gained = Heat lost

$$W_e \times 1 \times (10) + 50 \times 2 \times 10 = 400 \times 1 \times 10$$

$$10\ W_e = 4000 - 1000$$

$$W_e = \frac{3000}{10} = 300 \text{ g}$$

$$W_e = 300 \text{ g.}$$

47. $Q = ms\Delta t$; $Q = mL_V$

Heating curve: Solid converts to liquid then to gaseous state.

Cooling curve: Gas converts to liquid and then to the solid state.

48. $Q_{lost} = Q_{gained}$

49. Refer notes section under Determination of Specific Latent Heat of Vaporization by Method of Mixtures

50. $T = 1$ s, $t_i = 0$°C, $t_f = 50$°C

$\alpha = 2 \times 10^{5}$°C^{-1}

$\ell = \ell_0 (1 + \alpha\, \Delta T)$

$$T_0 = 1 \text{ s}, \quad \frac{T_0}{T_1} = \sqrt{\frac{l_0}{(l_0)(1+\alpha\Delta t)}}$$

$T_1 = ?$

$$\frac{1}{T_1} = \sqrt{\frac{1}{(1+2\times 10^{-5}\times 50)}}$$

$$T_1 = \sqrt{(1+10^{-3})} = 1.0005 \text{ s.}$$

Competition Wing

Level 1: Apply Your Concepts

Note: This is how you should frame your answer covering.

7. True. Expansion of a material depends upon the nature of the material.

8. P and R cannot be in thermal equilibrium.

9. Volume immersed in the liquid increases.

12. B C A D

Explanation for questions 26 to 35:

26. Near the coastal regions, when (c) the sun shines equally on the land mass as well as the sea giving an equal amount of heat energy. But, (*a*) the temperature of land rises rapidly as compared to the sea water, as the specific heat capacity of water is five times greater than that of land. So, water requires more heat energy to raise its temperature by 1°C. Then (*d*) the air above the land mass becomes hotter and lighter, and hence, rises up, which creates a low pressure over the land. (*b*) Due to the low pressure over the land mass, the cool air over the sea starts blowing towards the land, by this producing sea breeze.

27. The linear expansion of a metal rod of initial length l_0 is $\Delta l = \alpha l_0 \Delta t$. Linear expansion of a substance depends upon the original length, change in temperature and nature of the material.

28. Linear expansion of all the three are same their original length and change in temperature and the material are the same.

29. $\alpha = 11 \times 10^{-6}\,^\circ C^{-1}$

$$= \frac{11\times10^{-6}}{1.8^\circ F} = 6.11\times10^{-6\,\circ}F^{-1}$$

30. The distance between A and B increases when the temperature is increased.

31. The coefficient of linear expansion 'α' is half of the coefficient of a real expansion.

32. The coefficient of linear and a real expansion cannot be defined for liquids, as liquids do not have a definite shape.

33. (c) Initial temperature of water in the vessel is maintained at 10 °C. Due to freezing at the centre, the temperature of water begins to fall. The water contracts and its density increases. (*e*) As the density of water increases, the cold water goes to the bottom of the vessel and the temperature of water falls to 4 °C (*a*) as shown by the lower thermometer and this remains constant. (*d*) The temperature of water at the centre falls below 4 °C, then the water expands instead of contracting so that its density decreases, therefore, the water below 4 °C goes to the upper portion (*f*) The temperature of water falls till 0 °C, as shown by the upper thermometer. (*b*) Water at 0 °C freezes into ice and a layer of ice is formed at the top surface, because the density of ice is less than that of water. (*g*) Being a bad conductor of heat, ice prevents the loss of heat from water below it to the surroundings.

34. (a) C A E F B D.

35. Steam at 100°C can carry 540 cal of more heat energy per gram than the water at 100°C. It is possible because water is having high latent heat of vaporization.

Level 2: Review Your Concepts

Note: This is how you should frame your answer covering.

36. (i) The heat energy required by the system (containing both calorimeter and ice) to raise its temperature from −10°C to 0°C is

$Q_1 = m_c\, s_c\, (10) + m_i\, s_i\, (10)$

Substitute, mass of calorimeter, m_c mass of ice, m_i and specific heat capacities of calorimeter and ice and find Q_1

Find the heat energy absorbed by ice to convert into water at 0°C = $Q_2 = mL_F$

Substitute for latent heat of fusion, L_F and mass m of ice

Let the heat energy absorbed by the water and calorimeter to increase its temperature from 0°C to 50°C = Q_3.

$Q_3 = m_w\, s_w\, (50) + m_c\, s_c\, (50)$

The total heat supplied = $Q = Q_1 + Q_2 + Q_3$

The rate of heat supplied to the system = R = 50 cal s^{-1}

Time (t) taken by the system, $t = \dfrac{Q}{R}$

(ii) 9.4 minute

37. Water equivalent = 40 g

$$Q = m \times s \times \Delta t$$
$$= 40 \times 1 \times 20 = 800 \text{ cal.}$$

38. $t_1 = 50°C$

$t_r = 30°C$

$ms\ (50 - 30) = ms\ (30 - t)$

$20 = 30 - t$

$t = 10°C.$

39. (i) Observe the graph carefully and note the quantities represented on X and Y axes.

(ii) From the graph and using $Q = ms\Delta\theta_R$, find mass (m) of the solid.

(iii) Find L using the graph and $Q = mL$.

(iv) From the graph, find the specific heat capacity of liquid using $Q = ms\Delta\theta_R$.

(v) 0.75 cal $g^{-1}\ °C^{-1}$

40. (i) The loss of kinetic energy of the bullet

$= \frac{1}{2}mu^2 - \frac{1}{2}mv^2$

Here, $v = 0\ m\ s^{-1}$ and $u = 100\ m\ s^{-1}$

m = mass of the bullet $= \frac{50}{1000}$ kg

We know, $W = JQ$

Mechanical equivalent of work

Here, $J = 4.2\ J\ cal^{-1}$

$$Q = \frac{\frac{1}{2}mu^2}{4.2}\ \text{cal} \quad (1)$$

Now, this heat energy (Q) is used to melt the ice at 0°C $Q = mL_F$ (2)

Find the value of 'm' from (2)

$$m = \frac{Q}{L_F}$$

Take the value of $L_F = 80$ cal g^{-1}

(ii) 0.744 g

41. $t_1 = 20°C$, $h = 50$ m

$0.9 \times 500 \times 10 = 4200 \times \Delta t$

$$\Delta t = \frac{9 \times 500}{4200} = \frac{4500}{4200} = 1.07$$

$\therefore \quad t_f = 21.07°C.$

42. (i) Heat Q supplied to melt the ice at 0°C to water at 0°C = mL_F.

Here, L_F = latent heat of fusion of ice.

Heat supplied to increase the temperature from 0°C to 25°C = $ms\Delta t$

Here, $\Delta t = 25 - 0 = 25°C$

s = specific heat capacity of water.

m = mass of the substance.

Take 1 watt hour = 3600 J

(ii) 245.3 watt hour

43. (i) Use $Q = mL$ to find the heat absorbed by ice when it melts.

(ii) This heat is supplied over 8 minutes. Find heat supplied per minute.

(iii) Use $Q = ms\Delta\theta_R$ to find the heat required to raise the temperature of water from 0°C to 100°C.

(iv) Use heat supplied per minute × time = heat gained by water, to find time (t).

(v) 10 minutes

44. (i) Use:

Heat capacity = Mass of substance × Heat required per gram to raise its temperature by 1°C.

(ii) 2100 J $°C^{-1}$

45. $M \times 0.1 \times (90 - 60) = 300 \times 1 \times (60 - 25)$

$$M = \frac{35 \times 300}{3} = 3500\ \text{g}$$

Mass of one ball = 50 g

$\therefore \quad n \times 50 = 3500$

$n = 70.$

46. (i) In calorimeter X:

Find the initial temperature of metal A by using the principle,

Heat lost by metal A = Heat gained by liquid and calorimeter X

$m_A \cdot s_A \cdot (\Delta t)_A = \{50\ g \times 0.5 \times (30 - 25)\ °C + (5°C \times 10\ g)]\}$

$10 \times 0.4 \times (T - 30°C) = (50 \times 0.5 \times 5 + 50\ \text{cal})$ (1)

In calorimeter Y,

Find the initial temperature of metal B (2T).

The heat lost by metal B = Heat gained by (liquid + calorimeter).

$m_B\ S_B\ (2T - 40) = \{50\ g \times 0.5 \times (40 - 25)°C\} + (15\ °C \times 25\ g)$ (2)

(ii) $S_B = 0.2$ cal $g^{-1}\ °C^{-1}$

47. (i) Use $Q = ms\Delta\theta_R$ to find the heat absorbed by ice to raise its temperature from - 10°C to 0°C.

(ii) Use $Q = mL_{ice}$ to find heat absorbed by ice at 0°C to form water at 0°C.

(iii) Add 1 and 2 to find total heat absorbed.

(iv) Use $Q = mL_{vap}$ to find the heat lost by steam at 100°C when it condenses to water at 100°C.

(v) Use $Q = ms\Delta\theta_F$ to find the heat given when water at 100°C cools to 0°C.

(vi) Add 4 and 5 to find total heat given.

(vii) Equate 3 and 6 to find the mass of steam.

(viii) 42.5 g

48. (i) Let the total mass of the liquid = M =0.5 kg

Let, the mass of the liquid that is converted to solid = m

If L_v is the latent heat of vaporization and L_F latent heat of fusion, then $mL_F = (M - m)L_V$

Substitute the appropriate values and find the value of m.

(ii) 0.479 kg

49. (i) Use $Q_l = ms\Delta\theta_F$ to find heat lost by hot water.

(ii) Use $Q_g = ms\Delta\theta_R$ to find heat gained by cold water.

(iii) If H_v is the heat capacity of the vessel, use $H_v\Delta\theta_R$ to find heat gained by it.

(H_v = Mass of the vessel × Specific heat capacity of the vessel)

(iv) Add (ii) and (iii) and equate with (i) to find the heat capacity of the vessel.

(v) 756 J °C^{-1}

50. (i) Let the equilibrium temperature of the ball and water after the ball is dropped in to water be T.

Apply the principle of mixtures (or) calorimetry:

Heat lost by the hot body = Heat gained by the cold body.

$m_b\, s_b(\Delta t)_b = m_w\, s_w(\Delta t)_w$

$10 \times 0.1 \times (22\text{ g} - T) = 50 \times 1.$

$x\,(T - 25)$ (1)

Find the value of T from (1).

To find the temperature in new scale, use the formula

$$\left(\frac{T - LFP}{UFP - LFP}\right)_{scale\,1}$$

$$= \left(\frac{Length(x) - LFP}{UFP - LFP}\right)_{scale\,2} \qquad (2)$$

$$= \left(\frac{T - 0}{100 - 0}\right) = \left(\frac{X - 3}{15 - 3}\right)$$

(ii) 6.48 cm

51. $Q = 1050$ J

$m = 15$ kg

$\Delta t = 10$ °C

$$s = \frac{Q}{m\Delta t} = \frac{1050}{15 \times 10} = 7\,\text{Jkg}^{-1}\text{K}^{-1}$$

$$c = \frac{Q}{m\Delta t} = \frac{1050}{10}$$

$= 105$ J°C^{-1}

$$M = c = \frac{105}{4200} \times 1000$$

$= 25$ g $= 0.025$ kg

52. $mgh = ms\,\Delta t$

$10 \times 100 = s \times \Delta t$

$1000 = 4200\,\Delta t$

$$\Delta t = \frac{10}{42} = 0.238°\text{C}$$

53. Relative humidity

$$= \frac{\text{Amount of vapour present}}{\text{Amount of vapour at saturation}} \times 100\%$$

$$= \frac{11.48}{22.88} \times 100\% = 50\%.$$

54. RCC slab on houses as roofs are laid at a single stretch. By doing this, the slab behaves like a single plate and there will be a uniform expansion and contraction for temperature changes. Because of this, the building roof does not develop any cracks.

55. Given initial radius r_1 = 4 cm at temperature t_1 = 27°C, then $T_1 = t_1 + 27$ K

$T_1 = 273 + 27$

$T_1 = 300$ K Final diameter is $d_2 = 2r_2$

$$r_2 = \frac{d_2}{2}$$

Given $d_2 = 8.2$ cm, $r_2 = 4.1$ cm

and final temp $T_2 = t_2 + 273$

$= 127 + 273 = 400$K

Now, coefficient of areal expansion β.

$$= \frac{A_2 - A_1}{A_1(T_2 - T_1)} = \frac{[(4.1)^2 - (4)^2]\pi}{16\pi(400 - 300)}$$

$$= \frac{0.81}{16\pi(100)}$$

$= 0.05 \times 10^{-1} = 5 \times 10^{-3}$K^{-1}

Level 3: Assess Your Concepts

56. Heat gained by ice = heat lost by water

$Lm + (ms\Delta t) = (ms\Delta t)$

$80 \times 5 + 5 \times 1 \times (t - 0) = 5 \times 1 \times (20 - t)$

$$400 + 5t = 100 - 5t$$

$$10t = -300$$

$$t = -300$$

t cannot be less than zero.

Explanation:

Heat lost by water to change its temperature from 20°C to 0°C is $H_1 = ms\Delta t$

$$= 5 \times 1 \times 20$$

Heat required by ice to melt is

$H_2 = LM$

$= 5 \times 80$

$= 400$ cal

$H_1 < H_2$

Resultant temperature is 0°C.

57. (i) Find the ratio of the densities of A, B and C from given information.

Here, density $(d) = \frac{mass\,(m)}{volume\,(v)}$ (1)

When equal volumes of A and B liquids are taken, then find the ratio of their densities. Use principle of mixtures (or) calorimetry and find the ratio of specific heats of A and B. Get the equilibrium temperature of A and C from the given data.

Again, heat lost by 'A' liquid = heat gained by 'C' liquid. $m_A s_A (\Delta t)_A = m_C s_C (\Delta t)_C$

Given that $m_A = m_C$

Find the ratio of s_A and s_C

(ii) 2 : 1 : 4

58. (i) From the given data find the heat absorbed (Q) by the ice block per unit area in 1 minute (60 seconds).

(ii) If A is the area of the block, total heat absorbed is QA.

(iii) If t is the thickness of the block, its volume = At and mass = 917At

∵ Density of ice = 917 kg m^{-3} [given]

(iv) Heat absorbed during melting of ice = mL_{ice}

= 917 At × 336000 J

(∵ L_{ice} = 336000 J g^{-1})

(v) Equate 4 and 2 to find 't'.

(vi) 0.09 m

59. (i) Which one gets converted into water vapour hot water or cold water?

(ii) Engulfed water vapour reduces the supply of oxygen.

60. W_e = 200 g

Mass of water = 300 g

T_1 = 30°C

t_f = 70°C

Q = 200 × 1 × (70 – 30) + 300 (1) × (70 – 30)

= 500 (40)

20,000 cal.

61. Mass of ice = 10 g

Initial temperature = –20°C

Mass of water = 10 g

Temperature of water = 10°C

Heat absorbed by ice = 10 × (0.5) (20) + (10 × 80)

= 100 + 800 = 900 cal

Heat absorbed by ice = 10 × 0.5 × 20 = 100 cal

Heat lost by water ms Δt = 10 × 1 × 10 = 100 cal

∴ Temperature of the mixture = 0°C.

62. Let the lengths of copper and steel rods at 0°C be ℓ_c and ℓ_s, respectively.

Then let the lengths of copper and steel rods at 100°c be ℓ_c', ℓ_s', respectively.

We know, $\ell_2 = \ell_1[1 + \alpha(\Delta t)]$

Here, Δt = rise in temperature

Δt = 100°c – 0°c = 100°c

$\ell_c' = \ell c\,[1 + \alpha_c(100)]$

$= \ell c[1 + 1.7 \times 10^{-5} \times 100]$ cm

$= \ell_c\,[1.0017]$ cm

$\ell_s' = \ell_s\,[1 + \alpha_s\,(100)]$

$(100)] = \ell_s[1 + 1.1 \times 10^{-5} \times 100]$ cm

$= \ell_s[1.0011]$cm

Given ℓ_s = 100 cm

$\ell_s' = (100 \times 1.0011)$ cm = 100.11 cm

Given, $\ell_c' \sim \ell_s' = 5$ cm

$\ell_c' = 100.11 + 5$ cm = 105.11 cm

Consider, $\Delta \ell_c = (\ell_c' - \ell_c)$ and $\Delta \ell_s = (\ell_s' - \ell_s)$

Given the value of 'α_c' is greater than 'α_s' $\ell_c' = \ell_c + 100 \times 1.7 \times 10^{-5}$

$\ell_c = 105.11 - 0.0017 = 105.1083$ cm

The length of cu rod at 0°c is, $\ell_c = 105.1083$ cm

63. $t_0 = 2$ s, $t_1 = 10$°C

$t_2 = 110$°C

$\alpha = 2 \times 10^{-5}$°C^{-1}

$$\frac{t_1}{t_0} = \sqrt{\frac{l_0(1+\alpha\Delta t)}{l_0}}$$

$$t_1 = 2\sqrt{1+\alpha\Delta t}$$

$$= 2\sqrt{1+2\times10^{-5}\times100}$$

$$= 2\sqrt{1.002}$$

$$= 2\times1.001$$

$$= 2.002 \text{ s.}$$

64. The given alloy is in the liquid and solid state at the same temperature of 242 °C. This shows that 242° is the freezing or the melting point of the alloy. When the alloy in the solid state is immersed in water in a calorimeter, the temperature of the alloy falls down as it loses heat energy to the water and calorimeter.

Heat lost by the alloy in solid form = Heat gained by (1) (water + calorimeter)

Now, heat lost by the alloy = $m \times s \times \Delta\theta$

Where, $m = 100$ g, $s = ?$, $\Delta\theta = (242 - 14)$°C

Heat lost by alloy = $100 \times s \times 228$. (2)

Heat gained by (water + calorimeter)

$= m \times s \times \Delta\theta$

Substitute $m = (40 + 200) = 240$ g,

$S = 1$ cal g^{-1} °C^{-1}, $\Delta\theta = (14 - 12.1) = 1.9$ °C

Heat gained by (water + calorimeter)

$= 240 \times 1 \times 1.9$ (3)

Equating (2) and (3), we get

$100 \times s \times 228 = 240 \times 1 \times 1.9$

$$s = \frac{240\times1\times1.9}{100\times228}$$

s = 0.02 cal g^{-1} °C^{-1}.

When the alloy in the liquid stage is immersed in water in calorimeter, it is at its freezing point.

Heat lost by alloy = $(m\, L_F) + (m \times s \times \Delta\theta)$.

Substitute $m = 100$ g, $L_F = ?$, $s = 0.02$ cal g^{-1} °C^{-1}

$\Delta\theta = (242 - 22.1) = 219.9$ °C

Heat lost by the alloy = $100\, L_F + 100 \times 0.02 \times 219.9$ (4)

Substitute $m = 240$ g, $s = 1$ cal g^{-1} °C^{-1},

$\Delta\theta$ Q = 22.1 − 12.1 = 10 °C.

Heat gained by water + Calorimeter = $m \times s \times \Delta\theta$ $= 240 \times 1 \times 10 = 2400$ (5)

Equating (4) and (5)

$100\, L_F + (100 \times 0.02 \times 219.9) = 2400$

$L_F + 0.02 \times 219.9 = 24$

$L_F = 24 - 4.398$

$L_F = 19.602$ cal g^{-1}.

65. We know from co-ordinate geometry,

(i) Slope of (OP) $\tan\theta_1 = \dfrac{T_1 - 0}{(Q_1 - 0)}$

$$= \frac{T_1}{ms_1(T_1-0)} = \frac{1}{ms_1}$$

(ii) Slope of PQ = tan0° = 0. When solid converts liquid, the heat energy supplied to the substance is $Q = Q_2 - Q_1$.

Here, $Q = mL_F$ and L_F is latent heat of fusion.

(iii) Slope of $QR = \tan\theta_2$

$$= \frac{T_2 - T_1}{ms_2\,(T_2 - T_1)} = \frac{1}{ms_2}$$

(iv) Slope of RS = tan0° = 0

Here, the liquid converts to gaseous state. The heat energy supplied is $Q_4 - Q_3 = mL_V$. Here, L_V is latent heat of vaporization.

(v) Slope of $ST = \tan\theta_3 = \dfrac{T_3 - T_2}{Q_5 - Q_4}$

$$= \frac{(T_3 - T_2)}{ms_3(T_3 - T_2)} = \frac{1}{ms_3}$$

Given that, $\theta_1 > \theta_2 > \theta_3$

$$\Rightarrow \frac{1}{ms_1} > \frac{1}{ms_2} > \frac{1}{ms_3}$$

$s_1 < s_2 < s_3$

66. Heat gained = 50 g × 1 cal $g^{-1}°C^{-1}$ × (t°C – 30°C)
Heat lost = 150 g × 1 cal $g^{-1}°C^{-1}$× (90°C – t°C)
According to the principle of calorimetry, heat lost by a hot body = heat gained by a cold body
∴ 150 g × 1 cal $g^{-1}°C^{-1}$ × (90°C – t°C) = 50 g × 1 cal $g^{-1}°C^{-1}$ × (t°C – 30°C)
150 × 90 – 150 t = 50 t – 50 × 30
150 × 90 + 50 × 30 = 150 t + 50 t
200 t = 13500 + 1500 = 15000
t = 15000/200 = 75°C

67. According to the principle of calorimetry, heat lost by a hot body = heat gained by a cold body
Let the temperature θ_3 of the liquid of mass m3, be greater than that of θ_2 and θ_1.
Let θ be the equilibrium temperature of the mixture.
$\therefore m_3s_3\Delta\theta_3 = m_1s_1\Delta\theta_1 + m_2s_2\Delta\theta_2$
$m_3s_3(\theta_3 - \theta) = m_1s_1(\theta - \theta_1) + m_2s_2(\theta - \theta_2)$
$m_3s_3\theta_3 - m_3s_3\theta = m_1s_1\theta - m_1s_1\theta_1 + m_2s_2\theta - m_2s_2\theta_2$
$m_1s_1\theta_1 + m_2s_2\theta_2 + m_3s_3\theta_3 = m_1s_1\theta + m_2s_2\theta + m_3s_3\theta$
$= \theta\,(m_1s_1 + m_2s_2 + m_3s_3)$

$$\Rightarrow \theta = \frac{m_1s_1\theta_1 + m_2s_2\theta_2 + m_3s_3\theta_3}{m_1s_1 + m_2s_2 + m_3s_3}$$

68. Given, mass, m = 0.5 kg
Δθ = 40°C – 25°C = 15°C
Heat absorbed Q = 13.5 kJ
Let 's' be the specific heat capacity of castor oil.
We know, heat absorbed
Q = msΔθ

$$\Rightarrow s = \frac{Q}{m\Delta\theta} = \frac{13.5\text{kJ}}{0.5\text{kg} \times 15°\text{C}}$$

$= 1.8\text{kJ kg}^{-1}°\text{C}^{-1}$
$= 1.8\text{kJ kg}^{-1}\text{K}^{-1}$

69. Mass, m = 100 g = 0.1 kg
Heat absorbed, Q = 10500 J
Q = mL, where L is the specific latent heat of fusion.

$$\therefore L = \frac{Q}{m} = \frac{10500\text{J}}{0.1\text{ kg}}$$

$= 105000\text{J kg}^{-1} = 105\text{ kJ kg}^{-1}$

70. Heat gained
= 50 g × 80 cal g^{-1} + 50 g × 1 cal $g^{-1}°C^{-1}$× (t°C – 0°C)
Heat lost = 150 g × 1 cal $g^{-1}°C^{-1}$ × (60°C – t°C)
According to the principle of calorimetry, heat lost by a hot body = heat gained by a cold body
∴ 150 g × 1 cal $g^{-1}°C^{-1}$ × (60°C – t°C)
= 50 g × 80 cal g^{-1} + 50 g × 1 cal $g^{-1}°C^{-1}$× (t°C – 0°C)
150 × 60 – 150 t = 4000 + 50 t
150 × 60 – 4000 = 150 t + 50 t
200 t = 9000 – 4000 = 5000
t = 5000/200 = 25°C

JEE-NEET SPECIAL WING

Multiple-Answer Type Questions

1. Given, initial temperature in °C, $T_1 = 40$ °C
Final temperature in °C, $T_2 = 100$ °C
Change in temperature in °C, $\Delta T = 100 - 40 = 60°$ C
We have,

$$\frac{\text{Change in temp in °C}}{100} = \frac{\text{Change in temp in °F}}{180} = \frac{\text{Change in temp in K}}{100}$$

Now, $\frac{\text{Change in temp in °C}}{100} = \frac{\text{Change in temp in °F}}{180}$

$\Rightarrow \frac{60}{100} = \frac{\text{Change in temp in °F}}{180}$

$\Rightarrow$ Change in temp in °F $= 180 \times \frac{60}{100} = 108$ °F

Similarly,

$\frac{\text{Change in temp in °C}}{100} = \frac{\text{Change in temp in K}}{100}$

$\Rightarrow$ Change in temp in °C = Change in temp in *K*
Therefore, Change in temp in *K* = 60 *K*
Hence, the correct option is (a, d)

2. Given,
The specific heat capacity of alcohol,
$s = 2180$ J kg^{-1} K^{-1}
(a) Mass of alcohol, $m = 100\ g = 0.1$ kg
Then the heat capacity, $C = m \times s = 0.1 \times 2180$ $= 218$ J K^{-1}
(b) Heat energy supplied to alcohol to raise its temperature by 10 °C = $C \times 10$
$= 218 \times 10 = 2180$ J
(c) Given, $m_1 = 10\ g$ and $m_2 = 20\ g$
$T_1 = 20$ °C and $T_2 = 10$ °C
Let T be the common temperature of the mixture. Then
$m_1\, s\, (T_1 - T) = m_2\, s\, (T - T_2)$
$\Rightarrow m_1 (T_1 - T) = m_2 (T - T_2)$
$\Rightarrow 10 \times (20 - T) = 20 (T - 10) \Rightarrow 200 - 10T$ $= 20T - 200$
$\Rightarrow 30T = 400 \Rightarrow T = 400/30 = 13.33$ °C
$= 13.33 + 273 = 286.33$ *K*
(d) If the specific heat capacity of alcohol is 2180 J kg^{-1} K^{-1}, then its value is 0.52 cal g^{-1} °C^{-1} in common units.
Hence, the correct option is (a, b, c, d)

3. (a) Calorimeter uses the principle of mixtures to find the specific heat capacity of different bodies.
(b) The specific heat capacity of water is nearly five times that of land. That means water needs more heat than land to raise its temperature by 1°C.
(c) Heat absorbed or given out by a body is directly proportional to the change in temperature of the body.
(d) In cold countries, during winter, farmers water their fields in the evening because the temperature of the water does not fall quickly and protect the crop.
Hence, the correct option is (a, d)

4. From the graph,

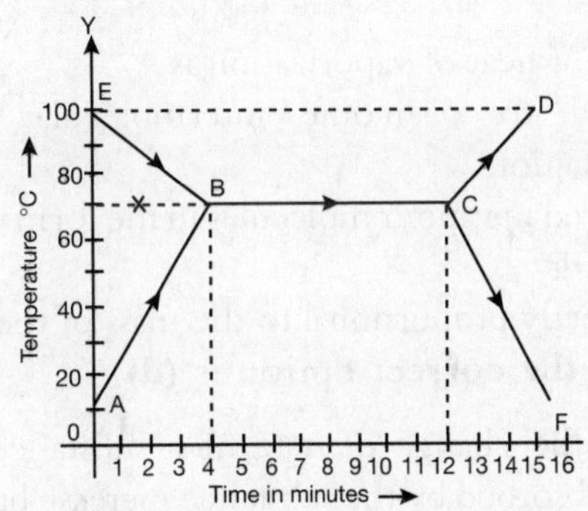

(a) The part BC of the graph shows the change in the state of naphthalene at constant temperature as the change of state of a substance happens at a constant temperature.
(b) Given, Heat absorbed, Q = 204 J
From the part AB of the graph, Change in temperature,
$\Delta T = 70 - 10 = 60$ °C
Then, Heat capacity, $C = \frac{Q}{\Delta T} = \frac{204}{60} = 3.4$ J °C^{-1}
(c) The part CD of the graph shows that the temperature of the liquid naphthalene increases on heating.
(d) The part CF of the graph shows that the temperature of the solid naphthalene decreases on cooling.
Hence, the correct option is (a, b, d)

5. Given, Mass of the calorimeter, $m = 70\ g$
Specific heat capacity of the calorimeter,
$s = 0.40$ J g^{-1} °C^{-1}
Mass of the water, $m' = 310\ g$
Initial temperature of water, $T_1 = 30$ °C
Specific heat capacity of water, $s' = 4.2$ J g^{-1} °C^{-1}
Mass of ice piece, $m'' = 50\ g$

Specific latent heat of fusion of ice,
L_{ice} = 336 J g^{-1} °C^{-1}

(a) The heat gained by the ice piece to form water = m'' L_{ice} = 50 × 336 = 16800 J.

(b) The heat energy gained by the water that formed from the ice = $m'' s' \Delta T$
= 50 × 4.2 × (15 – 0) = 3150 J

(c) The heat lost by the water (at 30 °C) in the calorimeter (if the final temperature of the water is 15 °C) = $m\, s'\, \Delta T$ = 310 × 4.2 × (30 – 15) = 19350 J

(d) According to principle of method of mixtures,
Heat lost by calorimeter + Heat lost by water (in the calorimeter) = Heat gained by the ice to form water + Heat gained by the water (formed from ice)
Hence, the correct option is (a, b, d)

Comprehension-Based Questions

6. The latent heat of vaporization is
   (i) used to overcome intermolecular forces of attraction
   (ii) stored in vapour molecules in the form of potential energy
   (iii) directly proportional to the mass of the substance
   Hence, the correct option is (d)

7. During the change of state of a substance, the heat energy absorbed by the substance increase but the temperature of the substance remains constant.
   Hence, the correct option is (c)

8. Given, The specific latent heat of the fusion of wax, L = 146 J g^{-1}
   Mass of the wax, m = 0.5 kg = 500 g
   Heat absorbed by the change of state from solid to liquid, Q = mL = 500 × 146 = 73000 J
   Hence, the correct option is (c)

9. One gram of water at 100 °C contains 100 cal of heat but 1 g of steam at 100 °C contains 640 cal of heat. The heat energy stored in vapour molecules in the form of potential energy = 640 – 100 = 540 cal
   Hence, the correct option is (a)

10. According to the principle of method of mixtures, the heat lost by hot body is equal to the heat gained by cold body, i.e., the total energy of the system remains constant.
    Hence, the correct option is (d)

11. F. Given, mass of the calorimeter, m = 50 g
    mass of the calorimeter with water, m' = 150 g
    Then the mass of the water, $m_w = m' - m$
    = 150 – 50 = 100 g
    A → c

    G. Given, mass of the calorimeter, m = 45 g
    specific heat capacity of calorimeter,
    s = 0.4 J g^{-1} °C^{-1}
    change in temperature of the calorimeter,
    ΔT = 5 °C
    The heat gained by the calorimeter = $m\ s\ \Delta T$
    = 45 × 0.4 × 5 = 90 J
    B → a

    H. Given, mass of the condensed steam, m = 10 g
    specific latent heat of vaporization,
    L = 2260 J g^{-1} °C^{-1}
    Then the heat lost by the steam = mL = 10 × 2260
    = 22.6 kJ
    C → e

    I. Given, mass of water, m = 100 g
    Initial temperature, T_1 = 35 °C
    Final temperature, T_2 = 45 °C
    Change in temperature, $\Delta T = T_2 - T_1$ = 45 – 35
    = 10 °C
    Specific heat capacity of water, s = 4.2 J g^{-1} °C^{-1}
    Heat absorbed by water = m s ΔT
    = 100 × 4.2 × 10 = 4200 J = 4.2 kJ
    D → b

    J. Given, mass of the calorimeter with water, m = 180 g
    Mass of the calorimeter with water and condensed steam, m' = 195 g
    Then the mass of the condensed steam = $m' - m$
    = 195 – 180 = 15 g
    E → d

Unit V

Electricity and Magnetism

In this Unit

CHAPTER

6

Electricity-II

Remember

Before beginning this chapter, you should be able to:

- State the different methods of charging bodies and the concept of electric field and electric potential.
- State the different properties of electric charges in motion.
- Learn the concept of electric current and electric resistances.

Key Ideas

After completing this chapter, you should be able to:

- Study the nature and properties of electric charges when they are at rest and in motion.
- Understand current in conductors and electrolytes.
- Discuss the heating effect, chemical effect and lighting effects of electricity and their applications.
- Study some laws such as Ohm's law, Joule's Law, laws of electrolysis, etc.
- Learn the detailed concept of resistances in series and parallel.

Scientific Crypt

A Tribute to Thomas Alva Edison (1847 – 1931)

Thomas Alva Edison, a legend in the field of technology, is an American inventor. He was born on 11th February, 1847 in Milano, Ohio. He was the seventh and last child of Samuel Edison, Jr. and Nancy Elliot Edison. He moved from Milano to Port Huron at the age of seven as his father became a carpenter at Fort Gratiot military post at Port Huron. He did his schooling in Port Huron. His teachers considered him a dull student but he was having difficulty following the lessons because of his hearing problems.

He set up his first laboratory in the basement of his house but he vacated it to an empty freight car because his mother could not bear the smell of the chemicals. By the age of 12, he started printing his weekly newspaper "Grand Trunk Herald". By 1869, Edison became a full-time inventor and entrepreneur and invented duplex telegraph, message printer, etc. He then opened a workshop in New York, New Jersey. From there, he produced universal stock printer, the automatic telegraph, the quadruplex, as well as other printing telegraphs. In 1877, Edison invented carbon – button transistor, tinfoil phonograph and with the help of leading financiers opened the Edison Electric light company and in 1879, he invented incandescent electric light bulb. He started new laboratory and research facility in West Orange, New Jersey and employed nearly 60 workers. From here he produced the commercial phonograph, the kinetoscope, the Edison storage battery, the electric pen, the mimeograph and micro taximeters. Thus, he patented more than 1000 discoveries. He was appointed as president of the U.S Navy Consulting Board.

This great inventor, who has contributed immensely to the shaping of modern society, left the world on 18th October, 1931 in West Orange, New Jersey.

FUN TIME

CROSSWORD

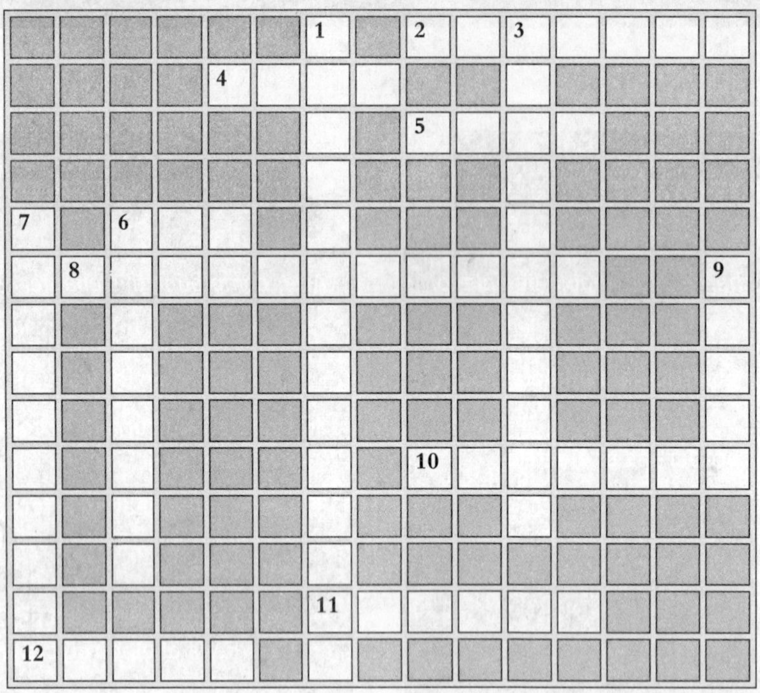

Across

2. Heat produced in a conductor is proportion to the square of this physical quantity.
4. A device which can maintain a potential difference for a long time.
5. A safety device used in electric circuits.
6. Potential difference between the terminals of a cell in open circuit.
10. Amount of electrical energy consumed by an electrical appliance per unit time.
11. In electroplating process the electrolyte used is nickel ammonium sulphate solution, which metal has to be used as anode what is the anode used.
12. Which pin is longer in a three pin plug?

Down

1. The process of depositing a layer of desired metal over another metal.
3. This electric property of a conductor does not depend upon its dimensions.
6. The charged particle which can flow through a conductor.
7. This electric property of conductor depends upon the dimension of the conductor
8. Substance in liquid state which conducts electricity.
9. Fuse is connected to this wire.

INTRODUCTION

In the chapter heat, you have studied that heat is a form of energy. Light, mechanical energy, chemical energy are the other forms of energy. Among all forms of energy, electric energy is the most useful and convenient for mankind. It can be converted to almost all forms of energy easily and can be stored and transmitted over long distances with very little wastage. Electric bulbs, motors, cell phones, air conditioners, heaters, computers and heavy machinery all use different effects of electric energy. In fact, it is difficult to imagine our lives without electric energy. The origin of electric energy lies in electric charges. The branch of physics which deals with the study of electric charges and their effects is called electricity.

In order to understand the topic of electricity better, we shall first recall some of the properties of electric charges which you have studied in detail in previous classes.

Electric Charge

Electric charge, basic property of matter carried by some elementary particles. Electric charge, which can be positive or negative, occurs in discrete natural units and is neither created nor destroyed.

Many fundamental, or subatomic, particles of matter have the property of electric charge. For example, electrons have negative charge and protons have positive charge, but neutrons have zero charge. The negative charge of each electron is found by experiment to have the same magnitude, which is also equal to that of the positive charge of each proton. Charge, thus, exists in natural units equal to the charge of an electron or a proton, a fundamen'al physical constant. A direct and convincing measurement of an electron's charge, as a natural unit of electric charge, was first made (1909) in the Millikan oil-drop experiment. Atoms of matter are electrically neutral because their nuclei contain the same number of protons as there are electrons surrounding the nuclei.

Following are the important properties of electric charge:

1. Electric charge is of two types, viz., positive and negative charge.

   Proton is said to be charged positively and electron is said to be charged negatively.

2. Like charges repel and unlike charges attract. Thus, a proton repels a proton and attracts an electron.

3. The force of attraction or repulsion between two point charges is given by Coulomb's law.

$$F = \frac{Kq_1q_2}{r^2}$$

   where, q_1 and q_2 are charges.
   K = constant of proportionality
   r = distance between the charges

4. Charge can neither be created nor destroyed. The charge from one body can be transferred to another body but the total charge of a system remains constant. This is called principle of conservation of charge.

5. Protons and electrons are elementary charged particles. Though the charge on them is opposite in nature, the magnitude of charge possessed by them is same, i.e., 1.6×10^{-19} C. It is denoted by 'e'. Charge on a body is always an integral multiple of this value. This property is called 'quantization of charge'.

6. When a body gains electrons, it becomes negatively charged. When it loses electrons, it becomes positively charged. The positive charge being bound firmly in the nucleus does not participate in charging.

Info Bytes!

The concept of electric charge was first observed by the ancient Greeks when they noticed that rubbing amber attracted lightweight objects like feathers.

The study of electricity is classified into two parts.

1. **Static Electricity:** It deals with electric charges at rest and their effects.
2. **Current Electricity:** It deals with charges in motion and their effects.

Conductors and Insulators

Current electricity is the study of charges in motion. Hence, it is of our interest to know the substances which allow charges to flow through them easily and which resist it. Accordingly, substances are classified as conductors and insulators.

Conductors

The substances which conduct electricity easily are called electric conductors.

Since positive charges cannot flow, the conduction of electricity is primarily due to flow of free electrons. Hence, conductors have large number of free electrons.

Examples: All metals are good conductors of electricity.

Konnect

Superconductors are materials that have zero electrical resistance at extremely low temperatures.

Insulators

The substances which do not conduct electricity are called electric insulators. Insulators do not have free electrons.

Examples: Wood, rubber, mica, etc.

Electric Current

The rate of flow of charge is known as electric current. It is denoted by *I*. If '*q*' is the net charge passing through any cross section of a conductor in time '*t*', then

$$\text{Current } (I) = \frac{\text{Charge}(q)}{\text{Time}(t)}$$

Current is a scalar quantity. S.I. unit of current is ampere (A). Multiple units of current are kiloampere (1 kA = 10^3 A), Megaampere (1 MA = 10^6 A).

Submultiple units are 1mA (1 milliampere = 10^{-3} A) and microampere (1 μA = 10^{-6} A).

One Ampere

Ampere is defined in terms of force between two thin and long current carrying conductor kept parallel to each other in vacuum. The current passing through a conductor is said to be one ampere when the net flow of charge per second through its cross section is one coulomb.

The charge transferred is always an integral multiple of the fundamental charge (charge of a proton). This property is referred to as **quantization of charge**.

i.e., $Q = ne$

Since current $(I) = \dfrac{Q}{t}$ or $I = \dfrac{ne}{t}$

where, e = magnitude of charge of an electron.

n = number of electrons flowing across any point in time 't'.

Info Bytes!

- Electric current was first discovered by Danish physicist Hans Christian Oersted in 1820.
- One ampere is named after French physicist André-Marie Ampère, one of the founding figures of electromagnetism.

Electric Potential

It is our common observation that water flows from a place at a higher level to a place at a lower level, irrespective of the amount of water at the two levels. Heat flows from a body at a higher temperature to a body at a lower temperature, irrespective of the amount of heat contained by the two bodies. Similarly, electric charges move from one point to another if there exists a difference in the electric potential irrespective of the concentration of charges at the two points. Thus, electric potential determines the direction of flow of electric current. Charge flows from a body at higher potential to a body at lower potential. By convention, a positively charged body is at a higher potential as compared to a negatively charged body. If positive charges like protons or positive ions are free to move, they would move from higher potential point to lower potential point. Usually, the movement of charges implies movement of electrons. Since electrons are oppositely charged (i.e., negatively charged), they move from lower potential point to higher potential point. This constitutes electronic current. Since the convention is that flow is always from higher to lower level, the conventional current is taken opposite to the electronic current. It should be remembered that conventional current implies the movement of positive charges whereas electronic current is the movement of electrons.

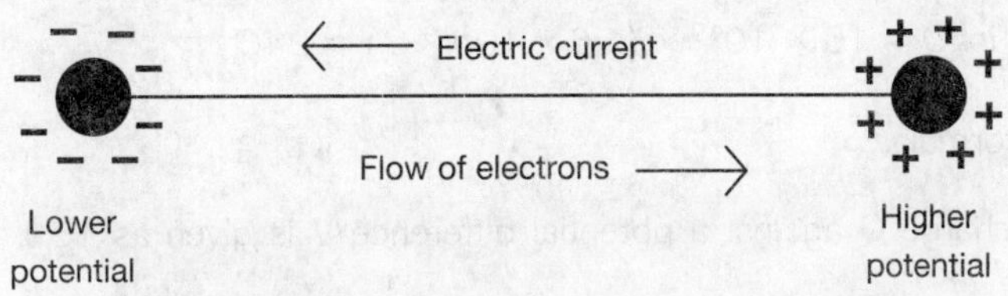

Figure 6.1 Electric potential of two bodies

As discussed earlier, concentration of charges determines the electric potential at a point. This can be increased by bringing charges at that point. In doing so some work has to be done on the charge. This work is stored as electric potential at that point. The electric potential can be measured in terms of work done and is defined as the work done in bringing a unit positive charge from infinity to a point in an electric field.

The electric potential is measured in volts (V). The electric potential at a point is said to be 1 volt if 1 joule of work is done in bringing a positive charge of 1 coulomb from infinity to that point.

Potential Difference

To bring a unit positive charge from infinity to a point in an electric field, some work has to be done which is called electric potential. Within an electric field, if a unit positive charge has to be moved from one point to another against the direction of the field, some work has to be done which is called potential difference between the two points.

Like electric potential, the potential difference is also measured in volts (V). Let Q coulomb charge be moved from point A to the point B in an electric field when work done is W. Let V be the potential difference between the two points. Therefore, the work done in moving unit positive charge is

$$= \frac{W}{Q}.$$

By definition, this work done is also the potential difference.

$$\therefore\ V = V_1 - V_2 = \frac{W}{Q}$$

where, V_1 = Potential at point A.

V_2 = Potential at point B.

When 1 joule of work is done in moving a positive charge of 1 coulomb from one point to another in an electric field, the potential difference between the two points is 1 volt.

i.e., $$1V = \frac{1 \text{ joule}}{1 \text{ coulomb}} = 1JC^{-1}$$

Info Bytes!

Since potential difference is measured in volts, it is sometimes called 'voltage' or 'voltage drop'.

EXAMPLE 6.1

15 joules of work is done in moving 15×10^{19} electrons from one point to another point in a conductor. What is the potential difference between the two points?

SOLUTION

The charge of one electron is approximately 1.6×10^{-19} Coulombs (*C*).

Charge *Q* on 15×10^{19} electron is: $Q = 15 \times 10^{19} \times (1.6 \times 10^{-19}\ C) = 24C$

Calculate *Q* based on the above formula.

The work done W to move this charge Q against a potential difference V is given as 15 J. Using this relationship, we have:

$$W = Q \times V \text{ or } V = \frac{W}{Q}$$

$$V = \frac{15J}{24C} = 0.625JC^{-1} \text{ or } 0.625 \text{ volts}$$

EXAMPLE 6.2

In a certain region of space, the electric potential at a specific point is 4 *V*. If a charge of 2 *C* is moved from infinity to this point, how much work was done by the external force?

SOLUTION

Given:

Electric potential (*V*) = 4 *V*

Charge (*Q*) = 2 *C*

Work done (*W*) = ?

Using the formula:

$W = Q \times V$

$W = 2C \times 4V$

$W = 8J$

So, the work done is 8 joules.

EXAMPLE 6.3 The electric potentials at the two ends of a conductor are 15 *V* and 7 *V*, respectively. 16 *J* of work needs to be done to move a certain amount of charge from the end at higher potential to the end at lower potential. Find the amount of charge moved.

SOLUTION

The potential difference between the two ends of the conductor (V) = 15 V − 7 V = 8V.

Work done (W) = 16 J

Charge (Q) = ?

$$\text{Potential difference} = \frac{\text{Work}}{\text{Charge}}$$

$$V = \frac{W}{Q} = \frac{16J}{8V} = 2 \text{ coulomb.}$$

Current in Conductors and Electrolytes

Rate of flow of charge is called current. We have already seen that charge moves from one point to another if there exists a potential difference between them. Thus, whether the current is flowing through a conductor or electrolyte, a potential difference is necessary for it. You have also studied in previous classes that cell or battery is used to provide potential difference.

Current in a Conductor

A potential difference can be produced between a conductor in the form of a metallic wire, if it is connected between the two terminals of a cell. The end of the wire connected to the positive terminal is at a higher potential while the end connected to the negative terminal is at a lower potential. A conventional current is set up between these two ends.

A conductor has of a large number of free electrons which are in random motion just like molecules in air. When it is connected across a cell or a battery, these free electrons begin to drift from lower potential to higher potential. This constitutes the electronic current. Thus, the free electrons are responsible for the flow of electric current in conductors. However, the direction of conventional current is taken opposite to that of electronic current, i.e., from higher potential to lower potential.

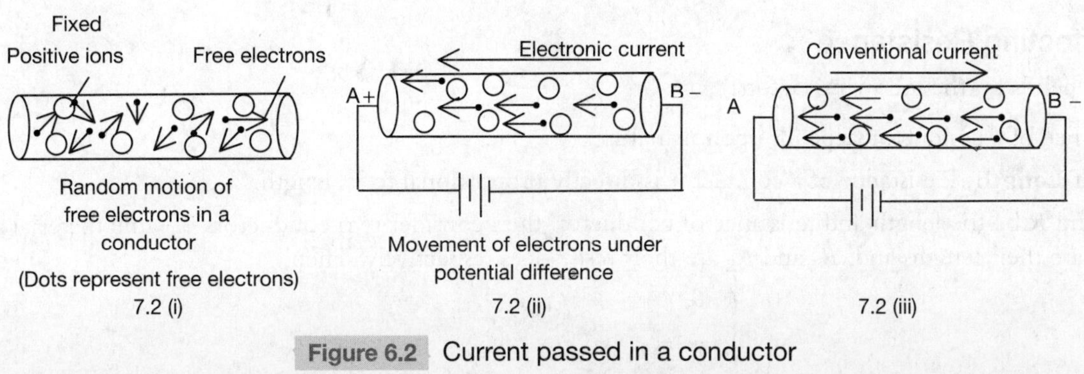

Figure 6.2 Current passed in a conductor

When the metallic wire is not connected to a battery, although the electrons are moving, the net flow in any particular direction is zero. Hence, no current flows through it in the absence of potential difference.

Current in an Electrolyte

A liquid or a solution which conducts electricity is called electrolyte. For example, copper sulphate ($CuSO_4$), sodium chloride (NaCl) or common salt solution.

When a potential difference is applied across an electrolyte, it undergoes a chemical change and decomposes into its constituents. This process is called electrolysis.

Take some water in a beaker and add common salt (NaCl) to it. Insert two metallic rods A and B in the solution. They are called electrodes. Connect A to positive and B to negative terminal of a cell. A is at higher or positive potential and is called anode while B which is at lower or negative potential is called cathode.

The solution dissociates into positive sodium ions (Na^+) and negative ions (Cl^-). The positive Na^+ ions move towards cathode B and gain electrons to form Na atoms. The negative Cl^- ions migrate towards anode A through electrolyte and form chlorine atoms by giving away electrons. The bubbles of chlorine gas can be seen coming out from A.

Thus, in an electrolyte, both positive and negative ions move through it towards opposite electrodes. The rate of flow of charge is electric current. However, the conventional current is taken as movement of positive ions through electrolyte towards cathode B. Through the external wire connecting the cell to the electrodes, electrons enter from cathode and move towards anode A. If a bulb is connected, it begins to glow confirming the flow of current.

Thus, in an electrolyte, the movement of ions is responsible for electric current.

Electrical Resistance

Conductors conduct electricity owing to the presence of a large number of free electrons. When a potential difference is applied across a conductor, these electrons begin to drift from the end at low potential to the end at high potential. While drifting, they collide with other electrons as well as fixed positive ions. The fixed ions are formed from the atoms which give free electrons. Thus, even as, conductor conducts electricity, at the same time it offers some obstruction to the flow of charges.

The obstruction offered by a conductor to the flow of electric current is called its resistance.

As the collisions suffered by drifting electrons increase, the resistance offered by the conductor also increases. Thus, the resistance depends basically on the arrangement of atoms and the configuration of electrons around the atoms of the conductor.

Units of Resistance

The SI unit of resistance is ohm. It is denoted by Greek symbol Ω (Omega).
Higher units of resistance

1. kilo-ohm(kΩ) = $10^3\ \Omega$
2. mega-ohm(MΩ) = $10^6\ \Omega$
3. giga-ohm(GΩ) = $10^9\ \Omega$

Factors Affecting Resistance

Resistance depends on the following factors:

1. Resistance of a conductor depends upon its nature.
2. **Law of Length:** Resistance of a conductor is directly proportional to its length.

   Let ℓ and R be the length and resistance of conductor, then consider two conductors of same material such that ℓ_1 and ℓ_2 are their lengths and, R_1 and R_2 are their resistances respectively. Then,

$$R_1 \propto \ell_1$$

$$R_2 \propto \ell_2$$

$$\therefore \frac{R_1}{R_2} = \frac{\ell_1}{\ell_2}$$

3. **Law of Area of Cross Section:** Resistance of a conductor is inversely proportional to its area of cross section.

Let a be the area of cross section of a conductor whose resistance is R.

$$R \propto \frac{1}{a}$$

Consider two conductors of area of cross sections a_1 and a_2 and resistances R_1 and R_2.

Then,

$$R_1 \propto \frac{1}{a_1}$$

$$R_2 \propto \frac{1}{a_2}$$

$$\therefore \frac{R_1}{R_2} \propto \frac{a_2}{a_1}$$

$$= \frac{\pi r_2^2}{\pi r_1^2} \quad (\because a = \pi r^2)$$

$$\frac{R_1}{R_2} = \frac{a_2}{a_1} = \left(\frac{r_2}{r_1}\right)^2$$

where, r_1 and r_2 are the radii of the two conductors.

Combining the 2nd and 3rd laws, we get

$$R \propto \frac{\ell}{a}$$

$$\therefore R = \rho \frac{\ell}{a}$$

where, ρ is the constant of proportionality.

Specific Resistance or Resistivity

We have seen that,

$$R = \rho \frac{\ell}{a}.$$

The constant of proportionality 'ρ' is called specific resistance or resistivity of a given conducting material like copper, aluminum, etc. It is a characteristic property of conducting material and independent of the size and shape of the conductor.

$$\rho = R\frac{a}{\ell}$$

Consider a conductor having unit area of cross section and unit length.

$$\rho = R\frac{1}{1}$$

$$\therefore \rho = R.$$

Thus, specific resistance or resistivity can be defined as the resistance of a conducting material having unit area of cross section and unit length.

Unit of Resistivity

$$\text{Unit of } \rho = \frac{\text{unit of } R \times \text{unit of } a}{\text{unit of } \ell}$$

$$= \frac{\text{ohm} \times (\text{metre})^2}{\text{metre}}$$

Unit of ρ = ohm–metre = Ω m

Sometime, a hybrid unit Ω cm is also used.

EXAMPLE 6.4 The length of copper wire is 100 m and its radius is 1 mm. Calculate its resistance if resistivity of copper is $1.72 \times 10^{-8}\ \Omega$ m.

SOLUTION

Length of copper wire (ℓ) = 100 m.

Area of cross section (a) = $\pi r^2 = 3.14 \times (10^{-3}\text{m})^2 = 3.14 \times 10^{-6}\text{m}^2$

Resistivity (ρ) of copper = $1.72 \times 10^{-8}\ \Omega$ m

Resistance offered by a conductor is given by,

$$R = \rho\frac{\ell}{A}$$

$$= \frac{1.72 \times 10^{-8} \times 100}{3.14 \times 10^{-6}} = 0.55\Omega$$

In this numerical, length of copper wire is 100 m. If the length is 1000 m, i.e., 1 km, the resistance offered by it would be 5.5 Ω which is very less. Thus, copper is a good conductor of electricity.

EXAMPLE 6.5 The resistance of 1 m of nichrome wire is 6 Ω. Calculate its resistance if its length is 70 cm.

SOLUTION

Given,

1st case

Length of nichrome wire (ℓ_1) = 1 m = 100 cm

Resistance of nichrome wire (R_1) = 6 Ω

2nd case

ℓ_2 = 70 cm

R_2 = ?

By 1st law of resistance,

$$\frac{R_1}{R_2} = \frac{\ell_1}{\ell_2}$$

$$\frac{6\Omega}{R_2} = \frac{100 \text{ cm}}{70 \text{ cm}}$$

$\therefore R_2 = 4.2\ \Omega$

EXAMPLE 6.6 Two wires made of German-silver are taken such that the length and area of cross-section of the second wire are twice and thrice, respectively, those of the first wire. If the resistance of the second wire is 12 Ω, find the resistance of the first wire.

SOLUTION

1st case

ℓ_1 = length of German silver wire

a_1 = area of cross section

R_1 = resistance

$$R_1 = \rho\frac{\ell_1}{a_1} \quad (1)$$

2nd case

ℓ_2 = length of wire = $2\ell_1$

a_2 = area of cross section of wire = $3a_1$

R_2 = resistance of wire = 12 Ω

$$R_2 = \rho\frac{\ell_2}{a_2}$$

$$\therefore 12 = \rho\frac{2l_1}{3a_1} \quad (2)$$

Dividing (1) by (2)

$$\frac{R_1}{12} = \frac{\rho\ell}{a_1} \times \frac{3a_1}{\rho(2\ell_1)} = \frac{3}{2}$$

$\therefore R_1 = 18\ \Omega$

Effect of Temperature on Resistance

The resistance of a conductor increases with an increase in temperature.

Let the resistance of a conductor at 0°C be R_0.

Let the resistance of the conductor at t°C be R_t.

Then, $R_t = R_0(1 + \alpha t)$,

where, 'α' is known as the **temperature coefficient of resistance**.

Pure metals have positive temperature coefficient of resistance. That is resistance of metals increases with an increase in temperature.

Alloys have a very less temperature coefficient of resistance. So, the resistance of alloys like Manganin and Constantan vary very little with an increase in temperature. Because of this property, they are used in making standard resistances.

Semiconductors like germanium, silicon and bad conductors like glass, pure water, etc., have negative temperature coefficient. The resistance of these materials decreases with an increase in temperature.

Effect of Impurities on Resistance

1. Resistance of conductors increases with addition of impurities.
2. Resistance of semiconductors decreases with addition of selected impurities.

Electrical Conductance

The reciprocal of resistance is known as electrical conductance. It is denoted by G. It is a measure of ease with which a charge can flow in a conductor.

$G = \frac{1}{R}$. Unit of conductance is mho or ohm^{-1} or siemen.

Electrical Conductivity

The reciprocal of resistivity is called conductivity.

It is denoted by σ. $\sigma = \frac{1}{\rho}$. The unit of conductivity is mho/metre or siemen/metre.

Super Conductors

Conductors exhibit a phenomenon known as super conductivity at a very low temperature known as critical temperature. At critical temperature, a metal offers zero resistance to the passage of electricity. These type of conductors are called superconductors.

The temperature below which a conductor offers no resistance to the flow of electric current is known as its **critical temperature**.

Electric Circuits and Circuit Diagrams

In order to make use of electric energy, the current has to be passed through various devices and electric components. For this they need to be connected properly with respect to each other and electric source. This systematic arrangement of electric components and devices with the electric source is called electric circuit. It is also important that the circuit arrangement be represented schematically. The schematic representation of an electric circuit is called circuit diagram. In order to draw a circuit diagram, various electric components and devices are represented by suitable symbols.

The table below gives conventional symbols for some common components.

Table 6.1 Conventional symbols for electrical components

Electrical Components	Symbol
A cell	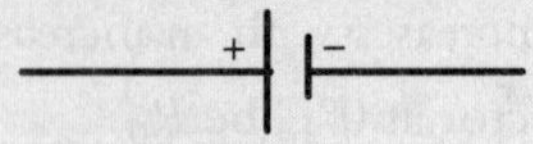
A battery	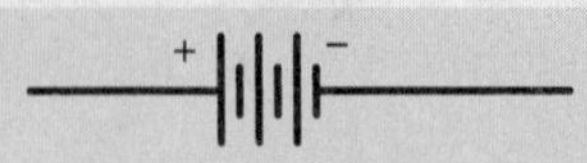
Alternating current source	
Plug key	
Switch	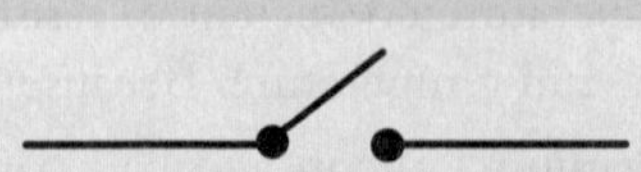
Tapping Key	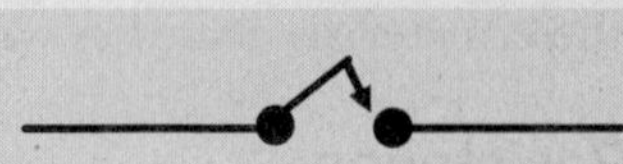
Conducting (connecting) Wire	

Table 6.1 Continued

Electrical Components	Symbol
An Ammeter	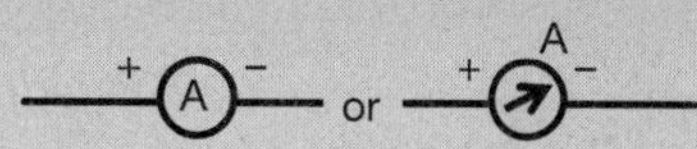
A Voltmeter	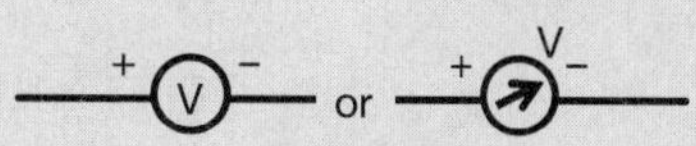
A resistance (fixed value)	
A variable resistance or rheostat	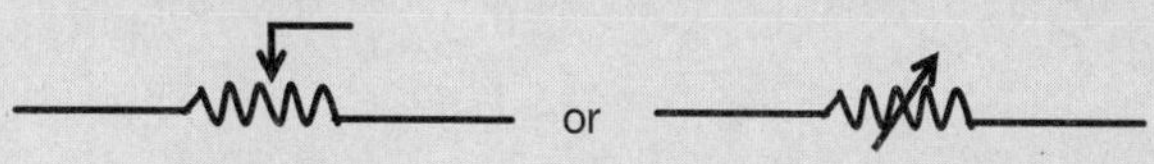
Galvanometer	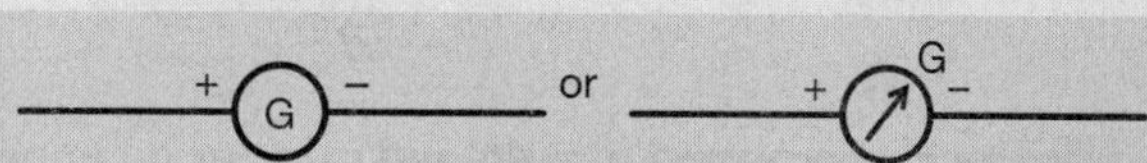
Load	
Heater	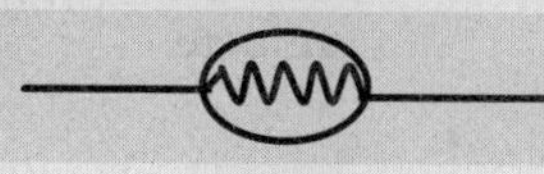
Bulb	

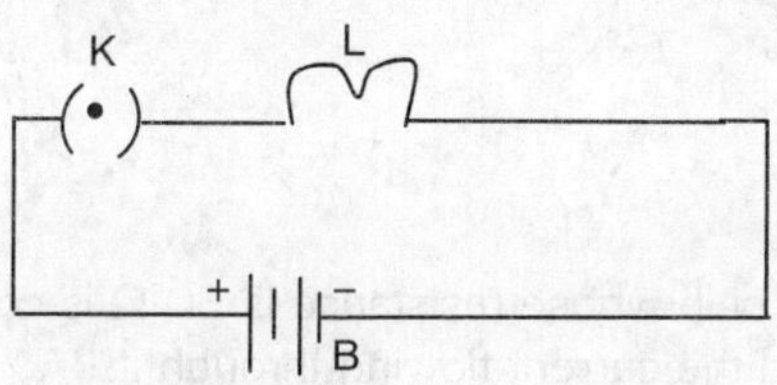

Figure 6.3 Basic circuit diagram

The Fig. 6.3 is a circuit diagram showing the connection of lamp (L) with a battery (B). The key (K) is used to connect or disconnect the lamp with the battery.

Ohm's Law

We have studied that when a potential difference is applied between the ends of a conductor, current begins to flow through it. George Simon Ohm, a German physicist performed a series of experiments to determine the exact relationship between the potential difference and the electric current. On the basis of these experiments, he formulated a law which is called Ohm's law and can be stated as, the potential difference (V) applied between the ends of a conductor bears a constant ratio with the electric current (I) flowing through it, provided the physical state of the conductor remains the same. The factors which constitute physical state of conductor are its length, area of cross section, temperature and material.

According to Ohm's law

$$V \propto I$$

i.e.,

$$V = (\text{constant})\ I$$

$$\frac{V}{I} = \text{Constant}$$

The constant in the above relation is called resistance (R) of the conductor.

$$\therefore \frac{V}{I} = R$$

$$V = IR$$

If the potential difference is measured in volts and current in amperes, the resistance of conductor is said to be in ohms.

$$\frac{\text{volt}}{\text{ampere}} = \text{ohm}$$

The resistance of a conductor is said to be 1 ohm if the potential difference of 1 volt causes a current of 1 ampere to pass through the conductor.

$$\frac{1\text{volt}}{1\text{ampere}} = 1\text{ohm}$$

EXAMPLE 6.7 An electric bulb whose resistance is 60 Ω is connected to a source of potential difference of 230 V. Find the current flowing through it.

SOLUTION

Potential difference (V) applied to the bulb = 230 V

Resistance (R) of bulb = 60 Ω

Current (I) flowing through bulb = ?

According to Ohm's law,

$$V = IR$$

$$\therefore I = \frac{V}{R}$$

$$= \frac{230\text{V}}{60\Omega}$$

$$\therefore I = 3.83\ \text{A}$$

EXAMPLE 6.8 Study the following circuit diagram.

Find the potential difference provided by the cell.

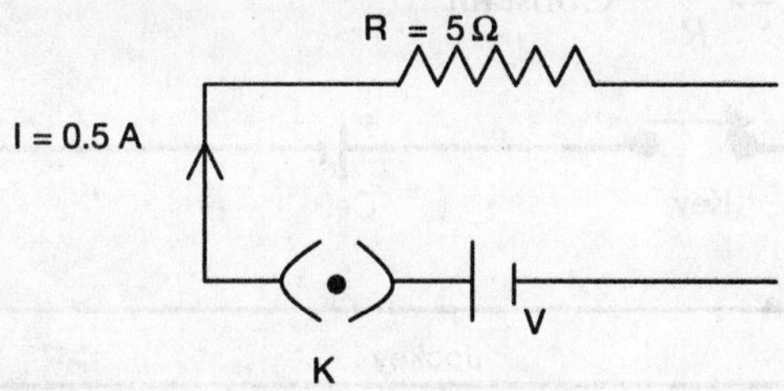

Figure 6.4 Circuit diagram consisting a resistance of 5 Ω

SOLUTION

Current (I) flowing through the resistor = 0.5 A

Resistance (R) of the resistor = 5 Ω

Potential difference (V) = ?

According to Ohm's law,

$V = IR$

$= 0.5\ \text{A} \times 5\ \Omega$

$V = 2.5\ \text{V}$

Experimental Verification of Ohm's Law

Voltmeter—Ammeter Method

Connect a battery (B), an ammeter (A), a resistor (R), a rheostat (Rh) and a voltmeter (V) as shown in the Fig. 6.5.

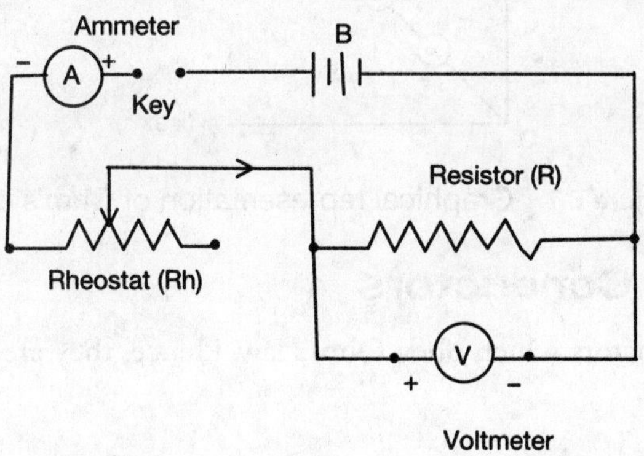

Figure 6.5 Experiment to verify Ohm's law

Move the slider position of the rheostat for different values of current in the circuit. The reading of current and voltage across the resistor for different positions of the slider switch are noted. In each case, the ratio of voltage to current is found.

It is observed that, the ratio V/I remains constant showing that the (voltage potential difference) is proportional to current ($V \propto I$).

Potentiometer Method

Connect a potentiometer (a resistance wire of 1 m length) AB stretched between two brass terminals, as shown in the Fig. 6.6.

Close the key and record the voltage in the voltmeter connected parallel to A and jockey at different points.

Experimental set up of potentiometer method.

The ratio of the voltage to the corresponding length at each reading will be constant showing $\frac{V}{L}$ = constant, but $L \propto R$

$$\Rightarrow \frac{V}{R} = \text{Constant}$$

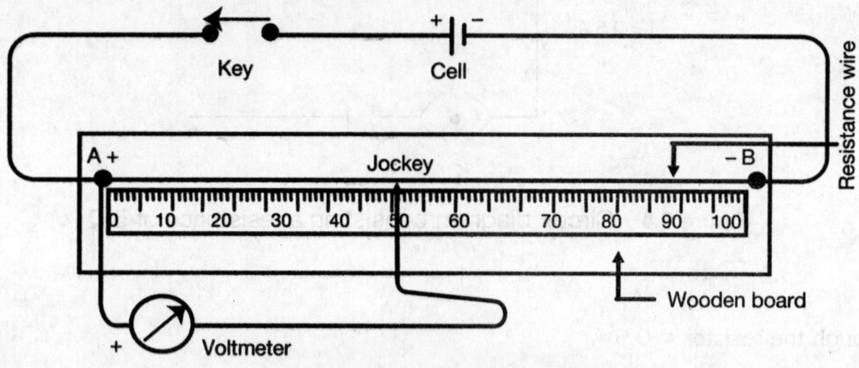

Figure 6.6 A potentiometer

Graphical Representation of Ohm's Law

Plot voltage (V) on x-axis and current (I) on y-axis.

Observation: A straight line passing through the origin is obtained (implies $V \propto I$).

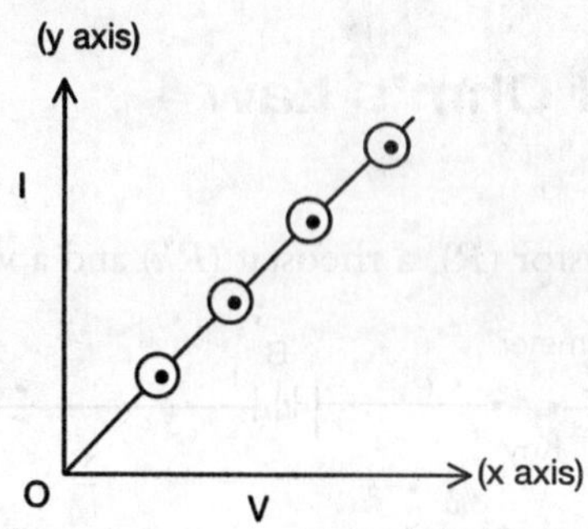

Figure 6.7 Graphical representation of Ohm's Law

Ohmic and Non-ohmic Conductors

Ohmic conductors are those conductors which obey Ohm's law. Hence, they are referred to as linear conductors.

Examples: All metals.

The conductors which do not obey Ohm's law are known as **non-ohmic conductors**.

Examples: Electrolytes, semiconductor devices like diodes, transistors, etc.

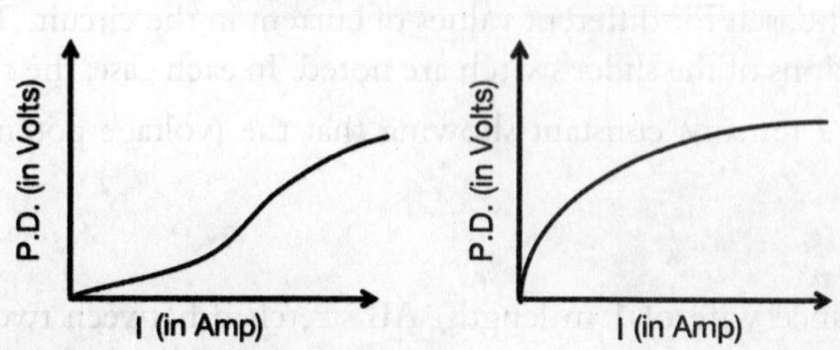

Figure 6.8 V-I graph for Ohmic & Non-Ohmic conductors

V-I graph for non-ohmic conductors is not linear. (not a straight line)

Resistors in Series

Resistors are said to be connected in series, when there exists only one path for the flow of current and the current through each resistor is same.

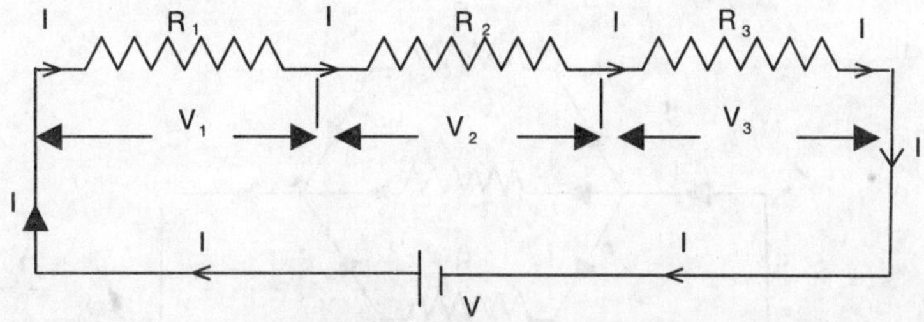

Figure 6.9 Resistors in series

Resistors R_1, R_2 and R_3 are connected in series as shown above. Apply a voltage 'V' across the series combination. Let V_1, V_2 and V_3 be the voltage drop across R_1, R_2 and R_3 respectively as shown in the Fig. 6.9. Let the current I flow through all the three resistances.

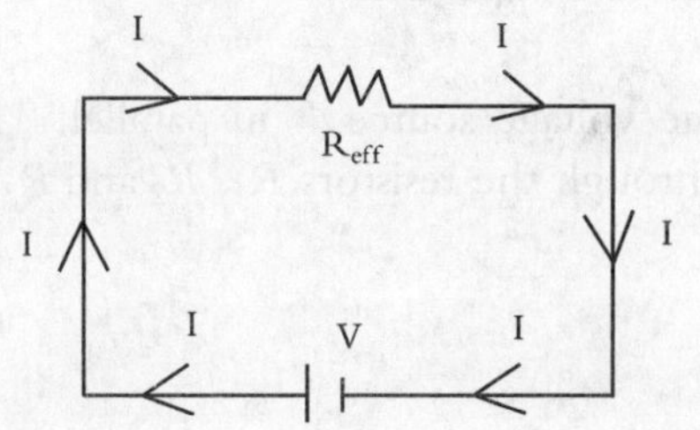

Konnect

In a series circuit, if one component fails, the entire circuit is disrupted. While in a parallel circuit, if one component fails, the other components can still function.

Therefore, the voltage V_1 across R_1 : $V_1 = IR_1$ (By Ohm's Law)

The voltage V_2 across R_2 : $V_2 = IR_2$

The voltage V_3 across R_3 : $V_3 = IR_3$

The applied voltage $V = V_1 + V_2 + V_3 = IR_1 + IR_2 + IR_3$

If R_{eff} is the effective resistance, or equivalent resistances of the combination, then, $V = IR_{eff}$

$IR_{eff} = IR_1 + IR_2 + IR_3$

$IR_{eff} = I(R_1 + R_2 + R_3)$

$\therefore R_{eff} = R_1 + R_2 + R_3$

Characteristics of a Series Circuit

1. Same current is flowing through all the resistances.
2. The effective resistance is the sum of the individual resistances. Effective resistance $R_{eff} = R_1 + R_2 + R_3$.
3. The applied voltage $V = V_1 + V_2 + V_3$

EXAMPLE 6.9 Find the effective resistance, when 1Ω, 10 Ω and 4 Ω resistances are connected in series.

SOLUTION

When resistors are connected in series, the effective resistance is given by,

$R_{eff} = R_1 + R_2 + R_3$

$R_{eff} = 1 + 10 + 4 = 15\Omega$

Resistors in Parallel

Resistors are said to be connected in parallel, when equal potential difference exists across all of them, i.e., the potential drop across each resistor is the same.

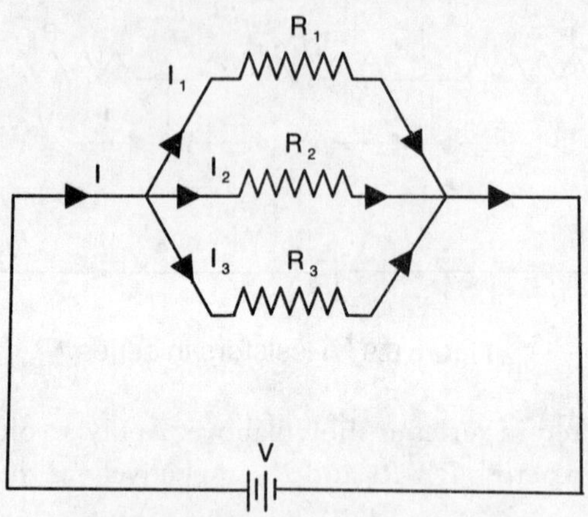

Figure 6.10 Resistors in parallel

Let three resistors R_1, R_2 and R_3 be connected across the voltage source V in parallel. The current I drawn from the battery is divided into three parts I_1, I_2 and I_3 flowing through the resistors R_1, R_2 and R_3, respectively as shown in Fig. 6.10.

The total current $I = I_1 + I_2 + I_3$

By Ohm's law to R_1, R_2 and R_3, we get,

$$I_1 = \frac{V}{R_1},\ I_2 = \frac{V}{R_2},\ \text{and } I_3 = \frac{V}{R_3}$$

$$\text{As } I = I_1 + I_2 + I_3$$

$$= \left(\frac{V}{R_1} + \frac{V}{R_2} + \frac{V}{R_3}\right) = V\left(\frac{V}{R_1} + \frac{V}{R_2} + \frac{V}{R_3}\right) \qquad (6.1)$$

Let R_{eff} be the effective resistance.

$$\text{Applying Ohm's law, } I = \frac{V}{R_{eff}} \qquad (6.2)$$

From equation (6.1) and (6.2), we get,

$$\therefore \frac{V}{R_{eff}} = V\left(\frac{1}{R_1} + \frac{1}{R_2} + \frac{1}{R_3}\right) \Rightarrow \frac{1}{R_{eff}} = \frac{1}{R_1} + \frac{1}{R_2} + \frac{1}{R_3}$$

Characteristics of a Parallel Circuit

1. The potential difference across each resistors is the same.
2. The reciprocal of the effective resistance is equal to the sum of the reciprocals of the individual resistances.
3. Current in the circuit $I = I_1 + I_2 + I_3 + \ldots\ldots.$
4. The effective resistance is less than the least resistance in the circuit.

EXAMPLE 6.10 Find the equivalent resistance when 3 ohm and 6 ohm resistances are connected in parallel.

SOLUTION

When resistances are connected in parallel, the equivalent resistance is given by,

$$\frac{1}{R_{eff}} = \frac{1}{R_1} + \frac{1}{R_2}$$

$$\frac{1}{R_{eff}} = \frac{1}{3} + \frac{1}{6} = \frac{2+1}{6} = \frac{3}{6} = \frac{1}{2}$$

$$R_{eff} = 2\Omega$$

EXAMPLE 6.11 For the given circuit, find the effective resistance between

(i) A and B

(ii) B and C

(iii) A and C

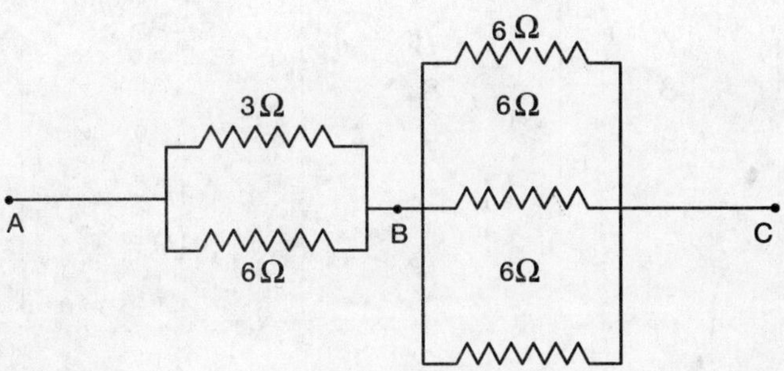

Figure 6.11 A circuit consisting resistors in series & parallel

SOLUTION

(i) Effective Resistance between A and B is

$$\frac{1}{R_{AB}} = \frac{1}{R_1} + \frac{1}{R_2} \Rightarrow \frac{1}{R_{AB}} = \frac{1}{3} + \frac{1}{6} = \frac{2+1}{6} = \frac{1}{2}$$

$$\therefore R_{AB} = 2\Omega$$

(ii) Effective Resistance between B and C is

$$\frac{1}{R_{BC}} = \frac{1}{R_1} + \frac{1}{R_2} + \frac{1}{R_3} = \frac{1}{6} + \frac{1}{6} + \frac{1}{6} = \frac{3}{6} = \frac{1}{2}$$

$$\therefore R_{BC} = 2\Omega$$

(iii) Resistance between A and C is obtained by drawing the simplified circuit as follows: Now, R_{AB} and R_{BC} are in series,

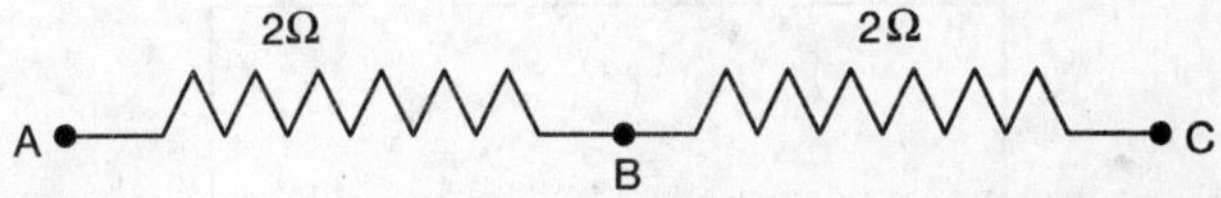

Figure 6.12 Simplified circuit consisting resistance in series

$$\therefore R_{AC} = R_{AB} + R_{BC}$$

$$R_{AC} = 2 + 2 = 4\Omega$$

Colour Coding of Resistors

The value of resistance is usually coded where by three bands of colours, followed by one band for the tolerance. The first two bands of colours indicate the first two digits. The third band gives the value of the multiplier and the fourth band gives the value of tolerance.

The following chart gives the colour code of resistances:

Table 6.2 Different colour code of resistances

Colour	First digit	Second digit	Multiplier	Tolerance
Black	0	0	10^0	-
Brown	1	1	10^1	-
Red	2	2	10^2	-
Orange	3	3	10^3	-
Yellow	4	4	10^4	-
Green	5	5	10^5	-
Blue	6	6	10^6	-
Violet	7	7	10^7	-
Grey	8	8	10^8	-
White	9	9	10^9	-
Gold	-	-	10^{-1}	5%
Silver	-	-	10^{-2}	10%
No colour	-	-	-	20%

1. Red, red, orange and no colour indicate the value of resistance = 22000 Ω ± 20%
2. Red, orange, orange and gold indicate the value of resistance = 23000Ω ± 5%

Circuit Diagram

The connection of electrical components in an electric circuit are discussed as follows:

Bulbs in Series

If the second terminal of a bulb is connected to the first terminal of the next bulb and so on, then the bulbs are said to be connected in series.

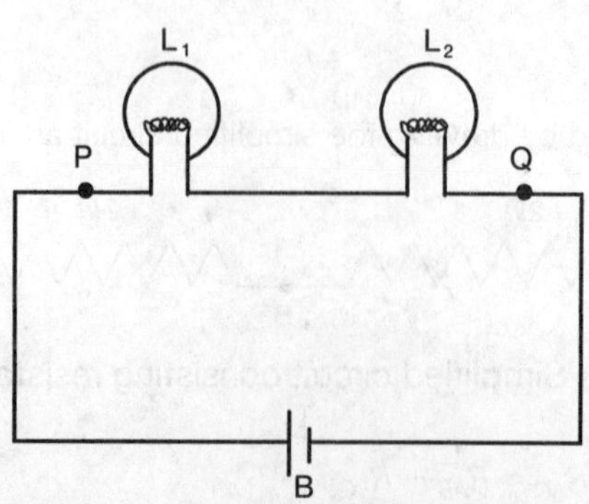

Figure 6.13 Bulbs in series in a circuit

If a voltage (V) is applied across the bulbs in series, then

1. voltage applied is divided among the bulbs.
2. same current exists in all the bulbs.
3. the brightness of each bulb depends on the number of bulbs connected
4. failure of any bulb leads to a break in the circuit.

Bulbs in Parallel

If the first terminal of all the bulbs are connected together and the second terminals of all the bulbs are connected together, then the bulbs are said to be connected in parallel.

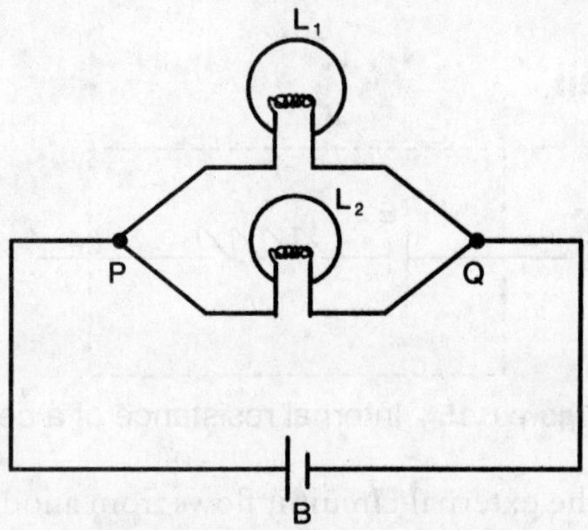

Figure 6.14 Bulbs in parallel

If a voltage (V) is applied across the bulbs connected in parallel, then

1. the voltage across each bulb remains the same.
2. the current is divided among the bulbs.
3. the power consumption of each bulb remains the same, even when the other bulb is removed.
4. the brightness of each bulb remains the same, even when the other bulbs are removed.
5. the failure of a particular bulb has no effect on the working of the other bulbs in parallel.

Electric Cell

An electric cell is a device which provides a constant potential difference between the ends of conductor connected across its two terminals. It converts chemical energy into electrical energy.

Open and Closed Circuits

As a result of constant potential difference provided by a cell, a current flows through the circuit connected to it. A circuit is a path through which the current flows. If the path is broken due to a open switch or if there is an insulator within the path, current cannot flow and such a path is called open circuit. The closed continuous path made of conductors is called closed circuit.

Electromotive Force of a Cell

When no current is drawn from a cell, i.e., it is open circuit, the potential difference between the terminals of the cell is called electromotive force (emf) of the cell.

In the older days, emf was an abbreviation for electron motive force. It was thought that a cell generates a force, which is responsible for the motion of electrons, i.e., flow of electricity.

The EMF is a characteristic of a cell and is different for different cells. For eg., EMF of a voltaic cell is 1.08 V and for Leclanche cell, it is 1.5 V. It is denoted by symbol *E*. The EMF is equal to the work done in taking a unit positive charge through the external circuit connected to the cell and the electrolyte inside the cell.

Terminal Voltage

The potential difference between the two terminals of the cell, when current is drawn from it, i.e., the cell is in closed circuit, is called its terminal voltage. It is denoted by '*V*'.

Terminal voltage is equal to the work done in taking a unit positive charge around the external circuit only, connected across the terminals of the cell. The terminal voltage is, therefore, always less than the EMF of cell.

The difference between *E* and *V* of a cell is called lost volt. The voltage is lost because of the resistance offered by the cell itself to the flow of current.

Internal Resistance of Cell

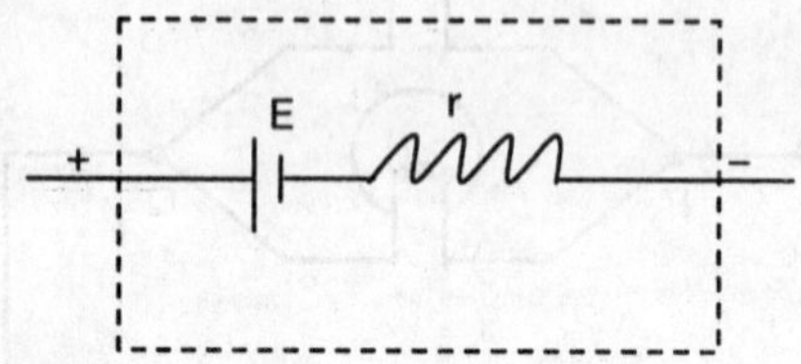

Figure 6.15 Internal resistance of a cell

When a current is drawn from a cell, in the external circuit it flows from anode to cathode and inside the cell through electrolyte, it flows from cathode to anode to maintain the continuity. The electrolyte offers certain resistance to the flow of current. This is called internal resistance of cell. It is denoted by symbol '*r*'. If current *I* is drawn from the cell, the lost voltage or voltage drop across the internal resistance '*r*' of the cell is given by,

$$v = Ir$$

The internal resistance is considered to be in series with the cell.

emf = terminal voltage + internal voltage drop.

$$E = V + v$$

The internal resistance of the cell depends upon the following factors:

1. It is directly proportional to the distance between the two electrodes.
2. It is inversely proportional to the area of cross section of the electrodes.
3. It depends upon the nature, concentration and temperature of the electrolyte.

The terminal voltage depends on external resistance, internal resistance and emf of the cell, whereas emf is independent of external and internal resistance.

Relation between emf, terminal voltage and internal resistance

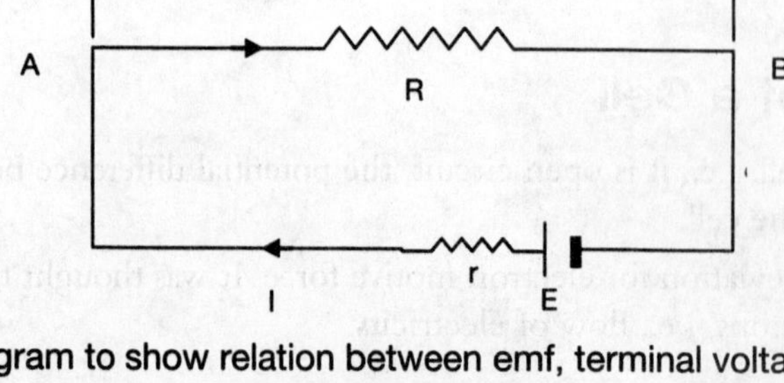

Figure 6.16 Circuit diagram to show relation between emf, terminal voltage and internal resistance

When the cell is connected to an external resistance 'R', a current 'I' is drawn from the cell. The total voltage 'E' of the cell is dropped across the internal resistance 'r' and the external resistance 'R'.

According to Ohm's law, the voltage drop across the internal resistance 'r' is equal to Ir.

Similarly, the voltage drop across the external resistance 'R' is equal to IR

Since both the resistances are connected in a series, $E= Ir +IR$.

Let the voltage across the terminals AB be V, then,

$$V = IR \text{ or } E = Ir + V.$$

$$\Rightarrow E - V = Ir \text{ or } r = \frac{E-V}{I}$$

Since $I = \frac{V}{R}$, $r = \frac{E-V}{V/R} = \left(\frac{E-V}{V}\right) \times R = \frac{E-V}{I} (\because V/R = I)$.

The smaller the internal resistance, the better is the cell. With the passage of time, the internal resistance of a dry cell increases.

Cells in Series

When the negative terminal of a cell is connected to the positive terminal of the next cell and so on, the cells are said to be in series.

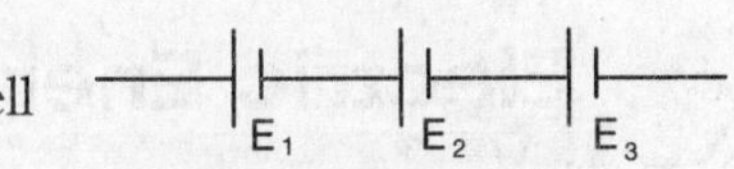

Figure 6.17 Cells in series

Cells connected in series are shown in Fig. 6.17.

When several cells are connected in a series, the total emf is the sum of the emf's of individual cells.

$$E = E_1 + E_2 + E_3$$

When the cells are connected in a series, the total internal resistance is equal to the sum of the internal resistances of the individual cells.

$$r = r_1 + r_2 + r_3$$

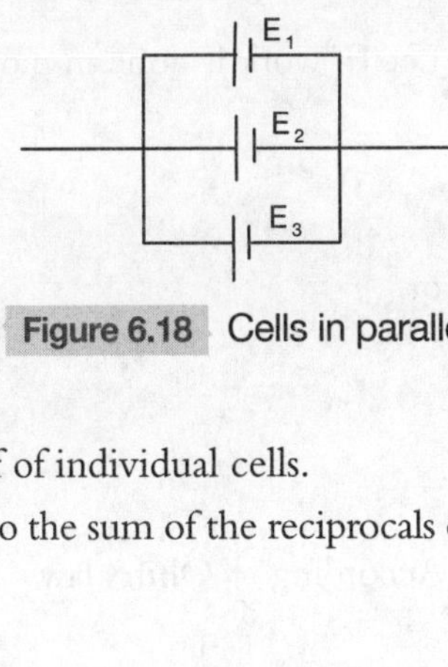

Figure 6.18 Cells in parallel

Cells in Parallel

When the negative terminals of all the cells are connected together and all the positive terminals are connected together, as shown in Fig. 6.18, then the cells are said to be in parallel.

When several identical cells are connected in parallel, the total emf is the same as the emf of individual cells.

When the cells are connected in parallel, reciprocal of the total internal resistance is equal to the sum of the reciprocals of individual internal resistances.

$$\frac{1}{r_{eq}} = \frac{1}{r_1} + \frac{1}{r_2} + \frac{1}{r_3}$$

If cells are identical, then $r_{eq} = r/n$

Heating Effect of Current

When a potential difference is applied between the ends of a conductor, current begins to flow through it. The current flows as large number of free electrons present in the conductor begin to drift from the end at lower potential to the end at higher potential. In the process, they constantly keep on colliding with positive ions of the conductor. The ions gain energy and begin to vibrate more vigorously about their mean positions. The average kinetic energy of atoms of conductor increases. This results in a rise in the temperature of the conductor and we say that the conductor has been heated. Thus, flow of current has a heating effect on the conductor. The heat produced (Q) depends on the following factors.

1. **Resistance of Conductor:** More the resistance of conductor, more is the number of collisions between free electrons and ions. Hence, if a conductor offers more resistance to the flow of current, the heat produced in it will be more.

$$Q \propto R$$

2. **Current Flowing through the Conductor:** Heat produced increases with the increase in the strength of the current flowing through conductor.

$$Q \propto I^2$$

3. **Time of Flow of Current:** As the time of flow of current increases, the heat produced also increases.

$$Q \propto t$$

Thus, a conductor having larger resistance will generate more heat when a stronger current passes through it for a longer time.

If I is the current flowing through a conductor of resistance R for time t, the heat produced (Q) is given by,

$$Q \propto I^2Rt$$

Electric Energy And Electric Work

The energy spent in moving an electric charge through a conductor is called electric energy. This energy is provided by a cell which converts chemical energy into electric energy.

The work done in moving an electric charge through a conductor, when some potential difference is applied at its ends is called electric work.

Let W work is done in moving charge Q under potential difference V.

$$V = \frac{W}{Q}$$

or,

$$W = VQ$$

$$\text{But } Q = It$$

$$\therefore W = VIt \tag{6.3}$$

According to Ohm's law,

$$V = IR \quad \text{Substitute this in equation (6.3)}$$

$$\therefore W = (IR)It$$

$$W = I^2Rt$$

$$\text{Also, } I = \frac{V}{R} \quad \text{Substitute this in equation (6.3)}$$

$$W = V\left(\frac{V}{R}\right)t$$

$$W = \frac{V^2}{R}t$$

∴ Electric work or energy can be expressed as

$$W = VIt = I^2Rt = \frac{V^2}{R}t = VQ$$

If the current is flowing through a heating element like in a heater, the electric energy is converted to heat energy.

Electric Power

The rate at which electric work is done is called electric power.

or

The amount of electric work done in one second is called electric power.

Let a cell do work W in time t, the power delivered by it is

$$P = \frac{W}{t}$$

Units of Electric Power

If work done is measured in joule and time in second, power is measured in watt (W).

$$\text{Watt} = \frac{\text{Joule}}{\text{Second}}$$

The power developed is 1 watt if 1 joule of work is done in 1 second.

$$1\ \text{Watt} = \frac{1\ \text{Joule}}{1\ \text{Second}}$$

Higher units of power

1 kilowatt (kW) = 1000 W = 10^3 W

1 Megawatt(MW) = 10^6 W

1 Horsepower (hp) = 746 W

1 kW = 1.34 hp

$$P = \frac{W}{t} \tag{6.4}$$

But $W = VIt$

$$\therefore P = \frac{VIt}{t}$$

$$P = VI$$

Power is also measured in volt-ampere

$$W = I^2 R t$$

Put in equation (6.4)

$$P = \frac{I^2Rt}{t}$$

$$\therefore P = I^2R$$

$$W = \frac{V^2}{R}t$$

Substitute in equation (6.4)

$$P = \frac{\frac{V^2}{R}t}{t}$$

$$P = \frac{V^2}{R}$$

$$\therefore P = \frac{W}{t} = VI = I^2R = \frac{V^2}{R}$$

Commercial Units of Electrical Energy

$$\text{Electric power} = \frac{\text{Electric work}}{\text{Time}}$$

$$= \frac{\text{Electric work}}{\text{Time}}$$

∴ Electric energy = Electric power × Time

Unit of electric energy = Unit of electric power × Unit of time = Watt × Second

The unit watt second gives the energy consumed by an electrical appliance, in t seconds whose power is P watt.

However, for practical purposes, higher units of energy are used. The higher units of electrical energy are watt-hour (W h) or kilowatt-hour (kW h).

If an electric appliance of power P watt is used for 1 hour, the energy consumed by it is 1 watt hour.

1 watt hour = 1 watt × 1 hour

= 1W × (60 × 60) s = 3600 W s

1 Watt hour = 3600 J. (W s = J)

One kilowatt hour is the energy consumed in 1 hour by an electric appliance whose power is 1 kilowatt.

1 kilowatt hour = 1 kilowatt × 1 hour

= 1 kW × (60 × 60) s

= 1000 W × 3600 s

1 kilowatt hour = 3.6×10^6 J

1 kW h = 3.6 MJ

The electric meter installed at our homes measures the energy consumed in kilowatt hour.

EXAMPLE 6.12

Two resistors of 15 Ω and 4 Ω in series are connected to a cell of EMF 2 V and internal resistance 1 Ω. Draw the circuit diagram and find the following:

(i) current in the circuit

(ii) voltage drop across each resistor

(iii) terminal voltage of the cell

(iv) lost voltage

SOLUTION

The circuit diagram based on the given information is shown in Fig. 6.19:

1. Current in the circuit:

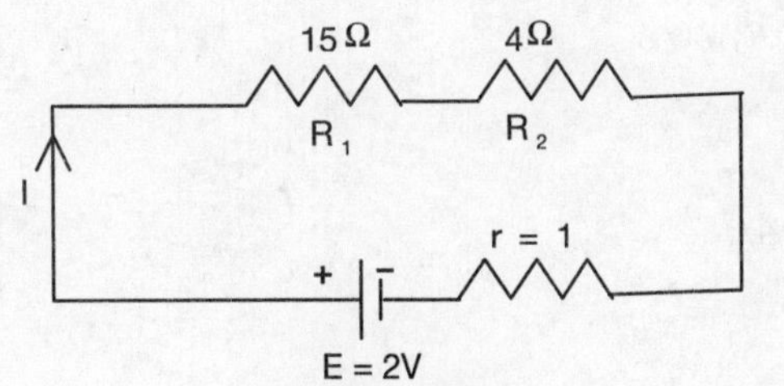

Figure 6.19

$$I = \frac{\text{EMF}(E)}{\text{Total circuit resistance }(R)}$$

The internal resistance of cell is in series with the external resistances.

$\therefore R = R_1 + R_2 + r = 15\ \Omega + 4\ \Omega + 1\ \Omega$

$$R = 20\ \Omega$$

$$I = \frac{2V}{20\Omega}$$

$$I = 0.1\ \text{A}$$

2. Voltage drop or potential difference (V_1) across R_1

$V_1 = IR_1$ (Ohm's law)

$V_1 = 0.1\ \text{A} \times 15\ \Omega$

$V_1 = 1.5\ \text{V}$

Similarly,

$V_2 = IR_2 = 0.1\ \text{A} \times 4\ \Omega$

$V_2 = 0.4\ \text{V}$

3. Terminal voltage

It is equal to the total voltage drop in external circuit.

$V = V_1 + V_2$

$= 1.5\ \text{V} + 0.4\ \text{V}$

$= 1.9\ \text{V}$

4. Lost voltage is the voltage drop across the internal resistance of cell.

$v = Ir$

$= 0.1 \times 1 = 0.1\text{V}$

Also,

$v = E - V$

$= 2\ \text{V} - 1.9\ \text{V} = 0.1\ \text{V}$

EXAMPLE 6.13 A 20 V electric bulb is connected to a 20 V battery of negligible resistance. The resistance offered by the bulb is 5 Ω. Find:

(i) Current flowing through the bulb.

(ii) Power of the bulb.

(iii) Electric energy consumed by it in 3 hours.

SOLUTION

Given,

Voltage of bulb (V) = 20 V

Resistance of bulb (R) = 5 Ω

Time (t) = 3 hours = 3 × 60 × 60 = 10800 s

1. Current (I) through bulb $= \frac{V}{R}$

$$I = \frac{20\text{V}}{5\Omega} = 4\text{A}$$

2. Power (P) = $V \times I$

$= 20\text{ V} \times 4\text{ A} = 80\text{ W}$

3. Electrical energy (W) = $V \times I \times t$

$= 80 \times 10800$

$= 864000\text{ J}$

$$W = \frac{864000}{3.6\times10^6}\text{ kW h} = 0.24\text{ kW h}$$

EXAMPLE 6.14 The resistance of a electric heater is 200 Ω and it draws a current of 1A. Calculate its power and potential difference at its ends.

SOLUTION

Given,

Resistance of heater (R) = 200 Ω

Current through heater (I) = 1 A

Power of heater (P) = ?

Potential difference (V) = ?

$P = I^2R$

$= (1)^2 \times 200$

$P = 200\text{ W}$

$V = IR = 1\text{A} \times 200\ \Omega$

$V = 200\text{ V}$

Watt Hour Meter

Watt hour is a unit in which the amount of electric energy consumed by a device is measured. A meter which measures the electric energy consumed by various electric appliances is called watt hour meter. It is commonly called electric meter which is installed at every house by the state electricity board.

It is connected before the main switch so that the total current drawn by all the appliances in the house passes through it and it can give the reading of energy consumed. The meter readings at the beginning and end of month are noted. The difference in the readings gives the energy consumed in that month in watt hour. This reading when multiplied by rate, fixed by the state electricity board per unit (one kWh), gives the monthly bill which has to be paid by the owner of the house.

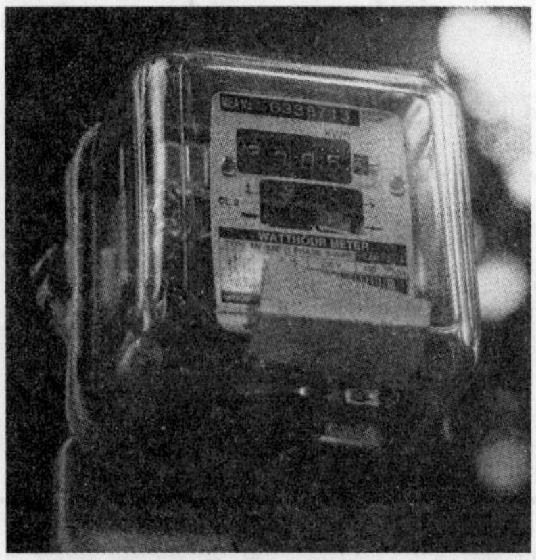
Credit line: Sunshine Studio / Shutterstock

Figure 6.20 Kilowatt hour meter

EXAMPLE 6.15 What should be the bill for the month of March for a heater of resistance 60.5 Ω connected to 220 V mains? The cost of energy is ₹ 2 per kWh and the heater is used for 3 hours daily.

SOLUTION

Given,

Resistance (R) of heater = 60.5 Ω

Potential difference (V) = 220 V.

Power (P) of heater is

$$P = \frac{V^2}{R}$$

$$P = \frac{220 \times 220}{60.5} = \frac{48400}{60.5}$$

$$= \frac{48400}{60.5}$$

$$P = 800 \text{ W}$$

Energy consumed by heater in a day = $P \times t$

= 800 W × 3 h

= 2400 W h

There are 31 days in the month of March.

∴ Energy consumed by heater in 31 days

= 2400 × 31

= 74400 Wh = 74.4 kWh

⇒ For 1 kWh, the charge is ₹ 2.

So, for 74.4 kWh, the charge will be = 74.4 × 2

= ₹148.8

EXAMPLE 6.16 Calculate the monthly bill if the following appliances are used as indicated below at the rate of ₹ 5 per unit.

(i) A heater of 1000 watt for 2 hours daily.

(ii) Ten 60 watt bulbs for 5 hours daily.

SOLUTION

Energy consumed by 1000 watt heater for 2 hours = 1000 × 2 = 2000 watt hour

Energy consumed by ten 60 watt lamp for 5 hours = 10 × 60 × 5 = 3000 watt hour

Total energy consumed per day = 2000 + 3000 = 5000 watt hour = 5 kW h

Total energy consumed for the month = 5 × 30 =150 kW h

Cost per kW h = ₹ 5

Cost for 150 kW h = 150 × 5 = ₹ 750

Wattage

The amount of electrical energy consumed by an electrical appliance per unit time is known as wattage.

$$\text{Wattage } (P) = I^2R \text{ or } = \frac{V^2}{R} \text{ or } VI$$

Unit of wattage is watt (W).
Multiple units are kW (10^3 W) and MW (10^6 W).

Joule's Law

If W is the mechanical work done by a body (in joule) and Q is the quantity of heat produced by it (in calories), then $W \propto Q$ or $W = JQ$, where, J is the mechanical equivalent of heat or Joule's constant. $J = 4.18$ J cal^{-1}.

We have seen that when electric current passes through a resistor, the electric energy spent or electric work done in moving the charges is converted into heat energy. In fact work done in any form, i.e., mechanical, chemical, etc., can be converted into heat energy. Joule conducted a series of experiments and found that the same work done in different forms produces the same quantity of heat in all cases. This is called Joule's law.

Joule showed that there is a definite relation between work done and heat produced by it.

Let W is the mechanical work done and Q is the heat produced in calories.

According to Joule's law,

$$W \propto Q$$

$$W = JQ$$

where, J is the constant of proportionality also called mechanical equivalent of heat.

$$J = \frac{W}{Q}$$

The value of J is 4.18 J cal^{-1} if work done and heat produced are measured in joules and calories, respectively. If both are measured in joules, then the value of J becomes unity.

Determination of the value of J using the Joule's calorimeter experiment

1. Take a calorimeter with a stirrer having a mass of w_1 g.
2. Take some quantity of water in a calorimeter, let the mass of the calorimeter with stirrer and water be w_2 g.
3. Place the calorimeter in a wooden box. Insert a thermometer and note the initial temperature of water. Let it be t_1°C.
4. Immerse a heater or coil (H) in water. Its two ends are connected to a plug key, a battery, an ammeter and a rheostat. A voltmeter is connected in parallel with the coil. (See Fig. 6.21).

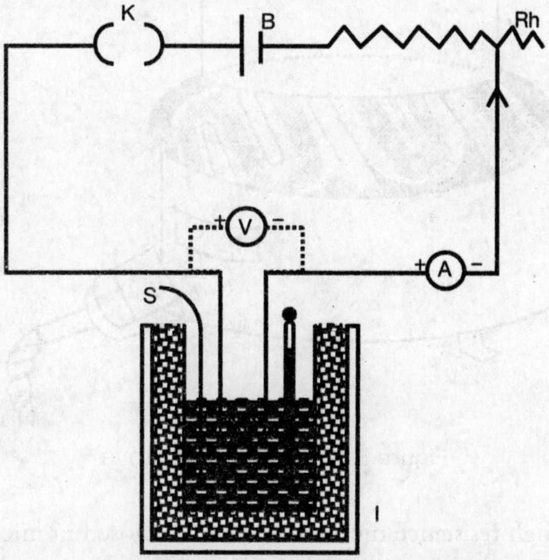

Figure 6.21 Joule's experiment

With the plug key (k) closed, adjust the rheostat so that a current of I ampere flows through the heater. Pass the current for a period of 30 minutes. Unplug the new key and note the new temperature of water. Let it be t_2°C.

The electrical work (w) done by heater = VIt

Heat developed by the heater (Q) is given by the sum of the heat gained by the calorimeter with stirrer (Q_1) and water (Q_2)

$\Rightarrow Q = Q_1 + Q_2$

$Q = w_1 s_c (t_2 - t_1) + m_w s_w (t_2 - t_1) = (t_2 - t_1)(w_1 s_c + m_w)$

where, w_1 = mass of the calorimeter with stirrer

s_c = specific heat of copper

s_w = specific heat of water

Mass of water, $m_w = (w_2 - w_1)$

According to Joule's law,

$$W = JQ$$

$$J = \frac{W}{Q} = \frac{VIt}{(t_2 - t_1)[w_1 s_c + m_w]}$$

Experimentally, it is found that $J = 4.18$ J cal^{-1}

Applications of Heating Effect of Electric Current

1. **Electric Heater:** It uses nichrome wire as a heating coil. The spiral coil of nichrome wire is placed in a groove in a porcelain frame in a zig zag manner. When current is passed through it, the wire gets red hot due to high resistance. The heat generated is used for cooking or heating purposes. Porcelain being an insulator of heat, does not become hot.

Figure 6.22 An electric stove

2. **Electric Iron:** The coil of high resistance nichorme wire is enclosed in mica sheets which are placed in a heavy metal block. The coil is connected to power supply and transfers its heat to the metal block which is used to iron clothes. The heating coil is embedded between mica sheets as mica is a good conductor of heat but bad conductor of electricity.

Lighting Effect of Electricity

When current passes through a conductor, it gets heated up. On being sufficiently heated, it may begin to emit light. This is called lighting effect of electricity.

Examples: electric bulbs and tubes.

Thus, electric lamps work on lighting effect of electricity. Following types of electric lamps are commonly used.

1. Filament lamp
2. Discharge lamp
3. Flourescent lamp
4. Electric arc lamp

Incandescent or Filament Lamp

Incandescence is a phenomenon in which an object emits light when heated to a high temperature.

This phenomenon is used in electric lamps which are called incandescent lamps. The element which is heated is connected in lamps in the form of a thin filament. Hence, it is also called filament lamp. Tungsten filament is most suitable for this purpose because of its following characteristics.

Info Bytes!

LEDs use the lighting effect of electricity more efficiently than traditional incandescent bulbs.

1. Its melting point is very high about 3665°C.
2. It offers high resistance. Hence, it gets heated quickly.
3. It does not get oxidized easily.

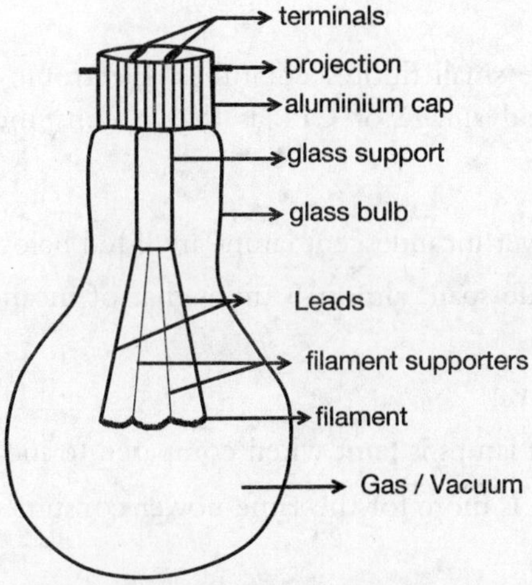

Figure 6.23 An electric bulb

The temperature of long thin tungsten filament can rise upto 3000°C. It is usually operated for a long period of time. Hence, it evaporates and condenses on the inner side of the glass surface of the bulb forming a layer on it. This decreases the life and efficiency of the lamp. To prevent this, the bulb is evacuated and filled with a gas at low pressure. The rate of evaporation decreases and filament can reach a higher temperature.

In olden days carbon filament was used in bulbs. The melting point of carbon is 1600°C which is low considering the heat generated in the bulb. On evaporation, black layer of carbon gets deposited on the inner side of bulb. Life of carbon filament bulb is short.

Discharge Lamps

They are so called because they use discharge tubes. Discharge tube is used to study conduction of electricity through gases. It consists of a glass tube having two electrodes fused to it and filled with one or more gases at very low pressure. A high potential difference is applied across the electrodes which ionizes the gases. The ions get accelerated towards electrode with opposite polarity during which they collide with neutral gas atoms. If the pressure of gas is 1.65 mm of Hg, the tube begins to glow due to successive collisions. The nature of gas determines the colour of light emitted.

Table 6.3 Colour of light according to the gas in the discharge tube

S. No.	Gas in the discharge tube	Colour of light
1	Neon	Orange
2.	Nitrogen	Red
3.	Sodium	Yellow
4.	Mercury	White
5.	Chlorine	Green
6.	Hydrogen	Blue

Fluorescent Lamps

Discharge lamp coated with fluorescent material from inside is called fluorescent lamp.

A high voltage applied to coils heat them which results in emission of electrons. These electrons collide with the atoms of mercury vapours present in the tube. These collisions cause emission of invisible ultraviolet (*uv*) material which emits visible bright light.

Compact fluorescent lamps (CFL) use small fluorescent tubes. Electronic circuits control the intensity of current. Main advantage of CFL is that it consumes small amount of electrical energy.

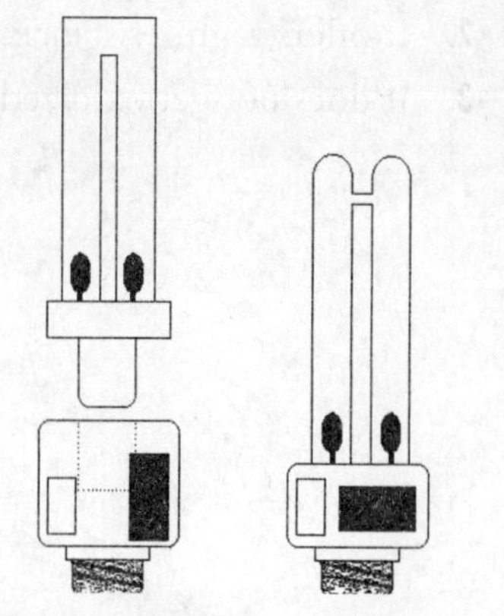

Figure 6.24 Fluorescent lamps

The advantages of fluorescent lamps over incandescent lamps are listed below:

1. Fluorescent lamps have a longer life span, almost 5 times that of incandescent lamps.
2. They consume less electrical energy.
3. The shadow formed by fluorescent lamps is faint when compared to incandescent lamps.
4. The brightness of fluorescent lamp is more for the same power consumed by them.

Electric arc Lamps

They are used to produce high intensity light as in search lights or cinema projector.

It consists of two carbon rods having pointed tips at one end. The tips are separated by a very small gap. A potential of about 40 V to 60 V is applied across the carbon rods and a glow is produced between the pointed tips. The glow emits very intense light. Using concave mirrors, this light can be focused on a point or can be converted to a parallel beam.

Household Distribution of Current

Fuse

Fuse is a very important safety device in an electric circuit. It is a thin wire which melts and breaks the electric circuit due to 1) overloading 2) short circuit 3) fluctuation in power supply.

Characteristics of Fuse

1. It should have a low-melting point. Generally a fuse wire is made from an alloy containing 50% lead and 50% tin. Its melting point is around 200°C.
2. Since fuse should melt before the excess of current reaches electric appliances and damages them, the temperature of fuse should rise quickly. This is possible if the resistance of fuse is very high.

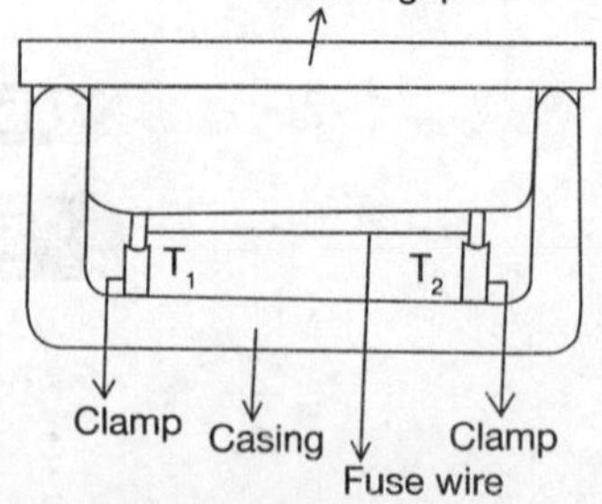

Figure 6.25 A fuse

A fuse wire is stretched between two terminals T_1 and T_2 fixed to porcelain casing or holder which fits into porcelain grip or socket. The porcelain socket is connected to live wire. For any reason, if excessive current begins to flow, the fuse wire gets heated up more quickly than conducting wires and melts, breaking the circuit. Thus, the excessive current is prevented from flowing through electric appliances, which may damage them.

Current Rating of Fuse

Different electric circuits can withstand certain maximum amount of current without getting heated up and damaging themselves. For example, for a lighting circuit, this limit is 5 A and for a heating circuit, it is 15 A. If current approaches this value, fuse wire will melt. Thus, the current ratings of fuse should be less than the maximum current that can safely flow through the circuit.

Fuse should be connected in live wire of a circuit. If it is connected to neutral wire, the fuse will melt when current exceeds its rating, but the appliance will still be connected to high potential of supply through live wire. If a person touches the appliance, his body provides a path for current to flow to earth which is at zero potential. Thus, person may get severe shock which may prove fatal. Hence, fuse is connected to live wire so that if it melts, the appliance is no longer connected to the high potential of the supply and possibility of electric shock is eliminated.

Earthing

When the insulation of live wire in a circuit inside a electric appliance melts due to some reasons, the live wire may touch the metal casing of the appliance. Thus, metal casing is connected to high potential. This metal casing of appliances such as mixer, fan, refrigerator, toaster, etc., is continuously touched by us by our bare hands. Hence, we may get a severe shock as current will flow through our body to earth which is considered as zero potential. To prevent this, metal casings of all appliances are connected to earth by a conducting wire. This is called earthing.

Thus, earthing involves connecting metal body of electric appliance to thick copper wire which is connected to a copper plate buried deep in the Earth. The copper plate is surrounded by a mixture of charcoal and common salt.

Earthing helps in two ways. When live wire comes in contact with metal casing, the current instead of flowing through the person touching it, flows through earth wire. Also when live wire touches wire, i.e., during short circuit, the current from metal body flows through earth wire which offers very less resistance. Thus, a large current is drawn which melts the fuse instantly. The appliance does not receive current any more, thus, preventing it from potential damage.

Household Distribution of Current

Electricity is supplied to houses through over head wires on poles or through underground cable. The electric cable consists of 3 wires, viz., live wire or phase wire, neutral wire and earth wire. The company which supplies electric power installs its fuse near the pole or before the kWh meter. If the house draws more than allotted current, this fuse which is called pole or company fuse melts and supply is cut off.

At the power station, neutral and earth wire are connected together so that both are at ground or zero potential. The live and electrical wire are connected to the input terminals of kWh meter and the earth wire to the body of meter. On the output side of kWh meter, fuse is connected in series with live wire. This fuse is called main fuse. After this, live and neutral wires are connected to the main switch.

The main switch is an iron clad double pole switch. It is operated by a single lever and can connect and disconnect both live and neutral wire simultaneously to the house. These two wires then carry power to whole house. The distribution of electric power in the house is done by two types of wiring system.

1. Tree type
2. Ring type

Tree System

Phase wire to different rooms is taken from the main board, through a fuse on the main board. Neutral and earth wire is common to all the circuits.

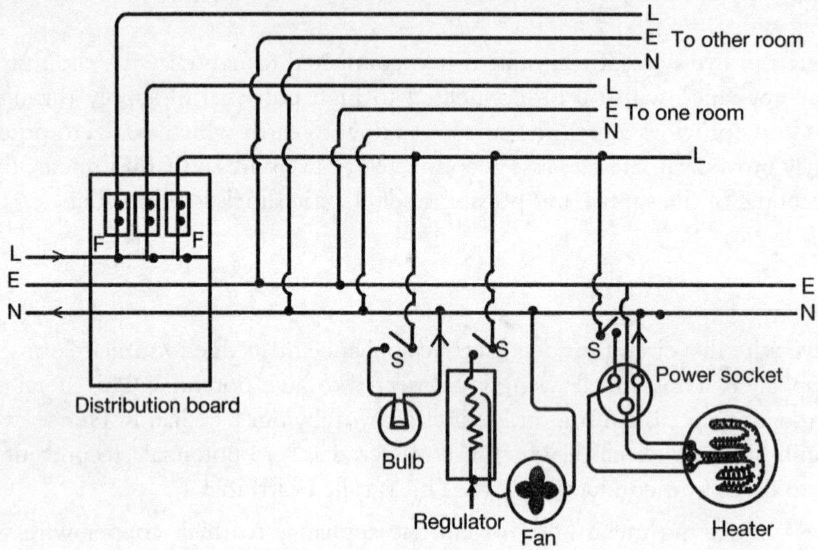

Figure 6.26 Tree system of wiring in household circuits

The different circuits coming from the main board are connected in parallel.

If there is a short circuit in one particular circuit, then only the fuse of that circuit is broken and the power supply to other parts of the circuit will not be affected. This is the major advantage of parallel circuit.

Disadvantages of Tree System

A long length of wire is required as all the wires are to be drawn from the main board itself. It increases the initial installation cost. When the fuse of a particular line melts, it affects all the appliances connected to that circuit.

Ring System

It consists of a ring formed by all the three wires-phase, neutral and earth and runs through all the rooms and comes back to the main board. Each appliance is connected to this ring. Appliances which are likely to get short circuited are protected by a fuse near the appliance.

Advantage

As one ring feeds the entire house, it requires less length of wire. It reduces installation cost.
As there is an individual fuse for each appliance, only faulty appliance will not work and all the other appliances will not be affected. It is easier to install.

Switch

Switch is a device to connect or disconnect an electric appliance.

1. Lever type switch is used for light, fan, heater, etc.
2. Push switch is used in devices like calling bell.

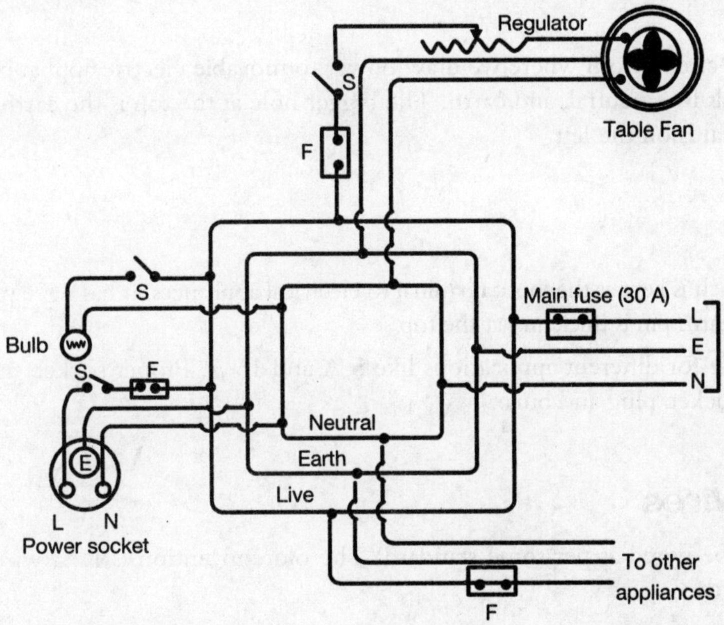

Figure 6.27 Ring system of wiring in household circuits

3. Single pole double throw switch is used for staircase lights.
4. One staircase bulb can be switched on or off either from the first floor or from the ground floor.

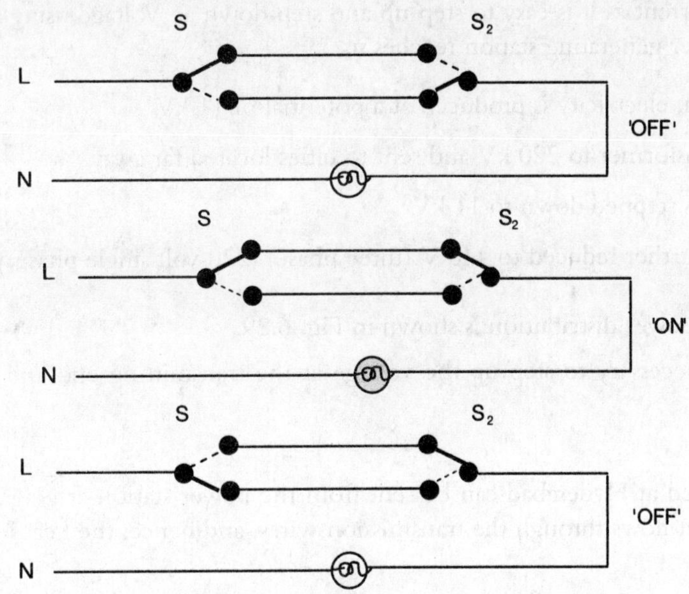

Figure 6.28 Switches in electric circuit

The same switch is used near the room entrance and near the bed so that we can switch on the light as we enter the room and switch it off when we go to bed.

We should always connect the switch in the live wire and not on the neutral wire. This is for safety reasons. Suppose the switch is connected to neutral wire, the live wire remains connected to the appliance even when the switch is in off position. This may prove fatal if proper earthing is not there. We should not touch the switch with a wet hand as it may act like a conducting path and one receives a fatal electric shock.

Socket

Sockets are elements of electric circuit from where we draw power to movable electric appliances like radio, electric iron, toaster, etc. It has three terminals live, neutral, and earth. The bigger hole at the top is the earth terminal, Live terminal is on the right and neutral terminal is on the left.

Plugs

It is the counterpart of socket which is kept as the input terminal to electrical appliances. It has three pins. Live pin is on the right, neutral pin is on the left and the earth pin is thick and at the top.

Plugs and sockets are available for different applications like 5 A and 15 A. Proper sockets and plugs are to be used as otherwise it will overheat the socket/plug and burn.

Colour Coding of Wires

All electrical appliances are to be wired as per some standard. The old convention is Red wire for Live, Black wire for Neutral and Green wire for Earth.

According to the specifications of a recent international convention, live wire is to be connected to brown, neutral wire to be connected to light blue and earth wire is connected to green or yellow wire.

Power Transmission

Mainly, we use alternating current as it is easy to step up and step down ac Voltage using a transformer. Now, let us see how the power from the power generating station reaches us.

- At the generating station, electricity is produced at a potential of 11 kV.
- It is stepped up by a transformer to 220 kV and sent to cities located far away.
- At the city outskirts, it is stepped down to 11 kV.
- At the street level, it is further reduced to 440 V (three phase) (220 volt single phase) and supplied to the houses.

The schematic diagram of power distribution is shown in Fig. 6.29.

Let us now see why it is necessary to step up the voltage at the transmitting end and step down the voltage at the receiving end.

We know *Power* = *VI*

For example, power required at Hyderabad can be sent from the power station at Nagarjunasagar in two ways. If we send at 220 volt a large current flows through the transmission wires, and hence, the heat loss due to transmission will be large.

This is because the power lost as heat is I^2R. Since current is more for a given conductor, the loss is more.

Further, we require thick wires which cost more.

If we send power at high voltage, then less current would flow for a given power, and hence, the loss will be minimized.

Further more, we can use thin wires as compared to earlier case. This reduces the cost of transmission wires.

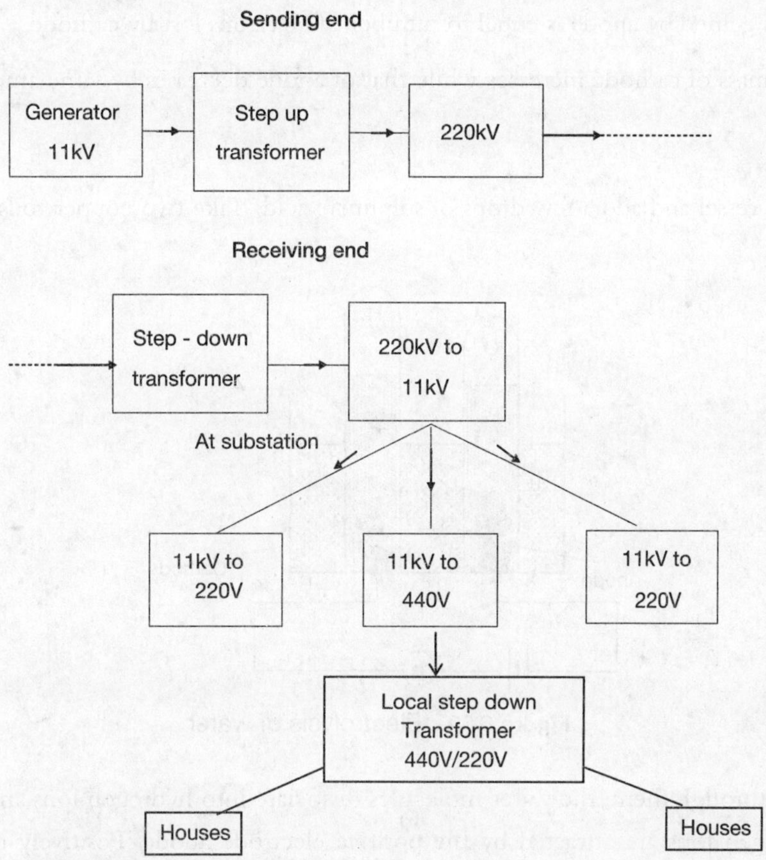

Figure 6.29 The schematic diagram of power distribution

Chemical Effect of Electricity

The most common chemical effect of current electricity is electrolysis. Just like solids, some liquids also conduct electricity. Such liquids are called electrolytes. When electric current passes through an electrolyte, it decomposes into its constituents.

Electrolysis

The process in which an electrolyte undergoes decomposition into its constituents when an electric current is passed through it is called electrolysis.

The plates inside the electrolyte through which the electric current is passed from the external battery are called **electrodes**.

The electrode which is connected to the positive terminal of the battery is called **anode**.

The terminal which is connected to the negative terminal of the battery is called **cathode**.

The vessel in which the electrolyte is kept is called **voltameter**.

Following are the characteristics of electrolysis process.

1. The concentration of electrolyte remains unaffected during electrolysis.

2. The anode gains electrons as negative ions come to it and cathode loses electrons to positive ions which are attracted to it.

3. Number of electrons gained by anode is equal to number of electrons lost by cathode.
4. During electrolysis, mass of cathode increases while that of anode decreases by same amount.

Electrolysis of Water

Take some water in a glass vessel and add a few drops of sulphuric acid. Take two copper rods and connect them to two terminals of a battery.

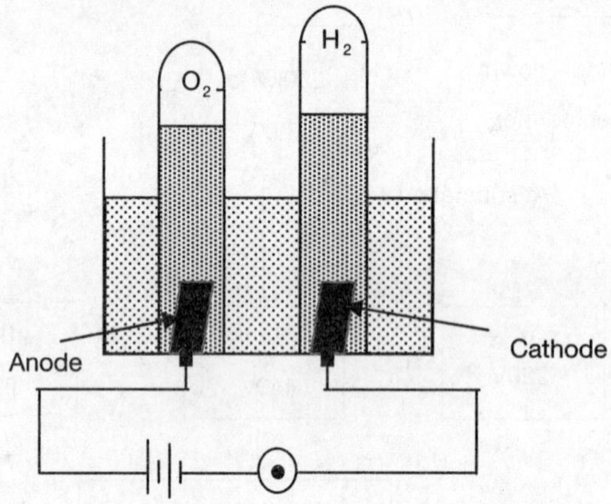

Figure 6.30 Electrolysis of water

When current is passed through them, the water molecules dissociate into hydrogen ions and oxygen ions.

Negatively charged oxygen ions are attracted by the positive electrode anode. Positively-charged hydrogen ions are attracted by the negative electrode cathode. So, hydrogen and oxygen ions are collected at the cathode and the anode, respectively.

Electrolysis of Copper Sulphate

Here copper sulphate is the electrolyte and both the electrodes are copper rods.

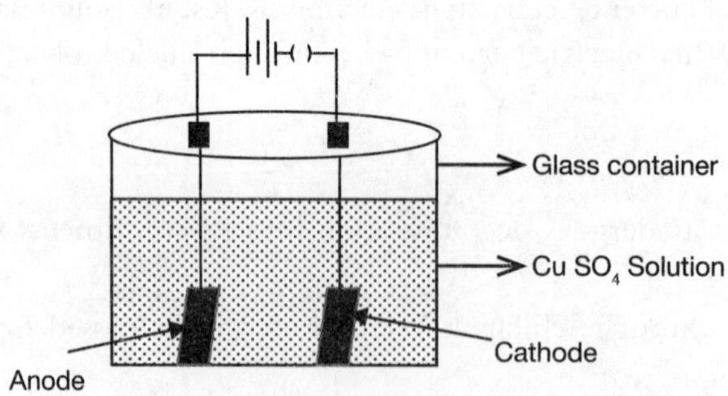

Figure 6.31 Electrolysis of copper sulphate

When current is passed through the copper sulphate solution, copper sulphate molecules split into copper ions Cu^{++} and sulphate ions SO_4^{--}

$$CuSO_4 \rightarrow Cu^{++} + SO_4^{--}$$

When current is passed, the positive copper ions are attracted by the cathode and a coating of copper is observed on the cathode. The negative sulphate ions are attracted by the anode. They react with copper and $CuSO_4$ molecules are formed, thereby, maintaining the concentration of electrolyte.

Uses of Electrolysis

Electroplating, extraction of metals from ore (i.e., Metallurgy), purification of metals, electrotyping, etc.

Electroplating

The process of depositing a thin layer of a desired metal over another metal by passing an electric current through some electrolyte is called electroplating.

The object to be electroplated is taken as cathode and the metal to be coated is kept as anode. Suitable electrolyte is used.

Some common electroplating applications

Copper Plating

Cathode	:	Article to be plated
Anode	:	Copper rod
Electrolyte	:	Copper sulphate solution

Silver Plating

Cathode	:	Article to be plated
Anode	:	A silver rod
Electrolyte	:	Silver nitrate solution $AgNO_3$

Nickel Plating

Cathode	:	Article to be plated
Anode	:	Nickel rod
Electrolyte	:	Nickel ammonium sulphate solution $NiSO_4(NH_4)_2\ SO_46H_2SO_4$

Chromium Plating

Cathode	:	Article to be plated
Anode	:	Chromium rod
Electrolyte	:	Chromic acid solution H_2CrO_4

Laws of Electrolysis

Michael Faraday carried out a series of experiments and proposed two laws which are known as 'Faraday's laws of electrolysis'.

Faraday's First Law of Electrolysis

The mass of the substance deposited at the cathode is directly proportional to the quantity of electricity, i.e., charge and the time for which the current is passed through the electrolyte.

Larger current passing through a given electrolyte for a given time or the same current passing for a longer time will deposit more mass on the cathode.

$$m \propto I; \text{ or } m \propto t; \quad m \propto It$$

Since $$Q = It, \; m = ZQ$$

The constant Z is known as **electrochemical equivalent** of the substance.

The electrochemical equivalent of a substance is defined as the mass of the substance which is produced during electrolysis by passing one coulomb of charge. The unit of Z is g C^{-1}.

Electro Chemical Equivalent

The mass of ions liberated at the electrode when 1 coloumb of electricity is passed through the electrolyte is known as electrochemical equivalent. It is denoted by Z and $Z = m/q$.

Units of Z are g C^{-1} or g A^{-1} s^{-1}.

Faraday's Second Law of Electrolysis

When the same quantity of electricity passes through different electrolytes, the masses of ions liberated at the respective electrodes are proportional to their chemical equivalents.

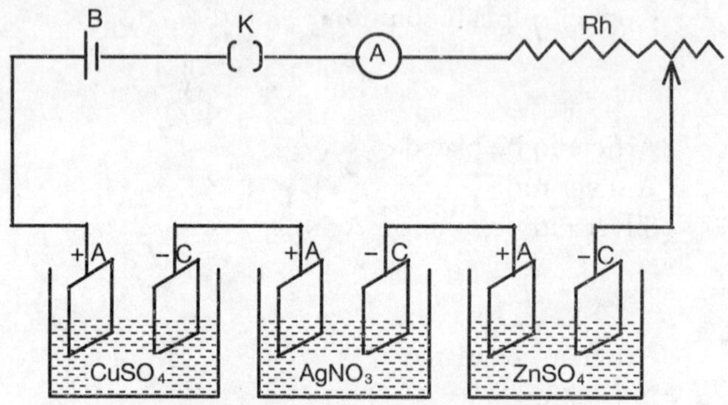

Figure 6.32 Faraday's experiment

If E_1, E_2 and E_3, are the chemical equivalents and Z_1, Z_2 and Z_3, are the electro chemical equivalents of three substances, say Cu, Ag and Zn, respectively, and their masses liberated are m_1, m_2 and m_3, when the same quantity of electricity is passed through their respective electrolyte, then according to Faraday's second law of electrolysis

$$\frac{m_1}{E_1} = \frac{m_2}{E_2} = \frac{m_2}{E_3} \text{ or}$$

$$m_1 : m_2 : m_3 : = E_1 : E_2 : E_3 \qquad (6.5)$$

This is one form of Faraday's second law. If we apply the first law, then

$$m_1 = Z_1\, q \qquad m_2 = Z_2\, q \qquad m_3 = Z_3\, q$$

$$m_1 : m_2 : m_3 : = Z_1 : Z_2 : Z_3 \qquad (6.6)$$

Combining equations (6.5) and (6.6), we get

$$Z_1 : Z_2 : Z_3 : = E_1 : E_2 : E_3$$

Chemical Equivalent (E)

The ratio of the atomic weight of an element to its valency is known as the chemical equivalent. It is denoted by E.

The amount of charge which on passing through an electrolyte liberates 1 gram equivalent of the substance at an electrode is called Faraday constant. The value of Faraday constant is 96,500 C.

EXAMPLE 6.17 The e.c.e. of silver is 1.12×10^{-3} gC^{-1}. If a current of 0.5 A is passed for 3 hours through a solution of silver nitrate, how much silver will be deposited on the cathode?

SOLUTION

Current (I) = 0.5 A

Time (t) = 3 hours = 10,800 seconds (since 3 hours × 60 minutes/hour × 60 seconds/minute = 10,800 seconds)

e.c.e. (Z) of silver = 1.12×10^{-3} g C^{-1}

Relationship Between Mass, Current, Time, and e.c.e.:

$m = ZIt$

$m = 1.12 \times 10^{-3}$ g $C^{-1} \times 0.5$ A $\times$ 10,800 s

$m = 1.12 \times 10^{-3} \times 5.4 \times 10^{3}$

$m = 6.048$ g

So, if a current of 0.5 A is passed for 3 hours through a silver nitrate solution, 6.048 grams of silver will be deposited on the cathode.

EXAMPLE 6.18 During copper plating, a 4*A* current is passed for 1500 seconds and 3.6*g* of copper is deposited. Find the electrochemical equivalent of copper.

SOLUTION

Given,

Mass (*m*) of copper deposited = 3.6 g

Time(*t*) from which current is passed = 1500 s

Current (*I*) = 4A

e.c.e. of copper (*Z*) = ?

Using the formulae: $Z = \frac{m}{It} = \frac{3.6g}{4A \times 1500s} = \frac{3.6}{6000} = 0.0006\ g\ C^{-1}$

Thus, the electrochemical equivalent of copper is $0.0006\ g\ C^{-1}$ or 0.0006 grams per Coulomb.

Dry Cell

A dry cell is a form of primary cell which is used widely in torches, transistor radios, electric toys, clocks, etc.

It consists of a zinc container at the centre of which a carbon rod is fixed. Carbon rod act an anode while the zinc body acts as cathode. The dry paste of ammonium chloride (NH_4Cl) and zinc chloride ($ZnCl_2$) serves as an electrolyte. The electrolyte is mixed with powdered coke. The carbon rod is surrounded by graphite and manganese dioxide. The top of carbon rod is connected to a brass cap to improve electrical conductivity. The container is sealed with sealing wax to make it air and water tight.

Zinc atoms from the container lose two electrons when the cell is connected to a electric circuit

$$Zn \rightarrow Zn^{2+} + 2e^-$$

These electrons flow through external conducting wire and reach carbon electrode. This constitutes electric current. The conventional current is taken from carbon rod to zinc body.

The ammonium chloride in the electrolyte dissociates as

$$NH_4Cl \rightarrow NH^{+}_4 + Cl^-$$

The electrons lost by zinc combine with positive ammonium ions (NH^+_4)

$$2NH^+_4 + 2e^- \rightarrow 2NH_3 + H_2$$

The hydrogen gas produced is reduced by manganese dioxide.

$$H_2 + 2MnO_4 \rightarrow H_2O + MnO_3$$

The positive zinc ions combine with negative chlorine ions to form zinc chloride.

$$Zn^{2+} + 2Cl^- \rightarrow ZnCl_2$$

The powered carbon present in electrolyte facilialtes the movements of charges.

Dry cell gives an emf of 1.5 V. Since it is primary cell, once the chemicals present in cell are used up, cell has to be replaced by a new cell.

There are many secondary cells or accumulators which are also in wide use nowadays in which chemical reactions can be reversed by passing current in reverse direction. For example, lead sulphuric acid battery is widely used in automobiles and industries. Cell phones are powered by battery which can be easily recharged.

POINTS TO REMEMBER

- ✔ Atoms of matter are electrically neutral because their nuclei contain the same number of protons as there are electrons surrounding the nuclei.
- ✔ The substances which conduct electricity easily are called electric conductors.
- ✔ The substances which do not conduct electricity are called electric insulators.
- ✔ The rate of flow of charge is known as electric current. It is denoted by *I*.
- ✔ The charge transferred is always an integral multiple of the fundamental charge (charge of a proton). This property is referred to as quantization of charge.
- ✔ The electric potential at a point is said to be 1 volt if 1 joule of work is done in bringing a positive charge of 1 coulomb from infinity to that point.
- ✔ The obstruction offered by a conductor to the flow of electric current is called its resistance.
- ✔ The reciprocal of resistance is known as electrical conductance.
- ✔ At critical temperature, a metal offers zero resistance to the passage of electricity. These type of conductors are called superconductors.
- ✔ The temperature below which a conductor offers no resistance to the flow of electric current is known as its critical temperature.
- ✔ The systematic arrangement of electric components and devices with the electric source is called electric circuit.
- ✔ According to Ohm's Law, V is directly proportional to I.
- ✔ Resistors are said to be connected in series, when there exists only one path for the flow of current and the current through each resistor is same.
- ✔ Resistors are said to be connected in parallel, when identical potential difference exists across all of them, i.e., the potential drop across each resistor is the same.
- ✔ An electric cell is a device which provides a constant potential difference between the

ends of conductor connected across its two terminals.

- ✔ When no current is drawn from a cell, i.e., it is open circuit, the potential difference between the terminals of the cell is called electromotive force (emf) of the cell.
- ✔ The potential difference between the two terminals of the cell, when current is drawn from it, i.e., the cell is in closed circuit, is called its terminal voltage.
- ✔ The energy spent in moving an electric charge through a conductor is called electric energy.
- ✔ The rate at which electric work is done is called electric power.
- ✔ The energy spent in moving an electric charge through a conductor is called electric energy.
- ✔ A meter which measures the electric energy consumed by various electric appliances is called watt hour meter.
- ✔ The amount of electrical energy consumed by an electrical appliance per unit time is known as wattage.
- ✔ If W is the mechanical work done by a body (in joule) and Q is the quantity of heat produced by it (in calories), then W μ Q or $W = JQ$ where J is the mechanical equivalent of heat or Joule's constant.
- ✔ Fuse is a very important safety device in an electric circuit. It is a thin wire which melts and breaks the electric circuit due to 1) overloading 2) short circuit 3) fluctuation in power supply.
- ✔ Switch is a device to connect or disconnect an electric appliance.
- ✔ The process in which an electrolyte undergoes decomposition into its constituents when an electric current is passed through it is called electrolysis.
- ✔ A dry cell is a form of primary cell which is used widely in torches, transistor radios, electric toys, clocks, etc.

DW

PRACTICE QUESTIONS CLASSROOM WING

Very Short Answer Type Questions

Directions for questions from 1 to 5:
Fill in the blanks.

1. The net charge flowing through a cross-section of conductor in unit time is called ________.
2. The unit of resistance is ____________.
3. Unit of electric charge is________.
4. Electric potential is measured in ______.
5. Fuse should be connected to ______ wire of the circuit.

Directions for questions from 6 to 25:
Answer the following questions.

6. What is the SI unit of electric current?
7. Find the total internal resistance of the cells when they are all connected in

   (a) series, and (b) parallel
8. What is the use of kilowatt-hour meter?
9. Define static and current electricity.
10. The electric field at a point is 200 N C^{-1}. Determine the acceleration of a charged particle of mass 100 g and charge 30 μC placed at that point.
11. A bulb is connected to a battery through a resistor. If another resistor is connected parallel to the first resistor, then what will happen to the brightness of the bulb?
12. What will be the resistance of a bulb rated 100 W - 230 V?
13. Define terminal voltage, internal resistance and lost voltage.
14. A bulb is rated 60 W – 230 V. How much will be the current (in A) flowing through it, when connected to 115 V?
15. What is the reason for conduction of electricity?
16. What is the SI unit of potential difference?
17. On increasing the temperature, what is the variation of the resistance of a metallic conductor and semi-conductor?
18. Define electric current.
19. Define electric energy or work.
20. Define electric potential, potential difference and EMF.
21. What is the relation between current (I), emf (E), terminal voltage (V) and internal resistance (r)?
22. Define electric power and give its unit in S.I. system.
23. What is meant by conventional and electronic current?
24. State Ohm's law and what are ohmic and non-ohmic conductors.
25. Match the statements of Column A with those of Column B.

Column A	Column B
A. Galvanometer	a. electrolysis
B. Rheostat	b. variable resistor
C. Voltameter	c. electric current

Short Answer Type Questions

26. Effective resistance of two resistors A and B, when they are connected in parallel combination, is 12 W. What would be the colour bands on B, if colour bands on resistor A are brown, yellow and black? (neglect tolerance)
27. It takes 20 minutes to boil water in an electric kettle. By change in the length of the coil in the kettle, using the same power supply, water is to be boiled in 14 minutes. Then the change in the length of the coil is ______ original length.
28. 200 J of work is done in moving a 10 C charged particle between two points in a uniform electric field of 64 V m^{-1} along the direction of the electric field. Find the distance between the two points.

29. A total of 10^{19} electrons flow through a conductor of resistance 20 W in one second. Find the potential difference between the terminals of the conductor.

30. Study the circuit given below and determine the effective resistance (in W) between A and B.

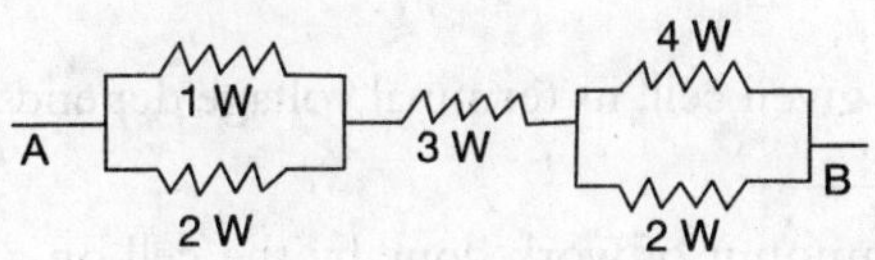

31. Calculate the value of resistor X.

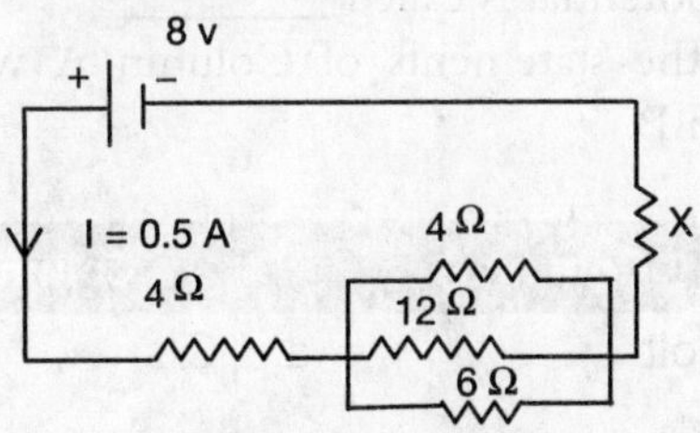

32. Effective resistance of two resistors A and B connected in parallel combination is x. Find the value of x if colour bands on A are blue, yellow, black and colour bands on B are red, yellow, black.

33. Two heaters of 200 W each and two bulbs of 40 W each operate 4 hours daily on the supply of 200 V. If the cost of energy is 3 rupees per kW h, find the bill for the month of April.

34. Give an expression for equivalent internal resistance when cells of different internal resistances are connected in series and parallel.

35. Find the equivalent resistance of the following circuit, between junction A and B.

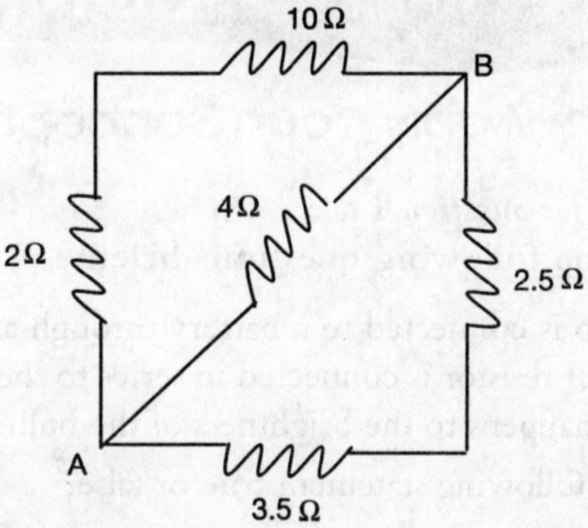

36. When does a fuse melt?

37. The length and area of cross section of a wire are 1m and 0.040 cm^2, respectively. If its resistance is 4 ohm, calculate its resistivity.

38. Derive $r = \dfrac{E-V}{I}$, where, r is internal resistance, E – emf, V – terminal voltage, I – current.

39. What is the need for a step up and step down transformers at various stages of power transmission?

40. Show that 1 kW h = 36 × 10^5 J.

Essay Answer Type Questions

41. The reading of ammeter shown in the circuit given below is 5 A. What will be the mass of copper deposited at the cathode in a voltameter connected across the terminals P and Q after 30 min? [Electrochemical equivalent (e.c.e.) of copper = 0.000332 g C^{-1}]

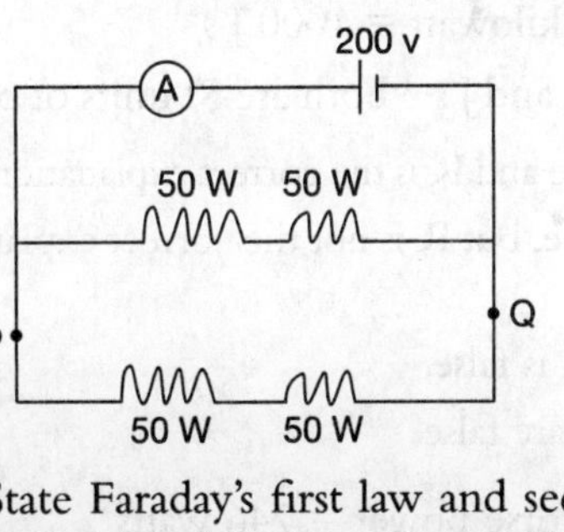

42. State Faraday's first law and second law of electrolysis and verify them experimentally.

43. Derive an expression for equivalent resistance of resistors connected in series.

44. A resistor is connected in series to a copper voltameter as shown in the circuit below. Determine the heat generated in the resistor in one hour if the mass of the ions deposited on the cathode is 3.294 g in 1000 s.

[e.c.e. of copper is 0.0003294 g C^{-1}]

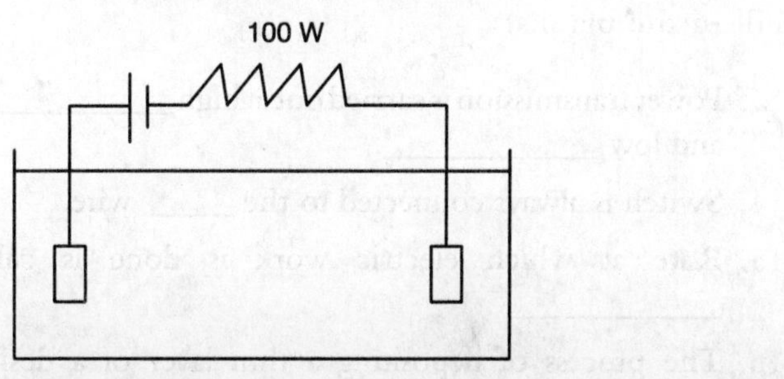

45. The ratio of the length of the two wires made of the same material is 1 : 3 and their volumes are in the ratio of 2 : 3. What is the ratio of their resistances?

PRACTICE QUESTIONS COMPETITION WING

Level 1: Apply Your Concepts

Directions for question 1 to 5
Answer the following questions briefly:

1. A bulb is connected to a battery through a resistor. If another resistor is connected in series to the first, then what happens to the brightness of the bulb?
2. Is the following statement true or false?
   The emf is a characteristic of a cell and is different for different cells.
3. What is a fuse and specify its uses?
4. What is Incandescence?
5. State laws of resistance and define resistivity.

Direction for questions from 6 to 12:
State whether the following statements are true or false.

6. Conventional current always flows from a body having high charge density to the body having low charge density.
7. At constant temperature, the resistance of a conductor changes according to the applied voltage.
8. The used up chemicals in a dry cell can be re obtained by charging it.
9. In an electrolyte, the movement of ions is responsible for electric current.
10. Electrotyping is an application of electrolysis.
11. Electric potential at a point in an electric field is defined as the work done in moving a unit positive charge from infinity to that point.
12. Earthing of electric appliances prevents electric shock.

Directions for questions from 13 to 19:
Fill in the blanks.

13. Power transmission is carried out at high ____________ and low ____________.
14. Switch is always connected to the _____ wire.
15. Rate at which electric work is done is called ____________.
16. The process of depositing a thin layer of a desired metal over another metal by passing an electric current through some electrolyte is called ________.
17. Conductance is the reciprocal of __________.
18. For a given cell, its terminal voltage depends on _____ and _____.
19. The amount of work done by the cell on a unit positive charge carrier to force it to go to the point of higher potential is called ________.
20. Match the statements of Column A with those of Column B.

	Column A		Column B
A.	volt	a.	C/s
B.	ampere	b.	volt/ampere
C.	ohm	c.	J/C

Direction for questions from 21 to 36:
For each of the questions, four choices have been provided. Select the correct alternative.

21. Calculate the strength of the electric field at a point, if a 20 μC charge is placed at the point experiences a force of 20 N.
    (a) 10^3 N m^{-1} (b) 10^6 N m^{-1}
    (c) 10^9 N m^{-1} (d) 10^{12} N m^{-1}
22. Which of the following is correct?
    (a) Resistance of a conductor depends on its mass.
    (b) Resistance of a conductor is directly proportional to its length.
    (c) Resistance of a conductor depends on temperature.
    (d) Both (b) and (c).
23. **Assertion (A):** 1 kilowatt = 1000 J s^{-1}
    Reason (R): watt and J s^{-1} both are SI units of power.
    (a) A and R are true and R is the correct explanation of A.
    (b) A and R are true, but R is not the correct explanation of A.
    (c) A is true but R is false.
    (d) Both A and R are false.
24. **(A) Assertion:** Horse power = 746 watts
    (R) Reason: Horse power is unit of electric potential.
    (a) A and R are true and R is the correct explanation of A.

(b) A and R are true, but R is not the correct explanation of A.

(c) A is true but R is false.

(d) Both A and R are false.

25. Among the following statements,

(A) A discharge lamp uses a discharge tube which is filled with a gas at a very low pressure.

(B) Always white light is emitted independent of gas taken in the lamp.

(a) Only A is true.

(b) Only B is true.

(c) Both A and B are true.

(d) Both A and B are false.

26. The quantity of heat produced by a current in a conductor is directly proportional to ______ in the conductor.

(a) the time of current flow.

(b) the square of magnitude of current.

(c) the resistance.

(d) All the above.

27. Which of the following graphs represents a ohmic conductor?

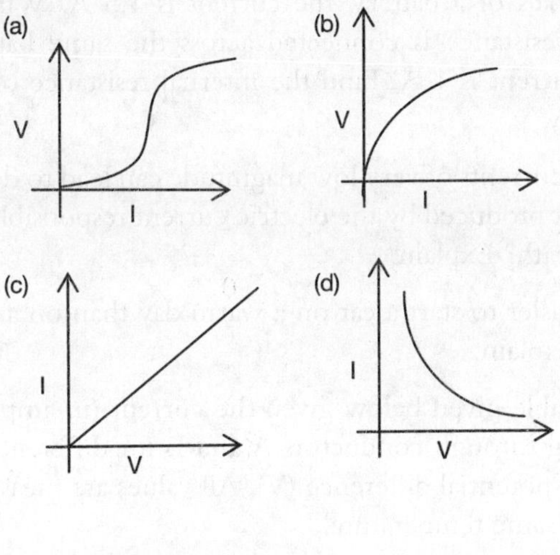

28. Arrange the following steps in proper sequence to verify the Ohm's law.

(A) Switch on the electric circuit.

(B) Move the position of the slider of the rheostat and note down the ammeter and voltmeter readings.

(C) Connect ammeter, key, battery, rheostat and resistor in series by using conducting wires.

(D) Note down the Ammeter and voltmeter reading.

(E) Connect a voltmeter across the resistor.

(F) Determine the ratio of voltmeter reading and ammeter reading in each case.

(G) Note that the ratio of voltmeter and ammeter reading are equal in each case.

(a) CAEDBFG (b) CEADBFG

(c) ABECDFG (d) BCEDFHG

29. Arrange the following steps in proper sequence to determine the resistivity of a material.

(A) Switch on the circuit and take the voltmeter and ammeter readings.

(B) Determine the resistance of the wire as resistance $R = V/I$

(C) Connect the wire, battery and ammeter in series.

(D) Determine the length (ℓ) and area of cross-section (A) of the wire.

(E) Connect a voltmeter across the wire. (*f*) The resistivity of the material is $\rho = RA/l$

(a) EBCDFA (b) ACBEDF

(c) CEABDF (d) BCADFE

30. An electric bulb marked 15 V is connected to a battery of 15 V which has a negligible resistance. If the resistance offered by the bulb is 5 Ω, the power of the bulb is ______ W.

(a) 225 (b) 75

(c) 30 (d) 45

31. During the electrolysis of $CuSO_4$ solution using copper electrodes, the

(a) mass of cathode increases.

(b) mass of anode increases.

(c) Both (a) and (b)

(d) None of these

32. Fuse should be connected to ______ wire of the circuit.

(a) earth (b) neutral

(c) phase (d) Any of the above

33. The mass of the substance deposited at the cathode is

(A) inversely proportional to quantity of electricity passed through electrolyte.

(B) directly proportional to quantity of electricity passed through electrolyte.

(C) directly proportional to the time for which electricity is passed through the electrolyte.

(D) inversely proportional to the time for which electricity is passed through the electrolyte.

(a) A and B are true. (b) B and D are true.

(c) B and C are true. (d) A and D are true.

34. Which of the following statements is true?
   (a) In tree type distribution of electric power, fuses are present only on the main board.
   (b) In ring type distribution of electric power, there is an individual fuse for each appliance.
   (c) Ring type distribution of electric power is advantageous than the tree type distribution.
   (d) All the above.

35. If 'i' is the current flowing through a conductor of resistance 'R' for time 't', then the heat produced (Q) is given by ______.
   (a) $\frac{i^2R}{t}$ (b) $\frac{iR^2}{t}$
   (c) i^2Rt (d) iRt^2

36. A fuse wire should have______.
   (a) high resistance (b) low-melting point
   (c) Both (a) and (b) (d) None of these

Level 2: Review Your Concepts

37. It takes 5 minute to boil water in an electric kettle. If the length of the coil in the kettle is changed to half of its original length, then what will be the time taken to boil the same amount of water, with the same power supply?

38. Calculate the amount of work done in moving a 20 C charge between two points separated by 20 cm in a uniform electric field of strength 200 V m^{-1}.

39. 32 V is connected across the terminals of a conductor of resistance 40 Ω. Determine the number of electrons flowing through the conductor in 2 s.

40. Study the circuit given below and determine the effective resistance (in Ω) between A and B.

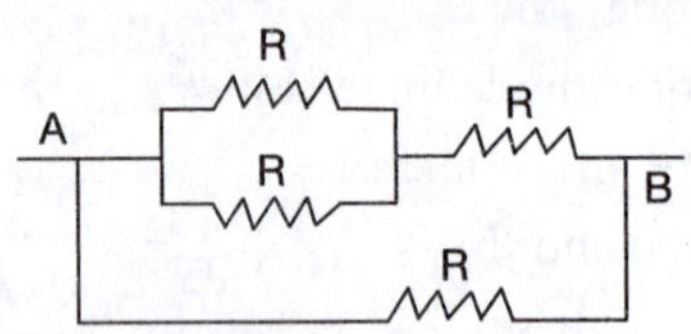

41. Four cells each of emf 1.9 V and internal resistance 1 Ω are connected to an external resistance of 18 Ω as shown in the figure. Find the terminal potential difference of this combination.

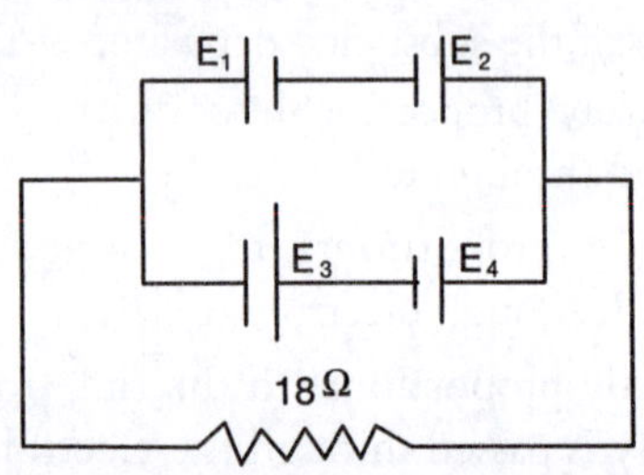

42. A technician has two resistance coils. By using them individually, in series or in parallel, he is able to obtain resistances of 3Ω, 4Ω, 12Ω and 16Ω (not in the same order). What is the resistance of the two coils?

43. The heat generated in the coil of resistance 180 Ω which is connected to a silver voltmeter is 364.5 k J. If a steady current is passed through the circuit for 15 min, find the mass of Ag that gets deposited on the cathode. Relative atomic mass of silver is 108 g and Faradays constant is 96500 C.

44. A 200W, 220V light bulb has a greater resistance than a 100W, 200V light bulb.

45. When a 3 Ω resistance coil is connected across the terminals of a battery, the current is 1.5 A. When a 5 Ω resistance is connected across the same battery, the current is 1 A. Find the internal resistance of the battery.

46. Even currents of very low magnitude can lead to death. Is heat produced by the electric current responsible for the death? Explain.

47. It is easier to start a car on a warm day than on a cold day. Explain.

48. The table given below given the current (in amperes) passing through conductors A and B for different values of potential difference (V). All values are measured at the same temperature.

A		B	
V	I	V	I
4	2.8	4	9
5	3.5	5	11.25
6	4.1	6	13.5

Which among A and B is an ohmic conductor? Also, find the resistance of that conductor.

49. Calculate the effective resistance between A and B.

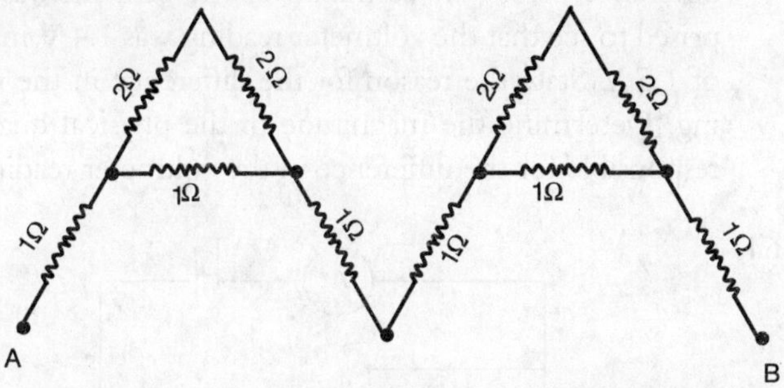

50. 'A current carrying conductor is electrically charged.' Explain with reason whether the statement is true or false.

51. Electric power of a heater is 1200 W when connected to a 240 V supply. The resistivity and area of cross section of the coil are 10^{-5} Ω m and 0.4 mm^2, respectively. If the radius of each turn is 7 mm, find the number of turns present in the coil.

52. When a body is rubbed with another body, a certain number of electrons are transferred. If the same number of electrons are allowed to flow through the cross section of a conductor in 2s, 10A electric current can flow through it. Determine the number of electrons transferred.

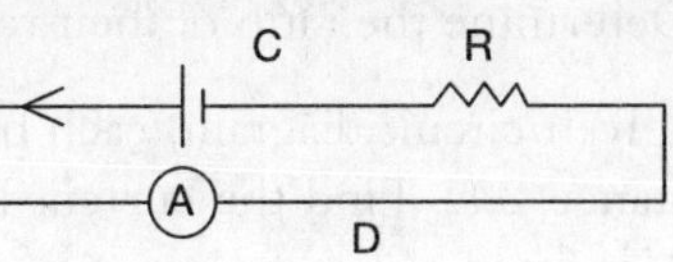

53. In the circuit diagram shown above, explain what happens if a wire is connected between the points C and D.

54. A current of 5A flows through a conductor. Calculate the number of electrons flowing through the conductor in 2s. (Take charge of electron as 1.6×10^{-19} C)

55. Calculate the work done to move a charge 5 C between two points A and B, if both the points are maintained at same potential of 6 V.

56.

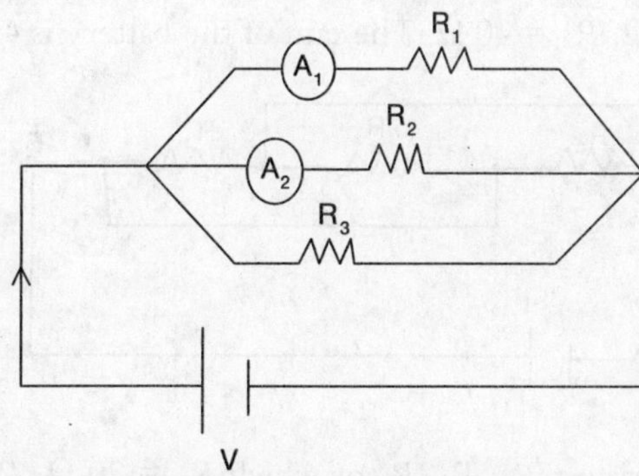

Three identical resistors are connected in parallel as shown in the figure. Explain, what happens to the ammeter readings in A_1 and A_2 when the resistor R_3 is removed.

Level 3: Assess Your Concepts

57. In the given circuit, find the power dissipated in the 6 Ω resistance.

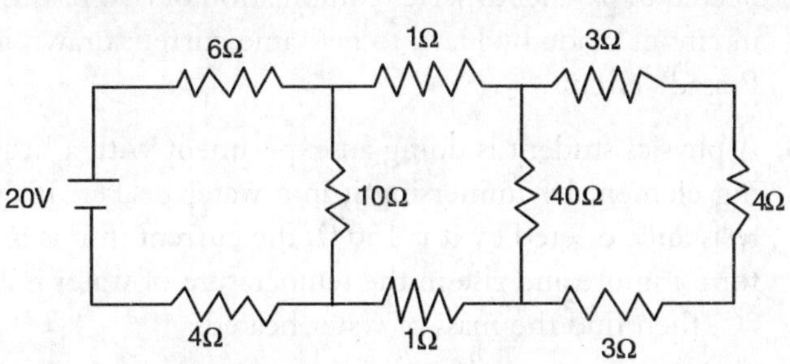

58. A copper voltameter is arranged as shown below. If the heat developed in the resistor after one hour is 3,60,000 J, then what will be the mass (in g) of copper deposited in the cathode after 1 h?

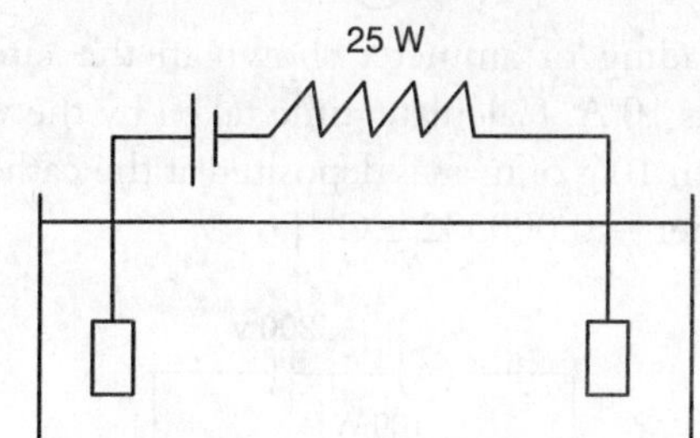

[The e.c.e. of copper is 0.0003294 g C^{-1}]

59. Three batteries with emf E_1, E_2 and E_3 are connected as shown in the figure. If their terminal voltages are 4 V, 2 V and 6 V, respectively, then find the ratio of their internal resistances.

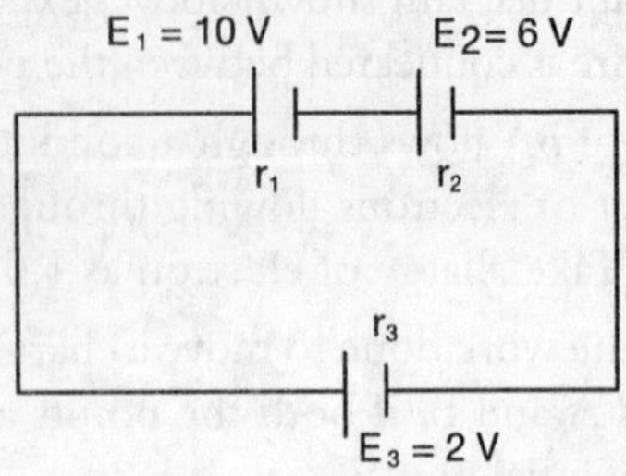

60. Find the current through the resistor R_4 if $R_1 = R_2 = R_3 = 20\ \Omega$, $R_4 = 40\ \Omega$. The emf of the battery is 4 V.

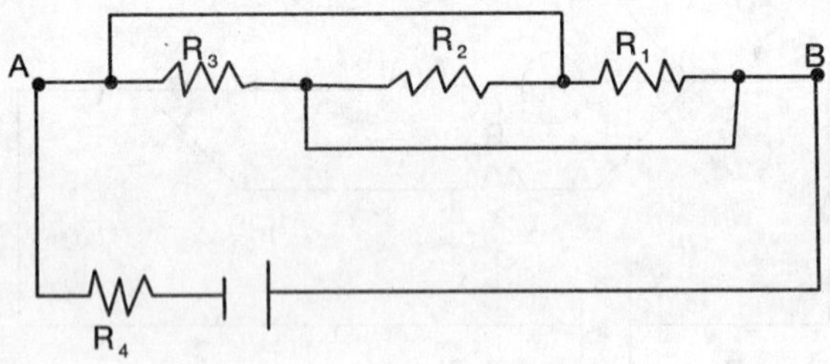

61. Three resistors R_1, R_2, R_3 of which $R_1 = 20\ \Omega$, $R_2 = 20\ \Omega$, $R_3 = 30\ \Omega$ connected to a battery of emf 24 V as shown in the figure. If the resistance of the voltmeter is 20 Ω, find the reading of the voltmeter.

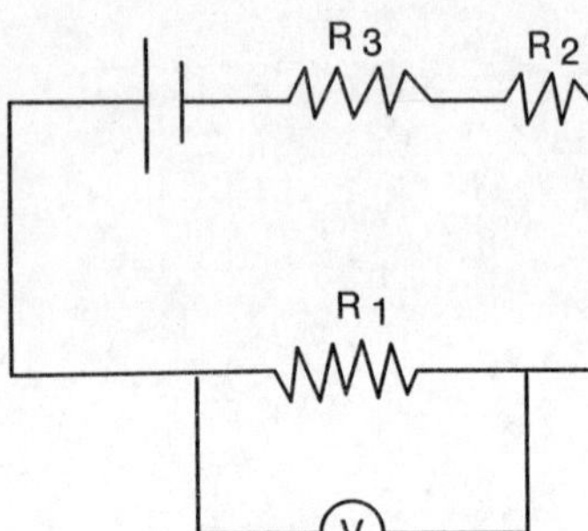

62. The reading of ammeter shown in the circuit given below is 10 A. Calculate time taken by the voltameter in which 10 g of mass is deposited at the cathode. [e.c.e of copper = 0.000332 g C^{-1}]

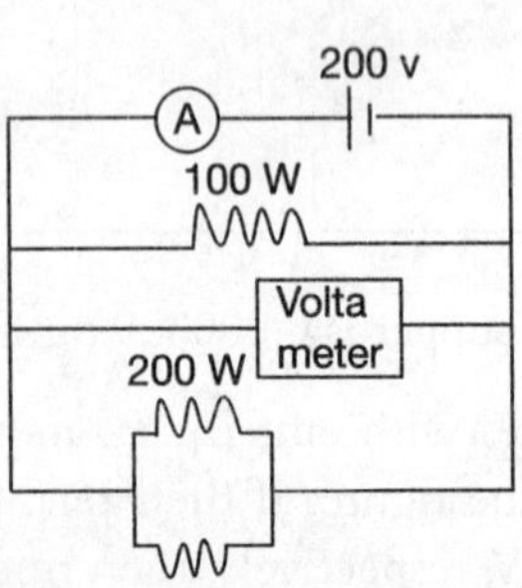

63. A student connected a dry cell of emf 1.5 V to an external resistance of 10 Ω. When he measured the potential difference across the terminals of the cell, he was surprised to see that the voltmeter reading was 1.4 V instead of 1.5 V. State the reason for the difference in the reading. Determine the magnitude of the physical quantity responsible for the difference in the voltmeter reading.

64.

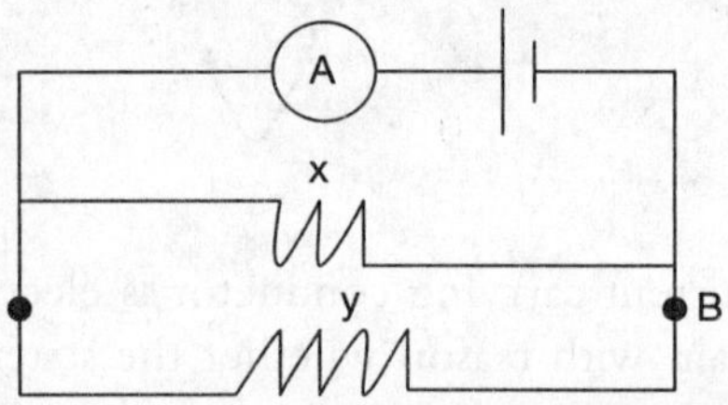

In the electric circuit shown below two identical coils x and y, each of resistance 100 Ω, are connected across a potential difference of 200 V. When a copper voltameter is connected across the terminals A and B, the ammeter reading is found to be 10 A. Determine the heat developed in the coil y and the mass of copper deposited at the respective electrode after 1 hour. (Given that e.c.e of copper = 0.000332 g C^{-1})

65. The area of cross sections of two coils made of the same material is 1 : 2 and the ratio of their volumes is 2 : 3. Determine the ratio of their resistance.

66. In the given circuit diagram, each bulb has a filament of resistance 2 Ω. Find the current in bulb 'C', when bulb 'A' is fused.

67. Two resistors of colour coding (red, red, orange) and (red, brown, yellow) are connected in series by Hari. And they are connected in parallel by Prasad. Electric source connected in the circuit is 10 V of DC voltage in both cases. Find the value of resistance which is connected in parallel to series combination of two resistors in circuit made by Hari, to get same current drawn by Prasad's circuit.

68. A physics student is doing an experiment with a heating element by immersing it in a water beaker. If the resistance offered by it is 150 Ω, the current in it is 5 A for 5 minute and rise in the temperature of water is 15 °C, then find the mass of water heated.

Take specific heat capacity of water as 1 cal g^{-1} $°C^{-1}$.

69. An ice block of mass 4 kg at 0 °C temperature is completely converted into water at 0 °C at the end of 5 minute when it is in contact with a heating coil. If 220-volt potential difference is applied to the coil, then find out the current passing through it.

70. In the experimental verification of Faraday's first law of electrolysis, the battery used is of 20 V and internal resistance 2 Ω. The rheostat used has a resistance of 8 Ω. When the circuit is closed for 1 hour, the mass of the copper cathode is increased by 2 mg. Find the resistance of $CuSO_4$ voltameter in the circuit. (Take electrochemical equivalent value of copper as 0.0003294 g/C).

AT

PRACTICE QUESTIONS JEE-NEET SPECIAL WING

Multiple-Answer Type Questions

Directions for questions 1 to 5: **Each question has FOUR options (a), (b), (c), and (d). ONE OR MORE THAN ONE of these four option(s) is/are the correct answer(s).**

1. When a current of 2 ampere is passing through a conductor, the number of electrons crossing a particular cross section per second is
   (a) 6.023×10^{23} (b) 1.6×10^{-19}
   (c) 1.25×10^{19} (d) 4.75×10^{19}

2. A copper wire of resistance 4 ohm is stretched to double its length. Then,
   (a) Its radius of cross section becomes half.
   (b) Its area of cross section becomes half.
   (c) the new resistance of the wire becomes 8 ohms.
   (d) the new resistance of the wire becomes 16 ohms.

3. Two wires made of aluminium and germanium are heated through the same temperature difference. Then
   (a) the resistance of aluminium increases and that of germanium decreases.
   (b) the resistance of aluminium decreases and that of germanium increases.
   (c) the resistance of both the wires increases.
   (d) germanium is non-ohmic conductor.

4. Find in the effective resistance in the given circuit:

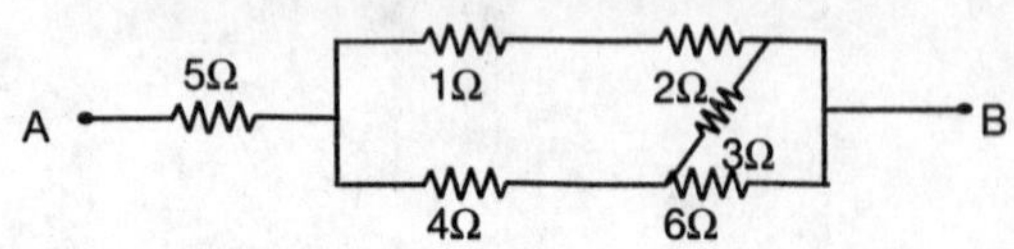

   (a) The effective resistance between points A and *B* is 6Ω.
   (b) The effective resistance between points A and *B* is 7Ω.
   (c) The effective resistance between 3Ω and 6Ω is 2Ω.
   (d) The resistances 3Ω and 6Ω are connected in parallel.

5. Four identical cells of emf 3 Volt and internal resistance 0.5 ohm each are connected in series as shown in the figure, across a resistor of resistance 1 ohm. Then, choose the correct option(s).

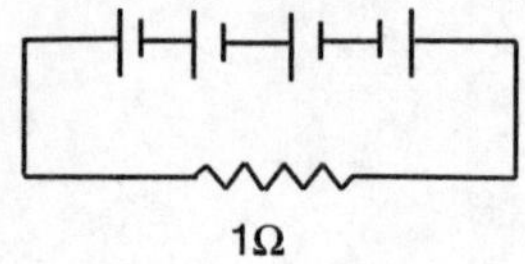

   (a) Potential difference across one ohm resistor is 6 Volt
   (b) Current in the circuit is 2 amperes.
   (c) Potential difference across one ohm resistor is 2 Volt
   (d) Current in the circuit is 4 amperes.

6. Which of the following is/are the units of electric power?
   (a) kWh (b) Watt
   (c) Siemen (d) Horsepower

7. Power ratings of an electric kettle are 2 kilowatts and 220 volts. Which of the following is/are true statements?
   (a) The resistance of the kettle is 59.4 Ω.
   (b) The current drawn by kettle is 3.2 A
   (c) The resistance of the kettle is 24.2 Ω.
   (d) The current drawn by kettle is 9.09 A.

8. Terminal voltage of a cell of emf 4 *V* is 3 *V* when a current of 2A is passing through it. Internal resistance of the cell is
   (a) 0.5Ω (b) 0.75Ω
   (c) 1Ω (d) 0.25Ω

9. A fuse wire should have
   (a) high resistance
   (b) low-melting point
   (c) high conductivity
   (d) low conductivity

10. Using colour coding, 5000 Ω ± 10% is denoted by
   (a) green, black, red, silver
   (b) red, blue, yellow, silver
   (c) orange, brown Violet gold
   (d) yellow, black, green, silver

Comprehension-Based Questions

Directions for questions 11 to 16: Read the paragraph and answer the questions given below:

A battery of emf 22 volt and negligible internal resistance is connected across two identical bulbs (B_1 and B_2) of resistance 4 ohm each and two resistors (R_1 and R_2) as shown in the figure. K_1 and K_2 represent the keys.
The ammeters and voltmeters connected in the circuit are ideal.

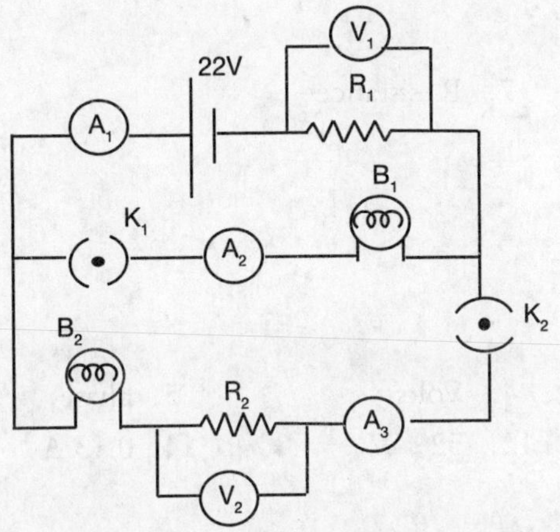

11. With the keys closed and resistances 8 ohm each, the current drawn from the battery is

(a) 1.5 A (b) 2.5 A
(c) 3 A (d) 2 A

12. With the keys closed and resistance 8 ohm each, A_2 reads

(a) 0.5A (b) 1.5A
(c) 2A (d) 1A

13. With the keys closed and resistance 8 ohm each, V_2 reads

(a) 14V (b) 11V
(c) 4V (d) 5.5V

14. With K_2 open and resistance 7 ohm each, V_1 reads

(a) 14V (b) 11V
(c) 4V (d) 5.5V

15. With K_2 open and resistance 7 ohm each, power drawn by the bulb B_1 is

(a) 12W (b) 16W
(c) 13.7W (d) 21.4W

16. Using the data given in the previous paragraph, match the following.

Column – A	Column – B
A. Ideal ammeter	a. 12
B. Ideal voltmeter	b. 4.8
C. When K_1 is open, $R_1 = 4\ \Omega$ & $R_2 = 3\ \Omega$, reading of V_1 in volt is	c. Zero resistance
D. When K_1 is open, $R_1 = 4\ \Omega$ & $R_2 = 3\ \Omega$, power dissipated in R_2 in watt is	d. 8
E. If K_2 is open and B_1 dissipates a power of 25 W, then R_1 in ohm is	e. Infinite resistance

ANSWER KEYS

Crossword

Across

2. Current 4. Cell 5. Fuse 6. EMF
10. Wattage 11. Nickel 12. Earth

Down

1. Electroplating 3. Resistivity 6. Electron 7. Resistance
8. Electrolyte 9. Phase

Classroom Wing

Very Short Answer Type Questions

1. electric current. 2. Ohm 3. Coulomb 4. Volts 5. phase
6. Ampere 10. 6×10^{-2} m s^{-2} 11. Increases 12. 529 W 14. 0.13 A
16. Volt 25. A-c, B-b, C-a

Competition Wing

Level 1: Apply Your Concepts

1. Decreases 2. True 6. False 7. False 8. False
9. True 10. True 11. True 12. True 13. voltage, current
14. phase/live 15. electric power 16. electroplating 17. resistance
18. external resistance, internal resistance 19. emf 20. A : R, B : P, C : Q
21. (b) 22. (d) 23. (a) 24. (c) 25. (a)
26. (d) 27. (c) 28. (b) 29. (c) 30. (d)
31. (a) 32. (c) 33. (c) 34. (d) 35. (c)
36. (b)

JEE-NEET SPECIAL WING

Multiple-Answer Type Questions

1. (c) 2. (b, d) 3. (a, d) 4. (b, c, d) 5. (b, c)
6. (b, d) 7. (c, d) 8. (a) 9. (a, b, c) 10. (a)

Comprehension-Based Questions

11. (d) 12. (b) 13. (c) 14. (a) 15. (b)
16. A-c, B-e, C-d, D-a, E-b

For answer key of Classroom wing and Competition wing, refer to Hints and Solutions

Hints and Explanations

CLASSROOM WING

Very Short Answer Type Questions

1. electric current.
2. Ohm
3. Coulomb
4. Volts
5. phase
6. ampere.
7. (a) In series connection, total internal resistance (r) is equal to the sum of the internal resistances of the individual cells;
   $r = r_1 + r_2 + r_3$
   (b) In parallel connection, total internal resistance is equal to the sum of the reciprocals of individual internal resistances.
   $$\frac{1}{r_{eg}} = \frac{1}{r_1} + \frac{1}{r_2} + \frac{1}{r_3}$$
8. Gives the reading of energy consumed.
9. (i) Charges at rest;
   (ii) Charges in motion.
10. $E = 200\ \text{N C}^{-1}$ $a = ?$
    $m = 100$ g; $q = 30\ \mu\text{C}$
    $F = Eq$
    $ma = Eq$
    $$a = \frac{Eq}{m} = \frac{200 \times 30 \times 10^{-6}}{10^2 \times 10^{-3}}$$
    $= 60 \times 10^{-3} = 6 \times 10^{-2}\ \text{m s}^{-2}$
11. When the resistors are connected in parallel, the effective resistance decreases, and hence, current increases. Therefore, the brightness of the bulb increases.
12. $$P = \frac{V^2}{R}$$
    $$100 = \frac{(230)^2}{R} \Rightarrow R = \frac{(230)^2}{100} = 23 \times 23$$
    $= 529$ W
13. (i) The P.D. between two terminals of the cell, when current is drawn from it, i.e., the cell is in closed circuit, is called its terminal voltage (V).
    (ii) The electrolyte offers certain resistance to the flow of current. This is called the internal resistance of cell (r).
    (iii) The difference between EMF (E) of the cell and terminal voltage (V) of a cell is called lost voltage
14. $$P = \frac{V^2}{R}$$
    $$60 = \frac{(230)^2}{R}$$
    $$R = \frac{(230)(230)}{60}$$
    $R = 881.67$
    $V = iR$
    $115 = i \times 881.67$
    $$i = \frac{115}{881.67} = 0.13\ \text{A}$$
15. It is primarily due to flow of electrons.
16. volt.
17. (i) The resistance of conductors increases with an increase in temperature.
    (ii) The resistance of semi conductors decreases with an increase in temperature.
18. The rate of flow of electric charges.
19. The energy spent or work done in moving an electric charge through conductor is called electric energy or electric work.
20. (i) Work done in bringing unit positive change from infinity to a point in an electric field is called potential (v).
    (ii) The work done in moving a unit positive charge from one point to another point against the direction of the field, is called as potential difference (P.D.) between two points.

(iii) The P.D. between the terminals of the cell, when no current is drawn from the cell, i.e., in an open circuit is called EMF.

21. $E - V = Ir$

22. The rate at which electric work is done is called electric power. In S.I., power = watt = 1 J s^{-1}.

23. (i) Positive charges flows from higher potential to lower potential.
(ii) If electrons moves from lower potential to higher potential, it constitutes electronic current.

24. (i) Ohm's law: The P.D. (V) applied between the ends of a conductor bears a constant ratio with the electric current (I) flowing through it, provided the physical state of the conductor remains the same.
(ii) Those which obeys Ohm's law are Ohmic conductor.
(iii) Those which do not obey Ohm's law are non Ohmic conductor.

25. Galvanometer – Electric current
Rheostat – Variable resistor
Voltameter – Electrolysis

Short Answer Type Questions

Note: This is how you should frame your answer covering.

26. $R_A = 14 \times 10^0 = 14$ W

$$R_p = \frac{R_A R_B}{R_A + R_B}$$

$$12 = \frac{14R_B}{14 + R_B}$$

$\therefore R_B = 84$

$= 84 \times 10^0$

Colours on B are Grey, Yellow and Black.

27. $\frac{v^2}{R}t = \frac{v^2 tA}{pl}$

$$Q\alpha\frac{t}{l}$$

$$\frac{Q_1}{Q_2} = \frac{t_1}{t_2} \times \frac{l_2}{l_1}$$

$$\frac{Q}{Q} = \frac{t_1}{t_2} \times \frac{l_2}{l_1}$$

$$\therefore l_2 = \frac{7}{10} l_1$$

$$\Delta l = l_1 - \frac{7l_1}{10} = \frac{3l_1}{10}$$

28. Work = 200 J
Distance = ?
$E = 64$ V m^{-1}: $q = 10$ C

$$E = \frac{F}{q}; F = E \times q$$

$W = F \times$ Displacement

$200 = 64 \times 10 \times s$

$$s = \frac{200}{640} = \frac{5}{16} \text{ m.}$$

29. $n = 10^{19}$, $R = 20$ W, $t = 1$ s
$V = iR$
$V = n \times e \times R/t$
$= 10^{19} \times 1.6 \times 10^{-19} \times 20 = 32$ V

30.
$$R = \left(\frac{2\times1}{3}\right) + 3 + \left(\frac{4\times2}{6}\right)$$

$$= \frac{2}{3} + 3 + \frac{4}{3}$$

$$= \frac{2+9+4}{3} = \frac{15}{3} = 5 \text{ W}$$

31. $R = R_1 + R_2 + R_3$, $\frac{1}{R} = \frac{1}{R_1} + \frac{1}{R_2} + \frac{1}{R_3}$,
$V = iR$
X = 10 Ω

32. $R_A = 64 \times 10^0 = 64$ W
$R_B = 24 \times 10^0 = 24$ W
Effective resistance (R_P)

$$Rp = \frac{R_A R_B}{R_A + R_B}$$

$$x = \frac{64 \times 24}{64 + 24}$$

$\therefore x = 17.5$ W.

33. Energy = (power)(time)
Total cost = (Energy)(price)
₹ 172.8

34. (i) $r = r_1 + r_2 + r_3 + \ldots\ldots\ldots$ (series)

(ii) $\frac{1}{r} = \frac{1}{r_1} + \frac{1}{r_2} + \frac{1}{r_3} + \ldots$(parallel)

35. $\frac{1}{R} = \frac{1}{R_1} + \frac{1}{R_2} + \frac{1}{R_3}$

2 Ω

36. If excessive current begins to flow the fuse wire gets heated up more quickly than the conducting wires and melts, breaking the circuit.

37. $R = \frac{\rho\ell}{a}$

Ans: 0.0016 Ω - cm.

38. Let "R" be external resistance. Then voltage drop across external resistance (R) is = *IR*, Voltage drop across the internal resistance (r) is = *Ir*.

39. (i) To increase and decrease the voltage.

(ii) By this, loss in power transmission can be decreased.

40. $1 \text{ kW h} = 1 \times 10^3 \times \frac{15}{15} \times 3600\ s$

$= 36 \times 10^5 \text{ J}$

Essay Answer Type Questions

Note: This is how you should frame your answer covering.

41. $R_p = \frac{v}{i} = \frac{200}{5} = 40\Omega$

$$\frac{1}{R_p} = \frac{1}{R_1} + \frac{1}{R_2} + \frac{1}{R_3}$$

$$\frac{1}{40} = \frac{1}{100} + \frac{1}{100} + \frac{1}{R_v}$$

$\therefore R_v = 200$ W

$R_1 : R_2 : R_v = 100 : 100 : 200$

$= 1 : 1 : 2$

$\therefore i_1 : i_2 : i_v = 2 : 2 : 1$

$i_v = \frac{5}{5} \times 1$

$= 1$ A

$m = Zit$

$= 0.000332 \times 10^{-3} \times 1 \times 30 \times 60$

$= 0.5976 \times 10^{-3}$ kg

$= 0.5976$ g

$\therefore$ Mass $= 0.5976$ g.

42. **1st Law** The mass of the substance deposited at the cathode is directly proportional to the quantity of electricity.

$m \propto I$

$m \propto It$

$m \propto st$

$m = Zit = ZQ$

$m_1{:}m_2{:}m_3 = z_1{:}z_2{:}z_3$

2nd Law:

The same quantity of electricity passes through different electrolytes, the masses of ions liberated at the respective electrodes are proportional to the chemical equivalents.

$m_1{:}m_2{:}m_3 = E_1{:}E_2{:}E_{30}$

$E_1{:}E_2{:}E_3 = z_1{:}z_2{:}z_3$

43. $V = V_1 + V_2 + V_3$; $V = iR$

44. $m = Zit$

$3.294 = 0.0003294 \times i \times 1000$

$\therefore i = 10$ A

$Q = i^2 Rt$

heat $= 100 \times 100 \times 3600$

$= 36 \times 10^6$ J

45. $\ell_1 : \ell_2 = 1 : 3$, $V_1 : V_2 = 2 : 3$

$$\frac{V_1}{V_2} = \frac{l_1 A_1}{l_2 A_2}$$

$$\Rightarrow \frac{2}{3} = \frac{1}{3} \times \frac{A_1}{A_2}$$

$$\frac{A_1}{A_2} = \left(\frac{2}{1}\right)$$

$$\frac{R_1}{R_2} = \frac{\frac{\rho \times l_1}{A_1}}{\frac{\rho l_2}{A_2}} = \frac{\rho l_1}{A_1} \times \frac{A_2}{\rho l_2}$$

$$= \frac{1}{3} \times \frac{1}{2} = \frac{1}{6}$$

Competition Wing

Level 1: Apply Your Concepts

1. When resistors are connected in series the effective resistance increases, and hence, the current decreases. Therefore, the brightness of the bulb decreases.

2. The emf of a voltaic cell is 1.08 V and for Leclanche cell, it is 1.5 V. It is different for different cells.

   Hence, the statement is true.

3. Fuse is a thin wire which melts and breaks the electric circuit due to (i) overloading (ii) short circuit (iii) fluctuation in power supply.

4. Incandescence is a phenomenon in which an object emits light when heated to a high temperature.

5. $R \propto \ell \Rightarrow \frac{R_1}{R_2} = \frac{\ell_1}{\ell_2}$

   $R \propto \frac{\ell}{a}$

   $\Rightarrow \frac{R_1}{R_2} = \frac{a_1}{a_1}$

   $R = \rho\frac{\ell}{a}$

   Specific Resistance or Resistivity (ρ) can be defined as the resistance of a conducting material having unit area of cross section and unit length.

8. volt → J/s
   ampere → C/s
   ohm → volt/ampere

21. $E = \frac{F}{q} = \frac{20}{20 \times 10^{-6}} = 10^6\,\text{N m}^{-1}$

    Hence, the correct option is (b).

22. $R = \rho\frac{l}{A'}$ R α T (for a conductor)

    Hence, the correct option is (d).

23. 1 kilowatt = 1000 watts

    1 watt = 1 J s^{-1}, watt and J s^{-1} both are SI units of power.

    Hence, the correct option is (a).

24. A is true but R is false.

    Hence, the correct option is (c).

Explanation for Questions 28 to 36.

28. Initially the ammeter, rheostat, resistor and the battery are connected in series by using connecting wires. Connect the voltmeter across the resistor. Switch on the electric circuit. Determine the ammeter and voltmeter reading and change the position of the slider of the rheostat and note down the ammeter and voltmeter readings. Change the magnitude of current flowing through the circuit and in each case determine the ratio of voltmeter and ammeter reading. It can be shown that the ratio is constant in all the cases.

29. Initially the wire, ammeter, battery and key are connected is series. Connect a voltmeter across the wire in parallel. Switch on the circuit and determine the voltmeter and ammeter readings. Determine ratio of voltmeter and ammeter reading. This gives the resistance of the wire. The length and area of cross-section of the wire are determined. Now the resistivity of the wire can be determined as $\rho = \frac{RA}{\ell}$

30. $V = 15\text{V}$
    $R = 5\Omega$

    $$P = \frac{V^2}{R} = \frac{15 \times 15}{5}$$

    $$P = 45\text{W}$$

31. During the electrolysis of $CuSO_4$ solution using copper electrode, the positive copper ions are attracted by the cathode and copper is deposited on cathode, so the mass of cathode increases.

32. Fuse should be connected to live / phase wire of the circuit. If it is connected to neutral wire, the fuse will melt when excess current flows, but the appliance will still be connected to high potential through live wire. Thus, if a person touches the appliance, he receives shock.

33. According to Faraday's First law of electrolysis, the mass of a substance deposited at the cathode is directly proportional to quantity of electricity passed and the time for which it is passed through the electrolyte. So, statements B and C are true.

34. In tree type distribution of electric power, fuses are present only on the distribution board where as in ring type, there is an individual fuse for each appliance. As there is an individual fuse for each appliance in ring type, only faulty appliance will not work and all the other appli-

ances will not be affected. It is easier to install. So, ring type is advantageous than that of tree type.

35. If 'I' is the current flowing through a conductor of resitance 'R' for time 't', then the heat produced (Q) is given by, $Q = I^2.R.t.$

36. A fuse wire should have high resistance and low-melting point.

Level 2: Review Your Concepts

Note: This is how you should frame your answer covering.

37. $Q = \frac{v^2}{R}t = \frac{v^2tA}{pl}$

$\frac{Q_1}{Q_2} = \frac{t_1}{t_2} \times \frac{l_2}{l_1}$

$\frac{Q}{Q} = \frac{5}{t_2} \times \frac{l_1}{2 \times l_1}$

$t_2 = 2.5$ min

38. $W = F \times S$

$F = Eq = 200 \times 20 = 4000$ N

$W = 4000 \times 0.2 = 800$ J.

39. $V = 32$ V, $R = 40$ W

$V = \frac{ne}{t}R$

$= \frac{n \times 1.6 \times 10^{-19}}{2} \times 40$

$n = \frac{3.2}{3.2 \times 10^{-19}}$

$n = 10^{19}$

40. 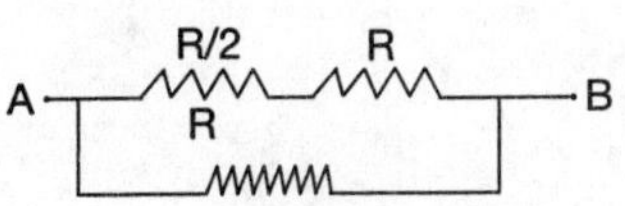

$$R_{AB} = \frac{\frac{3R}{2} \times R}{\frac{3R}{2} + R} = \frac{\frac{3}{2}R^2}{\frac{5R}{2}} = \frac{3R}{2} \times \frac{2}{5}$$

$R_{AB} = 3R/5.$

41. (i) When cells are connected in series $E = E_1 + E_2$.

(ii) When cells are connected in parallel $E = \frac{E_1r_2 + E_2r_1}{r_1 + r_2}$

(iii) 10.8 V

42. (i) The maximum resistance of 16 Ω is obtained when the resistors are connected in series.

The minimum value of 3 Ω is obtained when the resistors are connected in parallel.

(ii) 4 Ω and 12 Ω

43. (i) Heat generated $q = i^2Rt$

(ii) $m = Zit$

(iii) $m_1 : m_2 : m_3 = E_1 : E_2 : E_3$

(iv) 1.5 g

44. Determine the resistance of the two bulbs using the formula, $R = \frac{V^2}{P}$,

where, R is the resistance of the filament, V is potential difference and P is the power.

45. (i) Terminal voltage $V = E - ir$

(ii) 1 Ω

46. Remember that nerves are the carriers of electric signals. What is their current carrying capacity?

47. A car starts due to current supplied by the storage battery. The ionic dissociation of the electrolyte present in the battery is more at higher temperatures than at lower temperatures.

48. (i) Definition of ohmic resistor.

(ii) Conductor B, 0.5 Ω

49. (i) The equivalent resistance can be formed by successively simplifying the given circuit.

Find the equivalent resistance of the two 2 Ω resistors which are connected in series.

These together are connected in parallel to the 1Ω resistor. This combination is in series with the other resistors.

Thus, using the formulas for series and parallel connections, find the equivalent resistance in three steps.

(ii) 5.6 Ω

50. A body is charged when it loses or gains electrons. The number of electrons leaving from one end of the current carrying conductor is equal to the number of electrons entering through its other end.

51. (i) $R = \frac{V^2}{P}$

(ii) $R = \frac{\rho \ell}{A}$

(iii) Length of each turn = $2\pi r$

(iv) No. of turns = $\frac{L}{2\pi r}$

(v) 44

52. Electric current $I = \frac{Q}{t}$

$$10 = \frac{Q}{2} \Rightarrow Q = 20C$$

$$Q = ne$$

where, $\overline{e}$ is the of an electron

$\therefore 20 = n \times 1.6 \times 10^{-19}$ C

$$n = \frac{20}{1.6 \times 10^{-19}} = \frac{200}{16} \times 10^{19}$$

$$= 12.5 \times 10^{19} = 125 \times 10^{18}$$

53. If a wire is connected between C and D, the current flowing through the circuit increases, and hence, the ammeter reading rises suddenly. This is known as short circuiting.

54. Current flowing $i = \frac{Q}{t}$

Charge flowing, Q = it = 5 × 2 = 10 C

But Q = ne

Where, n is number of electrons passing through conductor in 2 s and e is the charge of electron 10 = n × 1.6 × 10^{-19}

number of electrons, $n = 6.25 \times 10^{19}$.

55. Since both the points A and B are at same potential, the potential difference between A and B is $V = 0$

Work done to move the charge between the points A and B is zero

56. When studies on electric current were done, the resistor R_3 is removed, the effective resistance in the circuit increases, and hence, the current flowing through the circuit decreases. Thus, the total current flowing through the circuit is less than that in the previous case. As less current is flowing between the two resistors, the ammeters A_1 and A_2 show a lower reading than in the previous case but have the same reading as the current flowing through the resistors R_1 and R_2 remains the same.

Level 3: Assess Your Concepts

Note: This is how you should frame your answer covering.

57.

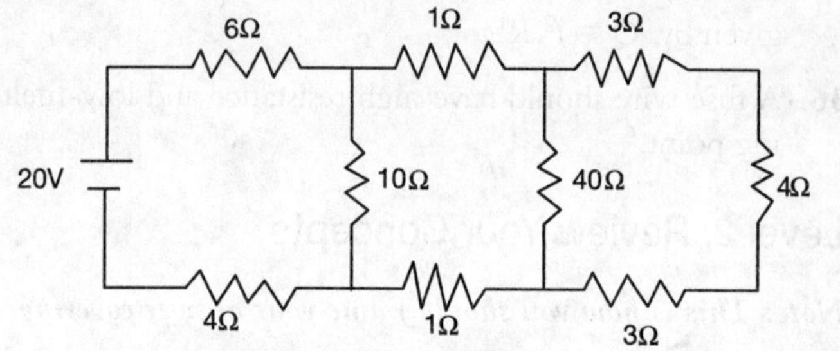

Effective resistance for the right most part of the circuit

$$= \left[\frac{1}{3+4+3} + \frac{1}{40}\right]^{-1}$$

$$= \left[\frac{1}{10} + \frac{1}{40}\right]^{-1} = \left[\frac{4+1}{40}\right]^{-1} = \left[\frac{5}{40}\right]^{-1} = \left[\frac{1}{8}\right]^{-1} = 8\Omega.$$

Effective resistance for the last two parts of the circuit

$$= \left[\frac{1}{1+8+1} + \frac{1}{10}\right]^{-1}$$

$$= \left[\frac{1}{10} + \frac{1}{10}\right]^{-1} = \left[\frac{2}{10}\right]^{-1} = \left[\frac{1}{5}\right]^{-1} = 5\Omega.$$

Effective resistance the circuit (R)

$= 6\Omega + 5\Omega + 4\Omega = 15\Omega.$

Current, $I = \frac{V}{R} = \frac{20}{15} = \frac{4}{3} A.$

Power through 6 Ω resistor, P = I^2R

$$= \left(\frac{4}{3}\right)^2 \times 15$$

$$= \frac{16}{9} \times 6$$

$$= \frac{32}{3} \sim 10.66W.$$

58. m = Zit

Q = i^2Rt

360000 = i^2 × 3600 × 25

$$i^2 = \frac{100}{25} = 4 \Rightarrow i = 2 \text{ A}$$

$m = Zit$

= 3294 × 10^{-10} × 2 × 3600 = 2.37 g.

59. (i) $E_{net} = E_1 + E_2 - E_3$

(ii) $I = \frac{E_{net}}{r}$

(iii) $V_1 = E_1 - ir_1$, $V_2 = E_2 - ir_2$, $V_3 = E_3 + ir_3$

(iv) Find the ratio of r_1, r_2, r_3.

(v) 3 : 2 : 2

60. (i) R_1, R_2, R_3 in parallel are in series with R_4.

(ii) $I = \frac{V}{R_{eff}}$

(iii) 46.7 Ω, 0.08 A

61. (i) Resistor R_1 and resistance of voltmeter are in parallel. Let Req = R_4

(ii) R_4, R_2, and R_3 are in series. Calculate the net effective resistance, R.

(iii) When resistors are in series $V_1 : V_2 : V_3 = R_4 : R_2 : R_3$

(iv) 4 V

62. $m = 10$ g

$$R_p = \frac{v}{i} = \frac{200}{10} = 20\Omega$$

$$\frac{1}{R_p} = \frac{1}{R_1} + \frac{1}{R_v} + \frac{1}{R_2}$$

$$\frac{1}{20} = \frac{1}{100} + \frac{1}{R_v} + \frac{1}{100}$$

$$\frac{1}{R_v} = \frac{1}{20} - \frac{1}{50}$$

$$\therefore R_v = \frac{100}{3} W$$

$$R_1 : R_v : R_2 = 100 : \frac{100}{3} : 100$$

$$= 3 : 1 : 3$$

$$\therefore i_1 : i_v : i_2 = 1 : 3 : 1$$

$$i_v = \frac{10}{1+3+1} \times 3$$

$$= \frac{10}{5} \times 3$$

$$= 6 \text{ A}$$

$$m = Zit = 0.000332 \times 10^{-3} \times 6 \times t$$

$$t = \frac{10 \times 10^{-3}}{0.000332 \times 10^{-3} \times 6} = 5020 \text{ s}$$

$$= 1.4 \text{ h}$$

63. The reason for the difference in reading is internal resistance offered by the cell.

$$E = V + Ir$$

where, the symbols represent quantities as in the above equation.

Putting the values as per the given data,

$1.4 = I \times 10;\ I = 0.14$

$1.5 = I(10 + r)$

$\therefore 1.5 = 0.14\ (10 + r)$

$\Rightarrow r = 0.71\ \Omega$.

64. Effective resistance

$$R = \frac{R_1 R_2}{R_1 + R_2} = \frac{100 \times 100}{200} = \frac{100}{2} = 50\Omega$$

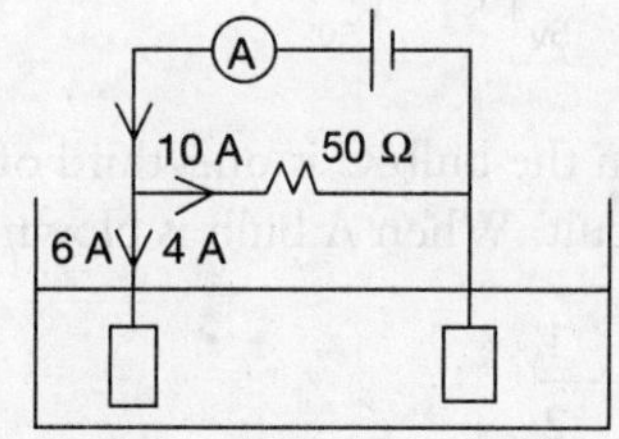

Current flowing through the 50 Ω resistor

$$i = \frac{V}{R} = \frac{200}{50} = 4\text{A}.$$

Current flowing though the electrolyte = 6 A.

Mass of copper deposited = Zit

= 0.000332 × 6 × 3600 = 7.1712 g

Current flowing through the resistor y = 2 A

Heat developed $Q = I^2.R.t$

$= 2^2 \times 100 \times 3600 = 400 \times 3600$

$= 144 \times 10^4$ J.

65. $\frac{A_1}{A_2} = \frac{1}{2}, \frac{V_1}{V_2} = \frac{2}{3}$

$$\frac{V_1}{V_2} = \frac{l_1}{l_2} \times \frac{A_1}{A_2}$$

$$\frac{2}{3} = \frac{l_1}{l_2} \times \frac{1}{2}$$

$$\frac{l_1}{l_2} = \left(\frac{4}{3}\right), \frac{R_1}{R_2} = \frac{\rho \times l_1}{A_1} \times \frac{A_2}{\rho l_2}$$

$$= \frac{4}{3} \times \frac{2}{1} = \frac{8}{3}$$

66. Total potential = 5 + 5 = 10 V

Total resistance in the circuit = R/3 Ω

Where R = 2 Ω

$$\text{Reff} = \frac{R}{3} = \frac{2}{3}\Omega$$

Total current $i = \frac{V}{Reff} = \frac{10}{2/3} = \frac{30}{2} = 15A$

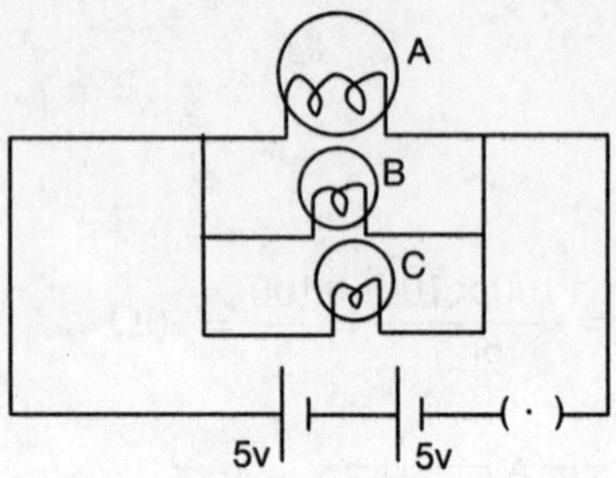

Current in the bulb C is one-third of the total current in the circuit. When A bulb is blown off then,

$R_{eff} = \frac{1}{2} + \frac{1}{2}$

$R_{eff} = 1\Omega$

$i = \frac{10}{1} = 10A$

$i_c = 5A$

67. R_1 (red, red, orange) = $22 \times 10^3\ \Omega$

R_2 (red, brown, yellow) = $21 \times 10^4\ \Omega$

Hari connected R_1, R_2 in series

$R_{eff} = R_1 + R_2 = 10^3(22 + 210)$

$R_{eff} = 232 \times 10^3\ \Omega$ (series)= 232 kΩ

Prasad connected R_1, R_2 in parallel.

$$R_{(p)eff} = \frac{R_1 \times R_2}{R_1 + R_2} = \frac{10^3 \times 22 \times 10^3 \times 210}{232 \times 10^3} = \frac{22 \times 210 \times 10^3}{232}$$

$$= \frac{4620 \times 10^3}{232} = 19.9 \times 10^3 \approx 20 \times 10^3\Omega = 20k\Omega$$

$R_{(s)eff} > R_{p(eff)}$

$$i_s = \frac{V}{R_s} = \frac{10}{232 \times 10^3} = 0.0431 \times 10^{-3}\ A = 43\ \mu A$$

$$ip = i_p = \frac{V}{R_p} = \frac{10}{20 \times 10^3} = 0.5 \times 10^{-3}\ A = 0.5\ mA$$

Let 'R' is the value of new resistance connected in Hari's circuit to get current as Prasad then

$$\frac{1}{20 \times 10^3} \times \frac{1}{232 \times 10^3} + \frac{1}{R}$$

$$\frac{1}{R} = \left(\frac{1}{20} - \frac{1}{232}\right) \Rightarrow R = 21.886\ k\Omega$$

68. R = 150 Ω

i = 5 A

t = 5 min = 5 × 60 = 300 s

Δt (change in temperature) = 15° C

M = ? S_w = 1 cal g^{-1} °C^{-1} = 4200 J kg^{-1} °C^{-1}

msΔt = i2Rt

$$m = \frac{i^2Rt}{s\Delta t} = \frac{5^2 \times 150 \times 300}{4200 \times 15} = 17.857\ kg$$

69. L_{ice} = 80 cal g^{-1} = 80 × 4200 J kg^{-1}

m = 4 kg t_1 = 0 °C

ice completely converted into water.

T = 5 min = 5 × 60 = 300 s

V = 220 V

I = ?

Q = mL = Vit

$$i = \frac{mL}{Vt} = \frac{4 \times 80 \times 4200}{220 \times 300} = \frac{4 \times 4 \times 14}{11} = 20.3636\ A$$

i = 20.4 A

70. In Faraday's first law of electrolysis experiment, V = 20 V

Internal resistance = 2 Ω

Rheostat resistance = 8 Ω

t = 1 h = 3600 s

Δm_{Cu} = 2 mg

R_{CuSo4}= ?

Total resistance = internal resistance of cell + rheostat resistance + resistance of $CuSO_4$ voltameter.

$R_{Total} = 2\Omega + 8\Omega + R_{CuSO4} = 10 + R_{CuSO4}$

m = Zit

$$i = \frac{m}{Zt} = \frac{2 \times 10^{-3}}{0.0003294 \times 3600} = \frac{2 \times 10^4}{3294 \times 3600} = \frac{20{,}000}{11858400}$$

i = 0.001686568171 A

$R = \frac{V}{i}$

$$10 + R_{CuSO4} = \frac{20}{0.0017}$$

$10 + R_{CuSO4} = 11858.4$

R_{CuSo4} =11858.4 −10 = 11848.4 Ω

JEE-NEET SPECIAL WING

Multiple-Answer Type Questions

1. $I = \frac{q}{t} = \frac{ne}{t}$

$\Rightarrow n = \frac{it}{e}$

$= \frac{2\times 1}{1.6\times 10^{-19}} = \frac{2\times 10^{19}}{1.6} = 1.25 \times 10^{19}$

Hence, the correct option is (c)

2. Volume remains constant.

$V_1 = V_2$

Volume $= A \times l$

$\Rightarrow A_1 l_1 = A_2 l_2$

$Al = A_2 (2l)$

$\therefore A_2 = \frac{A}{2}$

$R = p\frac{l}{A}$

$\Rightarrow \frac{R_1}{R_2} = \frac{l_1}{A_2} \times \frac{A_2}{l_2}$

$\frac{4}{R_2} = \frac{l}{A} \times \frac{\frac{A}{2}}{2l}$

$\therefore R_2 = 16\ \Omega$

Hence, the correct option is (b, d)

3. Aluminum, being a metal, has a positive temperature coefficient of resistance. Hence, its resistance increases with an increase in temperature.
On the other hand, germanium is a semiconductor with negative temperature coefficient of resistance. So, it is the resistance decreases with increase in temperature. So, germanium is non-ohmic conductor.
Hence, the correct option is (a, d)

4. Equivalent circuit of the given circuit is

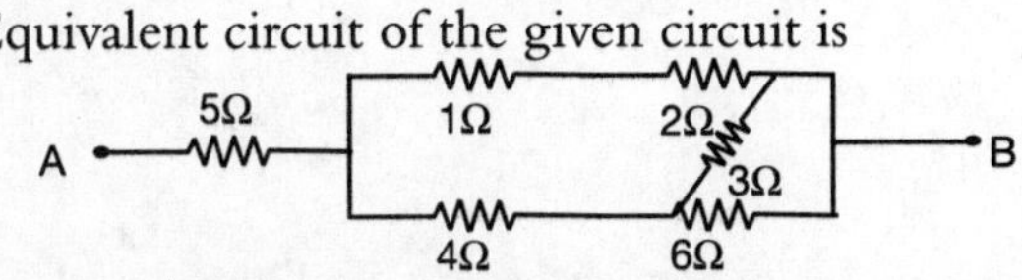

The resistances 3Ω and 6Ω are connected in parallel. The resistances 1Ω and 2Ω are connected in series.

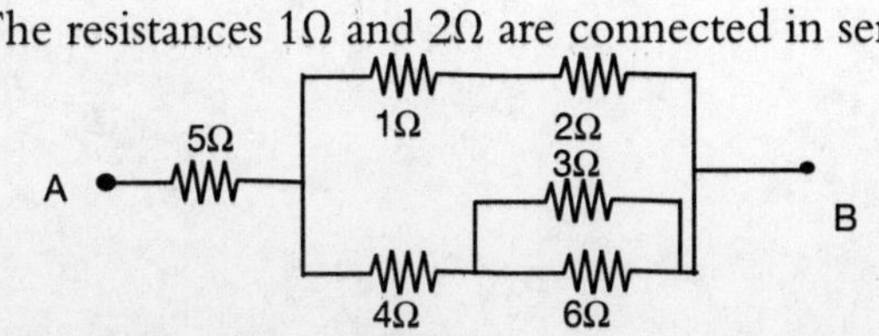

3Ω and 6Ω are in parallel

$\therefore$ its resultant $= \frac{3\times 6}{3+6} = 2\Omega$

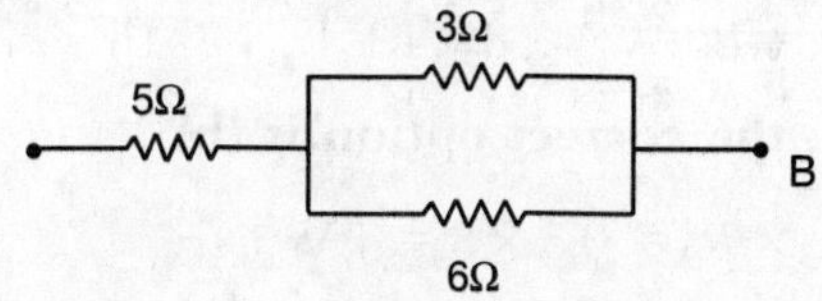

$\therefore R_{AB} = 7\Omega$

Hence, the correct option is (b, c, d)

5. $\varepsilon_{eff} = \varepsilon + \varepsilon + \varepsilon - \varepsilon$

$\Rightarrow \varepsilon_{eff} = 3 + 3 + 3 - 3 = 6V$

$R_{eff} = R + r + r + r + r$

$= 1 + 0.5 + 0.5 + 0.5 + 0.5 = 3\Omega$

By ohm's law, $i = \frac{\varepsilon_{eff}}{R_{eff}} = \frac{6V}{3\Omega} = 2A$

$V_{1\&} = iR = 2 \times 1 = 2V$

Hence, the correct option is (b, c)

6. Options (b) and (d) follow.
Hence, the correct option is (b, d)

7. Given $P = 2\text{kW} = 2 \times 10^3\text{Wb}$

$V = 220V$

$P = \frac{V^2}{R} \Rightarrow \frac{V^2}{P}$

$= \frac{220 \times 220}{2000} = 24.2\Omega$

$P = V.i \Rightarrow i = \frac{P}{V} = \frac{2000}{220} \simeq 9.09A$

Hence, the correct option is (c, d)

8. Terminal Voltage, $V = \varepsilon - ir$

$\Rightarrow r = \frac{\varepsilon - v}{i} = \frac{5-4}{2} = 0.5\ \Omega$

Hence, the correct option is (a)

9. Options (a), (b) and (c) follow.
Hence, the correct option is (a, b, c)

10. Option (a) follows.
Hence, the correct option is (a)

Comprehension-Based Questions

11. $R_{eff} = \frac{4\times 12}{4+12} + 8 = 3 + 8 = 11\Omega$

$\therefore i = \frac{22V}{11\Omega} = 2A$

Hence, the correct option is (d)

12. $i_1 = \left(\dfrac{R_2}{R_1 + R_2}\right) I_T$

$$\frac{R_2 + B_2}{R_2 + B_2 + B_1} \times A_1 = \frac{8+4}{8+4+4} \times 2 = \frac{12}{16} \times 2 = 1.5A$$

Hence, the correct option is (b)

13. $V_2 = A_3 \times R_2 = 0.5 \times 8 = 4$ V

Hence, the correct option is (c)

14. When K_2 is opens, $R_{eff} = B_1 + R_1 = 4 + 7 = 11\Omega$

$\therefore i = \dfrac{22}{11} = 2$A

$v_1 = R_1 \times i = 7 \times 2 = 14\ v$

Hence, the correct option is (a)

15. From the above solution i = 2A

$\therefore$ power $= i^2R = (2)^2 \times 4 = 16W$

Hence, the correct option is (b)

16. **A → (c)**

B → (e)

C. Effective resistance, $R = 4 + 3 + 4 = 11\Omega$

$\therefore i = \dfrac{\varepsilon}{R} = \dfrac{22}{11} = 2$A

$V_1 = iR_1 = 2 \times 4 = 8V$

Hence, the correct option is (d)

D. $R = 11\Omega$

$\Rightarrow i = 2$A

Power $= i^2R_2 = (2)^2 \times 3 = 12W$

Hence, the correct option is (a)

E. $P = i^2R \Rightarrow 25 = i^2 \times 4$

$\Rightarrow i = \dfrac{5}{2} = 2.5$A

$i = \dfrac{\varepsilon}{4 + R_1} \Rightarrow 2.5 = \dfrac{22}{4 + R_1}$

$\Rightarrow 4 + R_1 = \dfrac{22}{2.5} = 8.8$

$\therefore R_1 = 4.8\Omega$

Hence, the correct option is (b)

CHAPTER

7

Magnetism-II

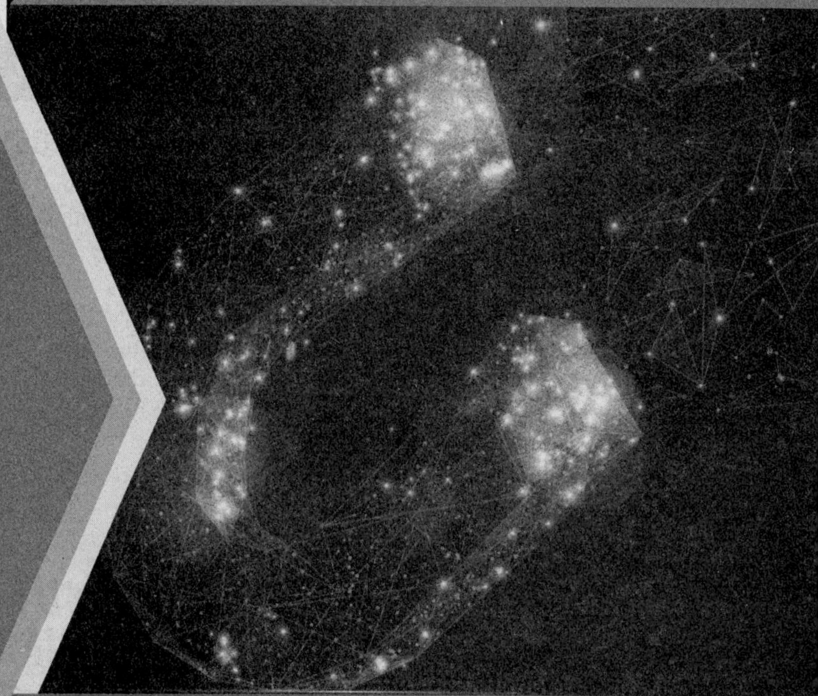

Remember

Before beginning this chapter, you should be able to:

- Learn the important terms such as a magnet, magnetic field, modern theory of magnetism.
- Classify various magnetic substances.
- Learn about the different elements of Earth's magnetic field, magnetic field produced by bar magnet in the Earth's magnetic field in different orientations.
- Understand the concept of electromagnetism and different instruments using magnetic effect of electric current.

Key Ideas

After completing this chapter, you should be able to:

- Learn the important properties of magnets, magnetic field and field lines, Ewing's Molecular Theory, inverse square law of magnetism, magnetic induction, modern electron theory, classification of magnetic materials and terrestrial magnetism.
- Study Oersted's Experiment, rules that help to find the direction of magnetic field.
- Find magnetic field due to a long straight and circular current carrying wires, solenoid and application of Fleming's left-hand rule.
- Understand Faraday's experiments and laws of electro magnetic induction including Lenz's Law and Fleming's right-hand rule.
- Study about electric generator, RMS voltage and peak voltage, self and mutual induction, transformer, eddy currents, etc.

Scientific Crypt

A Tribute to Hans Christian Oersted (1777 – 1851)

Hans Christian Oersted was born on 14th August 1777, in Rueljobing, Denmark. He was more interested in literature and philosophy.

In the year 1800, Volta discovered galvanic battery. Oersted was inspired by this and in order to carry out more scientific research, he arranged a scientific tour. Upon returning from the tour, he found that the university building was damaged by fire. While he was waiting to start a suitable work he began giving open lectures.

He became the assistant professor of physics at the university. He published a book on mechanical physics.

Every month he used to present his new scientific advances during his lectures. The year 1820 was fruitful for him. That year, he presented his discovery that a current carrying conductor produces a magnetic field around it. This historic discovery not only accelerated the development of physics, but also resulted in the birth of a new branch in physics called 'electromagnetism'.

The Danish government presented him a country house but he did not get to live in it. This great intellectual, inventor who revolutionised the field of science with his inventions, passed away in Copenhagen on 9th March, 1851.

FUN TIME

CROSSWORD

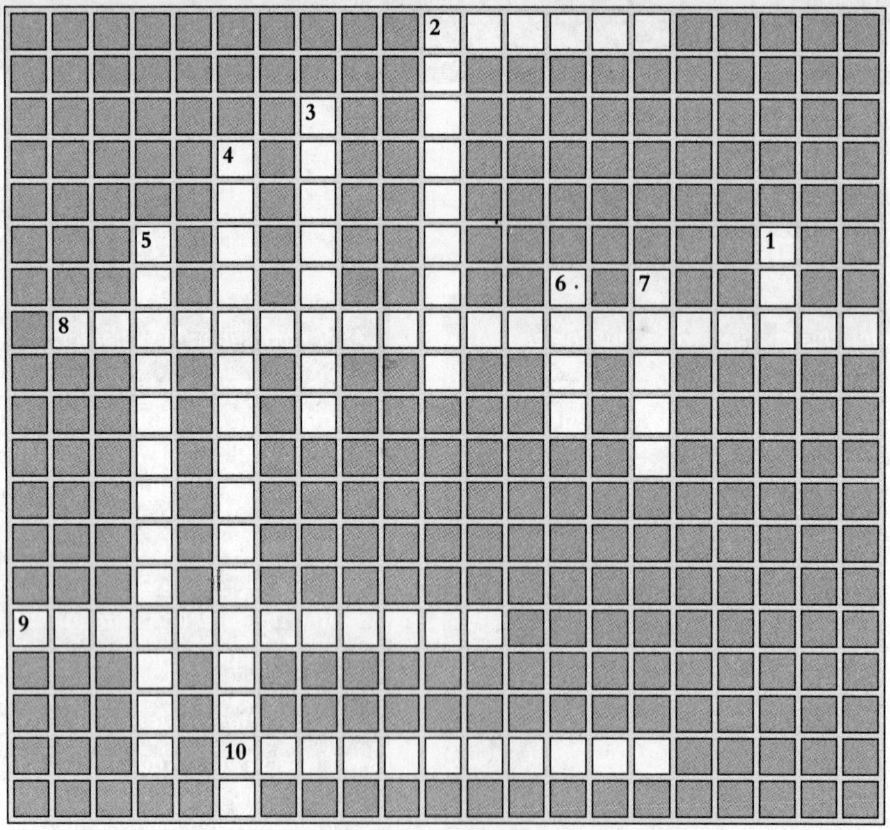

Across

2. Device which converts mechanical energy into electrical energy.
8. The property of a medium that allows itself to be influenced by magnetic field.
9. The core of transformer is made of _____.
10. Induced current produced in a solid core placed in changing magnetic filed _____.

Down

1. Moving coil microphone works on this principle.
2. If the magnitude of the current in the wire decreases, the number of magnetic lines of force _____.
3. Magnetic susceptibility for diamagnetic substances is _____.
4. A part of the energy is wasted on account of the magnetic flux in the soft iron core.
5. According to right hand thumb rule the direction of fingers encircling the wire conducting electricity shows the direction of_____.
6. The net magnetic moment of an atom of wood is _____.
7. The symbol for unit of magnetic flux.

INTRODUCTION

In 1820, Hans Christian Oersted discovered that current carrying conductor produces a magnetic field around it. Later Michael Faraday showed that current can be induced in a conducting coil, when there is relative motion between the coil and a magnet. Thus, electric current has magnetic effect and changing magnetic fields can induce electricity. Together, their study forms a very important branch of physics called electromagnetism. Large-scale generation of electricity worldwide and most of the devices which work on it are based on the principles of electromagnetism.

In the previous chapter, you studied electricity. Before we begin the study of electromagnetism, let us understand some important aspects of magnetism.

Magnetism

Since ancient times it was known that ferrous oxide (Fe_3O_4) had the ability to attract substances like iron, nickel, etc. Substances having this ability are called magnets. Fe_3O_4 is called natural magnet as it is naturally occurring while those substances in which this ability is artificially imparted are called artificial magnets.

The substances which are attracted towards a magnet and can become magnets are called magnetic substances.

Examples: iron, nickel, cobalt, etc.

The substances which are not attracted towards a magnet and cannot be magnetized are called non-magnetic substances.

Examples: wood, paper, plastic, etc.

Important Properties of Magnets

1. **Property of Attraction:** Magnets attract small pieces of materials like iron, nickel, and cobalt. The property of a magnet to attract small pieces of iron seems to be concentrated in small regions at the ends of the magnet. These regions are called magnetic poles.
2. **Property of Direction:** A freely suspended magnet always aligns itself in the North-South direction. The pole which points towards geographic north is called North pole of the magnet and the pole which points towards geographic south is called South pole of the magnet.
3. Like-poles of magnets repel each other and unlike-poles attract each other, just as like-charges repel and unlike-charges attract. Since a magnet can attract small pieces of iron and also the opposite pole of another magnet, property of attraction is not a sure test to find whether a given piece is a magnet or not. Repulsion is a sure test to confirm whether a given piece is a magnet or not.
4. **Property of Induction:** A magnet can induce magnetism in substances like soft iron, cobalt, nickel, etc.
5. Breaking a magnet successively into smaller pieces would still produce tiny magnets each with a north pole and south pole. The above phenomena is observed till we reach molecular stage.
6. Magnetic poles always exist in opposite pairs.

Magnetic Field and Field Lines

The area surrounding magnet, in which its effect can be felt, is called magnetic field of the magnet.

Place a bar magnet on a cardboard. Randomly sprinkle iron filings on the cardboard and tap it lightly. The iron filling arrange themselves in a particular pattern. Draw lines along these patterns. These lines form continuous, closed curves between the poles of the magnet. Place a magnetic needle near the north pole of bar magnet and mark the north pole end of needle. Now place the needle with its S-pole at this mark and mark the new position of its N-pole. It is found that the needle always traces a path formed by above mentioned curved lines. These lines are called magnetic lines of force. Thus, a magnetic field can be represented by lines of force.

Magnetic lines of force are those lines in a magnetic field along which an imaginary free isolated north pole moves.

1. Lines of force are continuous lines.
2. Outside a bar magnet, the lines of force are directed away from North pole and towards the South pole.
3. Inside a bar magnet, the lines are directed from South pole to the North pole.
4. Lines of force do not intersect.
5. The magnetic field is strong at places where the lines of force are crowded and weak where the lines of force are far apart.
6. The direction of magnetic field at a point is tangential to the line of force at that point.

Ewing's Molecular Theory of Magnetism

If we break a magnet into two parts, each part becomes a magnet with a north pole at one end and a south pole at the other end. If we break it further, we observe the same behaviour. This will continue even if we break the magnet to its molecular level.

Each molecule of a magnetic substance is an independent magnet irrespective of whether the substance is magnetized or not, these tiny magnets are called molecular magnets.

In an unmagnetized state [Fig 7.1 (a)], the molecular magnets are arranged in random manner. Therefore, the net magnetic effect is zero.

In the magnetized state [Fig. 7.1 (b)], these molecular magnets are arranged in an order. All the south poles are aligned in one direction and the north poles in the other direction. Therefore, a strong magnetic field is created.

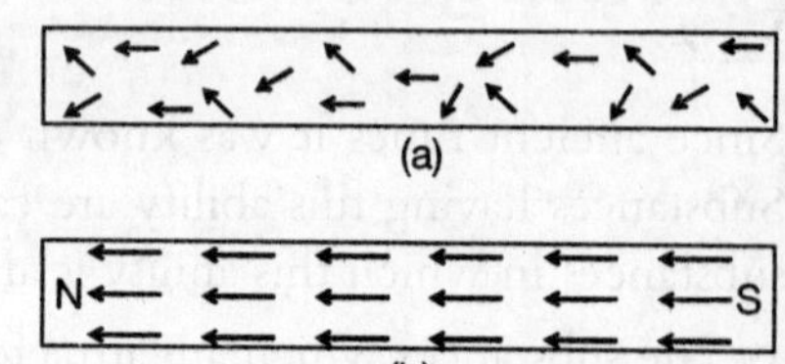

Figure 7.1 (a) An unmagnetized state, (b) A magnetized state

In general, perfect alignment of all the molecular magnets in the entire magnet is difficult to obtain. When this condition is obtained, it is called point of saturation and magnetizing the magnet further cannot increase the strength of the magnet. These postulates are known as Ewing's molecular theory named after the scientist who proposed them.

However, Ewing's molecular theory could not explain why the individual molecules of a magnetic substance like iron behave as tiny magnets. Also it failed to explain, why molecules of non-magnetic substances, like brass, do not behave like magnets. The theory could not explain the fact that substances like bismuth, copper are repelled by strong magnets.

Inverse Square Law of Magnetism

The ability of the pole of a magnet to attract or repel another magnetic pole is called its pole strength. It is denoted by 'm'. Its SI unit is ampere-metre.

Consider two hypothetical isolated magnetic poles of pole strengths m_1 and m_2 separated by a distance 'r'.

According to inverse square law of magnetism, given by Coulomb, the force of attraction or repulsion between two magnetic poles is directly proportional to the product of their pole strengths and inversely proportional to the square of the distance between them and acts along the line joining the poles.

Mathematically,

$$F \propto m_1 \times m_2$$

$$\text{and } F \propto \frac{1}{r^2},$$

$$\text{or, } F = K\frac{m_1 m_2}{r^2}$$

where, K is the constant of proportionality. Its value depends on the magnetic properties of the medium surrounding the magnetic poles and the system of units used.

If we choose SI units, and if vacuum or air is the medium surrounding the poles, then the value of K is denoted by $\left(\frac{\mu_0}{4\pi}\right)$.

$$\therefore\ F = \left(\frac{\mu_0}{4\pi}\right)\frac{m_1 m_2}{r^2} \qquad (7.1)$$

where, μ_0 is called magnetic permeability of vacuum or air.

The value of μ_0 is $4\pi \times 10^{-7}$ henry metre^{-1}.

If any medium other than vacuum or air surrounds the poles, then

$$F_1 = \frac{\mu}{4\pi} \times \frac{m_1 m_2}{r^2} \qquad (7.2)$$

where, 'μ' is absolute magnetic permeability of the medium.

Info Bytes!

- The strongest magnet in the universe is actually a star known as a magnetar, with a magnetic field trillions of times stronger than Earth's.
- The term 'magnet' is derived from the ancient Greek word 'Magnesia,' a place where magnetic stones were first found.

Some Important Terms

Magnetic Permeability

Magnetic permeability (μ) of a medium is defined as its ability to allow the magnetic lines of force to pass through it or to allow itself to be influenced by magnetic field.

On dividing equation (7.2) by equation (7.1), we have

$$\frac{F_1}{F} = \frac{\mu}{\mu_0} = \mu_r \Rightarrow \mu = \mu_0 \mu_r$$

where, μ_r is called **relative permeability** and it is defined as the ratio of magnetic force in a medium to the magnetic force in vacuum.

μ_r being a ratio has no units. For air or vacuum, $\mu_r = 1$.

Unit Pole Strength

The unit magnetic pole is defined as that pole which repels an identical pole at 1 metre distance with a force of 10^{-7} N.

By taking $\mu_0 = 4\pi \times 10^{-7}$ henry metre^{-1}, $r = 1$ m and $m_1 = m_2 = 1$(A–m), we have

$$F = \frac{\mu_0}{4\pi} \times \frac{m_1 m_2}{r^2}$$

$$= \frac{\mu_0}{4\pi} \times \frac{1 \times 1}{1^2} = \frac{4\pi \times 10^{-7}}{4\pi} = 10^{-7}\text{ N}$$

Magnetic Flux Density 'B'

The space around the magnet where the influence of the magnet can be felt is called **magnetic field**. Let us imagine this field as constituted by magnetic lines of force. The total number of lines passing through the given area is called **magnetic flux 'ϕ'**. The unit of magnetic flux in S.I system is weber (Wb). If a magnetic substance exits in this field, then the lines of force pass through it. These lines of force are called magnetic induction lines as these lines induce magnetism in the magnetic substance.

Magnetic flux per unit area is called magnetic flux density or magnetic induction.

i.e.,
$$B = \frac{\phi}{A}$$

Magnetic induction can also be defined as the force experienced by a unit north pole kept in a magnetic field.

We know that the force experienced by two poles m_1 and m_2 is given by,

$$F = \frac{\mu_0}{4\pi}\frac{m_1 m_2}{(r)^2}$$

Let m_1 be the pole strength of unit N pole.

$$\therefore m_1 = 1 \text{ A} - \text{m}$$

Let $m_2 = m$

$$\therefore F = \frac{\mu_0}{4\pi}\frac{m}{r^2}$$

By definition magnetic induction at a point in a magnetic field is the force experienced by a unit north pole placed at that point.

$$\therefore B = \frac{\mu_0}{4\pi}\frac{m}{r^2}$$

The SI unit of flux density is Wb m^{-2} or tesla (T). The CGS unit of flux density is gauss (G).

$$1 \text{ T} = 10^4 \text{ G}$$

Its other unit is N $A^{-1}m^{-1}$. The force experienced by a north pole of pole strength 'm', kept in a magnetic field of induction 'B', is given by,

$$F = mB. \text{ or } B = \frac{F}{m}$$

Intensity of Magnetic Field (H)

The intensity of magnetic field refers to the strength of a magnetic field at a point in C.G.S. units.

We know that

$$F = K\frac{m_1 m_2}{r^2}$$

where, $K = \frac{1}{\mu}$ and μ is the permeability of free space which is equal to 1 in C.G.S system. In the above equation, if m_1 is unit north pole and $m_2 = m$, then

$$F = \frac{m}{r^2}$$

This force is called intensity of magnetic field (H).

$$\therefore H = \frac{m}{r^2}$$

Thus, intensity of magnetic field can be defined as the force acting on unit north pole independent of the medium. In S.I. system,

$$H = \frac{m}{4\pi r^2}$$

Since $K = \frac{1}{4\pi}$ in S.I system, the S.I. unit of H is ampere metre^{-1} (A m^{-1}).

In C.G.S. system, its unit is oersted.

Both H and B represent strength of magnetic field at a point, the difference being that H is independent of the medium. H and B are related as follows:

$$B = \mu_o H$$

Magnetic Moment 'M'

The magnetic moment of a bar magnet is given by the product of its length and pole strength. Let us take the length of the magnet as '$2l$' and magnetic pole strength of the magnet as 'm'. Then the magnetic moment of the magnet is given by,

$$M = (2l) \times m$$

S.I. unit of magnetic moment is ampere – metre^2(A m^2)

Magnetic Field Induction of a Bar Magnet on the Axial Line of the Magnet

The line joining the north pole and south pole of a magnet is called axial line. The magnetic induction 'B' of a short bar magnet on the axial line is given by,

$$B = \left(\frac{\mu_0}{4\pi}\right)\frac{2M}{d^3}$$

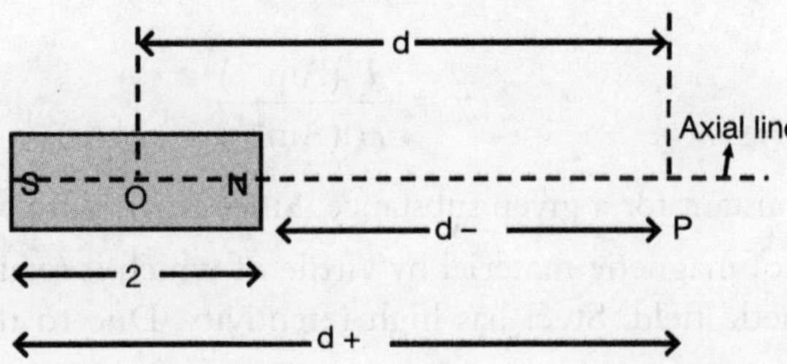

Figure 7.2 Diagram to show magnetic field induction of a bar magnet on the Axial Line of the Magnet

Where, μ_o is the permeability of free space, M is the magnetic moment of the magnet and 'd' is the distance of the point 'P' from the centre of the magnet. The direction of B is along the axis, parallel to $\overrightarrow{SN}$ vector.

Magnetic Field Induction of a Magnet on the Equatorial Line of the Magnet

A line perpendicular to the axis and passing through the midpoint of the magnet is called equatorial line. The magnetic induction 'B' of a short bar magnet on the equatorial line is given by

$$B = \left(\frac{\mu_0}{4\pi}\right) \cdot \frac{M}{d^3} \text{ N A}^{-1}\text{–m}^{-1},$$

where, μ_o is the permeability of free space, M is the magnetic moment of the given magnet and 'd' is the distance of the point 'P' on the equatorial line from the magnet.

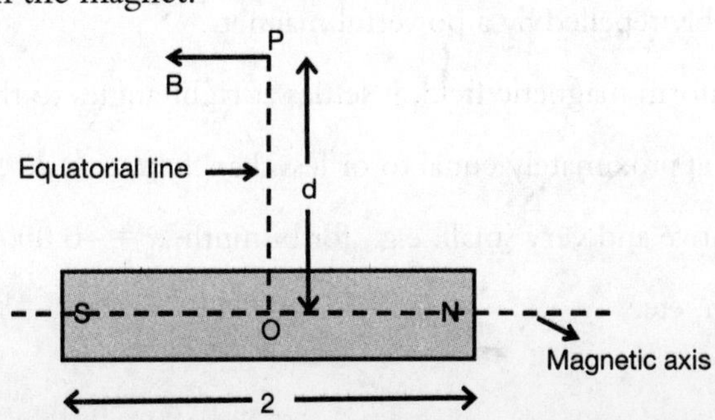

Figure 7.3 Diagram to show magnetic field induction of a magnet on the equatorial line of the magnet

The direction of B is parallel to the axis of the magnet and is in the $\overrightarrow{NS}$ direction.

Origin of Magnetism-Modern Electron Theory

One of the major drawbacks of Ewing's theory is that it fails to explain why molecules of magnetic substances like iron behave like tiny magnets while those of non-magnetic substances like wood do not. The modern electron theory offers an explanation to this. A molecule consists of two or more atoms. Each atom consists of electrons which revolve around the nucleus in orbits and rotate or spin about an axis. Since electrons carry negative charge, the orbital and spin motion of electrons give rise to electric current which produces a magnetic field.

For substances like iron, the net magnetic moment due to a molecule is not zero, hence, they are magnetic in nature. The net magnetic moment due to a molecule is zero in wood, hence, it is non-magnetic.

Magnetic Properties

1. **Intensity of Magnetization 'I':** It is the magnetic moment acquired per unit volume when a substance is placed in a magnetic field. Its unit is A m^{-1}.
2. **Magnetic Susceptibility 'χ':** It is the measure of capability of a medium to get magnetized. Susceptibility of a substance is defined as the ratio of intensity of magnetization '*I*' to the intensity of applied magnetic field '*H*'. Soft iron has high susceptibility.

$$\chi = \frac{I\ (\text{Am}^{-1})}{H\ (\text{Am}^{-1})}$$

   Magnetic susceptibility is a constant for a given substance. Since it is a pure ratio, it has no unit.
3. **Retentivity:** It is a property of magnetic material by virtue of which it retains the magnetic property even after removal of the applied magnetic field. Steel has high retentivity. Due to this reason, steel is used for making permanent magnets.

Classification of Magnetic Materials

Based on the magnetic properties, all materials can be classified as:

1. Diamagnetic substances
2. Paramagnetic substances
3. Ferromagnetic substances

Diamagnetic Substances

The resultant magnetic moment of an atom in a substance depends on the orientation of electron orbits and the axes about which electrons spin. The substances in which the net magnetic moment of any atom in them is zero are called diamagnetic substances.

1. A diamagnetic substance is feebly repelled by a powerful magnet.
2. When suspended in a non-uniform magnetic field, it settles at right angles to the direction of the field.
3. Its relative permeability (μ_r) is approximately equal to or less than 1 ($\mu_r \leq 1$).
4. Magnetic susceptibility is negative and very small, e.g., for bismuth, $x = -0.000015$

Example: air, water, copper, bismuth, etc.

Paramagnetic Substances

Those substances in which the orientation of electron orbits and axes of their spins are such that the net magnetic moment of any atom is not zero, are called paramagnetic substances. Those atoms which have unpaired electrons acquire resultant magnetic moment.

1. Paramagnetic substances are feebly attracted by a strong magnet.
2. When placed in a non-uniform external magnetic field, it aligns itself with the direction of the field and moves from weaker to stronger region of the field.
3. Its relative permeability is slightly greater than 1 ($\mu_r > 1$).
4. Its magnetic susceptibility (χ) is small and positive, e.g., for platinum, its value is 0.0001.

Example: aluminium, platinum, chromium, etc.

Ferromagnetic Substances

Like paramagnetic substances, the atoms of these elements have resultant magnetic moment. But unlike paramagnetic substances, they achieve high degree of magnetic alignment due to a special effect called 'exchange coupling'.

The elements Fe, Co, Ni, Gd and Dy are examples of ferromagnetic substances.

Ferromagnetic substances are those in which the resultant magnetic moments of individual atoms align themselves parallel to each other due to a special effect which leads to spontaneous magnetization.

1. They are strongly attracted by magnets.
2. They align in the direction of the applied field.
3. Their relative permeability is very high ($\mu_r >> 1$).
4. Magnetic susceptibility (χ) is very high and positive. Therefore, they can be easily magnetized and made into magnets.

Domain Theory

Domain theory explains the properties of ferromagnetic substances. According to domain theory, a large number of small local regions are formed in ferromagnetic substances, called **domains**. Within each domain, the magnetic dipoles of all the atoms align themselves parallel to each other giving rise to magnetism. The direction of magnetization in each domain is different from that in the other domains as indicated by arrows in the Fig. 7.4.

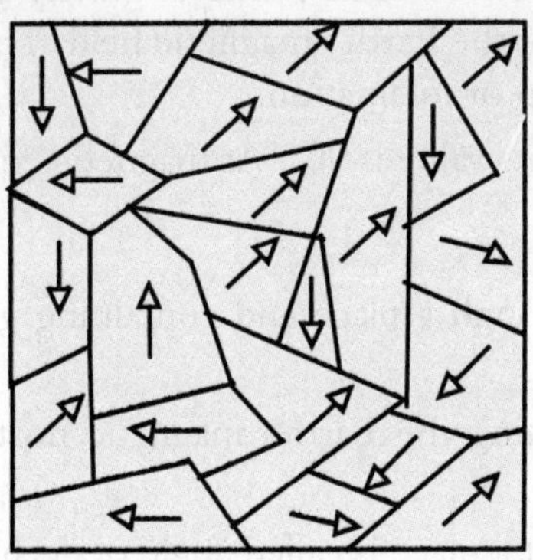

Figure 7.4 Different domain showing direction of magnetization by arrows

Konnect

Magnetic domains are like tiny neighbourhoods within a material where all the molecular magnets agree to point in the same direction.

In the diagram, boundary lines indicate different domains and arrows indicate direction of magnetization of respective domains. In the absence of applied magnetic field, the arrow of each domain point along different directions. As a result, the net magnetization of the specimen as a whole is zero. This explains why an iron rod is not a magnet by itself.

When a ferromagnetic specimen is magnetized, the domains expand and all arrows align parallel to each other in one direction. In an ideal magnet, there is a single domain with all the arrows pointing in one direction. This way the specimen becomes a magnet. Ferromagnetic substances exhibit retentivity because on demagnetising them, the original domains are not formed immediately, so that a certain amount of magnetization is still retained.

Terrestrial Magnetism

Our Earth behaves like a magnet. This is proved by the fact that a freely suspended bar magnet or a compass needle always come to rest in north–south direction. It is as if a huge bar magnet is buried at the centre of the Earth with its south pole at the geographic north and vice versa. The axis of the Earth's magnet makes an angle of about 17° with the geographic axis.

It is supposed that electric currents in the molten outer core rich in iron give rise to the Earth's magnetism. The study of the Earth's magnetism and its various elements constitutes terrestrial magnetism.

Info Bytes!

Earth's magnetic field is not uniform. It varies from point to point and changes over time.

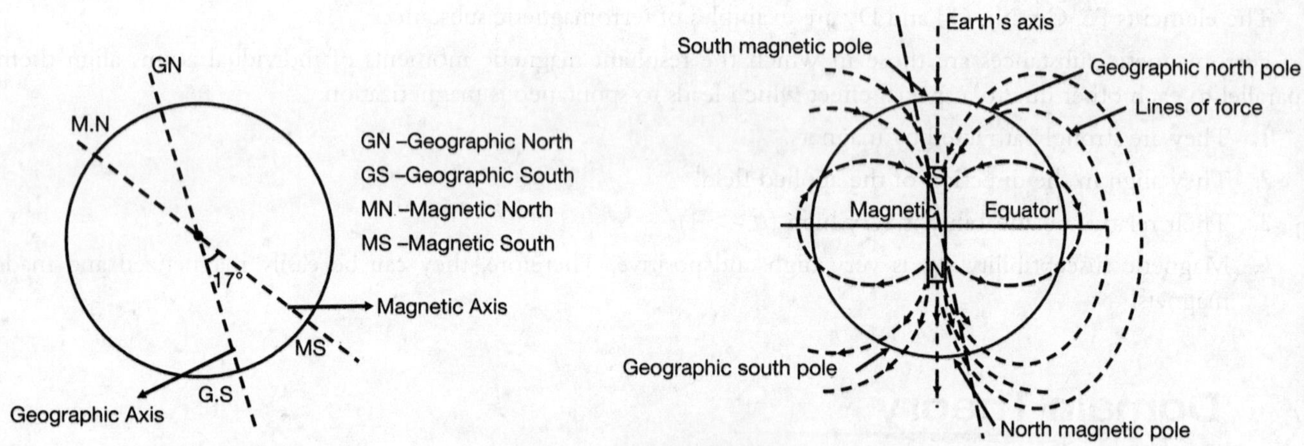

Figure 7.5 Terrestrial magnetism

Elements of Earth's Magnetism

1. **Angle of Dip or Inclination:** A magnetic needle suspended at its centre of gravity and free to rotate in vertical and horizontal planes comes to the rest in the direction of the Earth's magnetic field. The angle made by the axis of magnetic needle with the horizontal is called angle of dip or inclination.

   The angle of dip is maximum at the magnetic poles and its value is 90°. At magnetic equator of the Earth, its value is zero.

2. **Angle of Declination:** The vertical plane passing through a place and containing geographic north and south poles is called geographic meridian.

   The vertical plane passing through a place and containing the Earth's magnetic north and south pole is called magnetic meridian.

   The angle between geographic and magnetic meridian at a place is called angle of declination.

Mapping Neutral Points

The magnetic field due to a bar magnet consists of number of lines of force which emerge from its north pole and enter the south pole. At the same time, the effect of the horizontal component (B_H) of the Earth's magnetic field is also felt at a given place. The magnetic field induction (B) due to the bar magnet is large near it and decreases with the distance, whereas B_H remains constant in magnitude and direction at a given place. Thus, within the magnetic field of a bar magnet, the lines of force represent the net effect of B and B_H. There are some points within the magnetic field where B and B_H are equal in magnitude and opposite in direction and cancel each other. These points where the resultant magnetic field is zero are called 'neutral points'. The location of neutral points also depends on the orientation of the bar magnet.

1. **North pole of the bar magnet facing the geographical north of the Earth:** At the geographical north pole lies the magnetic south pole of the earth and vice versa. The Earth's magnetic lines of force are, thus, directed from geographical south to north. Hence, the horizontal component (B_H) of the Earth's magnetic field neutralizes the magnetic field induction (B) of the bar magnet at two diametrically opposite points lying on the equatorial line of the bar magnet.

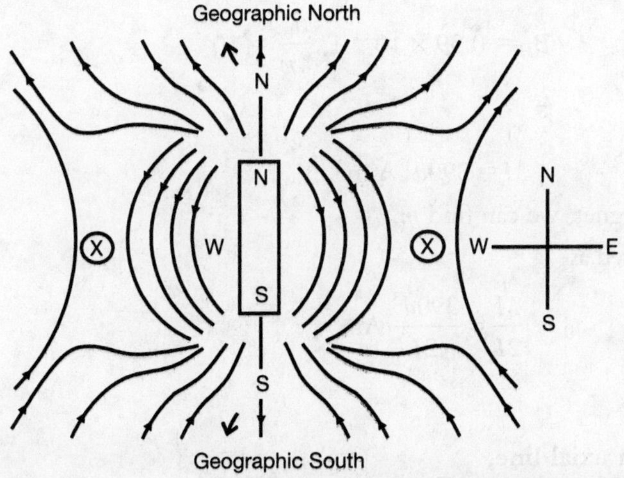

Figure 7.6 Magnetic field around a bar magnet whose N-pole is facing the geographical north of the Earth

These points are the neutral points when N-pole of the bar magnet points towards geographic north. If a compass needle is placed at any of these points, it points in any random direction.

2. **South pole of the bar magnet facing geographical north pole of the Earth:** In this orientation, the south pole of the bar magnet faces the magnetic south pole of the Earth.

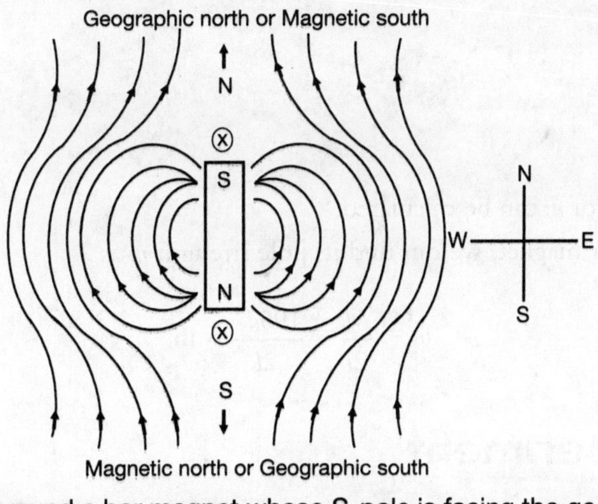

Figure 7.7 Magnetic field around a bar magnet whose S-pole is facing the geographical north of the Earth

Along the axial line of the bar-magnet, the lines of force due to the magnetic fields of the Earth and bar magnet are oppositely directed. Hence, at two particular points along the axial line, one nearer to the south pole and the other closer to the north pole of the bar magnets, the B_H nullifies the B. These two points represent the neutral points.

Calculation of Magnetic Moment of a Bar Magnet

At the neutral points, the magnetic field intensity due to a bar magnet equals horizontal component of Earth's magnetic field (B_H). Knowing B_H at a given place (which is 0.39×10^{-4} T in Andhra Pradesh) and distance 'd' of neutral point, we can determine magnetic moment, M.

Case I:

When neutral points lie on equatorial line,

$$B = \frac{\mu_0}{4\pi} \times \frac{M}{d^3} \text{ w}$$

Substituting $\qquad B_H = 0.39 \times 10^{-4}$ T, $\frac{\mu_0}{4\pi} = 10^{-7}$

> **Info Bytes!**
> The strongest permanent magnet ever created has a magnetic moment that is more than a million times that of a typical refrigerator magnet.

Simplifying,

we get $\qquad M = 390d^3$ A m^2.

Knowing the length of the magnet, we can find *m*.

The value of *m* can be calculated as

$$m = \frac{M}{2l} = \frac{390d^3}{2l} \text{ Am}$$

Case II:

When neutral points are on axial line,

$$B = B_H = \frac{\mu_0}{4\pi} \frac{2M}{d^3}$$

Substituting the values of B_H and $\mu_0/4\pi$, we get

$$\frac{2M}{d^3} = 390,$$

and we get

$M = 195d^3$ A m^2

Knowing the value of *d*, the value of *m* can be calculated.

If we know the length of the bar magnet, we can find its pole strength *m* as

$$m = \frac{M}{2l} = \frac{195d^3}{2l} \text{ A m}$$

Oersted's Experiment

Oersted was the first to put forth the direct relation between electricity and magnetism. He conducted several experiments to determine the magnetic effect of a current carrying wire. The following describes the Oersted experiment conducted to establish that a current carrying wire acts as a magnet.

A long straight wire is connected to an external battery and an electric current is passed through it. When a magnetic needle is placed below the wire such that the wire is parallel to the axis of the magnetic needle and the current flows in the south to north direction, a deflection in the needle is observed. It is observed that the north pole of the needle is deflected westwards and as the magnitude of current is increased, the deflection increases till the north pole of the needle turns towards exact west. It is also observed that if instead of placing the magnetic needle below the wire, if it was placed above the wire, the north pole of the magnetic needle is deflected eastwards. From this experiment, Oersted concluded the following facts.

1. Any current carrying wire produces a magnetic field around it, as it can deflect a magnetic needle placed near it.
2. The intensity of the magnetic field is proportional to the magnitude of the current passing through the wire.
3. The magnetic field setup acts at right angles to the direction of the flow of current.
4. The direction of the magnetic field depends upon the direction of the flow of current.

The direction of the magnetic field produced due to a current carrying wire may be determined using any one of the following rules.

Ampere's Swimming Rule

Imagine a man swimming along the conductor in the direction of current, facing a magnetic compass kept near and below the conductor. Then the north pole of the needle will be deflected towards his left hand.

Ampere's Right-Hand Thumb Rule

Imagine you are holding the current carrying wire with your right-hand, with the thumb pointing the direction of current. Then the direction of fingers encircling the wire show the direction of magnetic field.

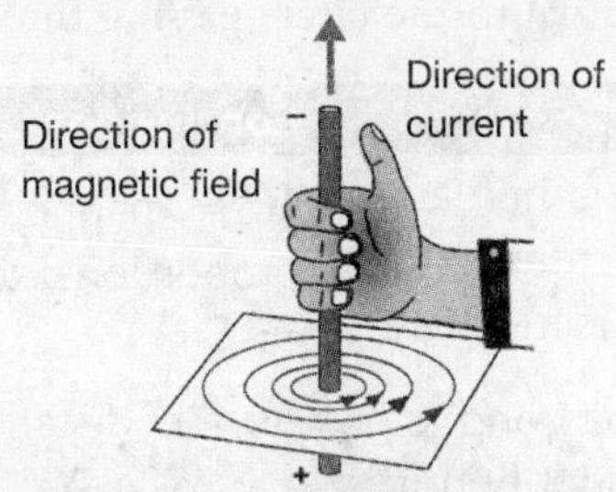

Figure 7.8 Ampere's right-hand thumb rule

Maxwell's Cork Screw Rule

Imagine a right-handed cork screw held by your hand. Rotate the screw's head such that its tip advances in the direction of the current. Then the direction in which the head rotates gives the direction of the magnetic field.

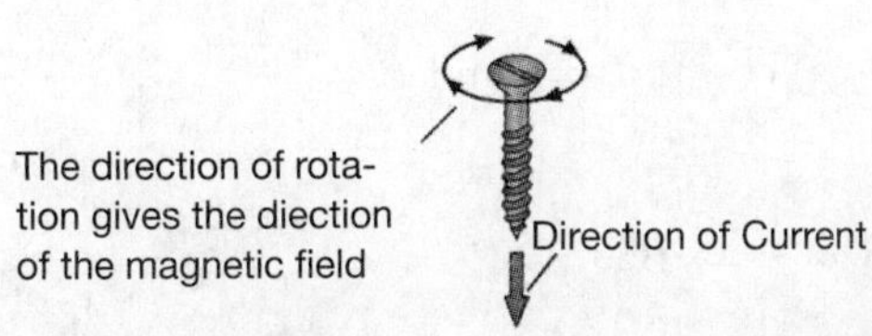

Figure 7.9 Maxwell's Cork Screw Rule

Magnetic Field Due to Current

The expression for magnetic field due to different carrying conductors are discussed as follows:

Magnetic Field due to a Long Straight Current Carrying Wire

The following experiment helps us study the magnetic field around a long straight current carrying wire.

Take a cardboard and fix a white paper over it. Make a small hole at its centre. Clamp this cardboard, to a stand in a horizontal position. Sprinkle some iron filings over it. Pass an insulated copper wire through the small hole at the centre of the cardboard and perpendicular to it.

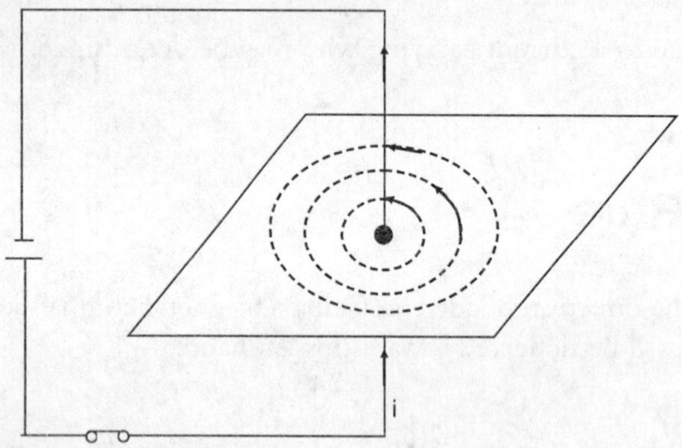

Figure 7.10 Magnetic field due to a long straight current carrying wire

Info Bytes!

The strongest magnetic field ever created in a lab is over 1,200 teslas—many times stronger than the magnetic field of Earth!

A battery, a switch and a variable resistance are connected in series to the wire and when the circuit is closed, a current (i) flows through the wire. The iron filings on the cardboard form concentric circles around the wire showing that a current carrying conductor sets up a magnetic field around the conductor. The direction of the magnetic field at any point is in the plane of the paper and is always tangential to the circle passing through that point.

Observations	Conclusions
If the magnitude of the current in the wire is increased, then the number of concentric circles increases (i.e., the number of magnetic lines of forces increases).	The magnetic field induction ($\vec{B}$) is directly proportional to the current flowing through the wire. $\Rightarrow B \propto i$
If a magnetic needle is brought near the conductor, the deflection in the needle is more and when it is moved away, the deflection decreases.	As the distance from the wire increases, magnetic field ($\vec{B}$) decreases. The magnetic induction (B) at a point is inversely proportional to the distance of the point from the wire. Hence, $B \propto \frac{1}{r}$

From these conclusions, we have

$$B \propto i \text{ and } B \propto \frac{1}{r}$$

$$\therefore \quad B \propto \frac{1}{r} \Rightarrow B = \frac{Ki}{r}$$

Where, K is the constant of proportionality and may experimentally be verified to be equal to $\frac{\mu_0}{2\pi}$ (in S.I system), where, μ_0 is called permeability constant of free space or vacuum, whose value is given as

$$\mu_0 = 4\pi \times 10^{-7} \text{ T m A}^{-1}$$

Hence,
$$B = \frac{\mu_0 i}{2\pi r}$$

EXAMPLE 7.1 Two infinitely long wires are placed parallel to each other as shown below. Determine the ratio of the magnetic field due to A and B at the point P.

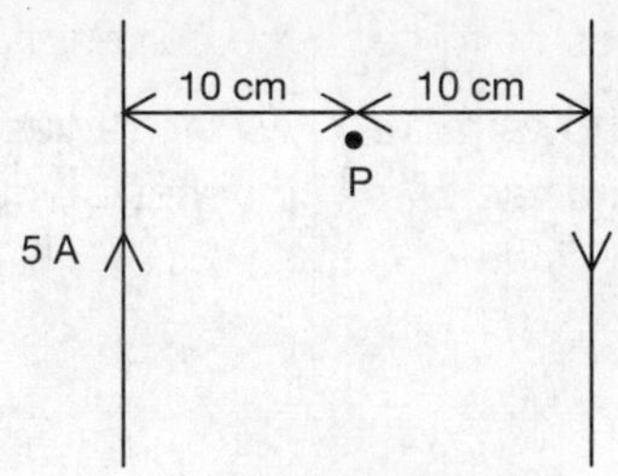

Figure 7.11

SOLUTION

$$B = \frac{\mu_0}{2\pi_r} \times i$$

$$\frac{B_1}{B_2} = \frac{\frac{5}{10}}{\frac{20}{10}} = \frac{5}{20} = \frac{1}{4}$$

So, the ratio is 1 : 4.

Magnetic Field due to a Circular Current Carrying Wire

Let us now study the magnetic field due to a circular current carrying conductor. Take a copper wire, bend it in the form of a circular coil. Connect this coil to a battery with a rheostat and a switch in series. Pass this copper wire over two holes of a cardboard covered with a white paper. Sprinkle iron filings on the cardboard.

It is observed that iron filings arrange themselves in concentric circles as shown in the figure below.

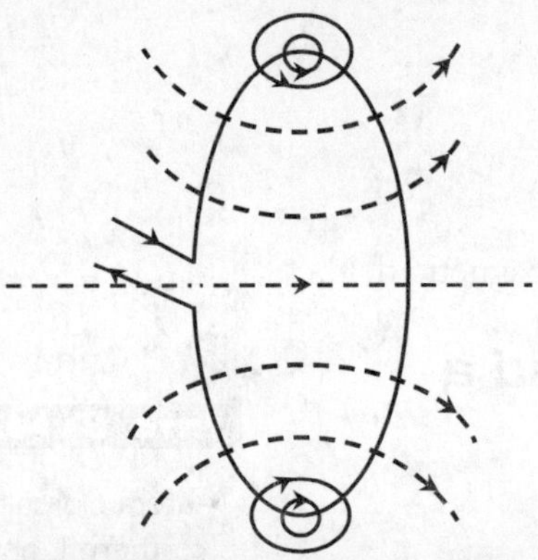

Figure 7.12 Magnetic field lines due to a circular current carrying conductor

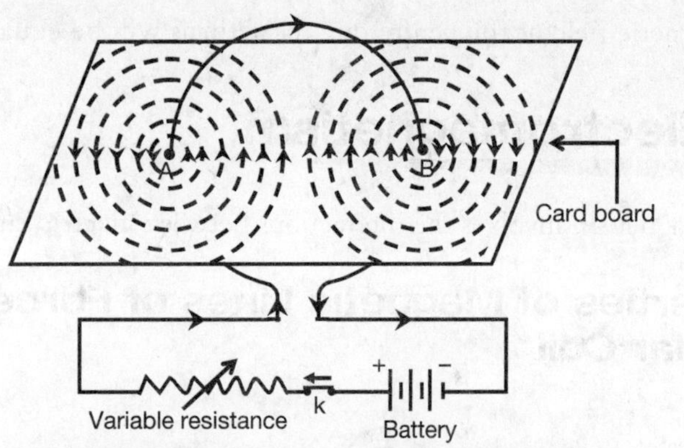

Figure 7.13 Magnetic field due to a circular current carrying wire

Observations	Conclusions
An increase in the magnitude of the current in the coil increases the number of magnetic lines of force.	Magnetic field induction is directly proportional to the current flowing in the wire.
It is observed that a magnetic compass shows more deflection if the circular coil is bent into a circle of less radius compared to a coil bent into a circle of larger radius.	As the radius of circular coil increases, the magnetic induction decreases. It means, $B \propto \frac{1}{R}$

Near the conductor, the field is circular and the direction of the field is given by right-hand thumb rule. As we move away from the wire towards the centre of the coil, the radius curvature of magnetic lines increases, i.e., they become straighter and almost parallel to each other. At the centre of the coil, the magnetic line of force is perpendicular to the plane of the coil.

The magnitude of the magnetic field at the centre of the circular current carrying wire is found to be:

1. directly proportional to the strength of the current passing through the wire.
2. inversely proportional to the radius of the circular coil.

$\therefore$ If B is the magnetic field at the centre, then

$$B \propto i$$

$$B \propto \frac{1}{r}$$

$$\therefore \quad B = K\frac{i}{r},$$

where, K is the proportionality constant and is equal to $\frac{\mu_0}{2}$ (in S.I. system)

$$\therefore\ B = \frac{\mu_0}{2}$$

where, μ_0 as defined earlier is the permeability constant of vacuum and is equal to $4\pi \times 10^{-7}$ T m A^{-1}.

If there are 'n' turns in the circular coil, then each turn will contribute to the magnetic field at the centre. So, the total magnetic field at the centre due to 'n' turns will be equal to $\frac{n\mu_0 i}{2r}$.

Electromagnetism

Electromagnetism involves the interactions between electric current and magnetic field.

Properties of Magnetic Lines of Force Around a Circular Coil

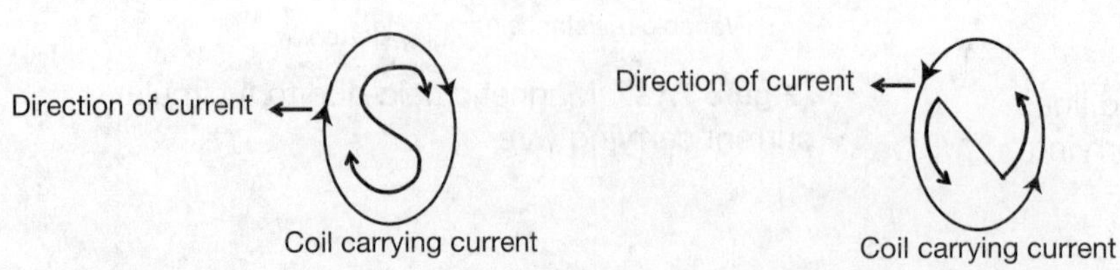

Figure 7.14 Sign conventions for magnetic field around a circular coil

Info Bytes!

Aurora Borealis, the Northern Lights, are a product of Earth's electromagnetism interacting with charged particles from the sun.

1. At the points where current enters or leaves coil is like a straight wire. Hence, the lines of force around these points are almost circular.
2. The lines of force inside coil are in same direction.
3. Magnetic field near the centre of coil is uniform as the lines of force are parallel to each other.
4. At the centre, the plane of magnetic field is perpendicular to the coil. The magnetic field strength increases with the increase in current.
5. Looking at a face of coil, if current is flowing in clockwise direction, the face develops south polarity. If it is in anti clockwise direction, the face develops north polarity.

EXAMPLE 7.2 Determine the amount of current flowing through a circular coil, if the strength of magnetic field at the centre of the coil is 4×10^{-5} T and its radius is 4 cm.

SOLUTION

$$B = \frac{\mu_0}{2r} \times i$$

$$4 \times 10^{-5} = \frac{4\pi \times 10^{-7}}{2} \times \frac{i}{4 \times 10^{-2}}$$

$$4 \times 10^{-5} = \frac{\pi}{2} \times 10^{-5} \times i$$

$$i = \frac{8}{\pi} A$$

EXAMPLE 7.3 Find the ratio of the magnetic fields, at distances 5 cm and 50 cm from a long straight current carrying conductor.

SOLUTION

Let the fields be B_1 and B_2 at distances 5 cm and 50 cm, respectively. As current remains same, we can write

$$B \propto \frac{1}{r}$$

$$\Rightarrow \frac{B_1}{B_2} = \frac{r_2}{r_1} \quad (1)$$

Substituting the value of r_1 and r_2 in equation (1), we get

$$\frac{B_1}{B_2} = \frac{50}{5} = 10$$

∴ The ratio of fields is 10 : 1.

EXAMPLE 7.4 A circular coil of radius π cm and 100 turns is carrying a current of 10 A. Find the magnitude of the magnetic induction field at the centre of the coil.

SOLUTION

The induction field at the centre of the coil is given by,

$$B = \frac{n\mu_0 i}{2r} \tag{1}$$

In the problem, the values given are, $r = \pi$ cm $= \pi \times 10^{-2}$ m, $n = 100$, $i = 10$ A

$$B = ?$$

Substituting the above values in equation (1), we get

$$B = \frac{100 \times 4\pi \times 10^{-7} \times 10}{2 \times \pi \times 10^{-2}} = 2 \times 10^{-2}\ \text{T} = 0.02\ \text{T}$$

Magnetic Field due to a Solenoid Carrying Current

An insulated copper coil wound around some cylindrical cardboard or some other core such that its length is greater than its diameter is called solenoid or helix.

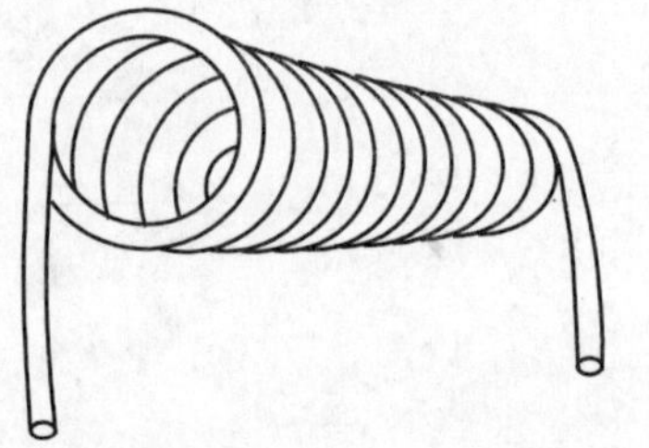

Figure 7.15 A Helix of Solenoid

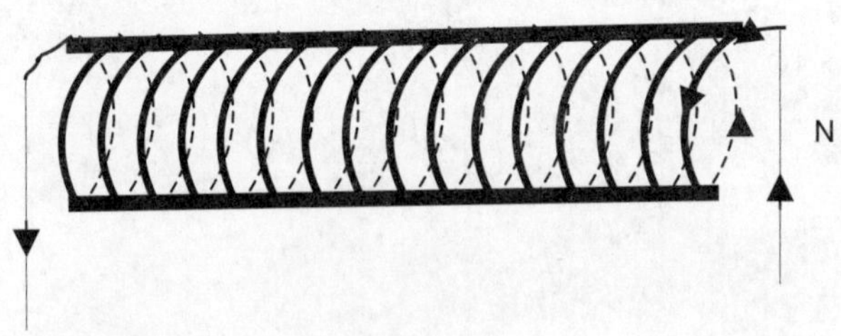

Figure 7.16 An insulated copper coil wound around a solenoid

When an electric current flows in the solenoid then each turn of the coil behaves like an independent magnet. All these magnets are arranged in order, and therefore, the total magnetic strength of the solenoid depends upon the number of turns. Thus, the solenoid acts like a bar magnet.

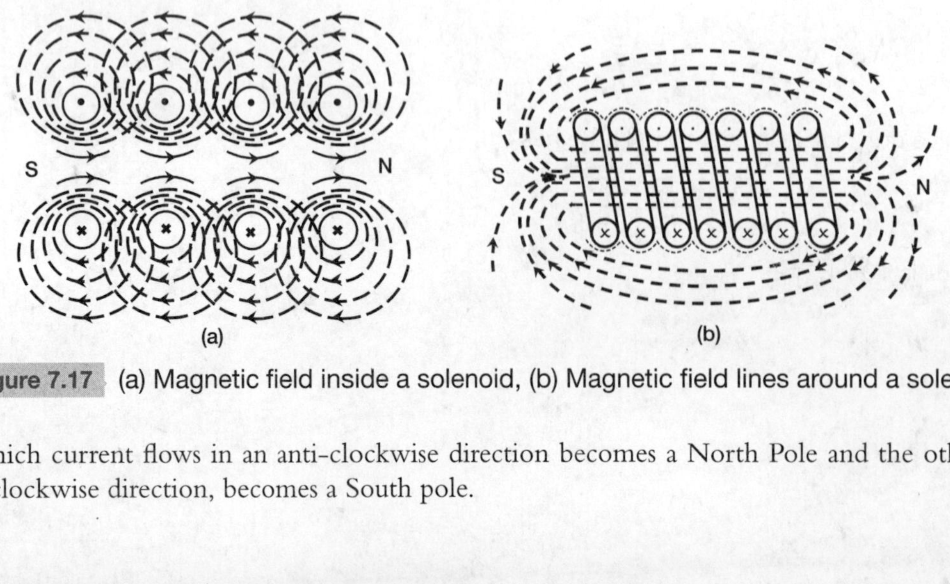

Figure 7.17 (a) Magnetic field inside a solenoid, (b) Magnetic field lines around a solenoid

The end in which current flows in an anti-clockwise direction becomes a North Pole and the other end where the current flows in clockwise direction, becomes a South pole.

Properties of a Solenoid

1. The magnetic field due to solenoid is directly proportional to the number of turns per unit length of the solenoid.
2. The magnetic field due to the solenoid is directly proportional to the current passing through the solenoid.
3. The field depends upon the nature of material on which the coil is wound.
4. If an iron core is kept inside the solenoid, the field becomes stronger.
5. Laminated soft iron core increases the intensity of the magnetic field inside a solenoid.
6. The magnetic lines of force within the solenoid are almost parallel to each other and to the axis of solenoid.

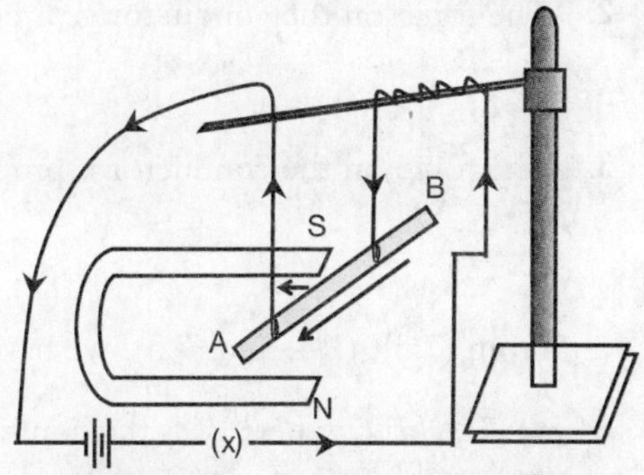

Figure 7.18 A current carrying rod, AB experiences a force perpendicular to the length and the magnetic field

Force on a Current Carrying Conductor Kept in a Magnetic Field

It is observed that when a current carrying conductor is kept in a magnetic field, it experiences a force.

Explanation

The lines of force representing the magnetic field between the poles of a horseshoe magnet would be straight and parallel to each other as shown in Fig. 7.19 (a) below.

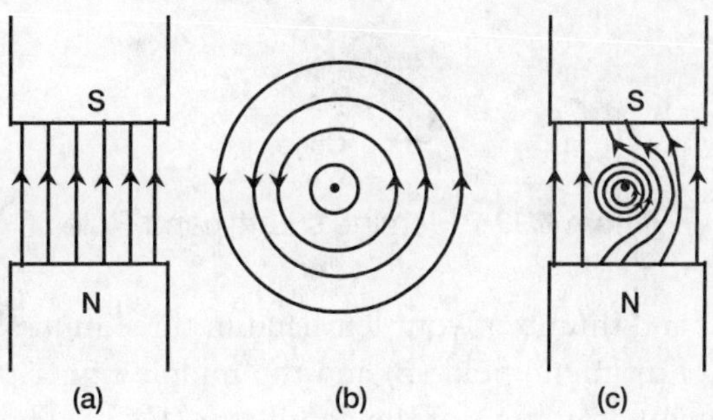

Figure 7.19 (a) Parallel magnetic field lines between the poles of a horseshoe magnet, (b) The magnetic field lines around a current carrying conductor, (c) Magnetic field lines when circular current carrying conductor is placed between poles of permanent magnet

The magnetic field lines around a current carrying conductor would be as shown in Fig. 7.19 (b). When this conductor is placed between the poles of the permanent magnet, the two fields would superimpose and there would be a tendency for the lines to crowd on the right side. These lines acting like stretched elastic strings would tend to straighten themselves, and thus, push the conductor towards the left. If the current in the conductor is reversed, the effect would be opposite.

The force acting on the current carrying conductor depends upon the following factors:

1. The force on the conductor is directly proportional to the current in the wire.

$$F \propto i \tag{7.3}$$

2. The force on the conductor is directly proportional to the strength of the magnetic field.

$$F \propto B. \tag{7.4}$$

3. The force on the conductor is proportional to the length of the conductor.

$$F \propto \ell \tag{7.5}$$

From (7.3), (7.4) and (7.5), we have $F \propto Bi\ell$

$\Rightarrow F = kBi\ell$, where 'k' is the constant of proportionality.

4. Let the force on a conductor of length 1m, carrying 1 current of 1A and placed in magnetic field of induction 1 T be 1N, then

$$1\text{ N} = K \times \frac{1\text{N}}{\text{Am}} \times 1\text{ A} \times 1\text{ m}$$

$$\because K = 1$$

$$\therefore F = Bil$$

The equation is applicable only when the current carrying conductor is placed at a right angle to the direction of the magnetic field B.

To find the direction of the force acting on the current carrying conductor, Fleming's Left-hand Rule is used which states as follows:

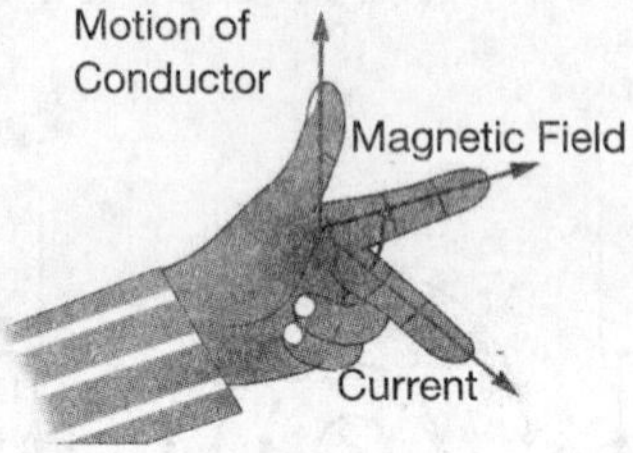

Figure 7.20 Fleming's Left-hand Rule

Stretch the forefinger, middle finger and thumb of your left hand in three mutually perpendicular directions. Now, if the forefinger points in the direction of magnetic field (B) and the middle finger points in the direction of current (i), then the thumb will point in the direction of motion of the conductor (F), i.e., the force acting on it.

If the magnetic field is not perpendicular to the current carrying wire, then the magnitude of force is given by, $F = Bi\ell\sin\theta$, where, θ is the angle which the current carrying wire makes with the direction of the magnetic field.

Moving Coil Galvanometer (Suspension Type)

Principle

A current carrying coil kept in a magnetic field experiences a couple which is proportional to the current. It is used to detect and find the direction of the flow of current. Voltmeter and ammeter are modified forms of a galvanometer.

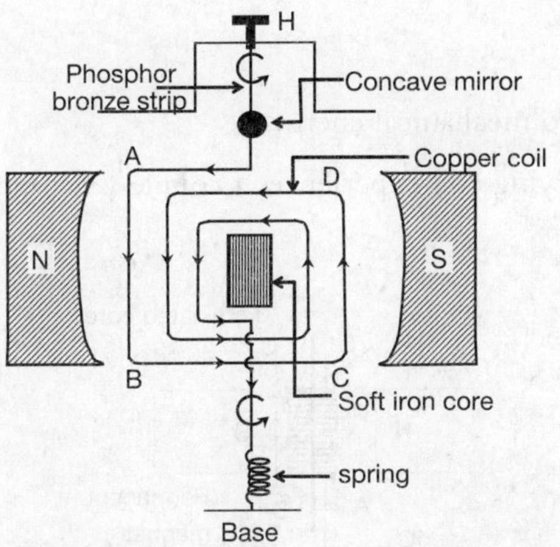

Figure 7.21 Moving coil galvanometer

> **Info Bytes!**
> Moving coil galvanometers are so sensitive, they can detect a current as minute as a nanoampere.

Construction

A moving coil galvanometer consists of a rectangular coil of thin, insulated copper wire suspended between the poles of a strong horseshoe magnet NS by means of a strip of phosphor bronze. It is attached to a torsion head 'H'. There is a small mirror attached to the phosphor bronze strip. This is to observe the deflection produced by the coil, when a current is passed through it. Current enters through the torsion head 'H' and leaves through the spring at the phosphor bronze bottom.

The magnet is made concave in shape so that its magnetic field is always parallel to the plane of the coil when the coil rotates and the magnitude of the magnetic field is the same at every point of time. This type of magnetic field is called radial magnetic field. Furthermore, soft iron core is kept suspended within the coil to increase the magnetic field.

Working

The current carrying coil ABCD is kept in a magnetic field such that the direction of the current and the field are perpendicular to each other. The direction of the current in the arms AB and CD are equal and opposite, therefore, both of them experience equal and opposite forces, forming a couple which tries to rotate the coil. This is called deflecting couple. The direction of the rotation of the coil is given by Fleming's left-hand rule.

As the coil rotates, the suspension wire and the loose spring of phosphor bronze get twisted, thus, opposing the rotation of the coil. This gives rise to an opposing couple called restoring couple. As the phosphor bronze wire is highly tensile, it does not break when the spring and wire are twisted.

When the moment of force produced by the deflecting couple is equal to the moment of force due to restoring couple, the coil comes to rest, at a new position.

The angle through which the coil has rotated can be measured by lamp and scale arrangement. It is found that the tangent of the angle of deflection is directly proportional to the strength of the current.

$$\tan \theta \propto i.$$

$$\therefore \quad i = k \tan \theta,$$

where, k is a constant and its value depends on:

1. The number of turns in the coil,
2. The area of cross section of the coil, and
3. The strength of the magnetic field.

The value of k is given by the manufacturers of galvanometers and knowing the deflection, we can calculate the current. Most often, using the given k the scale is directly calibrated in terms of current for a given galvanometer.

DC motor

A motor is a device which converts electrical energy into mechanical energy.

Principle: It works on the principle that a current carrying coil experiences a couple when placed in a magnetic field, which sets it into continuous rotations.

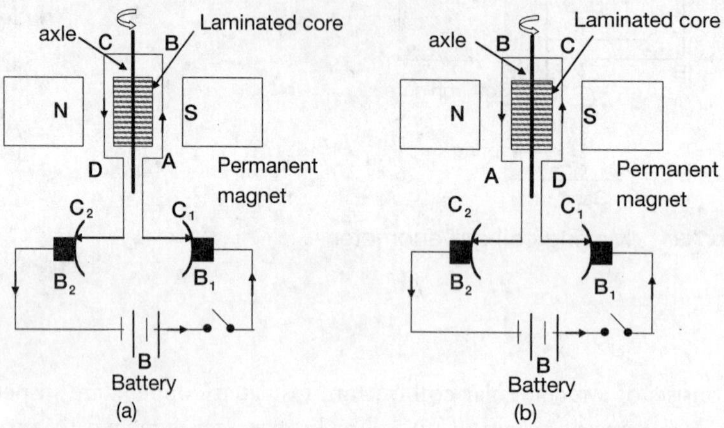

Figure 7.22 (a) Clockwise rotation of a motor by passing current, (b) Commutator reverses the current in DC motor.

The main parts of a motor are:

1. Permanent magnet N, S
2. Armature coil A, B, C, D
3. Commutator C_1, C_2
4. Brushes B_1, B_2
5. Battery B

The permanent magnet produces the necessary magnetic field. Its poles are made concave in shape so as to give radial field. In big motors, in order to have strong magnetic field, electromagnets are used.

Armature coil consists of a large number of insulated copper coils wound on a laminated soft iron core. The function of the coil is to set up magnetic field when a current is passed through it. The core is laminated to avoid any eddy current loss, and to provide strong magnetic field when current flows through the coil.

Commutator

The ends of the wire are connected to the two split rings C_1 and C_2 of the commutator. The function of the commutator is to change the direction of the current after half a rotation of the coil.

Brushes

The function of the two brushes B_1 and B_2 is to give electrical connection from the battery wire to the rotating coil, i.e., between the stationary parts and the moving parts of the electric circuit.

Battery

The function of the battery is to give the motor the necessary electrical energy.

Working of the Motor

The current from the positive terminal of the battery passes through the brush B_1, split ring C_1, and the armature coil ABCD returns via split ring C_2, brush B_2, to the negative terminal of the battery. The coil is placed in such a way that the magnetic field created by it is perpendicular to field due to magnets.

The current carrying coil is kept in the magnetic field of the permanent magnet. Therefore, it will experience a torque.

As per Fleming's left-hand rule, the arm AB of the coil experiences a force perpendicular to the plane of the paper and into the paper. The arm CD experiences a force perpendicular to the plane of paper and outwards (opposite to that of end AB) as shown in Fig. 7.22(a). These two forces constitute a couple and the motor rotates in clockwise direction.

When the coil turns through 90°, the magnetic field due to the coil and the field due to the permanent magnet become parallel to each other. Therefore, rotation should stop as there will not be any couple when the two fields are parallel. But due to the inertia of motion, it continues to rotate and it turns through 180°.

Now the commutator reverses the direction of the current which flows along DCBA. (as shown in Fig. 7.22(b). The arm CD of the wire experiences a force perpendicular to the plane of the paper and into the paper, and the arm AB experiences a force perpendicular to the plane of the paper and outwards (opposite to that of end AB). Thus, the motor rotates continuously in one direction.

The revolutions per minute of a motor coil depends on the following:

1. The number of the turns of the coil
2. The area of the coil
3. The magnitude of the current
4. The strength of the magnetic field

Electromagnetic Induction

We have seen that when current flows through a conductor, it produces a magnetic field. Michael Faraday, through series of experiments, showed that current can be induced in a coil if it is moved in a magnetic field or if magnet is moved relative to coil. Due to the relative motion between them, the magnetic flux (ϕ_0) linked with the coil, i.e., the number of lines of force passing normally through it, changes. This sets up an emf at the end of which causes current to flow. Faraday found that the current flows as long as there is continuous change in the magnetic flux passing through the conducting coil. Thus, even if both the coil and magnet are stationary, current can still be induced in coil, if the magnetic field is changed continuously which is possible by using electromagnets. This phenomenon of inducing current by changing the magnetic field associated with an electric circuit containing no source is called electromagnetic induction.

Faraday's Experiments

When a magnet is moved towards a coil with its north pole facing the coil as shown in the Fig. 7.23, Faraday observed a deflection in the galvanometer. The amount of deflection is found to be more if the speed of magnet is more.

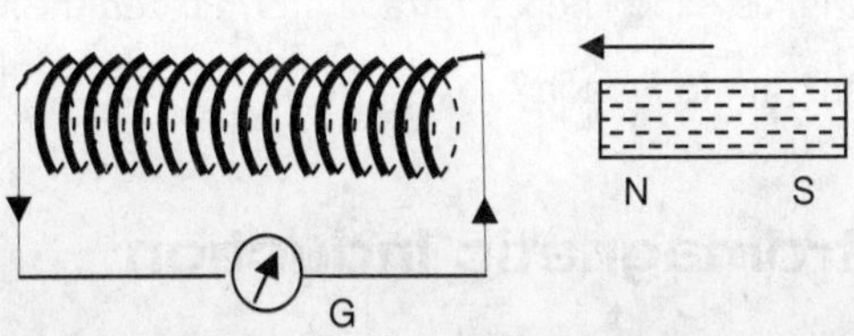

Figure 7.23 A magnet moved towards a coil with its north pole facing the coil

When the magnet is moved away from the coil, then it produces a deflection in the opposite direction as compared to the case, when the magnet is moved towards the coil.

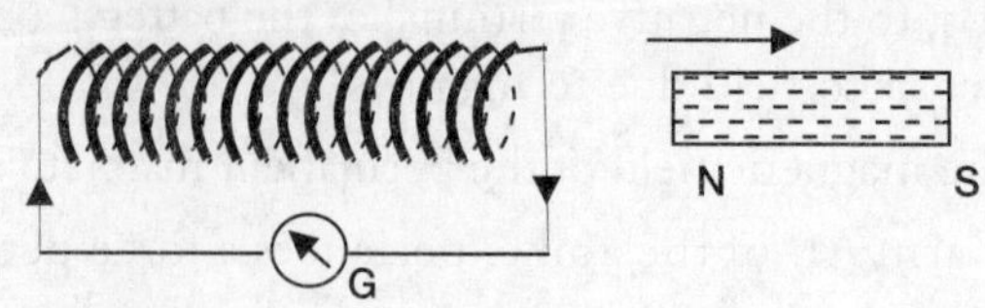

Figure 7.24 A magnet moved away from the coil

When the magnet is moved towards the coil with its south pole pointing towards the coil, then it produced a deflection in the opposite direction as compared to the case, when the north pole was pointing towards the coil.

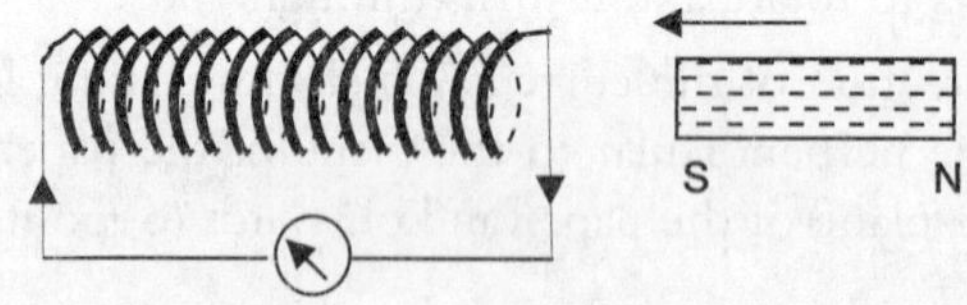

Figure 7.25 A magnet moved towards the coil with its south pole pointing towards the coil

Once again, if the magnet is moved away from the coil with the south pole pointing towards the coil, then it produces deflection in the opposite direction as compared to the case when the magnet is moved towards the coil.

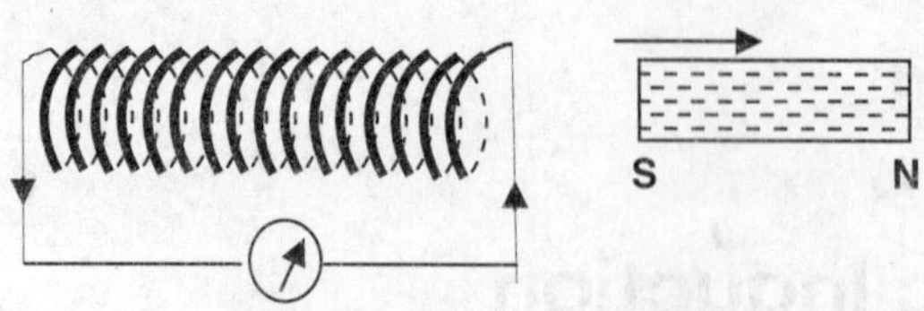

Figure 7.26 A magnet moved away from the coil with the south pole pointing towards the coil

Similar observations were made when the coil was moved towards or away from a stationary magnet. The deflections in the galvanometer were governed by the orientation of the magnet and the direction of the motion of the coil.

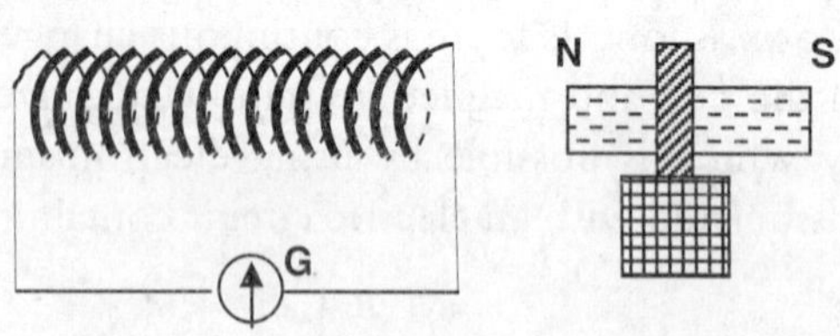

Figure 7.27 The coil moved towards or away from a stationary magnet.

Now, if we fix both the magnet and the coil such that there is no relative motion, then no deflection is observed in the galvanometer.

On the basis of the observations made in his experiments, Faraday formulated the following laws.

There are only two laws of EM induction, due to Faraday.

Faraday's Laws of Electromagnetic Induction

1. Whenever the magnetic flux linking a coil changes, then an emf is induced in the coil.
2. The magnitude of the induced emf is directly proportional to the rate of the change of flux.

From the above observations, we can conclude that if there is a relative motion between the magnet and the coil, an emf is induced in the coil.

1. This emf lasts so long as there is a relative motion between the magnet and the coil.
2. If there is no relative motion, no emf is induced.
3. The magnitude of emf depends upon the relative speed.
4. The magnitude of emf depends upon the number of turns in the coil.

Following the above conclusions, Faraday formulated the law for induced emf in a coil as, the induced emf in a coil is equal to the negative rate of the change of magnetic flux linked with the coil.

Thus,
$$E = -N\frac{d\varphi}{dt}$$

The observations of Faraday's experiments on electromagnetic induction and his laws can also be studied by replacing the permanent magnet with an electromagnet.

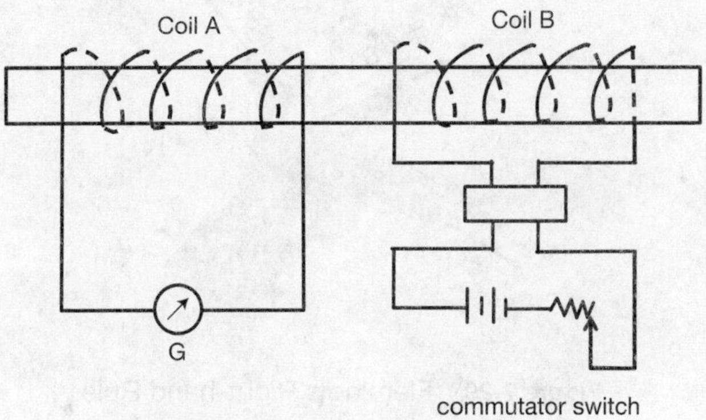

Figure 7.28 Faraday's Experiment

Wind two coils on a soft iron core separated by some distance, connecting the ends of coil A to a galvanometer and the ends of B to a battery through a rheostat (to vary the current) and a commutator switch (to reverse the current). It is observed that the needle of the galvanometer instantly deflects to one side and returns to zero quickly whenever the key is closed. When the key is opened, thus, disconnecting the coil from the battery, a greater deflection is observed is the galvanometer, but in the opposite directions.

Repeating the experiment after reversing the direction of current in coil B, similar observations are recorded.

Lenz's Law

According to Lenz's law, the direction of induced current is such that it opposes the very cause that produces it.

Consider a bar magnet moving towards a coil with its north pole facing the coil. Due to movement of the magnet see Fig. 7.23, current is induced in anti-clockwise direction in the coil when it is viewed from magnet. The face pointing towards the magnet becomes north pole and opposes its movement. When magnet is pulled away such that its north-pole leaves the coil, (Fig. 7.24) current is induced in clockwise direction giving the face of the coil pointing towards magnet a south polarity. Thus, the movement of magnet which is responsible for induced current, is always opposed by the current itself.

Let $d\phi_B$ be the change in the magnetic flux in a short interval of time dt. The induced emf (E), according to Faraday's law is given by,

$$E = \frac{-d\phi_B}{dt} \tag{7.6}$$

According to Lenz's law, the induced emf is such that it opposes the cause producing it. Hence, equation (7.6) on application of Lenz's law becomes

$$E = \frac{-d\phi_B}{dt} \tag{7.7}$$

If the coil contains N turns, equation (7.7) becomes

$$E = -N\frac{d\varphi_B}{dt}$$

Fleming's Right-hand Rule

To determine the direction of induced current in a conductor, when it is moved across a magnetic field, Fleming proposed the 'Right-hand rule'.

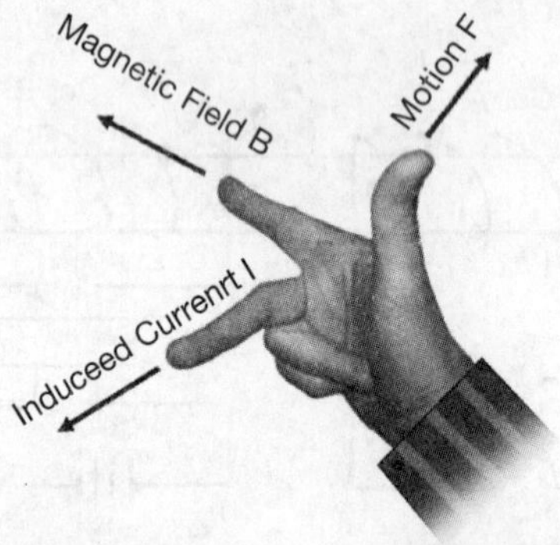

Figure 7.29 Fleming's Right-hand Rule

Stretch the forefinger, middle finger and thumb of your right-hand in three mutually perpendicular directions, such that the forefinger points in the direction of magnetic field (B), the thumb indicates the direction of motion (M), then the middle finger represents the direction of induced current (i) in the conductor.

Moving Coil Microphone

It is a device which converts sound energy into electric energy. It works on the principle of electromagnetic induction.

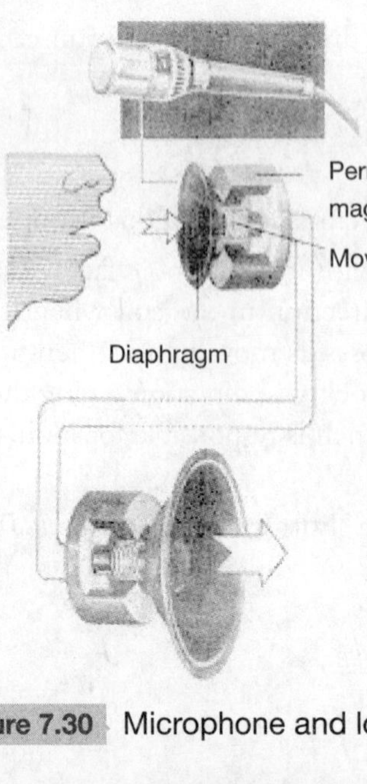

Figure 7.30 Microphone and loudspeaker

It consists of a diaphragm, a moving coil and a permanent magnet. The coil is kept in the magnetic field. As a person speaks into microphone, diaphragm is set into vibrations. The moving coil connected to it begins to vibrate accordingly. It being under magnetic field, a electric current is induced in it whose variations represent the vibrations of original sound. This electrical signal is amplified and then fed to a loud speaker.

Loud Speaker

It converts electric energy into sound energy. It consists of a permanent magnet, moving coil and a diaphragm in the form of paper cone as shown in the Fig. 7.31.

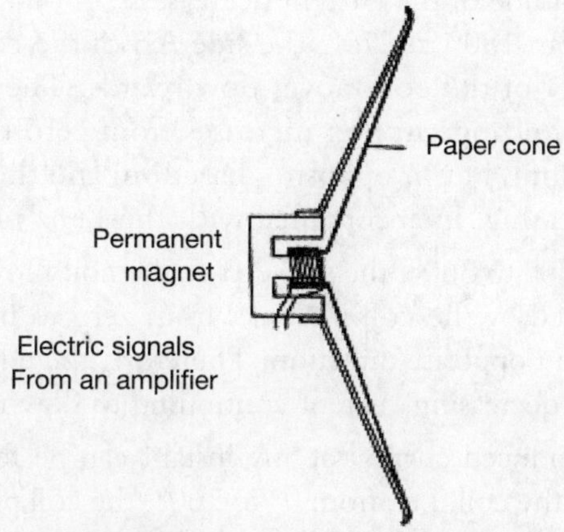

Figure 7.31 Parts of a loud speaker

The electrical signal corresponding to the variations of original sound from the microphone is fed to the coil placed between the poles of permanent magnet. The coil begins to vibrate and sets the paper cone into vibrations. The air around the loudspeaker vibrates reproducing the original sound more loudly.

Electric Generator

An electric generator is a device which converts mechanical energy into electrical energy. When a coil is rotated in a magnetic field, an emf is induced in it. The mechanical energy required to rotate the coil is converted into an electrical energy. Hence, an electric generator converts mechanical energy into electrical energy.

There are two types of generators—Alternating Current (AC) generator and Direct Current (DC) generator. In the former, the current changes direction after every half-rotation. In the latter, the current is unidirectional throughout.

The Alternating Current Generator

The main parts of an AC generator are the horseshoe magnet, armature (coil), slip rings and carbon brushes.

Construction

The construction of an electric generator is similar to that of an electric motor. An AC generator consists of a rectangular coil ABCD known as armature. This armature is rotated rapidly between the poles of a permanent horseshoe magnet. The ends of the rectangular coil A and D are connected to two circular metal pieces called slip rings A_1 and A_2. The slip rings rotate along with the coil. The two pieces of carbon brushes B_1 and B_2 are kept in contact with the slip rings. The carbon brushes are capable of tapping the current produced in the rotating coil.

Working

1. Assume that the rectangular coil ABCD is in horizontal position initially [See Fig. 7.32 (1)].
2. Let the rectangular coil ABCD be rotated from 0° to 90°, such that during its rotation, the side AB of the coil moves downwards and the side CD of the coil upwards. Hence, the flux linked decreases, but the rate of change in the flux increases from zero to maximum. Hence, emf induced increases from zero to maximum, (according to Faraday's laws of electromagnetic induction). The current flows in the direction ABCD according to Lenz's Law.
3. On further rotation from 90° to 180°, the side AB of the coil starts moving upwards while the side CD of the coil moves down. Hence, flux linked increases from zero to maximum. But the rate of change in flux decreases from maximum to zero. The emf induced in the coil decreases from maximum to zero. The current continues to flow in the direction ABCD, but the magnitude of the current decreases.
4. On further rotation of the coil from 180° to 270°, the side AB of the coil which is now once again horizontal moves upwards while the side CD of the coil moves downwards. The flux linked by the coil decreases from maximum to zero. But the rate of change in flux increases from zero to maximum in the opposite direction. Hence, the emf induced is maximum, but in opposite direction, and the current starts flowing in the direction DCBA, with the magnitude increasing, in accordance with the Lenz's Law.
5. On further rotation of coil from 270° to 360°, the side AB of the coil moves downwards while the side CD of the coil moves upwards. The flux linked by the coil increases from zero to maximum and the rate of change in flux decreases from maxiumum to zero in opposite direction. Therefore, the emf induced also decreases from maximum to zero in opposite direction, with decreasing current continuing to flow in the direction DCBA.

In the above figure, the direction of induced current at any instant can be found using Fleming's right-hand rule or Lenz's Law. For one complete rotation of the coil, i.e., from 0° to 360°, the coil produces an alternating voltage (AC). The variation in the current produced for various positions of the coil is shown in the graph.

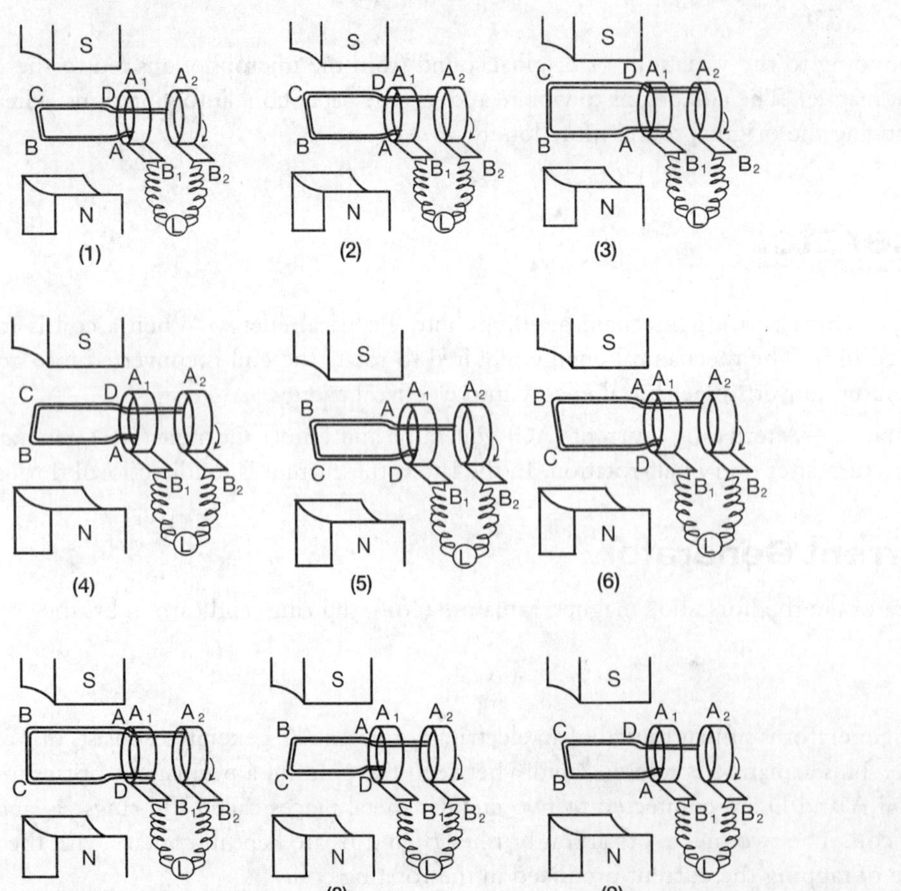

Info Bytes!

The world's largest electric generator is the Three Gorges Dam hydroelectric power station in China.

Figure 7.32 Working of an AC Generator in various steps showing positions of coil.

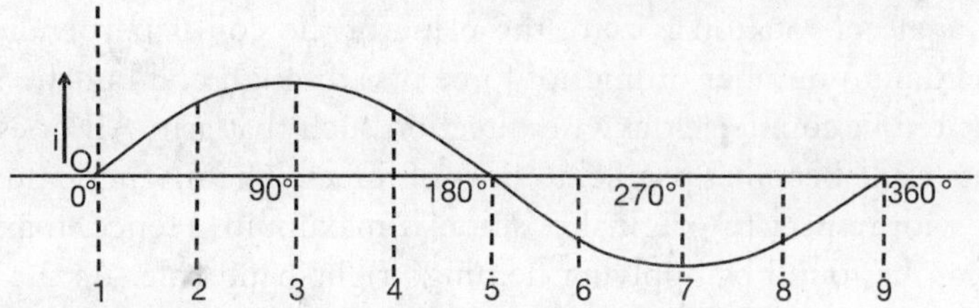

Figure 7.33 The variation in the current produced for various positions of the coil

Alternating Current (AC) Dynamo

Principle

When a conducting coil in a closed circuit in a constant uniform magnetic field rotates, the magnetic flux passing through it changes continuously producing an induced emf or current in the circuit.

Construction

It consists of four major parts.

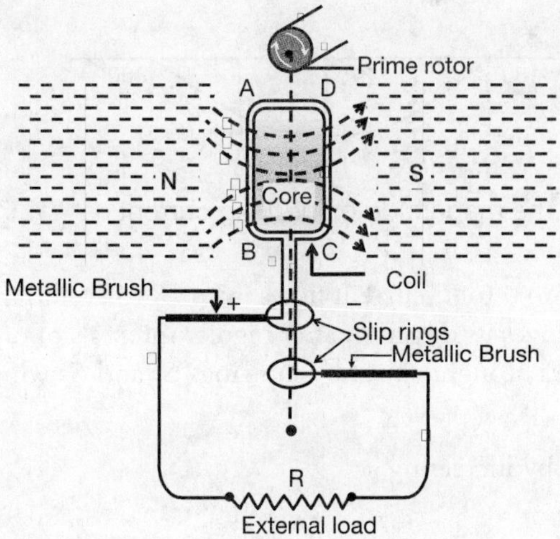

Figure 7.34 An Alternating Current (AC) Dynamo

Info Bytes!

- Alternating current (AC) generators are more commonly used than DC generators due to their efficiency in long-distance power transmission.
- The world's oldest working AC dynamo is over 130 years old and is still operational.

1. **Armature:** It consists of insulated copper coil wound over a rectangular frame and soft iron core which a laminated. In the Fig. 7.34, ABCD represents armature.
2. **Slip rings:** S_1 and S_2 are two metallic rings connected to the ends of the rectangular coil. They rotate along with the coil about the same axis.
3. **Carbon brushes:** B_1 and B_2 are two carbon brushes used as electrical contact between moving parts (S_1 and S_2) and stationary part (load R).
4. **Permanent magnet:** N-S is powerful horseshoe magnet having concave cylindrical poles. It produces a uniform radial magnetic field.

Working

As the amature ABCD is rotated between the poles of magnet, the magnetic flux linked with it changes continuously resulting in generation of induced emf which causes current to flow through the coil and load resistance R. As the position of amature coil changes due to its rotation, the magnitude of induced current also changes as shown in following diagram.

In its initial position where angle of rotation is zero, the plane of the coil is perpendicular to the magnetic lines of force or magnetic flux (ϕ_B). Maximum number of lines of force pass through coil but the induced current is zero as coil is stationary. Let the coil be rotated in counter clockwise direction such that arm AB goes down and CD comes up. As the coil rotates by 90° or $\pi/2$, its plane becomes parallel to lines of forces. The magnetic flux linked with it is zero but the change in magnetic flux ($d\phi_B$) with respect to original position is maximum. Hence, maximum induced current flows. The direction of this current can be found by applying fleming's right-hand rule. As the arm AB moves in downward direction and lines of force are from right to left, current flows from B to A in the arm AB. Arm CD has moved in upward direction, hence, current through it flows in opposite direction, i.e., from D to C. Through the load R, it flows from B_1 to B_2. As the coil rotates further by 90°, it again becomes perpendicular to magnetic flux with AB below CD. The magnetic flux passing through the coil is same as in initial position. Hence, the change $d\phi_B$ is zero causing the induced current to decrease from maximum to zero in the same direction. From this position as the coil rotates by 90°, AB moves up and CD down such that its plane is parallel to magnetic flux. As the change in the flux ($d\phi_B$) is maximum with respect to 'O' the induced current increases from zero to maximum in opposite direction which can be verified by applying Fleming's right-hand rule. Now the current flows from A to B, in AB, C to D in CD and B_2 to B_1 in R. As the coils comes back to its original position by rotating more by 90°, current decreases from maximum to zero in the same direction. This cycle is repeated as coil continues its rotational motion.

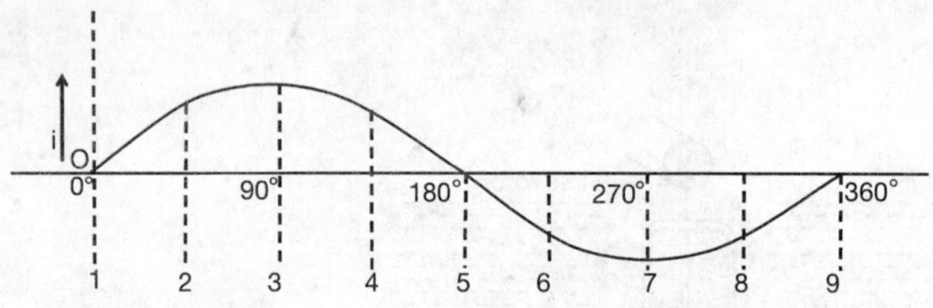

Figure 7.35 Graph of the magnitude of induced current

It can be seen that during 1st half of rotation, i.e., from 0 to π, current flows from B_1 to B_2 in R, while during 2nd half from π to 2π, it flows from B_2 to B_1. Thus, current changes its direction after regular intervals of time. Hence, alternating current is generated. This reversal in current direction is brought about by slip rings S_1 and S_2 which alternately connect the two ends of coil to B_1 and B_2.

The magnitude of induced current can be increased by increasing:

1. The number of turns in coil.
2. The area of cross section of coil.
3. The intensity of magnetic field.
4. The speed of rotation of coil.

RMS Voltage and Peak Voltage

In this type of a generator, we observe that the induced voltage across the output terminals alternates between $+V_0$ and $-V_0$ as shown in the Fig. 7.35. The alternation from $+V_0$ to $-V_0$ and again back to $+V_0$ (or $-V_0$ to $+V_0$ to $-V_0$) is referred to as one cycle, and if the frequency is n Hz, it implies that n cycles are completed in one second. The voltage V_0 is called peak value.

If the terminals of this generator are connected across a resistor, the current flowing through the circuit would also alternate at the same frequency and is referred to as alternating current. Thus, such a source of electrical energy is referred to as AC source or AC supply. The symbol for an AC source is. (~)

If a heater coil is connected to an AC supply of peak voltage V_0, the heater coil gets continuously heated even though the direction of current alternates. It is found that the heating effect produced by such a source would be the same as that caused by a constant voltage source such as a cell of terminal p.d. equal to $V_0/\sqrt{2}$. It can be shown that this value is the square root of the mean of the squares of the instantaneous voltages across the terminals of the AC supply. Hence, it is called Root Mean Square (RMS) value.

$$\therefore \quad V_{RMS} = \frac{V_0}{\sqrt{2}} \text{ and } I_{RMS} = \frac{I_0}{\sqrt{2}}$$

EXAMPLE 7.5 Find the RMS value of +5, +3, +1, –1 and –3.

SOLUTION

Let $x_1 = 5$, $x_1 = 3$, $x_1 = 1$, $x_1 = -1$ and $x_1 = -3$.

Now, squaring each number we have,

$(x_1)^2 = (5)^2 = 25$

$(x_2)^2 = (3)^2 = 9$

$(x_3)^2 = (1)^2 = 1$

$(x_4)^2 = (-1)^2 = 1$

$(x_5)^2 = (-3)^2 = 9$

Add up the squared numbers: $\therefore x_i^2 = 25 + 9 + 1 + 1 + 9 = 45$

Dividing the sum by the total number of values ($n = 5$):

$$\therefore \frac{x_i^2}{n} = \frac{45}{5} = 9$$

Finally, take the square toot of the result $RMS = \sqrt{9} = 3$

So, the RMS value of the given number is 3.

EXAMPLE 7.6 If an AC supply is rated as 110 V, find the peak voltage.

SOLUTION

The rating of an AC supply refers to its RMS value.

Thus,

$V_{RMS} = 110V$

The relationship between RMS voltage and peak voltage for a sinusoidal waveform is:

$V_{RMS} = \frac{V_0}{\sqrt{2}}$, where V_0 is the peak voltage.

Given that $V_{RMS} = 110V$

We can arrange the equation to solve for V_0:

$V_0 = V_{RMS} \times \sqrt{2}$

$V_0 = 110 \times \sqrt{2} \Rightarrow 155.54V$

Therefore, the peak voltage is approximately 155.54V.

The Direct Current Generator

When the current flows continuously in one direction, the current is referred to as direct current. To obtain such a DC current, the AC generator is modified by replacing the slip rings with a commutator (half-slip rings or split rings) S_1S_2.

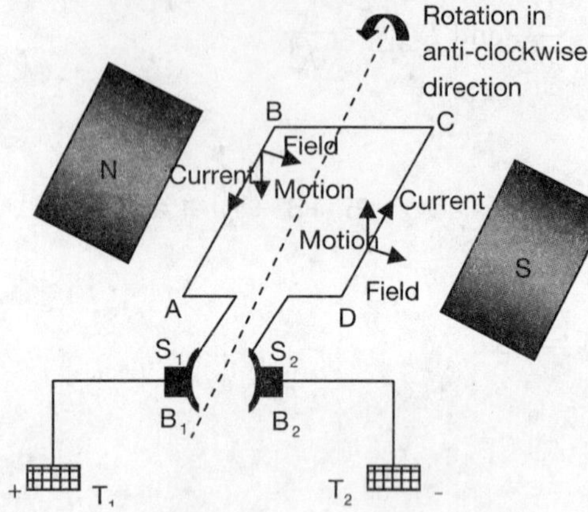

Figure 7.36 DC Generator

Working

Let the generator coil ABCD be initially in the horizontal position. Let the coil be rotated in an anti-clockwise direction as shown in the Fig. 7.37, side AB downwards and side CD upwards. According to Fleming's right-hand rule, the induced current flows in the direction BA in the side AB and in the direction DC in the side CD. Thus, induced current flows in the direction DCBA during the first half of rotation.

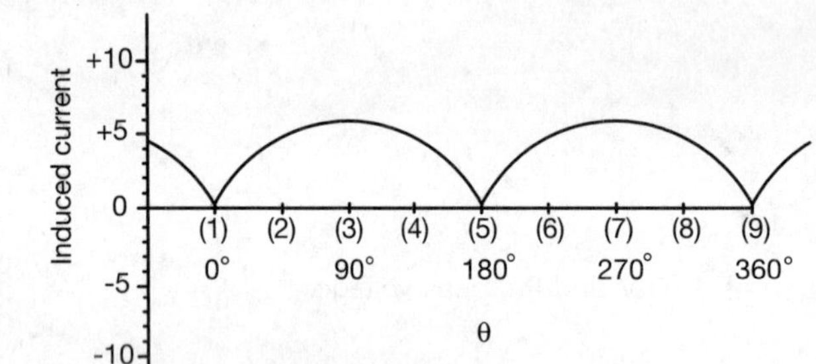

Figure 7.37 Graph of direct current

Konnect

Early DC generators were used to power street lamps before the widespread adoption of AC power.

After half rotation, arms AB and CD interchange their positions. When the coils interchange their positions, the commutator split rings S_1 and S_2 automatically change their contact with the carbon brushes. Due to this, the current flowing in the load remains in one direction. Thus, the brush B_1 remains always positive and the brush B_2 remains always negative. Thus, the current would always be flowing out from the terminal T_1.

Inductance of a Coil

The relative motion of a coil and a magnet induces an emf in the coil. This emf is referred to as dynamically induced emf, an since the emf is induced due to the actual motion of either the magnet or coil. If a change in the current in one coil induces an emf in another coil (due to changing magnetic field linked with each other), then the emf induced in the second coil is referred to as statically induced emf.

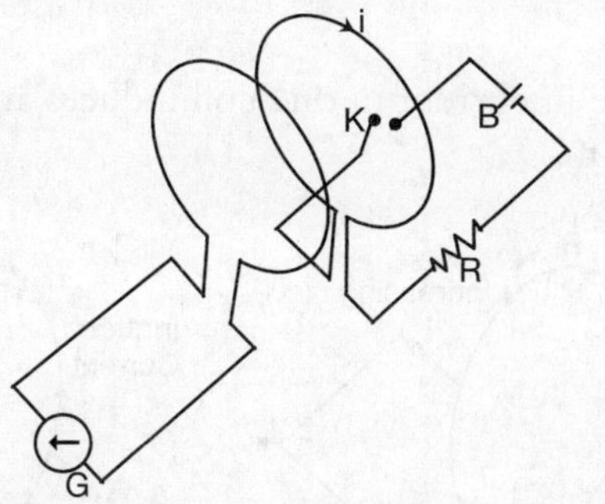

Figure 7.38 Circuit diagram to show a coil and a magnet induces an emf in the coil

Inductance is the property of a coil to induce emf in the same coil or another coil placed near it due to the changes in the current in the coil.

Self-Induction

Every current carrying coil produces a magnetic field which is linked to the same coil. When the current in the coil changes, the magnetic flux produced also changes and is linked to the coil itself. According to Faraday's law of induction, this change in magnetic field produces an induced emf which opposes the change.

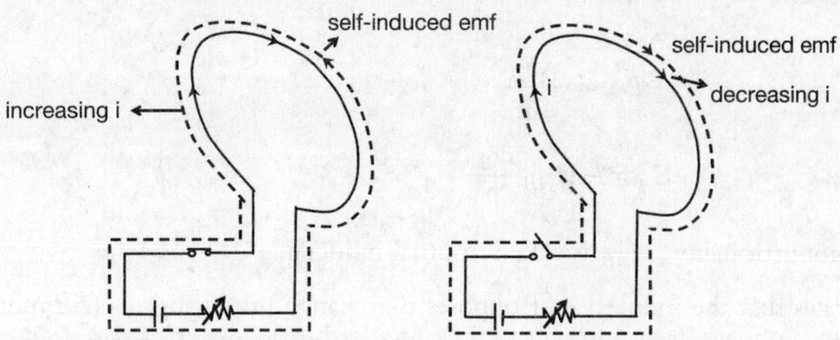

Figure 7.39 Self-induction in current carrying coils

This phenomenon in which an induced emf is produced in a coil due to a change in the current in the same coil is called self-induction, and the induced emf is generally referred to as self-induced emf.

The induced emf is equal to the rate of change of flux.

$$E \alpha -\frac{d\phi}{dt}$$

The negative sign indicates the induced emf opposes the applied emf.

But $\frac{d\varphi}{dt} \propto \frac{di}{dt}$ and so $\frac{d\varphi}{dt} = L\frac{di}{dt}$

$\therefore E = -L\frac{di}{dt}$ where 'L' is the constant of proportionality and is called self-inductance of the coil.

$$L = \frac{-E}{\left(\frac{di}{dt}\right)}$$

The self inductance 'L' of a coil is numerically equal to the ratio of the induced emf to the rate of change of current in the coil.

Mutual Induction

The phenomenon, due to which a change in current in one coil induces an emf in another coil held close to it, is called 'mutual induction'.

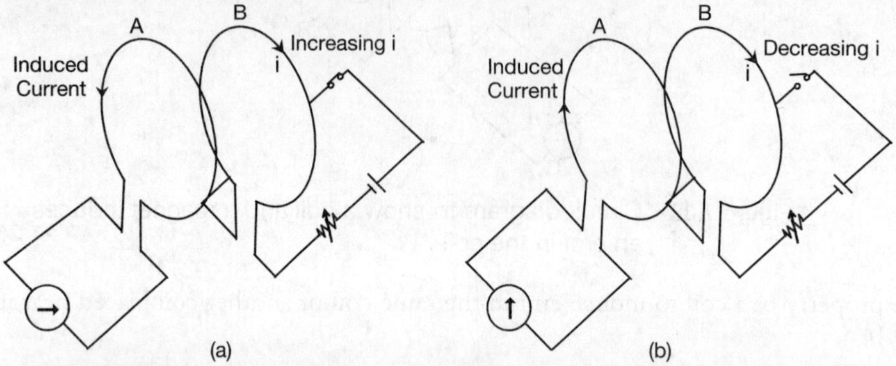

Figure 7.40 (a) Induced emf in coil A on increasing current in coil B, (b) Induced emf in coil A on decreasing current in coil B

Here, the current is changing in coil 'B'. Therefore, the flux associated with the coil B is changing. If we place one more coil 'A' near it, the changing magnetic field in coil 'B' will produce an emf in the second coil 'A'. This phenomenon is known as mutual induction.

$$E_A \propto -\frac{di_B}{dt}$$

$$E_A = -M_{AB}\frac{di_B}{dt}$$

Here, the constant of proportionality 'M_{AB}' is called 'mutual inductance'.

The negative sign indicates that the induced emf opposes the change producing it. The mutual inductance of a coil is numerically equal to the ratio of the induced emf in the coil to the rate of change of current in the another coil, placed near it.

$$M_{AB} = -\frac{E_A}{di_B/dt}$$

The unit of inductance (self-inductance and mutual inductance) is Henry (H) and 1 H = 1 V s A^{-1} (volt second per ampere).

Transformer

It is a static electrical device used to step-up a low voltage to a high voltage or to step-down a high voltage into a low voltage and is used on AC circuits. Transformer works on the principle of mutual induction. The main parts of a transformer are:

1. A soft iron laminated core
2. A primary coil
3. A secondary coil

Core

The core is made up of a rectangular frame made up of silicon steel. Each sheet is insulated from the neighbouring sheet by varnishing it.

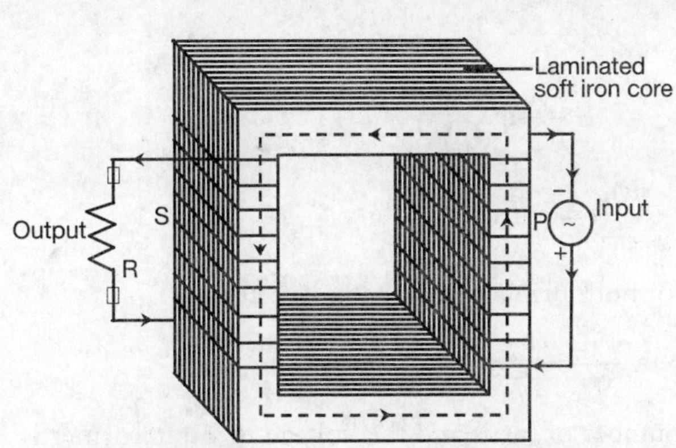

Figure 7.41 The core of a transformer

1. It is made up of soft iron to increase the magnetic permeability.
2. It is made up of laminations to avoid eddy current loss.

Primary Coil

The input of the alternating voltage is connected to this coil. Since the voltage changes with respect to time, changing magnetic flux is introduced by this coil. This changing flux is coupled to the secondary coil through the core.

Secondary Coil

The output from the transformer is taken from this coil. The changing flux due to changing voltage in the primary coil is coupled to the secondary coil. This will produce an alternating voltage.

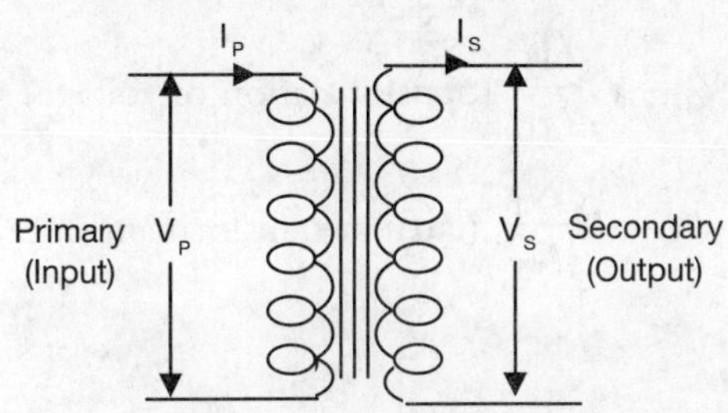

Figure 7.42 Secondary coil

Step-Up Transformer

A step-up transformer steps the primary (incoming) voltage up to a higher value. If the number of turns of the secondary coil is more than the number of turns of the primary coil, it is called step-up transformer. In this case, the secondary voltage will be more than the primary voltage. The secondary current is less than the primary current.

Step-Down Transformer

A step-down transformer steps the primary voltage down to a lower value. If the number of turns of the secondary coil is less than that of the primary coil, it is called step-down transformer. In this case, the secondary voltage will be less than the primary voltage. The secondary current is more than the primary current in a step-down transformer.

Working

If an AC voltage V_1 is applied to the primary coil of N_1 turns, an alternating current flows in the primary coil and produces a changing magnetic flux. This magnetic flux is linked to the N_2 turns of the secondary coil, thereby, an emf is induced in the secondary coil. Let it be V_2.

According to Faraday's law of induction,

$$E = -N\frac{d\varphi_B}{dt}$$

i.e., emf per turn, $E_{tum} = \frac{E}{N} = -\frac{d\varphi_B}{dt} = \text{constant}$

Thus, emf per turn is the same for both primary and secondary coils.

$$\therefore \frac{V_1}{N_1} = \frac{V_2}{N_2}$$

Thus, the relation between the number of turns and the voltage in a transformer is given by,

$$\frac{V_1}{V_2} = \frac{N_1}{N_2} \quad (7.8)$$

Since in an ideal transformer, there is no loss of power,

power in the primary = power in the secondary coils. If I_1 and I_2 are the currents in the primary and secondary coils, respectively,

$$P = V_1 I_1 = V_2 I_2$$

$$\frac{V_1}{V_2} = \frac{I_2}{I_1} \quad (7.9)$$

From. (7.8) and (7.9),

$$\frac{N_1}{N_2} = \frac{V_1}{V_2} = \frac{I_2}{I_1}$$

$$V_2 = V_1\frac{N_2}{N_1} \text{ (transformation of voltage)}$$

$$I_2 = I_1\frac{N_1}{N_2} \text{ (current transformation)}$$

$\therefore N_2 > N_1 \Rightarrow$ step-up transformer

$\therefore N_2 < N_1 \Rightarrow$ step-down transformer.

Konnect

- Step-up transformers are commonly used in power distribution networks to send electricity over long distances with minimal loss.
- Step-down transformers are what make it safe for you to use electrical appliances at home by lowering the voltage from power lines.

Energy Loss in Transformers

1. Due to the finite resistance of the primary and secondary coils, there will be a power loss in the primary and secondary coils due to heat energy developed in them. This is known as copper loss or heat loss.
   Copper loss = I^2R
2. A part of the energy is wasted on account of the magnetic flux in the soft iron core. This is known as magnetic loss or hysteris loss.
3. A part of energy is wasted on account of the eddy current. This is known as eddy current loss. This is minimized by using laminated core.
4. Loss due to flux leakage.

Uses of a Transformer

1. At the generating station, a transformer is used to step-up the voltage before transmitting it for long distances to avoid losses. At the receiving end, it is used to step-down to the required level to supply to the domestic users. It is used to change the voltage to required level.
2. In a radio, TV, X-ray tube, etc., either the step-up or step-down transformers are used.
3. In stabilizers, step-up–cum–step-down transformers are used to control the fluctuations in voltage.

EXAMPLE 7.7 In a transformer, the ratio of the number of turns of a primary to a secondary coil is 2 : 5. If the current through the primary coil is 10 A and input power is 300 W, find the current and voltage in the secondary coil.

SOLUTION

The turn-ratio and currents are related as

$$\frac{N_1}{N_2} = \frac{I_2}{I_1} \quad (1)$$

In the problem, values given are $\frac{N_1}{N_2} = \frac{2}{5}$, $I_1 = 10$ A

Substituting the above values in (1) and solving for I_2, we get

$$\frac{2}{5} = \frac{I_2}{10}$$

$$\Rightarrow I_2 = \frac{2}{5} \times 10 \Rightarrow I_2 = 4 \text{ A}$$

In an ideal transformer, the input and the output powers are equal. Therefore, we can write

$$V_1 I_1 = V_2 I_2 \quad (2)$$

But the input power is given as 300 W. Substituting this in equation (2), we get

$$V_2 I_2 = 300$$

Substituting $I_2 = 4$ A in the above equation, we get

$$V_2 \times 4 = 300 \Rightarrow V_2 = \frac{300}{4}$$

$$\Rightarrow V_2 = 75 \text{ V.}$$

Eddy Currents

Induced currents produced in a solid core piece of metal placed in changing magnetic field is called eddy current. It has advantages and disadvantages.

Let us see why eddy currents are undesirable. The eddy currents produced heat up the metallic solid core. The heating of core by eddy currents is undesirable because

1. It results in the loss of useful energy.
2. It increases the risk of the breakdown of the insulation of the winding.

Eddy currents can be eliminated by the following methods.

1. The solid metal is cut in such a manner so as to increase the path for the eddy current. Hence, the resistance increases and eddy current reduces.
2. Eddy currents can be reduced by using a laminated core. Instead of using a solid core, if we use thin sheets packed together and insulated between two layers, the resistance increases and the eddy current is reduced. This is the reason why the coil of a transformer is wound on a laminated core and not on the solid core.

Konnect

Eddy currents are used in induction cooking, where they heat up the cooking pan directly without a heating element.

Uses of Eddy Current

We can make use of the eddy current for some useful purpose. Eddy currents produce heat in metals. Hence, metals can be melted using the eddy current. This is the principle of induction in melting and heating furnaces.

POINTS TO REMEMBER

- ✔ The substances which are attracted towards a magnet and can become magnets are caled magnetic substances.
- ✔ The substances which are not attracted towards a magnet and cannot be magnetized are called non-magnetic substances.
- ✔ The area surrounding magnet, in which its effect can be felt, is called magnetic field of the magnet.
- ✔ A magnetic field can be represented by lines of force.
- ✔ The ability of the pole of a magnet to attract or repel another magnetic pole is called its pole strength. It is denoted by 'm'. Its SI unit is ampere-metre.
- ✔ Magnetic permeability (μ) of a medium is defined as its ability to allow the magnetic lines of force to pass through it or to allow itself to be influenced by magnetic field.
- ✔ The unit magnetic pole is defined as that pole which repels an identical pole at 1 metre distance with a force of 10^{-7} N.
- ✔ The total number of lines passing through the given area is called magnetic flux 'ϕ'.
- ✔ The intensity of magnetic field refers to the strength of a magnetic field at a point in C.G.S. units.
- ✔ The magnetic moment of a bar magnet is given by the product of its length and pole strength.
- ✔ A line perpendicular to the axis and passing through the midpoint of the magnet is called equatorial line.
- ✔ The substances in which the net magnetic moment of any atom in them is zero are called diamagnetic substances.
- ✔ Those substances in which the orientation of electron orbits and axes of their spins are such that the net magnetic moment of any atom is not zero, are called paramagnetic substances.
- ✔ Ferromagnetic substances are those in which the resultant magnetic moments of individual atoms align themselves parallel to each other due to a special effect which leads to spontaneous magnetization.
- ✔ The angle made by the axis of magnetic needle with the horizontal is called angle of dip or inclination.
- ✔ The angle between geographic and magnetic meridian at a place is called angle of declination.
- ✔ Electromagnetism involves the interactions between electric current and magnetic field.
- ✔ A motor is a device which converts electrical energy into mechanical energy.
- ✔ The phenomenon of inducing current by changing the magnetic field associated with an electric circuit containing no source is called electromagnetic induction.
- ✔ According to Lenz's law, the direction of induced current is such that it opposes the very cause that produces it.
- ✔ Moving coil microphone is a device which converts sound energy into electric energy. It works on the principle of electromagnetic induction.
- ✔ An electric generator is a device which converts mechanical energy into electrical energy.
- ✔ Inductance is the property of a coil to induce emf in the same coil or another coil placed near it due to the changes in the current in the coil.
- ✔ The phenomenon in which an induced emf is produced in a coil due to a change in the current in the same coil is called self-induction.
- ✔ The phenomenon, due to which a change in current in one coil induces an emf in another coil held close to it, is called 'mutual induction'.
- ✔ Transformer is a static electrical device used to step-up a low voltage to a high voltage or to step-down a high voltage into a low voltage and is used on AC circuits.
- ✔ Induced currents produced in a solid core piece of metal placed in changing magnetic field is called Eddy current.

PRACTICE QUESTIONS CLASSROOM WING

Very Short Answer Type Questions

Directions for Questions 1 to 4
Fill in the blanks.

1. Materials that neither attract nor get magnetized by a magnet are referred to as ______________ substances.
2. The representation of the magnetic field around a magnet is illustrated using ______________ of force.
3. The product of a bar magnet's length and its pole strength determines its ______________ moment.
4. The type of materials in which individual atomic magnetic moments align in the same direction due to a specific effect are termed as ______________ substances.

Directions for Questions 5 to 25
Answer the following questions briefly:

5. What do we call substances that are attracted towards a magnet?
6. Name the area around a magnet where its effects can be observed.
7. What term represents the magnetic field by means of lines?
8. By which symbol is the pole strength of a magnet denoted?
9. What is the SI unit of pole strength?
10. Define the unit magnetic pole in terms of force and distance.
11. What is magnetic flux represented by?
12. Which type of substances have a net magnetic moment of zero?
13. What is the special characteristic of ferromagnetic substances regarding their atomic magnetic moments?
14. Define the term 'angle of declination.'
15. Give the principle of a transformer. State the types of transformers.
16. What is meant by electromagnetism?
17. Why is Ewing's theory called molecular theory of magnetism?
18. What is meant by a solenoid?
19. Why do magnetic lines of force pass through iron more freely than through air?
20. According to Ewing's molecular theory, why is steel used to make permanent magnets?
21. Which rule is used to find the force on a current carrying wire placed in a magnetic field?
22. Mention the energy conversions taking place in a loud speaker and a microphone.
23. Define magnetic induction field B. Intensity of magnetic field (H) and state their units.
24. What happens to the length of an iron bar when it is magnetized?
25. State the principle of a moving coil galvanometer.

Short Answer Type Questions

26. Compare the properties of
    (a) diamagnetic (b) paramagnetic
    (c) ferromagnetic substances
27. Explain how will you calculate magnetic moment (M) of a bar magnet using neutral points.
28. Explain domain theory.
29. Give the properties of a solenoid.
30. Calculate magnetic field induction B due to a long straight conductor carrying a current of 5 A at a perpendicular distance of 10 cm from it.
31. Write a note on important magnetic properties.
32. Give various characteristics of magnetic lines of force.

33. Describe Ewing molecular theory.

34. Calculate magnetic field induction 'B' at the centre of a circular coil having 500 turns, radius π cm and carrying a 5 A of current.

35. Explain Oersted's experiment.

36. Explain why isolated magnetic poles do not exist.

37. What is modern electron theory?

38. Explain Faraday's experiment using a magnet and a coil and state Faraday's laws of electromagnetism.

39. Explain magnetic induction 'B' and intensity of magnetizing field.

40. Distinguish between absolute and relative permeability of a medium.

Essay Answer Type Questions

41. Describe a moving coil galvanometer.

42. Explain in detail:
    (a) Electric motor (b) AC generator
    (c) DC generator (d) Transformer

43. Write a note on terrestrial magnetism.

44. Write a note on:
    (1) self-inductance (2) mutual inductance

45. How do you locate the neutral points when
    (1) the North Pole of a bar magnet faces geographical north and
    (2) when the south pole of bar magnet faces geographical north?

PRACTICE QUESTIONS COMPETITION WING

Level 1: Apply Your Concepts

Directions for Q 1 to 5:
Answer the following questions briefly:

1. What principle does a moving coil microphone operate on?
2. What does a motor primarily convert?
3. Which phenomenon leads to the induction of current in a coil due to change in a nearby coil's current?
4. What is the primary purpose of a transformer in AC circuits?
5. What are the currents called that are induced in a metal exposed to a changing magnetic field?

Direction for questions from 6 to 12:
State whether the following statements are true or false.

6. Statement: All substances that are attracted towards a magnet can also become magnets.
7. Statement: The intensity of the magnetic field is a measure of the number of lines passing through a given area.
8. Statement: A substance in which the net magnetic moment of any atom is zero is known as a paramagnetic substance.
9. Statement: The phenomenon of electromagnetic induction involves inducing current by changing the associated magnetic field without an external source.
10. Statement: A transformer is a device that works on the principle of mutual induction and is used in DC circuits.
11. Statement: Eddy currents are produced due to a change in magnetic field in a coil.
12. The angle between geographic and magnetic meridian is called angle of dip.

Direction for questions from 13 to 19:
Fill in the blanks.

13. The ________ converts sound energy into electric energy and is based on the principle of electromagnetic induction.
14. If a coil produces an induced emf in itself due to a change in its own current, the phenomenon is termed as ________.
15. A device used primarily on AC circuits to either increase or decrease the voltage is called a ________.
16. Fleming's left-hand rule is used to find the direction of ______ acting on the current carrying conductor placed in a/an ______ field.
17. ________ is the measure of the ability of a given magnetic pole to attract or repel another magnetic pole.
18. The product of pole strength of a magnet and its magnetic length is called its ________.
19. An emf is induced in a coil when ________ linked with it changes.

Direction for question 20:
Match the entries in Column A with appropriate ones from Column B

20. Match the following terms in Column A with their definitions in Column B.

Column A	Column B
A. Magnetic permeability (μ)	a. Angle between geographic and magnetic meridian.
B. Angle of declination	b. Ability of a medium to allow magnetic lines of force.
C. Transformer	c. Converts electrical energy into mechanical energy.
D. Motor	d. Used to step-up or step-down voltage in AC circuits.

(a) A-b, B-a, C-d, D-c
(b) A-c, B-b, C-a, D-d
(c) A-d, B-b, C-a, D-c
(d) A-a, B-b, C-c, D-d

Direction for questions 21 to 35:
For each of the questions, four choices have been provided. Select the correct alternative.

21. What is the term for the capability of a medium to allow magnetic lines of force to pass through it?
(a) Magnetic moment
(b) Pole strength
(c) Magnetic permeability
(d) Magnetic induction

22. In which type of substance is the net magnetic moment of any atom zero?
(a) Diamagnetic substances
(b) Paramagnetic substances
(c) Ferromagnetic substances
(d) Nonmagnetic substances

23. What phenomenon is observed when there's an induced emf in a coil due to a change in current in a nearby coil?
(a) Electromagnetic Induction
(b) Self-induction
(c) Mutual induction
(d) Eddy currents

24. Which of the following devices works on the principle of converting electrical energy into mechanical energy?
(a) Transformer
(b) Electric generator
(c) Moving coil microphone
(d) Motor

25. Induced currents formed within a solid metallic piece when exposed to a changing magnetic field are termed as?
(a) Mutual currents (b) Inductive currents
(c) Eddy currents (d) Magnetic currents

26. The magnetic induction field B around a current carrying straight conductor is
(a) perpendicular to the current.
(b) parallel to the current.
(c) opposite to the direction of flow of current.
(d) None of the above.

27. ________ is used to make permanent magnets.
(a) Soft iron (b) Steel
(c) Nichrome (d) Copper

28. A transformer works with
(a) AC voltages only.
(b) DC voltages only.
(c) Both (a) and (b).
(d) None of these

29. Eddy currents are produced in a metallic conductor when
(a) the magnetic flux linked with it changes.
(b) it is placed in a changing magnetic field.
(c) it is placed in a magnetic field.
(d) Both (a) and (b).

30. The self or mutual induction takes place when magnetic flux through a coil ________.
(a) remains steady (b) decreases
(c) increases (d) Both (b) and (c).

31. Which of the following statements is incorrect? In the process of electromagnetic induction, the magnitude of the induced emf depends on ________.
(a) the number of turns of the coil.
(b) the magnetic flux linked with the coil.
(c) the rate of change of magnetic flux linked with the coil.
(d) area of the coil.

32. Write the following steps in a sequential order to find the current and voltage in the secondary coil. The ratio of the number of turns of a primary to a secondary coil, current through the primary coil and input power are given.
(A) Let the given data be taken as $\frac{N_1}{N_2}$ (turn-ratio), i_1, (input current) and P (input power).
(B) Substitute the given values of $\frac{N_1}{N_2}$ and i_1, in the above formula and get the value of i_2.
(C) Write the relation between turn-ratio and the currents as $\frac{N_1}{N_2} = \frac{i_2}{i_1}$, where, i_2 is the current in the secondary coil.
(D) Write the relation between input power and output power in terms of V_1, i_1, V_2, i_2, i.e., $V_1\, i_1 = V_2\, i_2 = P$, where V_1 and V_2 are the voltage in the primary and secondary coils, respectively.
(E) Substitute the values of i_2 and P in the above relation to get the value of V_2.
(a) ADBCE (b) BCADE
(c) ACBDE (d) DBCAE

33. Write in the sequential order the following steps of an experiment to show that a current carrying conductor sets up a magnetic field around it.
(A) Pass the insulated copper wire through the small hole at the centre of the cardboard and perpendicular to it.
(B) Paste a white paper on a rectangular cardboard and make a small hole at its centre.
(C) Connect this wire to a battery, a switch and a variable resistor in series.

(D) Clamp this cardboard to a stand in a horizontal position and sprinkle some iron filings over it.

(E) Now, when the circuit is closed, the iron filings on the cardboard form concentric circles around the wire.

(a) BDACE (b) BACED
(c) ADBEC (d) EDABC

34. Write the following steps of an experiment (in a sequential order), to establish that a circular current carrying wire creates a magnetic field around it.

(A) Sprinkle iron filings on the cardboard and switch on the circuit.

(B) Make two holes on a piece of cardboard covered with white paper. Pass this copper wire through the two holes of a cardboard .

(C) Take a copper wire and bend it in the form of a circle.

(D) Now connect the ends of the copper coil to a battery with a rheostat and a switch in series.

(E) You observe that the iron filings arrange themselves in concentric circles.

(a) ACBDE (b) CBDAE
(c) CADBE (d) BCDAE

35. Two long parallel wires A and B separated by a distance d, carry currents i_1 and i_2, respectively, in the same direction. Write the following steps in a sequential order to find the magnitude of the resultant magnetic field at a point 'P', which is between the wires and is at a distance 'x' from the wire A. (All the physical quantities are measured in SI units.)

(A) Note the given values of i_1, i_2, d and x .

(B) Write the formula to find the magnetic field due to a long straight current carrying wire, i.e., $B = \frac{\mu_o i}{2\pi r}$.

(C) Find the directions of the magnetic field at 'P' due to two wires A and B, using right-hand thumb rule.

(D) Determine the magnetic field at P due to wire A, using $B_1 = \frac{\mu_o i_1}{2\pi x}$.

(E) If the directions of magnetic field are same, then the resultant magnitude is equal to the sum of B_1 and B_2.

(F) Determine the magnetic field B_2 due to wire B at point P, i.e., $B_2 = \frac{\mu_o i_2}{2\pi(d-x)}$.

(G) If the directions of magnetic fields are opposite to each other, then the resultant magnitude is equal to the difference of B_1 and B_2.

(a) DFCEGBA (b) CDFEGBA
(c) ACBDFEG (d) ABDFCEG

Level 2: Review Your Concepts

36. When a short magnet is placed with its south pole pointing the geographic north of the Earth, the neutral point is at a distance 10 cm. At what distance the neutral point will be formed, when the magnet is rotated through 180^0?

$$\left[\text{Take } \frac{1}{3\sqrt{2}} = 0.88(\text{app})\right]$$

37. If the pole strength of two magnets are equal and are denoted by 'm', and their lengths are L1 and L2 respectively, which magnet would have a greater magnetic moment and why?

38. Why are diamagnetic substances not influenced by external magnetic fields, considering their atomic structure?

39. A circular coil of area 1.5 m^2 is placed normal to a uniform magnetic field of induction 2 Wb m^{-2}. The field is increased uniformly to 4 Wb m^{-2} in 20 s. Calculate the induced emf.

40. At a given point in a magnetic field, is it possible to have different magnetic induction fields? At two different points in a magnetic field, is it possible to have same magnetic induction field? Explain.

41. How can electromagnetic induction be used to oppose the change in current in a circuit?

42. Why is a transformer not efficient when used with a DC supply?

43. Two identical circular coils are placed in the same plane side by side such that they do not touch each other. An increasing current is in the same plane and

passed through one of the coils in the clockwise direction. Do the two coils attract or repel each other? Explain.

44. A bar magnet of magnetic moment M is cut into 'n' parts along the axial line and 'm' parts perpendicular to the axial line. Find the magnetic moment of each piece.

45. Two infinitely long wires P and Q carry currents of 2 A and 8 A, respectively, in the same direction. Find at what distance from P the resultant induction field is zero, if they are kept parallel to each other at a distance of 10 cm.

46. How does the phenomenon of Eddy currents show both the advantageous and disadvantageous effects of electromagnetic induction?

47. A magnetized rod of moment M and length 'L' is bent in the form of an arc of a circle of radius r. If the arc length is $\frac{1}{4}$th the circumference of the circle, then find the magnetic moment of the arc, in terms of M.

48. Explain why two magnetic field lines can never intersect.

49. A cell is connected across AD of a square loop ABCD, made of a conductor of uniform area of cross section, as shown in the figure. Find the ratio of magnetic-fields at the centre produced by

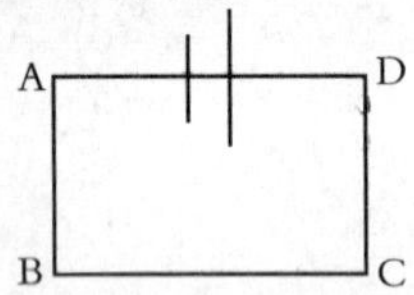

(a) sides AB and CD and

(b) sides AD and BC.

50. A bar magnet of magnetic moment M is cut into 'p' parts along the axial line and 'q' parts perpendicular to the axial line. Find the magnetic moment of each piece.

51. An experimentist placed two magnetic poles separated by 10 cm (in air), one having double the strength as the other and found that both repel each other with a force of 8×10^{-3} N. Calculate the pole strength of each pole.

52. If m is the pole strength, A is the area of cross section and I is the intensity of magnetization of a given magnet, prove that $I = \frac{M}{A}$.

53. Randheer's father gave him a short bar magnet of length 5 cm and asked him to find its pole strength. He also gave him information that the Earth's horizontal component of magnetic intensity is 50 μT at the given place. Experimentally Randheer found that the bar magnet produces a neutral point 15 cm away from its centre on the equatorial line and calculated its pole strength. Find the answer.

54. In a science fair, a student performed an activity with a magnet. First, he placed the magnet with its south pole pointing towards the geographic north of the Earth and rotated the magnet by an angle of 180°, then calculated how the angle made by the line joining the neutral points had rotated. Find the angle.

Level 3: Assess Your Concepts

55. Discuss the physical implications of Lenz's law. How does it relate to the conservation of energy, and in what practical applications can we observe its effects? Provide examples to support your answer.

56. The dipole moment of a semicircular magnet is 28 A m^2. It is straightened to form a bar magnet, which is then cut along its axial line to give two magnets. Find the magnetic induction at a point on the equatorial line 0.2 m away from the centre of one of the magnets. If the point is along the axis same distance away from the centre of the magnet, then find the magnetic induction.

57. Dive deep into the differences between diamagnetic, paramagnetic, and ferromagnetic substances. How do their atomic structures contribute to their magnetic behaviours? And how are these properties exploited in modern technologies?

58. Two magnetic poles of strengths 'm_1' and 'm_2' when placed in air at a distance of 'd' from each other, a force 'F' acts between them. If the pole strength of the poles is doubled, the distance between them is trebbled and the poles are placed in some other medium, the force between them reduces by 25%. Find the relative magnetic permeability of the medium.

59. A bar magnet is suspended in a uniform magnetic field. Find the ratio of the torques when it makes an angle of 30° and 60°, respectively, with the field.

60. Calculate magnetic field induction B due to a straight conductor carrying current 5 A at a perpendicular distance of 10 cm from it.

61. Explain the principle of electromagnetic induction and its significance in the development of electrical power generation. How have advancements in electromagnetic induction techniques shaped the evolution of power generation systems?

62. Describe the role of transformers in modern electrical distribution systems. What are the challenges faced in terms of energy losses, and how do engineers address these issues? Additionally, elucidate the principle behind the operation of transformers and their construction.

63. What are the underlying causes of eddy currents, and how do they manifest in electrical systems? Discuss both the advantageous and detrimental effects of eddy currents and methods employed to minimize their negative impacts.

64. In an experiment, a physics student named Rakesh took a magnet and a coil of resistance 10 Ω. He then performed an activity by moving the magnet towards the coil in such a way that the magnetic flux linked with the coil changes from 10 weber to 40 weber and he calculated the amount of charge that flowed through the coil during the motion. Find what his answer would be.

65. The figure shows two long parallel wires carrying currents i_1 and i_2 in opposite directions. What is the magnitude and direction of the resultant magnetic field at the point P?

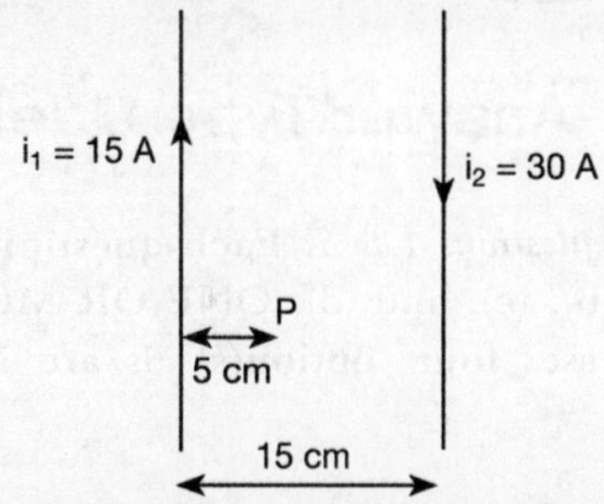

66. Find the ratio of the magnetic fields, at distances 5 cm and 50 cm from a long straight current carrying conductor.

67. In a transformer, the ratio of the number of turns of a primary to a secondary coil is 2 : 5. If the current through the primary coil is 10 A and input power is 300 W, find the current and voltage in the secondary coil.

68. What is the magnetic induction at a point on the axial line of a short bar magnet having magnetic moment 62.5 A m^2, which is at 50 cm from the centre of the magnet.

69. Two magnetic poles of strengths 10 A m and 200 A m are separated by 50 cm in air. What is the magnetic force between the two poles?

AT

PRACTICE QUESTIONS JEE-NEET SPECIAL WING

Multiple-Answer Type Questions

Directions for questions 1 to 5: **Each question has FOUR options (a), (b), (c), and (d). ONE OR MORE THAN ONE of these four option(s) is/are the correct answer(s).**

1. The pole strengths of two poles are doubled and distance between them also doubled.
   (a) The force between them remains same.
   (b) The force is inversely proportional to the square distance between the poles.
   (c) The force is directly proportional to the product of the strengths of the poles.
   (d) The force is inversely proportional to the product of the strengths of the poles.

2. A short bar magnet of magnet moment 10 A-m². Then magnetic field strength on the
   (a) axial line at a distance $2m$ from magnet is 2.5×10^{-7} T.
   (b) axial line at a distance $4m$ from magnet is 0.31×10^{-7} T.
   (c) equatorial line at a distance $2m$ from magnet is 1.25×10^{-7} T.
   (d) equatorial line at a distance $4m$ from magnet is 2.5×10^{-7} T.

3. In a transformer, the ratio of the number of turns of a primary to a secondary coil is $N_p : N_s$, the current through primary Coil is I_p, the current through secondary coil is I_S then
   (a) If $N_p : N_s$ is 1: 2; I_p = 10A, then I_s is 5A.
   (b) If $N_p : N_s$ is 2: 3; I_p = 10A, then I_s is 10A.
   (c) If $\frac{I_p}{I_s} = \frac{3}{2}$, then $\frac{N_p}{N_s} = \frac{2}{5}$.
   (d) If $I_p = 3I_s$, then $N_P = \frac{1}{3} N_s$.

4. If current 10 A flows through straight wire, then the
   (a) magnetic field at a distance $5m$ is $0.4T$.
   (b) magnetic field at a distance $5m$ is 0.4 μ T.
   (c) magnetic field at a distance $2m$ is = 1 μ T.
   (d) Magnetic field at a distance $4m$ is = $0.5T$.

5. A current carrying wire of 10 A placed in a magnetic field of $4T$. Which of the following is/are true statements?
   (a) If the length of the wire is 2 m, then force acting on the wire is $80N$.
   (b) If the length of the wire is 2 m, then force acting on the wire is $20N$.
   (c) If the length of the wire is 4 m, then force acting on the wire is $160N$.
   (d) If the length of the wire is 4 m, then force acting on the wire is $10N$.

Comprehension-Based Questions

Directions for Questions 6 to 10:

According to the oersted experiment, every current carrying wire produces a magnetic field around it. The magnetic field produced by the electric current depends on strength of current and direction of the current. Magnetic field produced by the electric current is directly proportional to electric current ($B \propto i$). Direction of magnetic field can be determined by using Ampere's right hand thumb rule. Magnetic field due to the current carrying wire at a radial distance 'r' from it is $B = \frac{\mu_{\circ i}}{2\pi r}$, magnetic field produced by the circular current carrying wire at center with 'n' turns given by: $B = \frac{\mu_\circ}{4\pi}\frac{i}{r}(\theta)$

Where 'r' is the radius. θ should be always in radian. Example – magnetic field produced by semi circular are at the centre of it is $B = \frac{\mu_\circ}{4\pi}\frac{i}{r}(\pi)$

$\because \theta = \pi$; $B = \frac{\mu_{\circ i}}{4r}$

6. A current 2A passing through the circular wire of radius πm, and 100 turns. The magnetic field at centre of the circle is

(a) 40T (b) 40μ T

(c) 20T (d) 20μ T

7. If $i_1 = 4$A, $i_2 = 6$A, $r_1 = r$, and $r_2 = 2r$, then the net magnetic field at the centre of the circle is

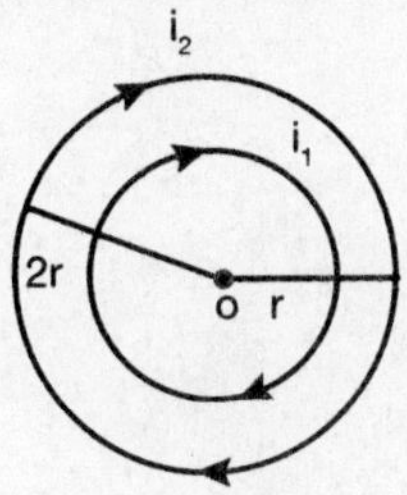

(a) Zero (b) $\frac{7\mu_\circ}{2r}$

(c) $\frac{11\mu_\circ}{r}$ (d) $\frac{11\mu_\circ}{r}$

8. If $i_1 = 2i_2$, then net magnetic field at the centre of the circle is

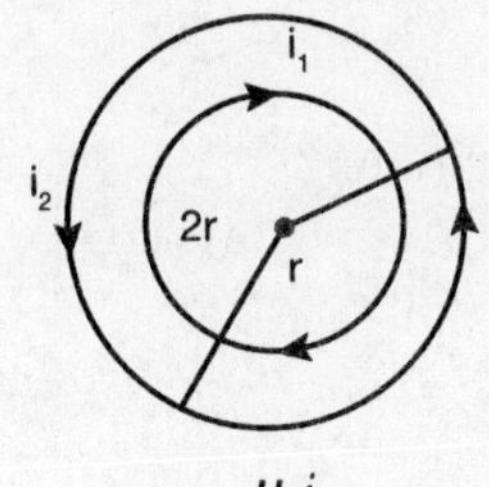

(a) $\frac{\mu_\circ i_2}{2r}$ (b) $\frac{\mu_\circ i_2}{4r}$

(c) $\frac{3}{4}\frac{\mu_\circ i_2}{r}$ (d) $\frac{4}{3}\frac{\mu_\circ i_2}{r}$

9. The magnetic field at centre of semi-circle is

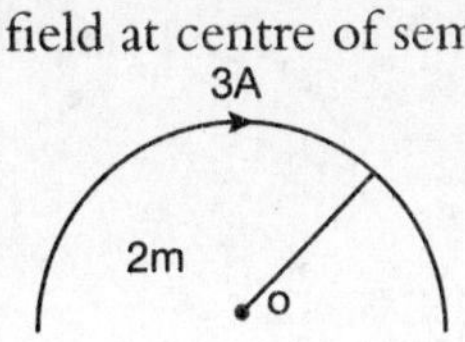

(a) $\frac{3\pi}{2} \times 10^{-7}$ outward (b) $\frac{3\pi}{2} \times 10^{-7}$ inward

(c) $3\pi \times 10^{-7}$ outward (d) $3\pi \times 10^{-7}$ inward

10. Two identical semicircular current t carrying wires are placed as shown in the figure. Radius of the semi-circle is 0.5*m*. Net magnet field at the centre 'O' is

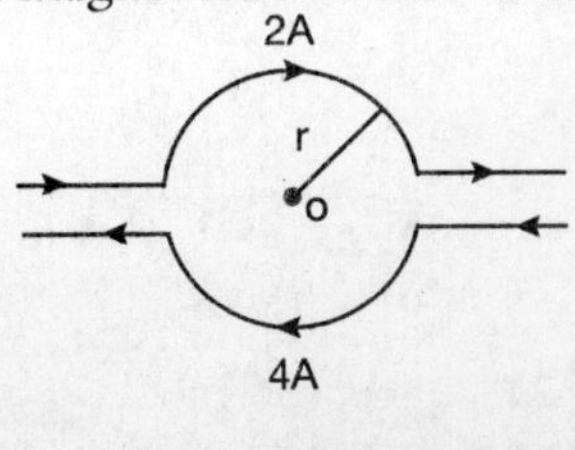

(a) $3\mu_\circ$ outward (b) $3\mu_\circ$ in ward

(c) $\mu_\circ$ outward (d) $\mu_\circ$ in ward

Directions for Questions 11 to 16: **These questions are based on the following diagram.**

A current carrying wire produces magnetic field $B = \frac{\mu_\circ i}{2\pi r}$ where is the current and r is the radial distance from it and current carrying wire also experiences force when it is placed in magnetic field. Let a current flowing in it and second current carrying wire (i_2 current through it) is placed at a distance 'r' from first wire, then force between them is $\frac{F}{l} = \frac{\mu_\circ i_1 i_2}{2\pi r}$. If the currents are in same direction they attract each other, if currents are opposites in direction, they repel each other

Two current carrying wires are placed as shown in the figure point 'o' is between the wires and 'p' is outside and near the second wire.

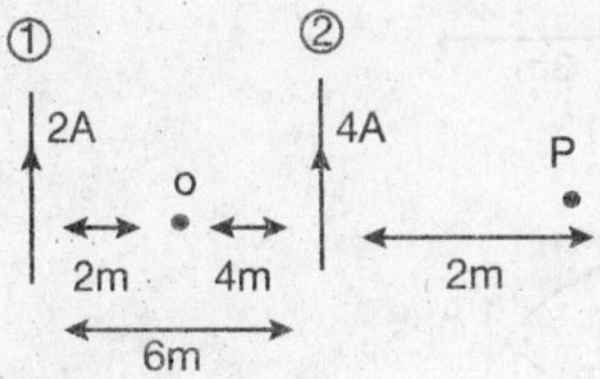

11. Magnetic field at 'o' due to wire '1' is

(a) 20μT inward (b) 20μT outward

(c) 40μT inward (d) 40μT inward

12. The ratio of magnetic fields at 'o' due to wire 1 and wire '2' is

(a) 1: 2 (b) 2: 1

(c) 1 : 1 (d) 1 : 4

13. The net magnetic field at 'o' is

(a) $\frac{\mu_\circ}{\pi}$ inward (b) $\frac{\mu_\circ}{\pi}$ outward

(c) Zero (d) None of these

14. The net magnetic field at 'p' is

(a) $\frac{\mu_\circ}{8\pi}$ inward (b) $\frac{\mu_\circ}{\pi}$ inward

(c) Zero (d) $\frac{9\mu_\circ}{8\pi}$ inward

15. The force per unit length between the wires is

(a) $\frac{8}{3}$ N attraction (b) $\frac{8}{3}$ N repulsion

(c) $\frac{3}{8}$ N attraction (d) $\frac{3}{8}$ N repulsion

16. Using above paragraphs match the following, find magnetic field at 'o'

Column – A	Column - B
A. 	a. $\frac{\mu_o}{4}T$
B. 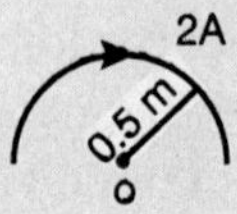	b. $\frac{\mu_o}{2}$ T
C. 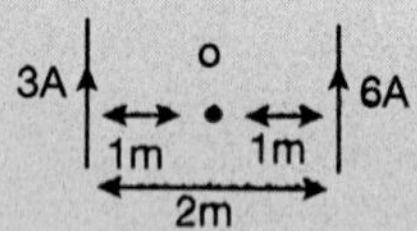	c. 6×10^{-7}T
D. 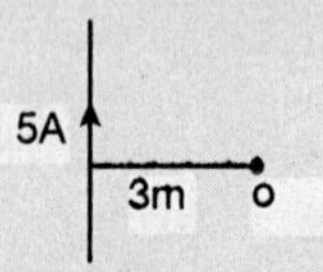	d. μ_o T
E. 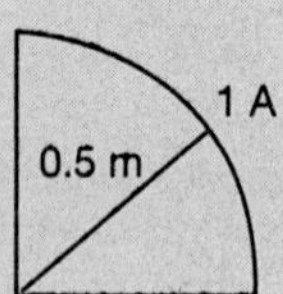	e. $\frac{10}{3} \times 10^{-7}$T

ANSWER KEYS

Crossword

Across

2. Dynamo
8. Magnetic permeability
9. Silicon steel
10. Eddy current

Down

1. EMI (Electromagnetic induction)
2. Decreases
3. Negative
4. Hysteresis losses
5. Magnetic field
6. Zero
7. Weber

Classroom Wing

Very Short Answer Type Questions

1. nonmagnetic
2. lines
3. magnetic
4. Ferromagnetic
5. Magnetic substances.
6. Magnetic field of the magnet.
7. Lines of force.
8. '*m*'.
9. Ampere-metre.
11. 'ϕ'.
12. Diamagnetic substances.

Competition Wing

Level 1: Apply Your Concepts

1. Electromagnetic induction.
2. Electrical energy into mechanical energy.
3. Mutual induction.
5. Eddy currents.
6. True
7. False
8. False
9. True
10. False
11. False
12. False
13. Moving coil microphone
14. self-induction
15. Transformer
16. force, magnetic
17. pole strength
18. Magnetic moment
19. the magnetic flux
20. (a) A : b, B : a, C : d, D : c
21. (c)
22. (a)
23. (c)
24. (d)
25. (c)
26. (a)
27. (b)
28. (a)
29. (d)
30. (d)
31. (b)
32. (c)
33. (a)
34. (b)
35. (d)

JEE-NEET SPECIAL WING

Multiple-Answer Type Questions

1. (a, b, c)
2. (a, b, c)
3. (a, d)
4. (b, c)
5. (a, c)

Comprehension-Based Questions

6. (b)
7. (b)
8. (c)
9. (c)
10. (b)
11. (a)
12. (c)
13. (c)
14. (d)
15. (b)
16. A-b, B-d, C-c, D-e, E-a

For answer key of Classroom wing and Competition wing, refer to Hints and Solutions

Hints and Explanations

CLASSROOM WING

Very Short Answer Type Questions

1. nonmagnetic
2. lines
3. magnetic
4. Ferromagnetic
5. Magnetic substances.
6. Magnetic field of the magnet.
7. Lines of force.
8. 'm'.
9. Ampere-metre.
10. A pole that repels an identical pole at 1 metre distance with a force of 10^(-7) N.
11. 'ϕ'.
12. Diamagnetic substances.
13. The resultant magnetic moments of individual atoms align themselves parallel to each other.
14. The angle between geographic and magnetic meridian at a place.
15. Electromagnetic induction.
    (i) step-up
    (ii) step-down transformers.
16. Magnetic effect of electricity
17. Each molecule of a magnetic substance is an independent magnet.
18. An insulated copper coil wound around some insulated core such that its length is greater than its diameter.
19. Iron has high magnetic permeability than air.
20. The retentivity is high.
21. Fleming's left-hand rule.
22. (i) Electric energy is converted into sound in loud speaker.
    (ii) Sound energy is converted into electrical pulses in microphone.
23. Magnetic flux per unit area is magnetic induction (B).
    Unit: N A^{-1} m^{-1}.
    Intensity of magnetic field (H) can be defined on the force acting on unit north pole independent of the medium.
    Unit: A m^{-1}
24. Increases
25. Fleming's left hand rule

Short Answer Type Questions

Note: This is how you should frame your answer covering.

26. (a) Diamagnetic substances-the substances in which the net magnetic moment of any atom in them is zero.
    (b) Paramagnetic substances-the substances in which the orientation of electron orbits and axes of their spins are such that the net magnetic moment of any atom is not zero.
    (c) Ferromagnetic substances-the atoms of these elements have resultant magnetic moment.
27. (i) $B = \frac{\mu_0}{4\pi}\frac{M}{d^3}$ at neutral points on equational line.
    (ii) $B = \frac{\mu_0}{4\pi}\frac{2M}{d^3}$ at axial neutral points.
    (iii) At neutral points $B = B_H$ i.e., horizontal component of Earth's magnitude field.
    $\therefore$ Put $B = B_H$ in above equation.
    (iv) Calculate M as B_H at a given place is constant and d distance of material point from magnet can be found.
28. (i) Domain theory used for ferromagnetic substances.
    (ii) Define domain.
    (iii) On magnetization, size of domains increase.
    (iv) On demagnetization, some magnetism is retained.

29. (i) The magnetic field due to solonoid is directly proportional to the number of tunes per unit length of the solenoid, the current passing through the solonoid.
(ii) The magnetic field depends upon the nature of material on which the coil is wound.
(iii) The magnetic lines of forces within the solonoid are almost parallel to each other and axis of solenoid.

30. (i) Use $B = \frac{\mu_0 I}{2\pi r}$

Ans: $10\ \mu T$

(ii) $\mu_0 = 4\pi \times 10^{-7}\ H\ m^{-1}$

31. Important magnetic properties, i.e.,
(i) Intensity of magnetization
(ii) magnetic susceptibility
(iii) Retentivity

32. Curved, closed, continuous lines

33. (i) Each molecule is a magnet.
(ii) Molecules are randomly oriented.
(iii) On magnetization, they align in one direction.
(iv) Explain saturation.
(v) Mention drawbacks.

34. (i) Use $B = \frac{n\mu_0 I}{2r}$

Ans: 0.05 T

(ii) $\mu_O = 4\pi \times 10^{-7}\ H\ m^{-1}$

35. (i) Magnetic needle placed near current carrying conductor is deflected.
(ii) Deflection is reversed on reversing the direction of current.
(iii) Deflection is increased on increasing the strength of current.
(iv) Thus, magnetic field is created around a current carrying conductor.

36. The smallest part belonging to a magnet also possess two poles.

37. (i) Electrons have orbital and spin motion.
(ii) Due to movement of electrons, current is produced creating a magnetic field.
(iii) In magnetic substances, net moment of electrons is not zero.
(iv) In non-magnetic substances, net moment of electrons is zero.

38. (i) When a magnet is moved in or out of a stationary coil, galvanometer connected to coil shows deflections, in opposite directions.
(ii) The deflection is also reversed if the polarity of magnet is reversed.
(iii) This current is called induced current and the phenomenon is called electromagnetic induction.

39. $B = \mu_0 H$

Essay Answer Type Questions

Note: This is how you should frame your answer covering.

41. (i) Mention working principle.
(ii) Find the deflecting couple, restoring couple.
(iii) Make use Fleming's left hand rule.
(iv) Mention important parts and their use.
(v) The tangent of the angle of deflection (Q) is directly proportional to the strength of the current (i).

$\tan\theta \propto i$

$i = k \tan\theta$

(vi) Mention on which the value of k depends.

42. (a) Mention working principle.
(b) Mention energy conversion, if any
(c) Mention important parts and their use.
(d) Mention working of the device and its uses

43. (i) Explain origin of Earth's magnetism.
(ii) Angle between magnetic and geographic is 17°.
(iii) Explain following elements of Earth's magnetism.
(a) Geographic and magnetic meridian.
(b) Angle of drop or inclination.
(c) Angle of declination.

44. (i) Define inductance.
(ii) Define self and mutual inductance.
(iii) Write expression for them and their units.

45. (i) Keep the bar given bar magnet with its north pole towards geographic north and draw its lines of force.
(ii) Earth's magnetic lines of force are from geographic south to north.
(iii) Locate the two points in the magnetic field where the lines of force due to earth and bar magnet are equal and opposite.
(iv) Repeat same process with south pole of bar magnet pointing towards geographic north.
(v) In 1st case, nuetral points are along equatorial line while in 2nd case, along axial line of the bar magnet.

Competition Wing

Level 1: Apply Your Concepts

Explanation for questions from 1 to 5:

1. Electromagnetic induction.
2. Electrical energy into mechanical energy.
3. Mutual induction.
4. To step-up a low voltage to a high voltage or to step-down a high voltage into a low voltage.
5. Eddy currents.
6. True.
7. False. (Explanation: The intensity of the magnetic field refers to the strength of a magnetic field at a point in C.G.S. units, whereas the total number of lines passing through a given area is referred to as the magnetic flux 'ϕ'.)
8. False. (Explanation: Substances in which the net magnetic moment of any atom is zero are called diamagnetic substances.)
9. True.
10. False. (Explanation: While a transformer does work on the principle of mutual induction, it is used in AC circuits, not DC.)
11. False. (Explanation: Eddy currents are induced currents produced in a solid core piece of metal placed in a changing magnetic field, not in a coil.)

20. (a) A : b, B : a, C : d, D : c

    (A) Magnetic permeability (μ) is the ability of a medium to allow magnetic lines of force to pass through it. (B) The angle of declination is the angle between the geographic and magnetic meridian. (C) A transformer is a device used on AC circuits to step-up a low voltage to a high voltage or to step-down a high voltage into a low voltage. (D) A motor is a device which converts electrical energy into mechanical energy.

21. (c). Magnetic permeability is defined as the ability of a medium to allow the magnetic lines of force to pass through it or to be influenced by a magnetic field.
22. (a). Diamagnetic substances are materials in which the net magnetic moment of any atom in them is zero.
23. (c). Mutual induction refers to the phenomenon where a change in current in one coil induces an emf in another coil held close to it.
24. (d). We know that a motor converts electrical energy into mechanical energy.
25. (c). Eddy currents are induced currents produced in a solid core piece of metal placed in a changing magnetic field.

Explanation for questions from 26 to 35:

26. The magnetic lines of force are concentric circles, with current carrying straight conductor at the centre and perpendicular to the plane of these concentric circles. The direction of the magnetic lines of force is clockwise or anti-clockwise depending on the direction of flow of current. The direction of B is obtained by drawing tangent to the concentric circles at any point on it. It is seen that different points on the concentric circle gives different directions of B and B is always perpendicular to the direction of current.

    Hence, the correct answer is (a).

27. The retentivity of steel is high. Hence, it is used to make permanent magnet.

    Hence, the correct answer is (b).

28. The working of a transformer is based on mutual induction. The change in the current flowing through one coil changes the flux passing through it. When this change in flux is linked to the other coil, the flux through it also changes, thereby, inducing an e.m.f. In AC, the current keeps on changing, and so, a transformer works with AC only.

    Hence, the correct answer is (a).

29. Eddy currents are produced in a solid piece of metal, when magnetic flux passing through it changes. When a metallic conductor is placed in a changing magnetic field, the magnetic flux passing through it changes and so eddy currents are produced.

    Also when magnetic flux around it changes, the magnetic flux passing through it changes and so eddy currents are produced.

    Hence, the correct answer is (d).

30. The self or mutual induction takes place when magnetic flux through the coil changes.

    Hence, the correct answer is (d).

31. The magnitude of induced emf depends on the rate of change of magnetic flux and not on the magnetic flux linked with the coil. Also, it depends on the area of cross section and number of turns of the coil.

    Hence, the correct answer is (b).

32. Let the given data be taken as $\frac{N_1}{N_2}$ (turn-ratio), i_1, (input current) and P (input power) (a). Write the relation between turn-ratio and the currents as $\frac{N_1}{N_2} = \frac{i_2}{i_1}$, where, i_2 is the current in the secondary coil (c). Substitute the given values of $\frac{N_1}{N_2}$ and i_1, in the above formula and get the value of i_2 (b). Write the relation between input power and output power in terms of V_1, i_1, V_2, i_2 i.e $V_1 i_1 = V_2 i_2 = P$, where, V_1 and V_0 are the voltages in the primary and secondary coils, respectively (d). Substitute the values of i_2 and P in the above relation to get the value of V_2.
Hence, the correct answer is (c).

33. Paste a sheet of white paper on a rectangular cardboard and make a small hole at its centre (b). Clamp this cardboard to a stand in the horizontal position and sprinkle some iron filings over it (d). Pass the insulated copper wire through the small hole at the centre of the cardboard and perpendicular to it (a). Connect this wire to a battery, a switch and a variable resistance in series (c). Now, when the circuit is closed, the iron filings on the cardboard form concentric circles around the wire (e).
Hence, the correct answer is (a).

34. Take a copper wire and bend it in the form of a circle (c). Make two holes on a piece of cardboard covered with a sheet of white paper and pass the copper wire through the two holes of the cardboard covered with the sheet of white paper (b). Now connect the ends of the copper coil to a battery with a rheostat and a switch in series (d). Sprinkle iron filings on the cardboard and switch on the circuit (a). You observe that the iron filings arrange themselves in concentric circles (e).
Hence, the correct answer is (b).

35. Note the given values of i_1, i_2, d and x (a). Write the formula to find the magnetic field due to a long straight current carrying wire, i.e., $B = \frac{\mu_0 i_1}{2\pi x}$ (b). Determine the magnetic field at P due to wire A, using $B_1 = \frac{\mu_0 i}{2\pi r}$

Determine B_2 due to wire B, i.e., $B_2 = \frac{\mu_0 i_2}{2\pi(d-x)}$ (f).

Find the directions of the magnetic field at 'P' due to two wires A and B, using right-hand thumb rule (c). If the directions of magnetic fields are same, then the resultant magnitude is equal to the sum of B_1 and B_2 (e). If the directions of the two magnetic fields are opposite, then the resultant magnitude is equal to the difference of B_1 and B_2 (g).
Hence, the correct answer is (d).

Level 2: Review Your Concepts

Note: This is how you should frame your answer covering.

36. (i) When south pole faces the geographic north, the null point is formed on the axial line. At null point, the axial field and horizontal component of Earth's magnetic field are equal.

$$B_H = B_{axial} = \frac{\mu_0}{4\pi} \times \frac{2M}{d_A^3} \quad (1)$$

Where, d_A = 10 cm = 0.1 m.

When the magnetic is turned through 180°, the null point is formed on the equatorial line.

$$B_H = B_e = \frac{\mu_0}{4\pi} \times \frac{M}{d_e^3} \quad (2)$$

Equating (1) and (2), find d_e.

(ii) 8 cm

37. The magnetic moment of a bar magnet is given by the product of its length and pole strength. So, the magnet with the longer length (either L1 or L2) will have a greater magnetic moment.

38. Diamagnetic substances have a net magnetic moment of zero for any atom in them, meaning they do not possess unpaired electrons that can align with external magnetic fields.

39. (i) Get the values of area (A) and initial magnetic induction (Bi). Find magnetic induction (Bf) and time (t) from the given data.

Use $E = \frac{\Delta\varphi}{t}$ and $\varphi = BA$.

Find φ_{final}, $\varphi_{initial}$ and from them, find $\Delta\varphi$ as well.

(ii) 0.15 V

40. (i) Can two magnetic lines of force intersect at a point in a magnetic field?

(ii) Magnetic field can be uniform or non-uniform. In uniform magnetic field it is possible to have same magnetic induction field at two different points.

41. According to Lenz's law, the direction of induced current is such that it opposes the very cause that produces it. By using this principle, devices such as inductors can be introduced in circuits to resist rapid changes in current.

42. A transformer operates on the principle of mutual induction, which requires a changing magnetic field. A DC supply provides a constant current, which means no changing magnetic field is produced in the primary coil, and hence no voltage is induced in the secondary coil.

43. Recall the principles of mutual induction and Faraday's experiments.

44. (i) When the magnet is cut along axial line, its area of pole decreases. If the area of poles decreases 'n' times, pole strength also decreases 'n' times.

The magnetic moment of each piece is $\frac{M}{n}$.

When each piece (obtained by cutting the magnet along the axial line) is divided into 'm' parts by cutting it perpendicular to the axial line, the length and the magnetic moment reduces to $\frac{1}{m}$th the original value.

(ii) $\frac{M}{mn}$

45. (i) Use $B = \frac{\mu_0 i}{2r}$, for both the wires.

If the resultant field at a point is zero, then at the point B due to P it is equal in magnitude and opposite in direction to B due to Q.

(ii) 2 cm

46. Eddy currents represent unwanted power losses in systems like transformers due to the resistive heating they produce. However, they can be advantageous in applications like induction heating for cooking and metal hardening.

47. (i) The pole strength of the magnet (m) is

$$m = \frac{M}{L} \quad (1)$$

When the rod is bent in the form of arc, it subtends 90^0 at the centre.

If 'd' is the distance between the poles, then

$$d = \sqrt{r^2 + r^2}$$

$$d = r\sqrt{2} \quad (2)$$

where, r is the radius of the arc.

The r is related to ℓ as

$$\ell = \pi r \quad (3)$$

Use (1), (2) and (3) and find the new magnetic moment (M_1)

M_1 = Pole strength × Distance between poles.

(ii) $\frac{2\sqrt{2}}{\pi} M$

48. Recall the definition of a magnetic field line.

Is it possible to have two directions for a given magnetic field at a given point in the field?

49. (i) Side AB and side CD carry equal currents. The distance of the centre from both the sides are equal. Therefore, fields produced by both sides are equal at the centre. Side AD and BC carry different currents. If R is the resistance of each side, then current through AD (I_D) is

$$I_D = \frac{3R}{4R} \times V \quad (1)$$

where, V is the terminal PD of the cell.

The current through BC is

$$I_{BC} = \frac{R}{4R} \times V \quad (2)$$

The ratio of currents gives the ratio of fields.

(ii) 1:1, 3:1

50. When a bar magnet is cut into 'p' parts along the axial line, its area becomes $(1/p)$th of the total area and the pole strength becomes $(1/p)$th of the pole strength. With decrease in pole strength, each part will have a magnetic moment (M/p). When the magnet is cut perpendicular to axial line, the magnetic moment becomes (M/p). Thus, the magnetic moment of each part is (M/p)

51. Let the pole strengths be 'm_1' and 'm_2'. Let $m_1 = m$, and hence, $m_2 = 2$ m

Distance between them, $d = 10$ cm $= 0.1$ m

Force of repulsion, $F = \frac{\mu_0}{4\pi} \frac{m_1 m_2}{d^2} = \frac{10^{-7}(m)(2m)}{(0.1)^2}$

Given, $F = 8 \times 10^{-3}$ N

$$\Rightarrow 8 \times 10^{-3} = \frac{10^{-7}(2m^2)}{0.01} \Rightarrow m = 20\,\text{Am}$$

Thus, the pole strengths are 20 A m and 40A m.

52. The intensity of magnetization is defined as magnetic dipole moment per unit volume.

$$I = \frac{M}{V}$$

where, M = dipole moment.

V = Volume of magnet

But $M = m \times 2l$; $V = A \times 2l$

where, $2l$ – length of magnet.

A – area of cross section.

$$\therefore \quad \therefore I = \frac{m \times 2\ell}{A \times 2\ell}$$

$$I = \frac{m}{A}$$

53. Let B = magnetic induction due to the bar magnet.

$B = \frac{\mu_0}{4\pi}\frac{M}{d^3}$, on the equatorial line.

where, M = magnetic moment

D = distance of a point from the centre of the magnet.

At neutral point, $B = B_H$, the horizontal component of the Earth's magnetic field.

$$\therefore \quad \therefore B_H = \frac{\mu_0}{4\pi}\frac{M}{d^3}$$

$$m = (B_H d^3)\frac{4\pi}{\mu_0} \times \frac{1}{2\ell}$$

where, $2\,\ell$ is length of the magnet.

$$m = \frac{10^7 \times (50 \times 10^{-6}) \times (0.15)^3}{5 \times 10^{-2}} = 33.75\,\text{Am}$$

54. When the south pole of a magnet points towards the north of the Earth, neutral points are obtained on the axial line. Thus, the line joining neutral points is along the axis of the magnet. When the poles are reversed, the neutral points are obtained along its equatorial line. Then the line joining the neutral points is the perpendicular bisector of the magnet. Thus, the line rotates by 90°.

Level 3: Assess Your Concepts

Note: This is how you should frame your answer covering.

55. Lenz's law is an embodiment of the principle of conservation of energy in the realm of electromagnetism. According to Lenz's law, the induced electromotive force (EMF) in any closed circuit is always in a direction to oppose the change in magnetic flux causing it. This opposition ensures that energy is not spontaneously or arbitrarily created or destroyed. In real-world scenarios, for instance, when we consider electromagnetic brakes, a metal disc moving in a magnetic field will experience an opposing force due to the currents (induced by the change in magnetic flux) that circulate within the disc. This opposition slows down the disc, converting its kinetic energy into other forms of energy but not destroying it, upholding the conservation principle.

56. (i) What is the expression for a magnetic moment of a semicircular magnet?

When the semicircular magnet is straightened, relate the distance between the two poles in the two cases to find the new length of the magnet.

Does the pole strength of the magnet change on straightening?

How does the pole strength change when the straight magnet is cut axially?

What is the magnetic moment of the newly formed (straightened) magnet?

Use $B_{\text{axial}} = \frac{\mu_0}{4\pi}\frac{2M}{d^3}$ and $B_{\text{equatorial}} \frac{\mu_0}{4\pi}\frac{M}{d^3}$

(ii) B equatorial = 0.0275 mT

B axial = 0.550 mT

57. At the atomic level, magnetic behaviour emerges predominantly from the spin and orbital motion of electrons. Diamagnetic substances possess electrons with paired spins, resulting in a net magnetic moment of zero. In contrast, paramagnetic substances have unpaired electrons, giving them a net positive magnetic moment. However, it's ferromagnetic substances that are particularly interesting; they not only have unpaired electrons but also exhibit strong interactions between neighbouring atoms leading to a parallel alignment of atomic magnetic moments. This alignment results in a macroscopic magnetization. Technologies like Magnetic Resonance Imaging (MRI) exploit the differential magnetic behaviours of tissues, allowing for detailed internal visualization.

58. (i) Use $F = \frac{\mu_0}{4\pi}\frac{m_1 m_2}{d^2}$, in both the cases.

Relate the quantities 'm_1', 'm_2', 'd' and 'F' in the second case with that in the first case using the given data. Then relate μ of the medium with μ_0 and find the value of μ_r of the medium.

(ii) 3

59. (i) The force on the poles of the bar magnet is mB. If the angle made by the bar magnet with the field is θ, then the perpendicular distance between the forces is $2\ell \sin\theta$ where '2ℓ' is the magnetic length, as shown in the figure below. The torque is given by,

Torque = Force × Perpendicular distance.

Torque = $mB \times 2\ell \sin\theta$

$\Rightarrow$ Torque $\propto \sin\theta$

(ii) $1 : \sqrt{3}$

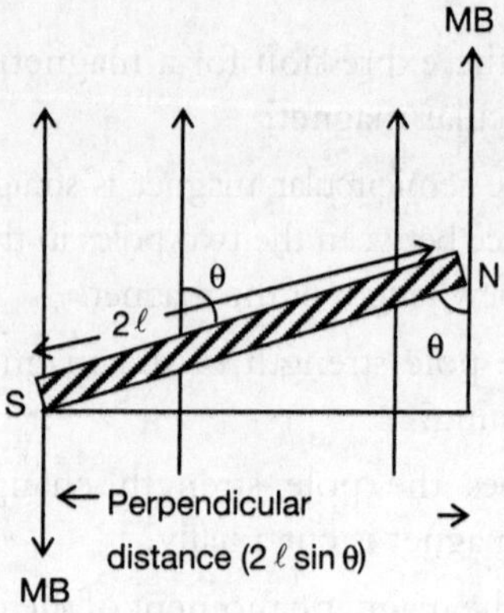

60. Given, $i = 5$ A

$r = 10$ cm $= 0.1$ m

$$\frac{\mu_0 i}{2\pi r} = \frac{4\pi \times 10^{-7} \times 5}{2\pi \times 0.1}$$

$$B = 10^{-5} T = 10 \times 10^{-6} T = 10 \mu T$$

61. Electromagnetic induction, discovered by Faraday, has been the cornerstone of power generation. The foundational principle is that a changing magnetic field within a closed loop induces an EMF, driving a current. In power plants, turbines (often driven by wind, water, steam, or other means) rotate magnets around conductors, or vice-versa, generating this change in magnetic field. The EMF produced is then harvested as electrical power. As societies developed, the capability to harness and efficiently utilize this principle has underpinned the evolution of modern electrical grids and power distribution systems.

62. Transformers, essential in modern electrical infrastructure, function on the principle of mutual induction. Within a transformer, two coils are placed close to each other. When alternating current (AC) flows through the primary coil, it produces a changing magnetic field, inducing a voltage in the secondary coil. The beauty of transformers is their ability to adjust voltages, essential for efficient power transmission over long distances. However, real-world transformers aren't perfect. They suffer from energy losses, predominantly from eddy currents and hysteresis within the core. To combat these, engineers often employ laminated or specialized cores to minimize the pathway for eddy currents and choose materials with low hysteresis loss.

63. Eddy currents represent a form of energy loss in many electromagnetic systems. When a conductor experiences a changing magnetic field, circulating currents, known as eddy currents, can be induced within the conductor. These currents can lead to resistive heating, representing a loss of energy. This effect is pronounced in transformer cores, motor cores, and other magnetic systems. However, the same principle that causes these losses can be harnessed beneficially, as in induction heating systems where the goal is to rapidly heat a material. To mitigate unwanted effects, engineers utilize laminated cores or employ non-conductive barriers to disrupt the flow of these currents.

64. $E = \frac{d\phi}{dt} = iR \Rightarrow i = \frac{E}{R} = \frac{d\phi}{R\,dt}$,

$dq = idt$

Here $q = idt = \frac{d\phi}{R}$

Given $d\phi = 40$ Wb $- 10$ Wb $= 30$ Wb and R $= 10\Omega$

$\therefore \quad dq = \frac{30}{10} = 3C$

Hence, a charge of 3 C flows through the coil, during the motion of the magnet.

65. The magnetic field B_1 at P due to i_1 is given as,

$$B_1 = \frac{\mu_0 i_1}{2\pi r_1} = \frac{\mu_0}{2\pi} \times \frac{15}{0.05} = \frac{150\mu_0}{\pi} T$$

The magnetic field B_2 at P due to i_2 is given as

$$B_2 = \frac{\mu_0 i_2}{2\pi r_2} = \frac{\mu_0}{2\pi} \times \frac{30}{0.10} = \frac{150\mu_0}{\pi} T$$

By the Right-hand thumb rule, we find that both B_1 and B_2 are in the same direction at P. Thus, the resultant magnetic field at P is

$$B = B_1 + B_2 = \frac{300\mu_0}{\pi}$$

$$T = \frac{300 \times 4\pi \times 10^{-7}}{\pi}$$

$$T = 1200 \times 10^{-7}$$

$$T = 1.2 \times 10^{-4} T$$

The direction of B is perpendicular to the plane of the conductors.

66. Let the fields be B_1 and B_2 at distances 5 cm and 50 cm, respectively.

As current remains same, we can write

$$B \propto \frac{1}{r}$$

$$\Rightarrow \frac{B_1}{B_2} = \frac{r_2}{r_1} = \frac{50}{5} = \frac{10}{1}$$

Hence, the ratio of the fields at the given distances is 10 : 1.

67. The turn-ratio and currents are related as

$$\frac{N_P}{N_s} = \frac{I_s}{I_P}$$

Given, $N_P : N_S = 2 : 5$ and $I_P = 10$ A; Input power $P_i = 300$ W

$$\therefore I_s = \frac{N_P}{N_s} \times I_P = \frac{2}{5} \times 10 = 4\text{A}$$

In an ideal transformer, the input and the output powers are equal.

Hence, we can get

$V_P I_P = V_S I_S$

$\Rightarrow V_S I_S = 300$

$$\Rightarrow V_S 4 = 300 \Rightarrow V_s = \frac{300}{4} = 75\text{V}$$

68. The magnetic induction at a point on the axial line of a short bar magnet is given by

$$B = \frac{\mu_0}{4\pi} \frac{2M}{d^3}$$

Given, $M = 62.5$ A m^2 and $d = 50$ cm $= 0.5$ m

$$B = \frac{4\pi \times 10^{-7}}{4\pi} \times \frac{2 \times 62.5}{0.5^3}$$

$$= 10^{-7} \times \frac{125}{0.125}$$

$$= 10^{-7} \times 1000 = 10^{-4}\text{T}$$

69. The magnetic force between two magnetic poles of strengths m_1 and m_2 separated by distance d in air is given by

$$F = \frac{\mu_0}{4\pi} \frac{m_1 m_2}{d^2}$$

Given, $m_1 = 10$ A m and $m_2 = 200$ A m; d = 50 cm = 0.5 m

$$\therefore F = \frac{\mu_0}{4\pi} \frac{m_1 m_2}{d^2}$$

$$= \frac{4\pi \times 10^{-7}}{4\pi} \times \frac{10 \times 200}{0.5^2}$$

$$= 10^{-7} \times \frac{2000}{0.25} = 8 \times 10^{-4}\text{N}$$

JEE-NEET SPECIAL WING

Multiple-Answer Type Questions

1. $F = \frac{\mu_o}{4\pi}\frac{m_1 m_2}{r^2}$

$F^1 = \frac{\mu_o}{4\pi}\frac{(2m_1)(2m_2)}{(2r)} = \frac{4}{4}, \frac{\mu_o}{4\pi}\frac{m_1 m_2}{r^2}$

$F^1 = F$

The force is inversely proportional to the square distance between the poles.

The force is directly proportional to the product of the strengths of the poles.

Hence, the correct option is (a, b, c)

2. $B_{axial} = \frac{\mu_o}{4\pi}\frac{2M}{d^3}$

a. $B_{axial} = \frac{10^{-7}\times 2\times 10}{(2)^3} = 2.5\times 10^{-7}\ T$

b. $B_{axial} = \frac{10^{-7}\times 2\times 10}{(4)^3} = \frac{5}{16}\times 10^{-7} = 0.31\times 10^{-7}\ T$

c. $B_{eq} = \frac{\mu_o}{4\pi}\times\frac{M}{d^3}$

$= \frac{10^{-7}\times 10}{2^3} = 1.25\times 10^{-7}\ T$

d. $B_{eq} = \frac{10^{-7}\times 10}{4} = 0.156\times 10^{-7}\ T$

Hence, the correct option is (a, b, c)

3. $\frac{N_p}{N_s} = \frac{I_s}{I_p}$

a. $\frac{1}{2} = \frac{I_s}{10} \Rightarrow I_s = 5A$

b. $\frac{2}{3} = \frac{I_s}{10} \Rightarrow I_s = \frac{20}{3}$ A

c. $\frac{N_p}{N_s} = \frac{I_s}{I_p} = \frac{5}{2}$

d. $\frac{N_p}{N_s} = \frac{I_s}{I_p} = \frac{1}{3} \Rightarrow N_p = \frac{N_s}{3}$

Hence, the correct option is (a, d)

4. $B = \frac{\mu_{o}i}{2\pi r}$

$B = \frac{4\pi\times 10^{-7}\times 10}{2\pi\times 5} = 4\times 10^{-7} = 0.4\times 10^{-6} = 0\ 4\mu\ T$

$B = \frac{4\pi\times 10^{-7}\times 10}{2\pi\times 2} = 10\times 10^{-7} = 10^{-6} = 1\mu\ T$

$B = \frac{4\pi\times 10^{-7}\times 10}{2\pi\times 4} = 5\times 10^{-7} = 0.5\times 10^{-6} = 0.5\mu\ T$

Hence, the correct option is (b, c)

5. F = Bil

$= 4\times 10\times 2 = 80\ N$

F = Bil

$= 4\times 10\times 4 = 160\ N$

Hence, the correct option is (a, c)

Comprehension-Based Questions

6. $B = \frac{\mu_{o}i}{2r} = \frac{4\pi\times 10^{-7}\times 10}{2\times\pi}\times 100$

$= 4\times 10^{-5} = 40\times 10^{-6}$

$= 40\mu\ T$

Hence, the correct option is (b)

7. $B = B_1 + B_2\ B = \frac{\mu_{o}i}{2r}$

$B_1 = \frac{4\pi\times 10^{-7}\times 4}{2r} = \frac{4\pi\times 10^{-7}\times 2}{r} = \frac{2\mu_o}{r}$

$B_2 = \frac{\mu_o 6}{2(2r)} = \frac{3}{2}\frac{\mu_o}{r}$

$B = B_1 + B_2 = \frac{\mu_o}{r}\left[2+\frac{3}{2}\right] = \frac{7}{2}\frac{\mu_o}{r}$

Hence, the correct option is (b)

8. $B_1 = \frac{\mu_o i_2}{2r}$ ⊗ (inward)

$B_2 = \frac{\mu_o i_2}{4r}$ ⊙ (outward)

$B_1 = \frac{\mu_o 2i_2}{2r} = \frac{\mu_o i_2}{r}$

$B_2 = \frac{\mu_o i_2}{4r}$

$B = B_1 - B_2$ (Currents are opposite in direction)

$= \frac{\mu_o i_2}{r}\left[1-\frac{1}{4}\right] = \frac{3}{4}\frac{\mu_o i_2}{r}$

Hence, the correct option is (c)

9. $B = \frac{\mu_o i}{4r} = \frac{4\pi\times 10^{-7}\times 3}{4\times 2} = \frac{3\pi\times 10^{-7}}{2}$

$B = \frac{3}{2}\pi\times 10^{-7}$ ⊗ inward

Hence, the correct option is (c)

10. $B_1 = \frac{\mu_o 2}{4\left(\frac{1}{2}\right)} = \mu_o$ (inward)

$$B_2 = \frac{\mu_\circ(4)}{4\left(\frac{1}{2}\right)} = 2\mu_\circ \text{ (inward)}$$

$B = B_2 + B_1 = 2\mu_\circ + \mu_\circ = 3\mu_\circ$ (inward)

Hence, the correct option is (b)

11. $B = \frac{\mu_\circ i}{2\pi r} = \frac{4\pi\times10^{-7}\times2}{2\pi\times2} = 2\times10^{-7} = 20\times10^{-6}$

$B = 20\mu T$ (inward)

Hence, the correct option is (a)

12. $B\,\alpha\frac{i}{r}\;\frac{B_1}{B_2} = \frac{i_1}{i_2}\times\frac{r_1}{r_2}$

$\frac{B_1}{B_2} = \frac{2}{4}\times\frac{4}{2} = \frac{1}{1}$

Hence, the correct option is (c)

13. $B_1 = \frac{\mu_\circ(2)}{2\pi(2)} = \frac{\mu_\circ}{2\pi}$ inward

$B_2 = \frac{\mu_\circ(4)}{2\pi(4)} = \frac{\mu_\circ}{2\pi}$ outward

$B = B_1 - B_2 = 0$

Hence, the correct option is (c)

14. $B_1 = \frac{\mu_\circ(2)}{2\pi 8} = \frac{\mu_\circ}{8\pi}$ inward

$B_2 = \frac{\mu_\circ(4)}{2\pi(2)} = \frac{\mu_\circ}{\pi}$ inward

$B = B_1 + B_2 = \frac{\mu_\circ}{\pi}\left[\frac{1}{8}+1\right] = \frac{9}{8}\frac{\mu_\circ}{\pi}$

Hence, the correct option is (d)

15. $\frac{F}{l} = \frac{\mu_\circ i_1 i_2}{2\pi r} \Rightarrow \frac{F}{l} = \frac{4\pi\times10^{-7}\times2\times4}{2\pi\times6}$

$\Rightarrow \frac{F}{l} = \frac{8}{3}N$

Hence, the correct option is (b)

16. **A.** $\frac{\mu_\circ i}{2\pi r} = \frac{\mu_\circ(1)}{2(1)} = \frac{\mu_\circ}{2}T$

B. $\frac{\mu_\circ i}{4r} = \frac{\mu_\circ(2)}{4\left(\frac{1}{2}\right)} = \mu_\circ T$

C. $B1 = \frac{\mu_\circ(3)}{2\pi(1)}$ $B2 = \frac{\mu_\circ(6)}{2\pi(1)}$

$B1 = \frac{4\pi\times10^{-7}\times3}{2\pi}$ $B2 = \frac{4\pi\times10^{-7}\times6}{2\pi}$

$B1 = 6\times10^{-7}$ in ward $B2 = 12\times10^{-7}$ outward

$B = B1 \sim B2$

$= 12\times10^{-7}\ldots 6\times10^{-7}$

$= 6\times10^{-7}T$

D. $B = \frac{\mu_\circ i}{2\pi r} = \frac{4\pi\times10^{-7}\times5}{2\pi\times3} = \frac{10}{3}\times10^{-7}$

E. $\frac{\mu_\circ i}{8r} = \frac{\mu_\circ(1)}{4(0.5)} = \frac{\mu_\circ}{4}T$

A ↔ b

B ↔ d

C ↔ c

D ↔ e

E ↔ a

Unit VI

Light

In this Unit

CHAPTER

8

Light

Remember

Before beginning this chapter, you should be able to:

- Study application of rectilinear propagation of light like the formation of shadows, working of pinhole camera, etc.
- Explain the phenomenon of refraction with the help of different examples.
- Understand the formation of rainbow, different colours of objects, etc.
- Understand the principle involved in the working of different optical instruments.

Key Ideas

After completing this chapter, you should be able to:

- Study reflection of light by plane mirrors and spherical mirrors.
- Study refraction through glass slab, prism, refractive index, total internal reflection and critical angle.
- Learn refraction through lenses and cause of dispersion.
- Study the basic terms related to visual photometry, laser and its working, construction and working of cameras, microscopes, telescopes, projectors, etc.

Scientific Crypt

A Tribute to Thomas Young (1773 – 1829)

Young was born in 1773, and was the eldest of ten children. He belonged to a Quaker family of Milverton. At the age of 14, Young learned Greek and Latin and was acquainted with 11 languages.

Young studied in London and received the degree "Doctor of Physics" in 1796 from Gottingen, Germany. In 1797 he entered Emmanuel college, Cambridge and in 1799, he established himself as a physician. Young published many of his first academic articles anonymously to protect his reputation as a physician. In 1801, Young was appointed as professor of natural philosophy at the Royal Institution. In two years he delivered 91 lectures, and in 1802, he was appointed as foreign secretary of the Royal society. In 1828, he was elected as a foreign member of the Royal Swedish Academy of Sciences.

One of his many achievements was to establish the wave theory of light with the help of a ripple tank. He demonstrated the interference phenomenon in the context of water waves. By the double slit experiment, he demonstrated interference phenomenon in the context of light as a wave. Young described the characteristics of elasticity, that came to be known as Young's modulus and is denoted as 'E'. Young is called founder of 'Physiological Optics'. He was the first to describe astigmatism. In 1804, Young developed the theory of capillary phenomenon on the principle of surface tension. Young also devised a rule of thumb for determining a child's drug dosage. In his encyclopedia Britannica article 'languages', Young also compared the grammar and vocabulary of 400 languages. He also developed Young temperament, a method of tuning musical instruments.

FUN TIME

CROSSWORD

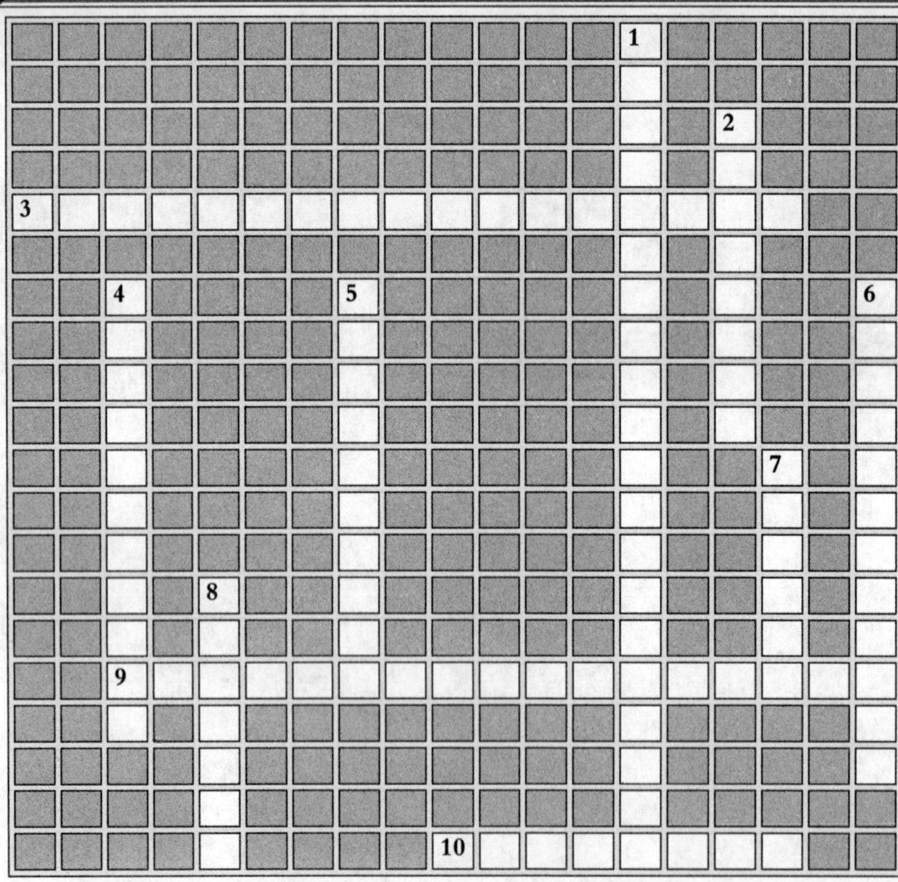

Across

3. A concave mirror is also known as this.
9. The change in the path of refracted ray on passing through hot air.
10. According to the sign convention, what should be the sign of the distances measured opposite to the direction of incident rays.

Down

1. What do you call the perpendicular displacement between an emergent ray and an incident ray produced?
2. Power of a lens is measured in ______.
4. The effect of eye corrected by using cylindrical lens.
5. This is formed when light rays meet after reflection or refraction.
6. A light ray passing through this point of a lens undergoes no deviation.
7. Images of trees seen on the road as a result of an optical illusion.
8. This phenomenon takes place mainly due to the dispersion of light.

INTRODUCTION

Nature around us is colourful and diverse. It is impossible to enjoy nature without light. Light causes sensation of sight. Investigation of nature of light has opened a treasure of knowledge and development.

Nature of Light

Light is a form of electromagnetic radiation and a non-mechanical wave. Non-mechanical waves do not require a material as a medium for propagation. Light exhibits dual nature, i.e., both particle nature as well as wave nature, and some phenomena of light can be explained by considering light as a wave (interference, diffraction and polarization) while other phenomena like, photoelectric effect, etc., can be explained by treating light as a particle.

Light travels at a speed of nearly 3×10^8 m s^{-1} in air or vacuum. Wavelength of visible light is from 400 nm to 800 nm (4000 Å – 8000 Å) and the corresponding frequency is 7.5×10^{14} Hz to 3.75×10^{14} Hz. Light travels along a straight line and this property is called rectilinear propagation. This straight line is called ray, and a bundle of rays is called beam of light.

When light is incident on a surface, a part of it is reflected, a part of it is refracted and the remaining part is absorbed. Light is reflected by highly polished surfaces (mirrors) and it is refracted partially by transparent media.

Light rays can be focused using mirrors and lenses. If light rays meet at a point after reflection or refraction by a mirror or through a lens, respectively, an image is obtained on a screen. These images are called real images.

Thus, real images are formed when the rays after reflection or refraction meet at a point. If the rays appear to meet when produced backwards, then the image formed is virtual. The real image can be caught on a screen but the virtual image cannot be formed on a screen.

Info Bytes!

- Light travels at a speed of about 299,792 kilometres per second in a vacuum.
- Isaac Newton initially thought that light was composed of particles, while Huygens believed it to be a wave. Turns out both were right; light has a dual nature.

Reflection of Light

When light is incident on a surface, separating two media, a part of the light is bounced back to the first medium. This is known as reflection.

AB is the surface, *PQ* is the incident ray and *QR* is the reflected ray.

$\angle$i = angle of incidence

$\angle$r = angle of reflection

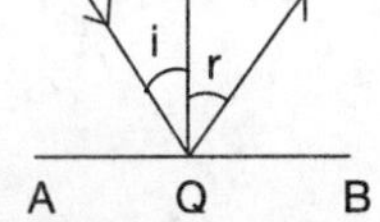

Figure 8.1 Reflection of a light ray incident on a plane mirror

Laws of Reflection

1. The incident ray, the reflected ray and the normal to the reflecting surface at the point of incidence lie in the same plane.
2. The angle of incidence is equal to the angle of reflection ($\angle i = \angle r$).

Reflection by a Plane Mirror

An object AB is placed at a distance 'u' on one side of the plane mirror. Each point of AB acts as a source. To find the distance and nature of the image, consider a ray AC incident along the normal and another ray AO incident on the mirror at an angle 'i'. The ray AC retraces its path since it is incident along the normal. But the ray AO is reflected along OD at an angle 'r'. The two reflected rays are produced backwards and they intersect at A'. Similarly B' is the virtual image of point B. Every point of the object will form the corresponding image between A' and B'. Thus, $A'B'$ is the virtual, erect image of the object AB.

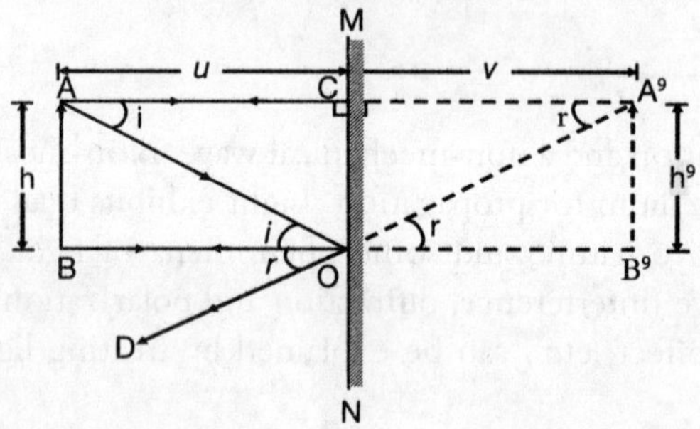

Figure 8.2 An extended object AB and its virtual image A' B' formed in a plane mirror MN

Features of an Image Formed by a Plane Mirror

1. The image is virtual and erect.
2. It is of the same size as that of the object.
3. The distance between the object and the mirror is the same as that between the image and the mirror.
4. It is laterally inverted.

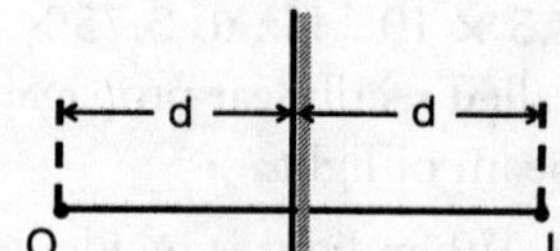

Figure 8.3 Distance of image and object from the mirror

Spherical Mirrors

Spherical mirrors are a part of a sphere. Consider a hollow sphere. Now consider slicing a portion out of a sphere and the surface of the portions are silvered on the inner or outer surface.

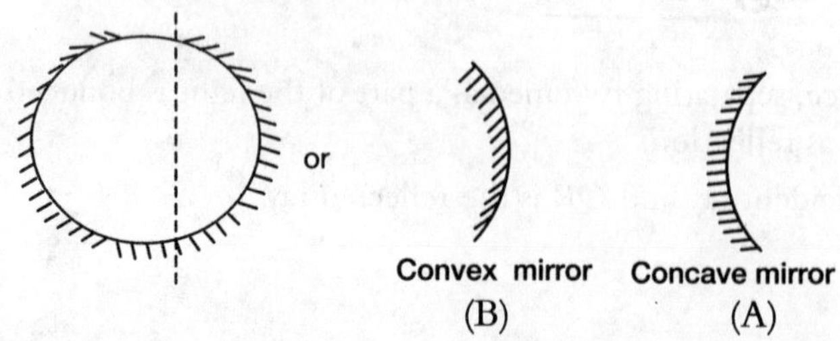

Figure 8.4 Convex and concave mirrors sliced from a spherical mirror

Generally, the smaller piece is used as a mirror. If a mirror is obtained from a sphere silvered on the outer side, it is called concave mirror (shown in Fig. 8.4[A]). If a mirror is obtained from a sphere silvered inside, it is called convex mirror (shown in Fig. 8.4[B]).

Terms Related to Spherical Mirrors

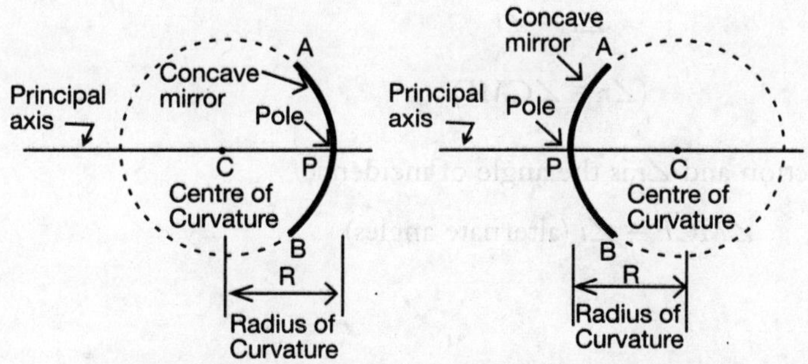

Figure 8.5 Terms related to spherical mirrors

Length AB is the measure of aperture, C is the centre of curvature, P is the pole, and PC is the principal axis.

1. **Aperture:** The portion available for reflection is called aperture; APB is the aperture.
2. **Pole:** It is the geometric centre of the reflecting surface. It is denoted by P.
3. **Centre of Curvature:** It is the centre of the sphere of which the mirror forms a part. C is the centre of curvature.
4. **Principal Axis:** It is a straight line passing through the centre of curvature and the pole. The line passing through P and C in the figure is the principal axis.
5. **Radius of Curvature (R):** It is the radius of the sphere of which the mirror forms a part. PC is the radius of curvature.
6. **Principal Focus:** Consider a parallel beam of light incident on a spherical mirror.

   In case of a concave mirror, the parallel beam after reflection converges at a point F which is called principal focus.

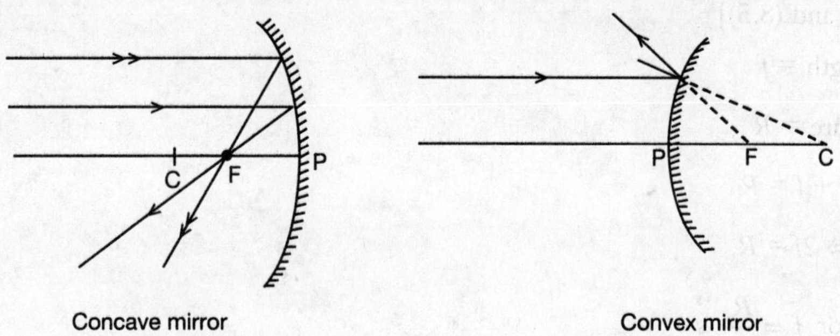

Figure 8.6 Reflection of a beam from spherical mirrors

   In case of a convex mirror, it appears to diverge from the focus (F). Thus, a concave mirror is called converging mirror and a convex mirror is called diverging mirror.

7. **Focal Length:** It is the distance between the pole and the principal focus. PF is the focal length. It is denoted by 'f'. It is measured in m or cm.

Relation between Focal Length and Radius of Curvature

Consider a concave mirror of small aperture. P is the pole of the mirror. PC is the radius of curvature = R

CM is the normal to the spherical surface.

PF is the focal length = f

OM is the ray parallel to principal axis and is incident on the mirror at an angle 'i'.

The ray OM after reflection passes through principal focus (F). A ray CM, incident normally, retraces its path after reflection.

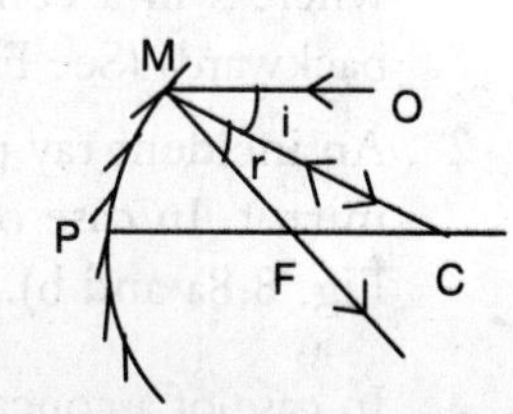

Figure 8.7 Reflection of ray OM incident on a concave mirror

From Laws of Reflection:

$$\angle i = \angle r \quad (8.1)$$

$$(\angle r = \angle CMF)$$

where, $\angle r$ is the angle of reflection and $\angle i$ is the angle of incidence.

$$\angle MCF = \angle i \text{ (alternate angles)} \quad (8.2)$$

From (8.1) and (8.2)

$$\angle MCF = \angle r \quad (8.3)$$

From geometry

$$FC = FM \quad (8.4)$$

($\because$ base angles of $\Delta\ CMF$ are equal)

Since we are considering a small aperture, $\angle PFM$ is small angle and PM is straight line. FM almost coincides with PF.

$$\therefore FM = PF \quad (8.5)$$

$$PF + FC = PC$$

$$PF + PF = PC \quad (8.6)$$

($\because PF = FC$) [from (8.4) and (8.5)]

PF is the focal length $= f$

PC is the radius of curvature $= R$

$$\because f + f = R$$

$$\Rightarrow 2f = R$$

$$\text{or } f = \frac{R}{2}$$

Thus, for a spherical mirror, the radius of curvature is twice its focal length.

Rules to Determine the Path of Reflected Rays

1. In case of a concave mirror, incident rays parallel to the principal axis on reflection pass through principal focus whereas in a convex mirror, the reflected rays only appear to pass through the principal focus, when produced backwards (See Fig 8.6).
2 An incident ray passing through the centre of curvature gets reflected along the same path in case of a concave mirror. In case of a convex mirror, the reflected ray only appears to pass through the centre of curvature (See Fig. 8.8a and b).
3. In case of a concave mirror an incident ray passing through the principal focus reflects parallel to the principal axis (See Fig. 8.8c). In case of convex mirror, an incident ray which appears to pass through the focus reflects parallel to the principal axis (See Fig. 8.8d).

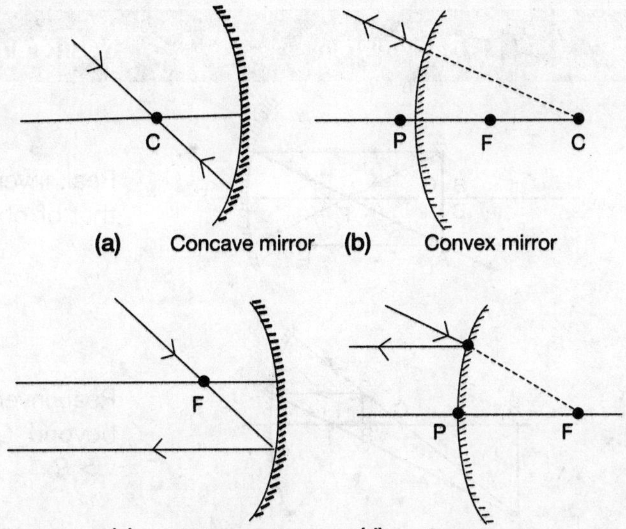

Figure 8.8 Incident ray passing through centre of curvature in figure (a) & (b); and through focus in figure (c) & (d)

Formation of Image by Convex Mirror

In the following ray diagrams, OJ is an extended object and IG is an image formed by a convex mirror of small aperture.

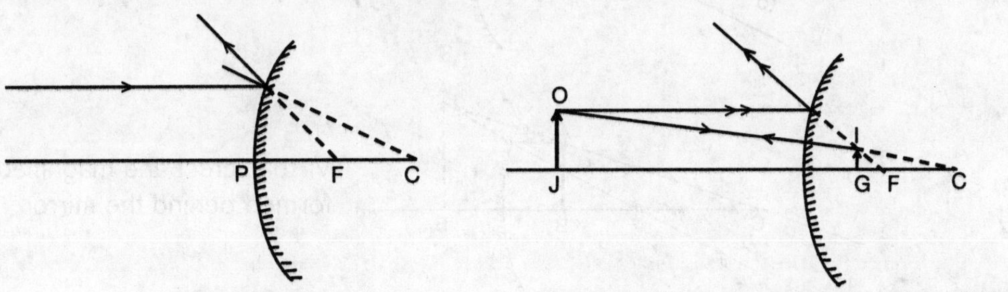

When object is at infinity

When object is at any position other than infinity

Figure 8.9 Formation of image by convex mirror

Formation of Image by Concave Mirror

In the following ray diagrams, AB is an extended object and A_1B_1 is an image formed by a concave mirror of small aperture.

Table 8.1 Image formation by Concave mirror

S. No.	Object distance	Ray diagram	Nature and position of image
1	$u = \infty$	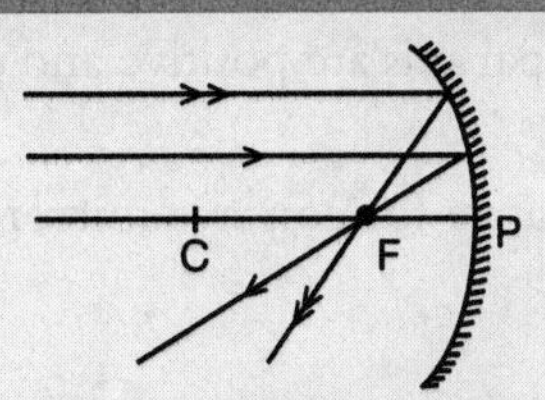	Real, inverted and highly diminished, $v = f$
2	$R < u < \infty$	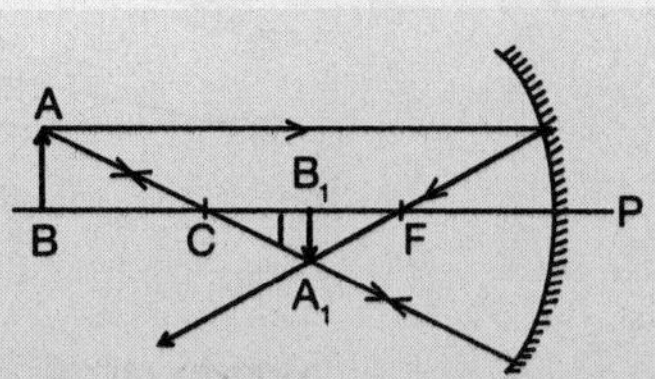	Real, inverted and diminished, lies between F & C *i.e.*, $f < v < R$.

(Continued)

S. No.	Object distance	Ray diagram	Nature and position of image
3	$u = R$	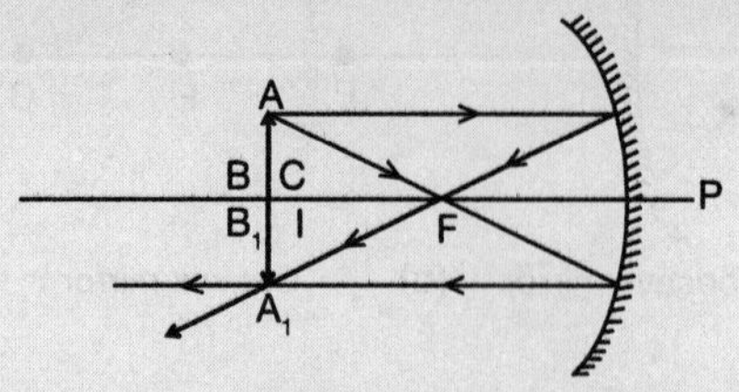	Real, inverted and of equal size as that of object, $v = R$. At C.
4	$f < u < R$	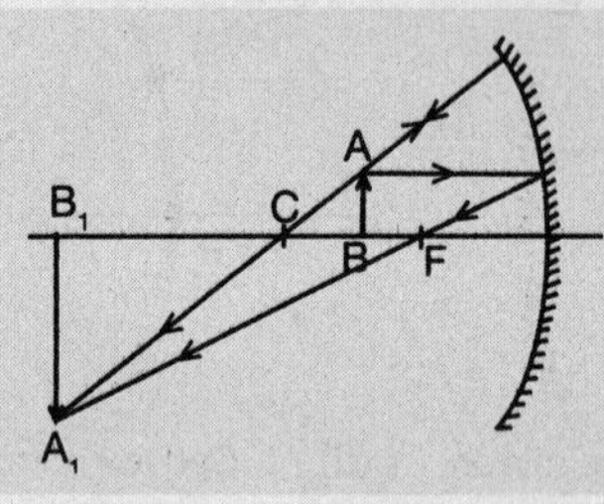	Real, inverted and magnified, beyond 'C'. $v > R$
5	$u = f$	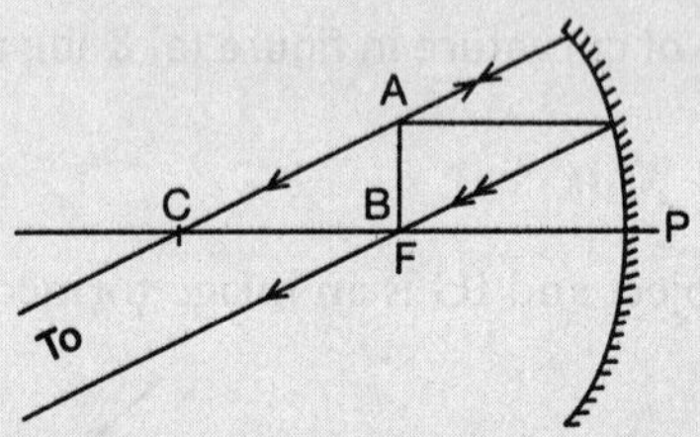	Real, inverted and highly magnified at $v = \infty$.
6	$u < f$	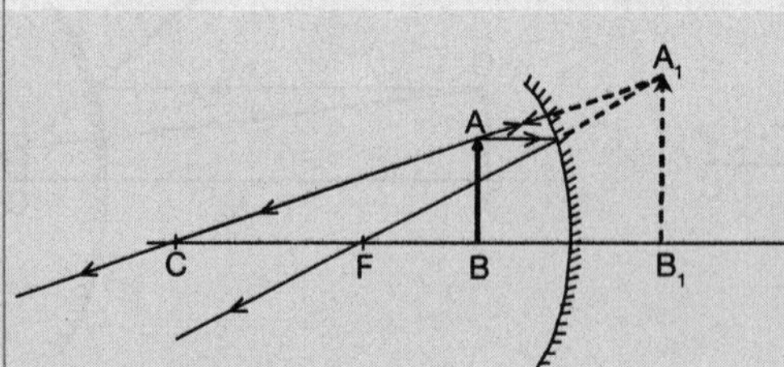	Virtual, erect and magnified and formed behind the mirror.

(Image formed by a mirror of large aperture is not distinct and the image suffers from defects and distortions.)

Sign Convention

New Cartesian sign convention of reflection by spherical mirrors:

1. All distances are measured from the pole (P) of the mirror.
2. Distances measured in the direction of the incident ray are taken as positive and the distances measured in the direction opposite to the incident ray are taken as negative.
3. Perpendicular distances (height) above the principal axis are positive and perpendicular distance below the principal axis are negative.
4. Thus, focal length and radius of curvature is negative for concave mirror and positive for convex mirror.

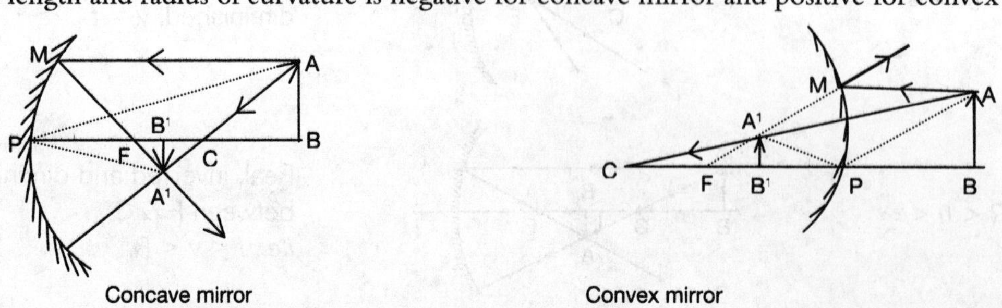

Figure 8.10 Formation of image by concave and convex mirror

Mirror Formula

Consider a spherical mirror (concave or convex mirror) of radius of curvature '*R*'. Let '*f*' be the focal length of the spherical mirror. *AB* is an object placed at a distance '*u*' from the pole *P*. A^1B^1 is an image of an object at a distance '*v*' from the pole *P*. *PC* is the radius of curvature. Triangle *ABP* and triangle A^1B^1P are similar.

Concave Mirror	Convex Mirror
$\therefore \frac{A^1B^1}{AB} = \frac{PB^1}{PB}$ Using Cartesian sign convention, we get $\frac{PB^1}{PB} = \frac{-v}{-u}$ $\frac{A^1B^1}{AB} = \frac{-v}{-u} = \frac{v}{u}$ (1) From similar triangles, ABC and A^1B^1C, we have $\frac{A^1B^1}{AB} = \frac{B^1C}{BC} = \frac{PC-PB^1}{PB-PC}$ Using Cartesian sign convention and (1) $\frac{v}{u} = \frac{-R-(v)}{-u-(-R)}$ $\frac{v}{u} = \frac{-R+v}{-u+R}$	$\frac{A^1B^1}{AB} = \frac{PB^1}{PB}$ Using Cartesian sign convention, we get $\frac{PB^1}{PB} = \frac{v}{-u}$ $\frac{A^1B^1}{AB} = \frac{v}{-u}$ (1) From similar triangles ABC and A^1B^1C, we have $\frac{A^1B^1}{AB} = \frac{B^1C}{BC} = \frac{PC-PB^1}{PC+PB}$ Using Cartesian sign convention and (1), we get $\frac{v}{-u} = \frac{R-v}{R+(-u)}$ $\frac{v}{-u} + \frac{R-v}{R-u}$
$-uv + vR = -uR + vu$ $\Rightarrow vR + uR = uv + uv \Rightarrow vR + uR = 2uv$ Dividing throughout by *uvR* $\frac{1}{v} + \frac{1}{u} = \frac{2}{R}$ $\frac{1}{u} + \frac{1}{v} = \frac{1}{f}$	$\Rightarrow vR - uv = -uR + uV$ $\Rightarrow uR + vR = uv + uv \Rightarrow uR + vR = 2uv$ Dividing throughout by *uvR* $\frac{1}{v} + \frac{1}{u} = \frac{2}{R}$ $\frac{1}{u} + \frac{1}{v} = \frac{1}{f}$

$$\because f = \frac{R}{2}$$

$\therefore$ The relation between object distance, image distance and the focal length for a mirror is $\frac{1}{f} = \frac{1}{u} + \frac{1}{v}$. This is called mirror formula.

Linear Magnification (*m*)

It is the ratio of image height to the object height

$$m = \frac{\text{Height of the image } (h^1)}{\text{Height of the object } (h^2)} = \frac{A^1B^1}{AB}$$

$$m = \frac{h^1}{h^2} = \frac{-v}{u} \quad \left(\because \frac{A^1B^1}{AB} = \frac{v}{u}\right)$$

(using Cartesian sign convention).

Magnification is positive if the image is erect (and virtual) and it is negative, if the image is (real and) inverted.

Konnect

The concept of magnification applies not just to mirrors but to all optical devices.

EXAMPLE 8.1 Find the radius of curvature of a concave mirror of focal length 40 cm.

SOLUTION

Focal length = $\frac{1}{2}$ radius of curvature (R)

Given,

$f = 40$ cm

$R = 2f = 2 \times 40 = 80$ cm

Since it is a concave mirror, 'R' is negative (from Cartesian sign).

So, $R = -80$ cm

EXAMPLE 8.2 A convex security mirror in a store has a focal length of 3 meters. If a shopper is standing 6 meters away from the mirror, determine the nature and distance of the image formed.

SOLUTION

Given that the mirror is convex, and focal length (f) = 3m; and, object distance (u) = –6 m.

(We use negative as the object distance is measured in the direction opposite to the incident rays)

Using the mirror formula, $\frac{1}{f} = \frac{1}{v} + \frac{1}{u}$

Substituting the values, we have

$$\frac{1}{3} = \frac{1}{v} - \frac{1}{6}$$

$$\Rightarrow \frac{1}{v} = \frac{1}{3} + \frac{1}{6} = \frac{1}{2}$$

Or

$v = 2$ m.

This means the image is formed 2 meters behind the mirror, indicating it's a virtual image.

For magnification (m):

$$m = -\frac{v}{u} = -\frac{2}{-6} = 0.3333$$

The magnification value less than 1 indicates the image is diminished, and since it's positive, it is erect.

In conclusion, the security mirror forms a virtual, erect, and diminished image of the shopper standing 6 meters from it. The image is formed 2 meters behind the mirror.

EXAMPLE 8.3

An object of height 2 cm is placed at distance 2.5 *f* from a concave mirror where '*f*' is its focal length. Find the height of the image.

SOLUTION

Height of the object = 2 cm

Focal length = $-f$ (for concave mirror, *f* is negative)

Object distance $u = -2.5\,f$ (from Cartesian sign convention)

Using the mirror formula, we get

$$\frac{1}{f}=\frac{1}{u}+\frac{1}{v}$$

$$\frac{1}{-f}=\frac{1}{-2.5f}+\frac{1}{v}\Rightarrow\frac{1}{v}=\frac{1}{-f}+\frac{1}{2.5f}\Rightarrow\frac{1}{v}=\frac{-1}{f}+\frac{2}{5f}$$

$$\frac{1}{v}=\frac{-5f+2f}{5f^2}\text{ or }v=\frac{-5f}{3}$$

$$\text{Magnification } m=\frac{h_1}{h_O}=\frac{-v}{u}$$

$$\frac{h_1}{2}=-\left(\frac{\frac{-5f}{3}}{\frac{-5}{2}f}\right)=\frac{-2}{3}\Rightarrow h_1=\frac{-2}{3}\times 2=\frac{-4}{3}$$

Image is 1.33 cm long. Minus sign shows that it is inverted.

EXAMPLE 8.4

A rod of length 10 cm lies along the principal axis of a concave mirror of focal length 10 cm in such a way that the end close to the pole is 20 cm away from it. Find the length of the image of the rod.

SOLUTION

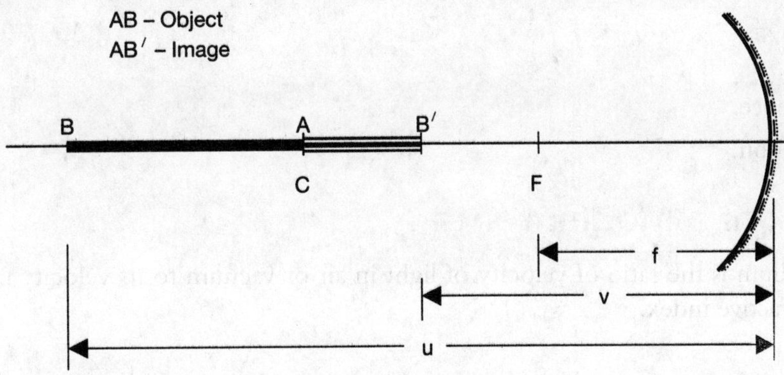

Figure 8.11 Rod AB placed at given distance from concave mirror

Focal length $f = -10$ cm

∴ Radius of curvature $R = 2f = -20$ cm

Length of the rod AB = 10 cm

Distance of the end A = 20 cm = R

Since the near end 'A' of rod is at the centre of curvature, its image A^1 will also be at 'C'.

Distance of the end B of the road= 20 + 10 = 30 cm

∴ $u = -30$ cm (from Cartesian sign convention)

$f = -10$ cm

$v = ?$

From mirror formula,

$$\frac{1}{f}=\frac{1}{u}+\frac{1}{v}$$

$$\frac{1}{-10}=\frac{1}{-30}+\frac{1}{v}$$

$$\frac{1}{v}=\frac{-1}{10}+\frac{1}{30}\Rightarrow\frac{1}{v}=\frac{-30+10}{30\times10}$$

$$\frac{1}{v}=\frac{-20}{300}$$

$$v=\frac{-30}{2}=-15\text{ cm}$$

Length of the image = A^1B^1 = 20 – 15 = 5 cm

Medium: The substance which allows the light to pass through it is called medium.

Refraction

When light passes from one medium to another medium, there is a change in the path of light in the second medium. This is known as refraction. Deviation in the path of light is due to the change in the speed of light when it passes from one medium to another. Refraction of light is shown in Fig. 8.12 and it shows:

PQ is the incident ray.

QR is the refracted ray.

MN is the normal.

∠*i* is the angle of incidence.

∠*r* is the angle of refraction.

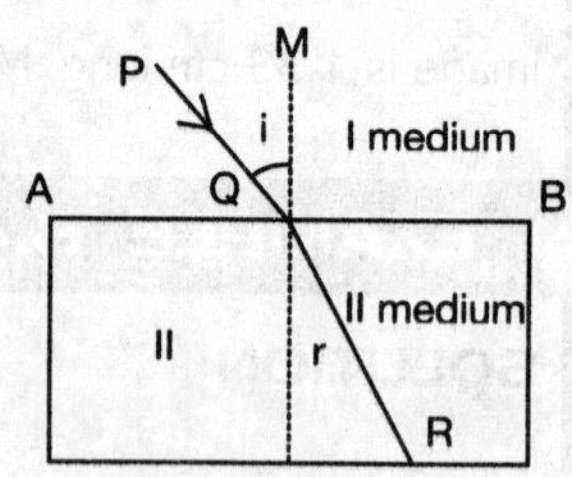

Figure 8.12 Refraction from one medium to another

Refractive Index of a Medium

Refractive index of a medium is the ratio of velocity of light in air or vacuum to its velocity in a given medium. This is known as the absolute refractive index.

$$\therefore \mu=\frac{\text{Velocity in air or vacuum }(c)}{\text{Velocity in given medium}}\Rightarrow\mu=\frac{c}{v}$$

where, μ is absolute refractive index. If μ_1 and μ_2 are the refractive indices of two media and v_1 and v_2 are the velocity of light in the medium one and medium two, respectively,

then,

$$\mu_1=\frac{c}{v_1} \tag{8.7}$$

$$\mu_2=\frac{c}{v_2} \tag{8.8}$$

Dividing (8.7) by (8.8), we get

$$\frac{\mu_2}{\mu_1} = \frac{\frac{c}{v_2}}{\frac{c}{v_1}}$$

$$\frac{\mu_2}{\mu_1} = \frac{v_1}{v_2} = {}^1\mu$$

where, $^1\mu^2$ is the relative refractive index of medium 2 with respect to medium 1.

Info Bytes!

Diamond has one of the highest refractive indices for natural materials, which gives it its characteristic sparkle.

Table 8.2 Absolute refractive indices of mediums

Medium	Absolute refractive index
Air	1.00
Water	1.33
Glass	1.5
Diamond	2.42

Rarer Medium: The medium of lower refractive index is called rarer medium.

Denser Medium: The medium of higher refractive index is called denser medium.

When a light ray is incident from rarer medium to the denser medium, the refracted ray bends towards the normal, i.e., $\angle i > \angle r$.

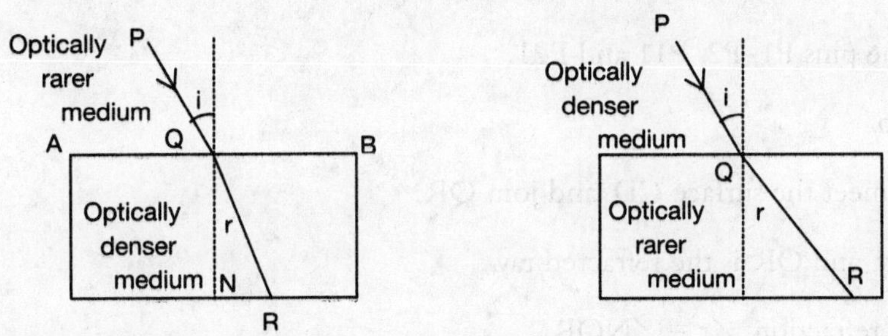

Figure 8.13 Refraction of light from rarer medium to denser medium and vice-versa

When a light ray travels from a denser medium to a rarer medium, the refracted ray bends away from the normal, i.e., $\angle i < \angle r$. Thus, the deviation of the ray of light depends on the optical density of the two media.

Laws of Refraction

First Law

The incident ray, the refracted ray and the normal to the surface separating the two media at the point of incidence, all lie on the same plane.

Second Law

The ratio of sine of angle of incidence to the sine of angle of refraction is a constant for a given pair of media and for a given colour of light. This law is also known as Snell's law.

$$\text{Mathematically, } \frac{\sin \angle i}{\sin \angle r} = \mu$$

where, μ is a constant called refractive index.

It is observed that, when a light ray travels along the normal, drawn to the interface of two medium, no refraction takes place, i.e., $\angle i = \angle r = 0$

$$\therefore \frac{\sin \angle i}{\sin \angle r} = \frac{0}{0} = \text{undefined}$$

So, snell's law is not applicable when angle of incidence is equal to zero, i.e., when the ray is incident along the normal.

Experiment to Verify Second Law of Refraction or to Find Absolute Refractive Index of a Glass

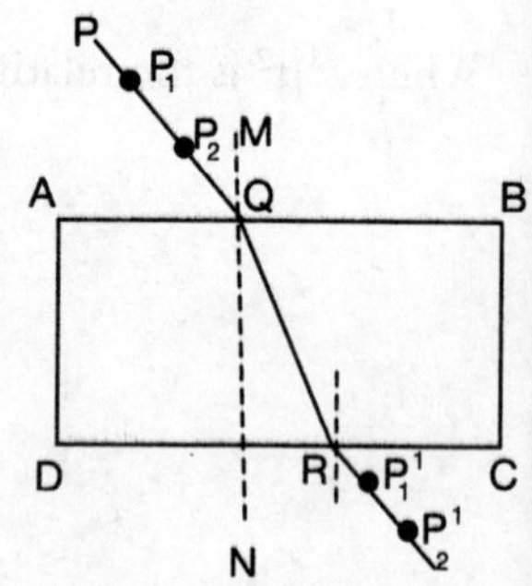

Figure 8.14 **Refraction through glass slab ABCD**

Take a glass slab and place it on a white paper which is fixed to a drawing board.

1. Trace the boundary ABCD of the glass slab and remove it.
2. Draw a normal *MN* to the glass surface AB, at point Q. Make a suitable angle (angle of incidence) with the normal. This is the line of incidence.
3. Fix two pins P1 and P2 on the line of incidence such that they are normal to the bond.
4. Replace the glass slab on the boundary traced, i.e., on ABCD.
5. Locate the image of the pins P1 and P2 looking through the opposite face of the glass slab through CD. How?
6. The image of the pins P11 and P21 appears to be in line with *P*1 and *P*2. Fix two pins at these points, i.e., P11 and P21.
7. Mark the points of the pins P1, P2, P11 and P21.
8. Remove the glass slab.
9. Join P11 and P21 to meet the surface CD, and join QR.
10. PQ is the incident ray, and QR is the refracted ray.
11. Measure the angle of refraction, $\angle r = \angle NQR$.
12. Find the refractive index of the glass, using

$$\mu = \frac{\sin \angle i}{\sin \angle r}$$

13. Repeat the experiment for different angles of incidence. Tabulate the results as shown below.
14. In each case, it is found that the ratio of sin i to sin r is a constant.

Trial No.	Angle of incidence $= \angle i$	Sin *i*	Angle of refraction $= \angle r$	Sin *r*	$\mu = \frac{\sin\angle i}{\sin\angle r}$

Principle of Reversibility of Light

If a ray of light travels from medium 1 to medium 2 along a certain path, it retraces the path when it travels from medium 2 to medium 1. Thus, the path of light is reversible. This property is called principle of reversibility of path (See Fig. 8.15).

AB is the refracting surface separating the two media. *MN* is the normal. A ray of light *PQ* is incident at an angle '*i*' and is refracted along *QR* at an angle '*r*'.

Refractive index of medium 2 with respect to medium 1 is

$$^1\mu_2 = {}_1\mu_2 = \frac{\sin \angle i}{\sin \angle r}. \quad (8.9)$$

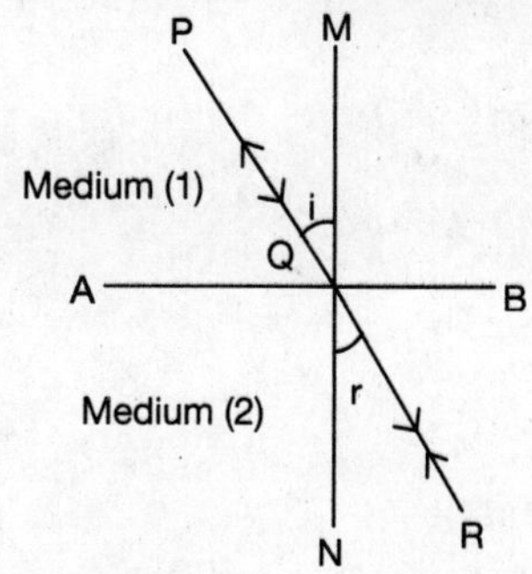

Figure 8.15 Reversibility of light

When a ray of light travels from medium 2 to medium 1, according to the principle of reversibility, *RQ* is the incident ray and *PQ* is the refracted ray, refracted at an angle '*i*'. Refractive index of medium 1 with respect to medium 2 is

$$^2\mu_1 = \frac{\sin \angle r}{\sin \angle i} \qquad \therefore \; {}_2\mu_1 = \frac{1}{{}_1\mu_2} \quad (8.10)$$

EXAMPLE 8.5 The velocity of light in a vacuum is 3×10^8 m/s. If the refractive index of glass is $\frac{3}{2}$, find the velocity of light in glass.

SOLUTION

Velocity of light in vacuum, $C = 3 \times 10^8$ m/s

Refractive index of glass, $n = \frac{3}{2}$

Using the formula for refractive index: $n = \frac{c}{v}$

Where, v = speed of light in the medium (in this case, glass).

So, $\frac{3}{2} = \frac{3\times10^8 \text{ m/s}}{v}$

$v \times \frac{3}{2} = 3\times10^8$ m/s

$v = \frac{2}{3} \times 3\times10^8$ m/s

$v = 2\times10^8$ m/s

So, the speed of light in glass is 2×10^8 m/s.

EXAMPLE 8.6 The angle of incidence of a ray of the light is 45°. If a ray of light travels from air to glass, find the angle of refraction. Refractive index of glass, $\mu_g = 1.5$.

SOLUTION

Given, $\angle i = 45°$ = Angle of incidence

Refractive index of glass = $\mu_g = 1.5$

Angle of refraction, r = ?Velocity of light in water is 2.25×10^8 m s^{-1}.

$$\mu = \frac{\sin \angle i}{\sin \angle r} \text{(from Snell's law)}$$

$$1.5 = \frac{\sin 45°}{\sin r}$$

$$1.5 = \frac{\left(\frac{1}{\sqrt{2}}\right)}{\sin r}$$

$$\sin r = \frac{1}{1.5 \times \sqrt{2}}$$

$\sin r = 0.4728$. From sine trigonometric table, we get $\angle r \approx 28°$.

EXAMPLE 8.7 The refractive index of water is 1.33, and the refractive index of ruby is 1.76. Calculate the refractive index of ruby with respect to water.

SOLUTION

$$\text{Relative refractive index of ruby with respect to water} = \frac{\text{Refractive index of Ruby}}{\text{Refractive index of Water}}$$

Given:

Refractive index of ruby, $m_r = 1.76$

Refractive index of water, $m_2 = 1.33$

$$\text{Relative refractive index} = \frac{m_r}{m_w} = \frac{1.76}{1.33} = 1.3233$$

So, rounded to three decimal places, the refractive index of ruby with respect to water is approximately 1.323.

Refraction through a Glass Slab

Consider a glass slab *ABCD* placed in air. A ray *PQ* incident from air to glass at an angle i_1 is refracted along *QR* at an angle i_2. The ray *QR* is incident on glass – air interface, then it undergoes refraction along *RS* at an angle i_3 (*RS* is called emergent ray).

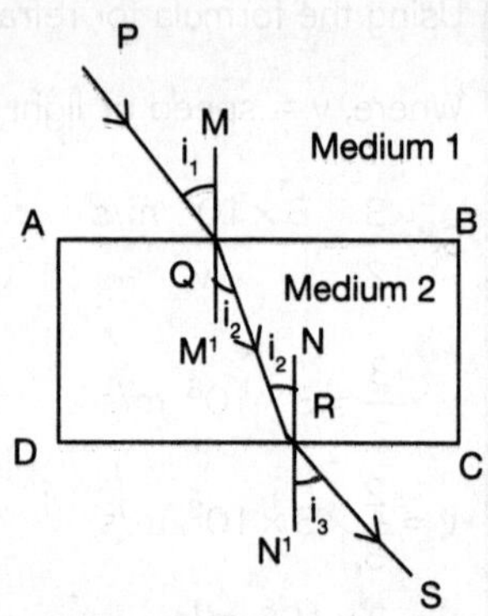

Figure 8.16 Refraction through a glass slab

From Snell's law, at the surface AB

$$^1\mu = \frac{\mu_2}{\mu_1} = \frac{\sin \angle i_1}{\sin \angle i_2} \tag{8.11}$$

where, μ_2 is refractive index of glass and μ_1 is refractive index of air.

From equation (8.11)

$$\mu_1 \sin \angle i_1 = \mu_2 \sin \angle i_2 \tag{8.12}$$

At the interface CD

From Snell's law
$$\frac{\mu_1}{\mu_2} = \frac{\sin \angle i_2}{\sin \angle i_3}$$

$$\mu_1 \sin i_3 = \mu_2 \sin i_2 \tag{8.13}$$

Comparing (8.12) and (8.13)

$$\mu_1 \sin i_1 = \mu_1 \sin i_3$$

Since $\mu_1 = 1$ (refractive index of air),

$$\text{Sin } i_1 = \sin i_3 \therefore i_1 = i_3$$

MM^1 and NN^1 are parallel to each other.

Thus, the emergent RS ray is parallel to the incident PQ ray.

Lateral Displacement

Consider an optical medium (*ABCD*) of thickness '*t*'. *PQ* is the incident ray, incident at an angle '*i*', the ray *PQ* undergoes refraction along *QR* at an angle '*r*'. In the absence of an optical medium the ray, *PQ* would have travelled straight without any deviation along *PQT*. Due to the presence of a medium, the incident ray undergoes shift. This is known as lateral displacement. Thus, lateral displacement is the perpendicular distance between the emergent ray and the incident ray produced. *RT* measures lateral displacement.

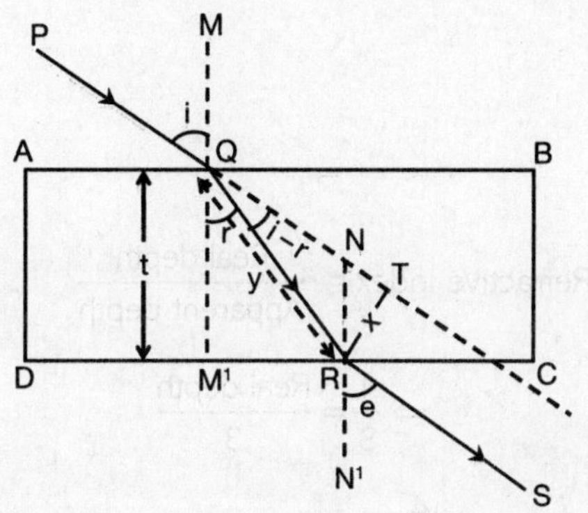

Figure 8.17 Lateral displacement shown by refraction of light through glass slab

The lateral displacement depends on the following factors:

1. **Thickness of the medium:** Lateral displacement is directly proportional to the thickness.
2. **Refractive index of the medium:** Lateral displacement is directly proportional to the refractive index of the medium.
3. **Angle of incidence:** Lateral displacement varies directly as the angle of incidence.

Real and Apparent Depth

Consider an object '*O*' placed in an optically denser medium. A ray *OM* passes without deviation, since it is incident along the normal. A ray *OP* incident at an angle *i* undergoes refraction at an angle '*r*' along *PR*. When refracted ray *PR* is produced backwards, it meets the normal at *I*. The object appears to come from *I* and not from *O*. *I* is the virtual image of the object *O*. *IM* is the apparent depth and *OM* is the real depth.

$$\text{Refractive index of the medium} = \frac{\text{Real depth}}{\text{Apparent depth}}$$

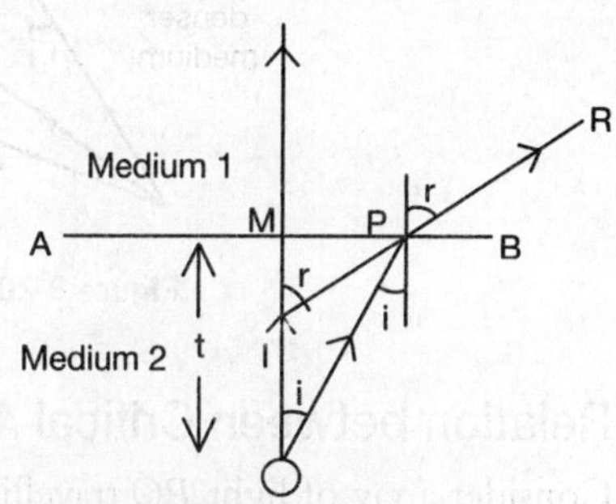

Figure 8.18 Showing to show real and apparent depth

Where real depth–it is the actual depth of the object.

Apparent depth–it is depth of the image of the object.

Examples:

1. The floor of a swimming pool appears to be raised when seen from the diving board. This is due to refraction.
2. Sun appears before it actually rises. This is due to refraction of light.
3. A stick immersed obliquely in water appears to be bent. This is refraction of light. When a ray of light passes from water to air, it bends away from the normal. Hence, the stick appears to be bent and short.

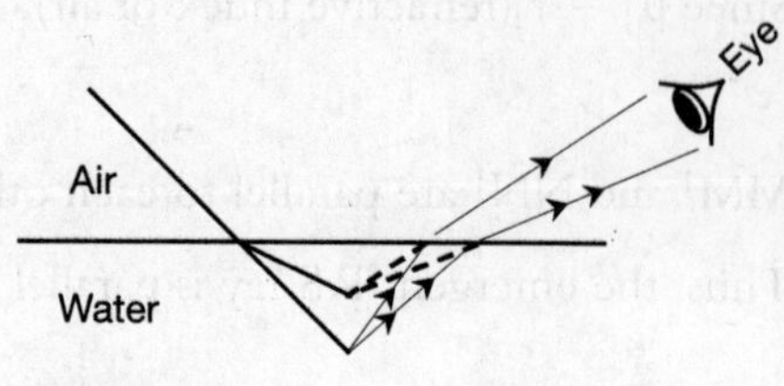

Figure 8.19 Apparent bent in a stick

EXAMPLE 8.8 A coin placed in a beaker containing water appears at a depth of 3 cm from the water surface. What is the real depth of the coin? Refractive index of water $= \frac{4}{3}$.

SOLUTION

Real depth = ?

Apparent depth = 3 cm

Refractive index of water $= \frac{4}{3}$

$$\text{Refractive index} = \frac{\text{Real depth}}{\text{Apparent depth}}$$

$$\Rightarrow \frac{4}{3} = \frac{\text{Real depth}}{3}$$

$$\frac{4}{3} \times 3 = \text{Real depth}$$

$$\therefore \text{Real depth} = 4 \text{ cm}$$

Critical Angle

The angle of incidence in the denser medium at which angle of refraction is 90° is called critical angle.

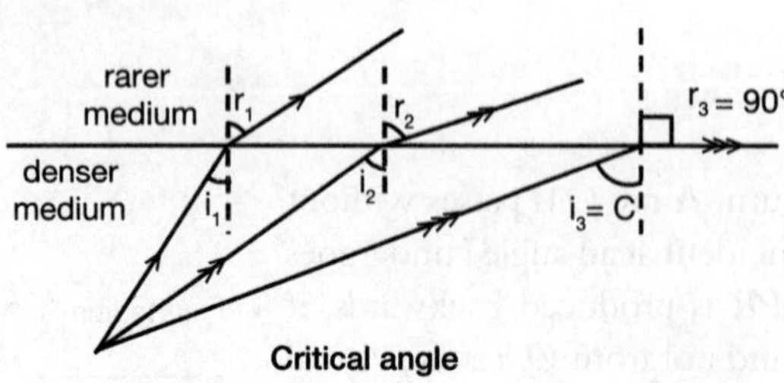

Figure 8.20 Formation of critical angle

Relation between Critical Angle and Refractive Index

Consider a ray of light *PQ* travelling from denser to rarer medium. Let the ray be incident at the critical angle. The angle of refraction will be equal to 90°.

From Snell's Law,

$$^1\mu_2 = \frac{\sin i}{\sin r} \qquad (8.14)$$

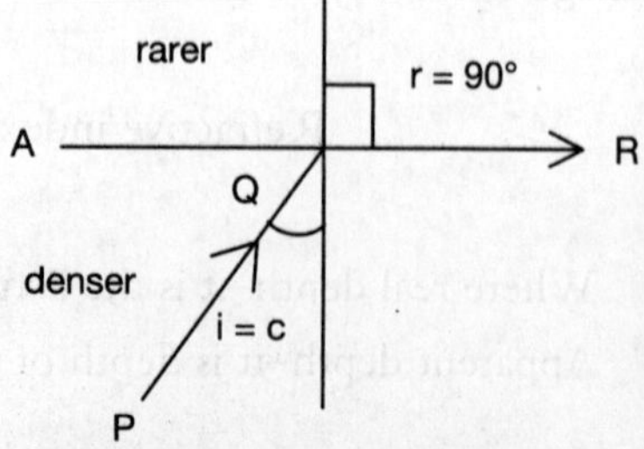

Figure 8.21 A ray PQ refracting from denser to rare medium

But $i = c$ and $r = 90°$

$$^1\mu_2 = \frac{\sin c}{\sin 90}$$

$$^1\mu_2 = \frac{\sin c}{1} \quad (\because \sin 90 = 1) \Rightarrow \frac{\mu_2}{\mu_1} = \sin\sqrt{C}$$

$[^1\mu_2 = \frac{\mu_2}{\mu_1}$ from relative refractive index]

If the second medium is air, then, $\mu_2 = 1$ and $\mu_1 = \mu \Rightarrow \mu = \frac{1}{\sin}$.

Total Internal Reflection

When a ray of light passes from denser to rarer medium, the refracted ray bends away from the normal. Hence, the angle of refraction is greater than the angle of incidence. Gradually if the angle of incidence increases, angle of refraction also increases. At a particular angle of incidence, the refracted ray just grazes the refracting surface making the angle of refraction is equal to 90°. This angle of incidence in the denser medium is called 'critical angle'. If the angle of incidence is further increased, the ray does not undergo refraction, it gets reflected into the same optically denser medium. This is known as total internal reflection.

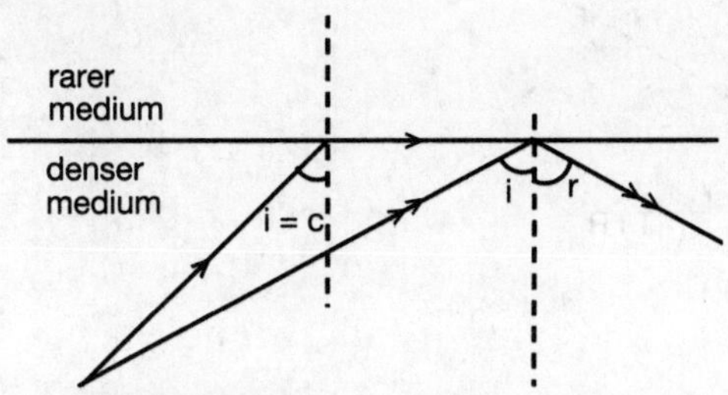

Figure 8.22 Total internal reflection

Konnect

In total internal reflection, 100% of the light is reflected back into the medium, unlike regular reflection where some light may be absorbed or scattered.

When angle of incidence in the denser medium is greater than the critical angle, the light reflected back into same medium. This phenomenon is called total internal reflection.

Conditions for Total Internal Reflection

1. The light ray should travel from denser medium to rarer medium.
2. Angle of incidence in the denser medium should be greater than the critical angle.

Differences between Reflection and Total Internal Reflection

Reflection	Total internal reflection
For reflection to take place, smooth polished surface is required.	No smooth polished surface is required for total internal reflection to occur.
It takes place at all angles of incidence.	Total internal reflection can occur only if the angle of incidence is greater than critical angle and light tends to travel from denser medium to rarer medium.
Some percentage of light rays are absorbed by the reflecting material.	No light energy is absorbed.

Example: Diamonds are cut into sharp angles. This gives rise to a number of refracting surfaces. Light rays entering diamond suffer total internal reflection. Light rays strike the diamond-air interface at greater than 24° (which is the critical angle of diamond). Thus, the light rays get trapped. These trapped light rays make the diamond sparkle.

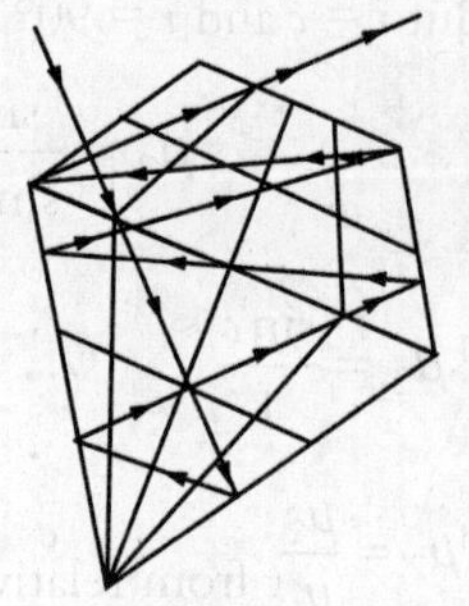

Figure 8.23 Diamond

Mirage

Inverted images of distant objects on the ground are usually seen during hot summer days. These images are seen as a result of an optical illusion called mirage. Such an illusion caused due to perceived presence of water though in reality water is non-existent.

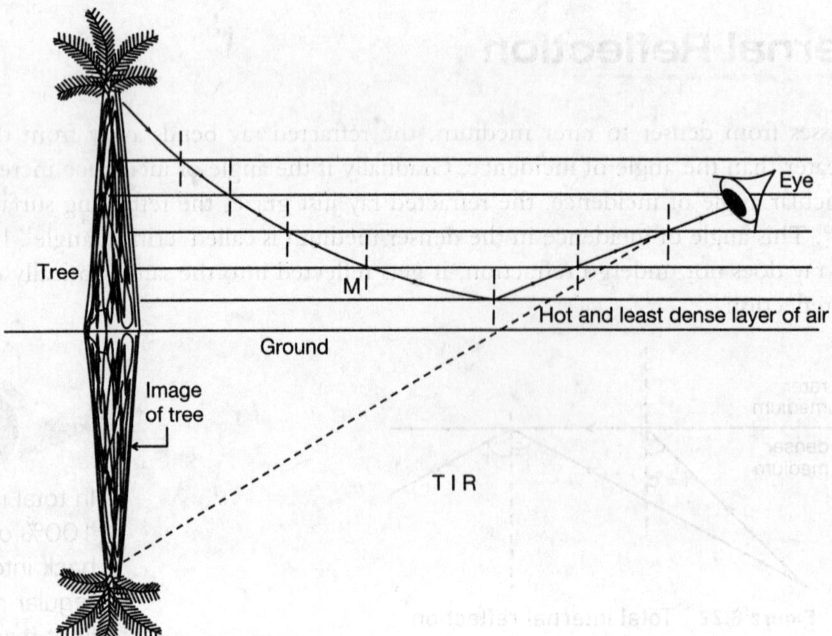

Figure 8.24 Formation of mirage

During peak summer days, the layer of air just above the Earth is less dense than the air above it. Light travelling from distant or tall object passes from layer of high refractive index (denser medium) to layer of low refractive index (rarer medium). Thus, the refracted ray bends more and more away from the normal.

This happens till the angle of incidence is equal to the critical angle. Once the angle of incidence is greater than the critical angle, light rays undergo total internal reflection and reach the eye, and the person sees the image of the tree, as there is water under the tree.

Mirage: Appearance of water without its actually presence is called mirage.

Twinkling of Stars

Twinkling of stars is due to atmospheric refraction. Light from stars undergoes continuous refraction as it enters the Earth's atmosphere. The refracted ray bends towards the normal stars appear at different position and appear slightly higher than their actual positions. The apparent position of the star changes gradually due to change in the Earth's atmosphere. Thus, the apparent position of the star fluctuates. As a result, the path of light from the star varies. (amount of light entering the eye also varies)

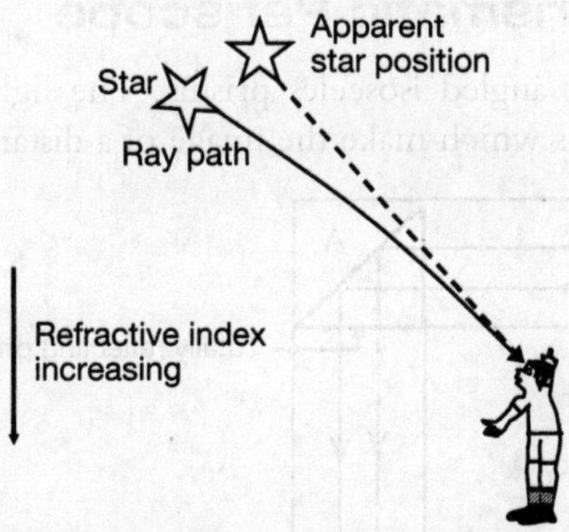

Figure 8.25 Apparent star position due to atmospheric refraction

Due to change in the light flux, star appears brighter some times and fainter at the other time. Thus, the twinkling of stars is due to fluctuation of apparent position of the star.

Planets do not twinkle they appear bigger than stars. A planet can be considered as a collection of a large number of point sized objects which nullify the twinkling effect.

Total Reflecting Prisms

Total reflecting prisms are right angled isosceles prisms. They are based on the principle of total internal reflection. These prisms are used to rotate light through 90° or 180°. These prisms are also used to obtain erect images of an inverted object.

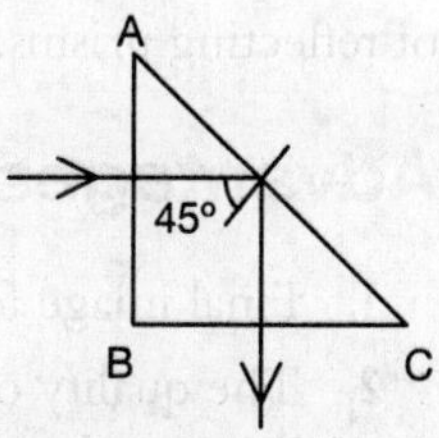

Figure 8.26 Total reflecting prisms

Deviation through 90°

When a ray of light is incident normally on the surface of a right angled isosceles prism, it does not undergo refraction. But it strikes the surface *AC* at an angle 45°, which is greater than the critical angle of glass, i.e., 42°. The ray undergoes total internal reflection and strikes the face *BC* normally and emerges out of it. Thus, the ray is rotated through 90°. Surface *AC* acts like a mirror.

Deviation through 180°

When a ray of light is incident normally on the surface *AC* of the prism, it passes without deviation and it strikes the surface *AB* at angle 45°, which is greater than the critical angle for glass. Total internal reflection takes place and the ray further strikes the surface *BC* at an angle 45°. The ray undergoes another total internal reflection and then it emerges out through *AC*, because the ray strikes the surface normally.

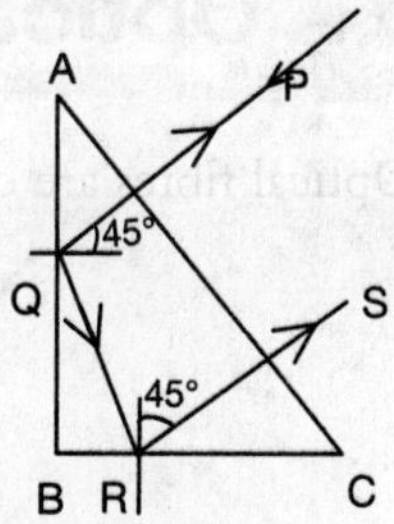

Figure 8.27 Total internal reflection in a prism

Erecting Prism or Non-deviation Prism

Rays after refraction from the surface *AB* strike the surface *AC* at an angle 45°, which is greater than the critical angle for glass and it undergoes total internal reflection. At surface *BC*, the rays undergo refraction and emerges out from the surface *BC* and the image *MN* appears as inverted.

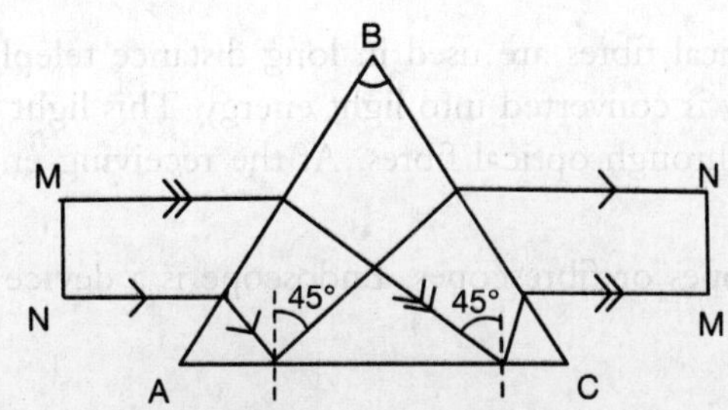

Figure 8.28 Erecting prism

Refracting Periscope or Prismatic Periscope

Refracting periscope consists of two right angled isosceles prisms. The light rays entering the periscope are rotated through 180° by the totally reflecting prisms which make the image of a distant object visible.

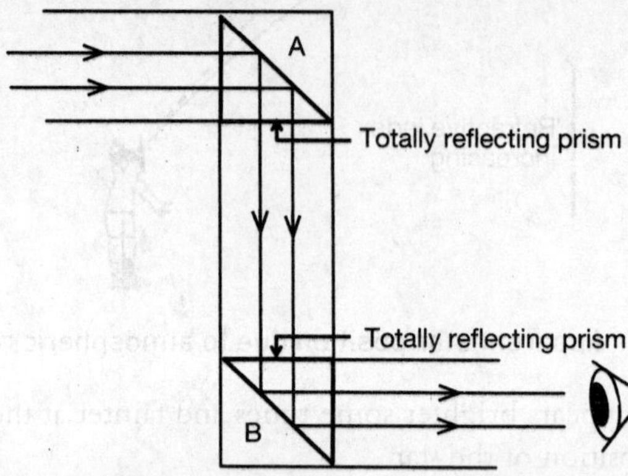

Figure 8.29 Prismatic periscope

This periscope is similar to that of reflecting periscope, but the reflecting periscope makes use of plane mirrors instead of reflecting prisms.

Advantages of Refracting Periscope Over Reflecting Periscope

1. Final image formed by the refracting periscope is bright and sharp, since no rays of light are absorbed.
2. The quality of the image is affected by the presence of dust and moisture in reflecting periscope. Moisture and dust does not have any appreciable effect on the image quality in refracting periscope.

Optical Fibres or Light Pipes

Optical fibres are devices used to transmit light in any desired path. It works on the principle of total internal reflection.

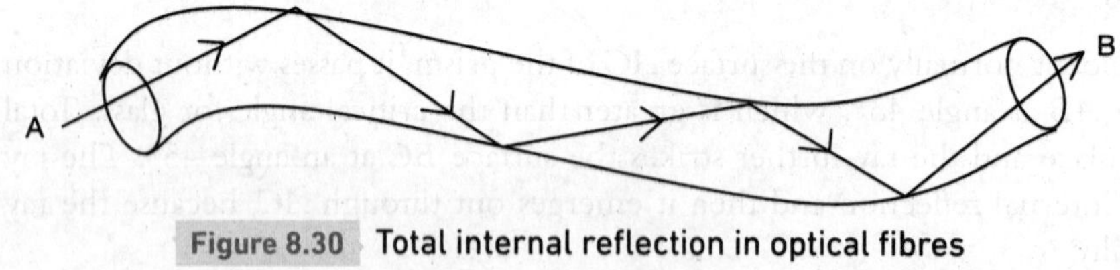

Figure 8.30 Total internal reflection in optical fibres

It consists of a thin fibre glass. When a ray of light enters a fibre, it suffers a series of total internal reflections and finally emerges out from the other end. Since the light energy is not absorbed, intensity of light is not lost.

Uses of Optical Fibres

1. **Used in communication:** Optical fibres are used in long distance telephony. Sound energy is converted into electrical energy. Electrical energy is converted into light energy. This light energy is fed to optical fibres and it is transmitted over a long distance through optical fibres. At the receiving end, light energy is finally converted to sound energy.
2. Optical fibres are used as endoscopes or fibrescopes. Endoscope is a device used to examine internal organs of a human body by physicians.

EXAMPLE 8.9 The refractive index of a certain gemstone is 2.42 when measured against air. What is the critical angle for light trying to exit from this gemstone into air?

SOLUTION

For light passing from the gemstone (with refractive index m_{gem}) to air (with refractive index m_{air}), the critical angle c is given by: $\sin c = \dfrac{m_{air}}{m_{gem}} = \dfrac{1}{2.41} = 0.4132$

(since, it is air $m_{air} = 1$)

So, we have $c = \sin^{-1}(0.4132) = 24.6°$

Thus, the critical angle for the gemstone is approximately 24.6°.

Refraction through Prisms

Prism is a transparent medium. It is bounded by two triangular surfaces and three rectangular surfaces.

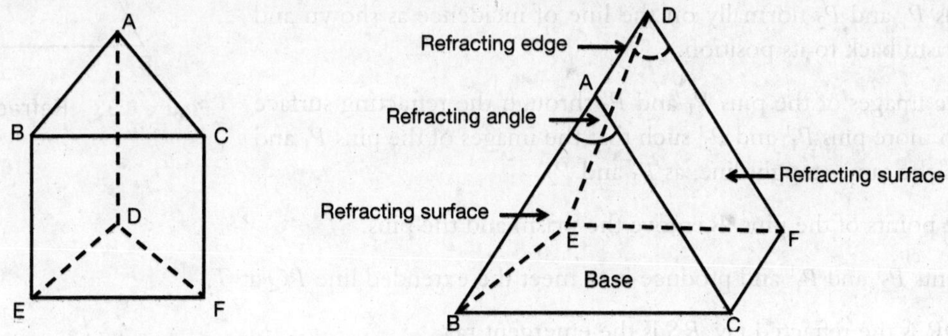

Figure 8.31 Prism

Rectangular surfaces are called refracting surfaces. The angle between the two refracting surfaces is called refracting angle or the angle of the prism. The line joining the refracting surfaces is called refracting edge. Section of a prism perpendicular to the refracting edge is called principal section.

Deviation of Light by Prism

ABC is the principal section of an equilateral prism. ∠*A* is the angle of the prism. *PQ* is the incident ray, incident at an angle i_1. Since the ray *PQ* is travelling from optically rarer medium to denser medium, the refracted ray *QR* bends towards the normal. r_1 is the angle of refraction on the face *AB*. The ray *QR* is incident at an angle r_2 on the surface *AC* of the prism and emerges out along *RS* at an angle i_2. i_2 is called angle of emergence.

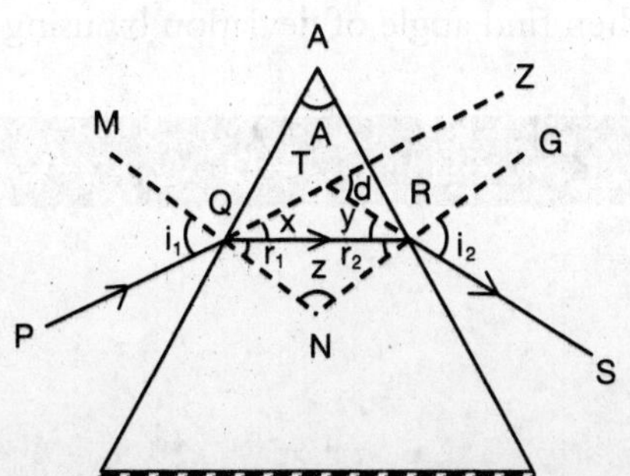

Figure 8.32 Deviation of light by prism

The angle between incident ray produced (PQ) and the emergent ray (RS) is called angle of deviation. Angle of deviation = $\angle STZ = \angle d$

The angle of deviation depends on the following factors.

1. Angle of incidence
2. Refractive index of the material of the prism
3. Angle of the prism

Konnect

The deviation of light by a prism is the basis for instruments like spectrometers, which can break down light into its component wavelengths.

Dependence of Angle of Deviation on Angle of Incidence

EXPERIMENT I

1. Place an equilateral prism on a white paper fixed to a drawing board. Trace the principal section ABC of the prism and remove it.
2. Draw normals MN and NK to the refracting surfaces AB and AC, respectively.
3. Make a suitable angle (i) with the normal. This line is the incident ray (PQ).
4. Fix two pins P_1 and P_2 normally on the line of incidence as shown and bring the prism back to its position.
5. Look for the images of the pins P_1 and P_2 through the refracting surface AC. Fix two more pins P_1^1 and P_2^1 such that the images of the pins P_1 and P_2 appear in the same straight line, as P_1 and P_2.
6. Encircle the points of the pins. Remove the prism and the pins.
7. Join the points P_2^1 and P_1^1 and produce it to meet the extended line PQ at T.
8. Join QR, QR is the refracted ray. RS is the emergent ray.

   $\angle SRK = i_2$ represents the angle of emergence.

   $\angle r_1$ is the angle of refraction on the surface AB.

   $\angle r_2$ represents the angle of incidence on the surface AC of the prism.

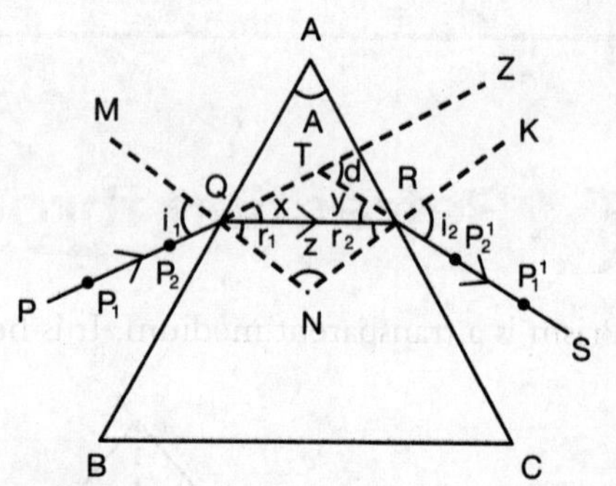

Figure 8.33 Refraction through prism

9. Produce the incident ray (PQ) and the emergent ray (RS) backward. The rays PQ and RS intersect at a point T.

   $\angle STZ$ is the angle of deviation = $\angle d$

   It can be proved that angle of deviation, $\angle d = \angle i_1 + \angle i_2 - \angle A$ (1)

   where, $\angle A = \angle r_1 + \angle r_2$

10. Measure $\angle i_1$, $\angle i_2$, $\angle r_1$ and $\angle r_2$ and then find angle of deviation by using equation (1).

Trial No.	$\angle i_1$	$\angle i_2$	$\angle r_1$	$\angle r_2$	$\angle A$	$\angle d = \angle i_1 + i_2 - \angle A$

It is found that the angle of deviation decreases with increase in the angle of incidence upto a particular angle. This particular angle of incidence where the angle of deviation is minimum is called minimum deviation position of the prism. Further as the angle of incidence is increased, the angle of deviation also increases. It is found that at the minimum deviation position,

1. Angle of incidence is equal to angle of emergence, i.e., $\angle i_1 = \angle i_2$
2. Angle of refraction r_1 is equal to angle of refraction r_2, i.e., $\angle r_1 = \angle r_2$.

   Then $d = 2\angle i - \angle A$ and $\angle A = 2\angle r$.

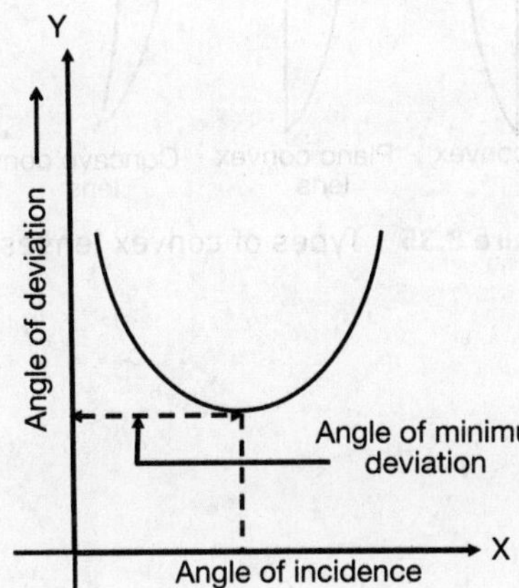

Figure 8.34 Graph to show relation between angle of deviation and angle of incidence

Dependence of Angle of Deviation on Refractive Index

If the hollow glass prism is filled with transparent liquids like water, benzene, etc., and the experiment is conducted as explained above, it is found that as the refractive index of the material increases the angle of deviation also increases.

Dependence of Angle of Deviation on the Colour or the Wavelength of Light

The experiment is repeated as explained above, but the pins are first painted red and the angle of deviation is found out. In the next trial, the pins are painted violet and the angle of deviation is found out for the same angle of incidence as that of the red pins. It is found that angle of deviation for violet is greater than the angle of deviation of the red colour.

∴ Lesser the wavelength, greater is the angle of deviation.

Dependence on Angle of the Prism

Repeat the experiment by taking prism of different angles (of the prism). (90°, 60°, 30° prism). It is found that the angle of deviation decreases with increase in the angle of the prism.

Refraction through Lenses

Lens: A lens is a transparent material which is bounded by two spherical surfaces or one spherical surface and one plane surface.

Lenses are of two types namely,

1. Convex lens or converging lens.
2. Concave lens or diverging lens.

Convex lens:

Convex lens has one or two spherical surfaces, such that it is thicker at the centre than at the edges. Convex lenses are of three types, namely,

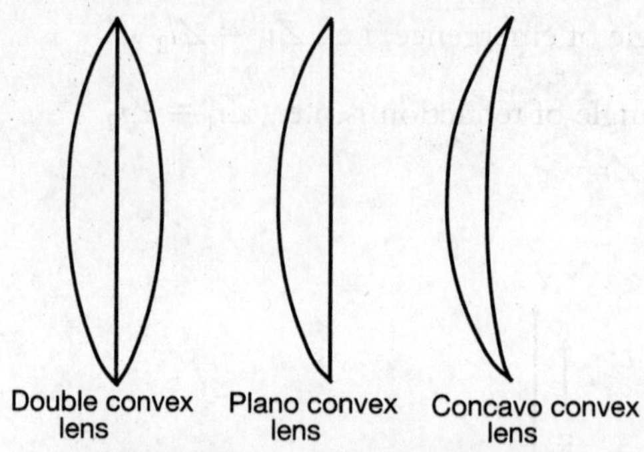

Figure 8.35 Types of convex lenses

1. Double convex lens
2. Plano convex lens
3. Concave–convex lens

Concave lens: Concave lens has one or two spherical surfaces, such that it is thinner at the centre than at its edge.

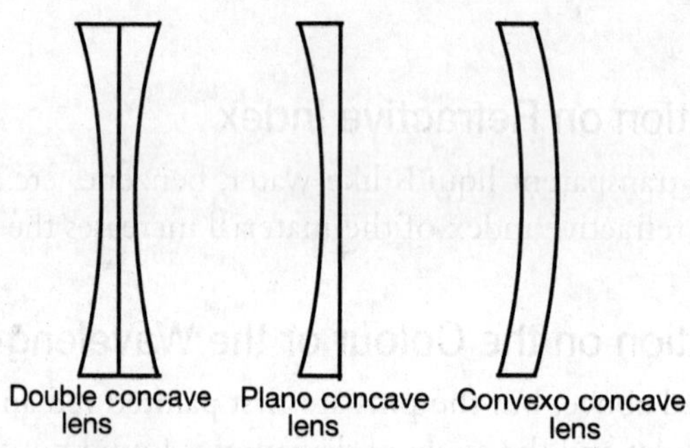

Figure 8.36 Types of concave lenses

Concave lens are also of three types, namely,

1. Double concave lens
2. Plano concave lens
3. Convexo–concave lens

Convergent Action of Convex Lens

A lens can be considered to be made up of prisms. The bases of the prisms are downwards in the upper half and prisms in the lower half have their bases upwards. Prisms at the edges have greater refracting angle.

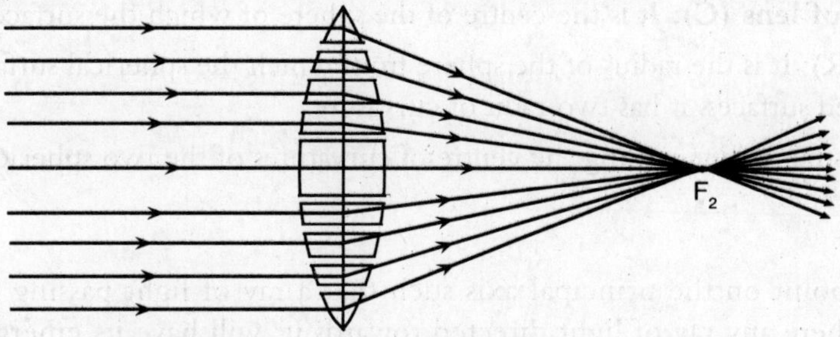

Figure 8.37 Rays converging from a convex lens

When a ray of light is passed through a prism, the emergent ray always bends towards the base (broader side) of the prism and greater the refracting angle, lesser will be the deviation. Thus, the rays from the outer edges are deviated more towards the base line and the light ray passing along the principal axis or principal focus passes without deviation. All these rays converge at a point which is called focus or principle focus.

When a convex lens is held facing the Sun and the screen is placed on the other side of the lens, by adjusting the distance between the screen and the lens, a sharp and bright spot is obtained on the screen. Thus, a convex lens is a converging lens.

Diverging Action of Concave Lens

Concave lens too can be considered to be made up of prisms. The prisms in the upper half have their bases upwards or their refracting angles downwards and the prisms in the lower half have their refracting angles upwards. The rays near the outer edges of the lens are deviated maximum towards the bases of prism and the central ray goes without deviation. These rays do not meet but when they are produced backwards, they meet at a point. This point is called focus.

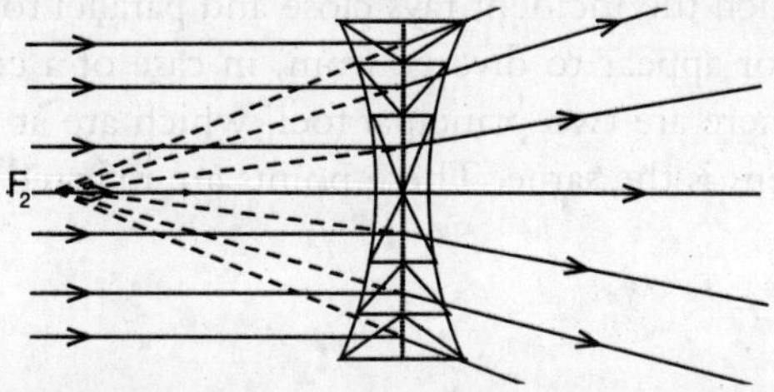

Figure 8.38 Rays diverging from a concave lens

When smoke is produced around the concave lens, held in sunlight, the emergent rays are seen to move away from each other. Hence, a concave lens is a diverging lens.

Some Definitions

Each surface of a lens is a part of a sphere. Surface 1 is a part of a sphere S_1 and surface 2 is a part of a sphere S_2.

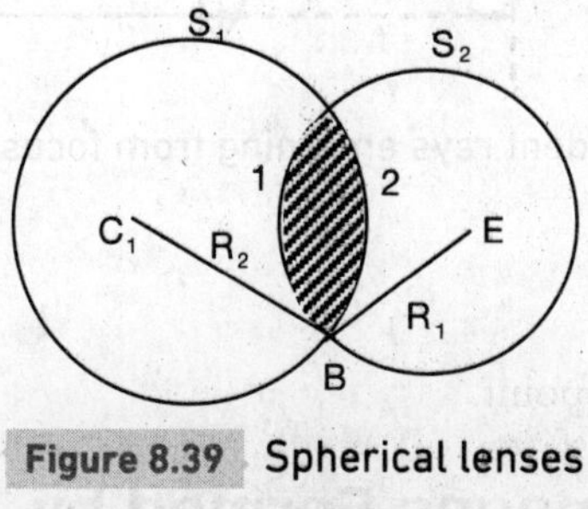

Figure 8.39 Spherical lenses

1. **Centre of curvature of lens (C):** It is the centre of the sphere of which the surface of a lens form S a part.
2. **Radii of curvature (R):** It is the radius of the sphere from which the spherical surface was obtained. Since a lens generally has two curved surfaces, it has two radii of curvature.
3. **Principal axis:** It is a straight line joining the centre of curvatures of the two spherical surfaces of the lens.

Optical Centre

In case of thin lens, it is a point on the principal axis such that a ray of light passing through it emerges without deviation or it is a point, where any ray of light directed towards it, will have its emergent ray coinciding with the direction of incident ray. Optical centre is denoted by '*O*'

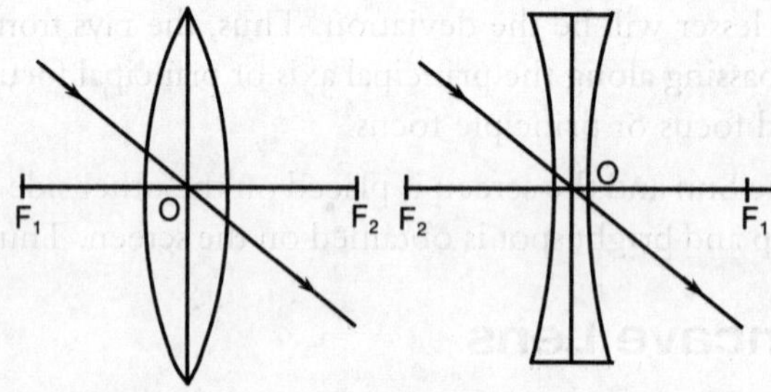

Figure 8.40 Incident ray passing through optical centre of spherical lenses

Principal Focus

It is the point on the principal axis to which the incident rays close and parallel to the principal axis of the lens converge after refraction, in case of a convex lens or appear to diverge from, in case of a concave lens. Since the light ray can be incident in either direction of the lens, there are two principal foci, which are at equal distance from the optical centre, provided the medium on either side of lens is the same. These points are referred to as first focal point and second focal point.

Focal Length

Distance between optical centre and the principal focus is called focal length and is denoted by *f*.

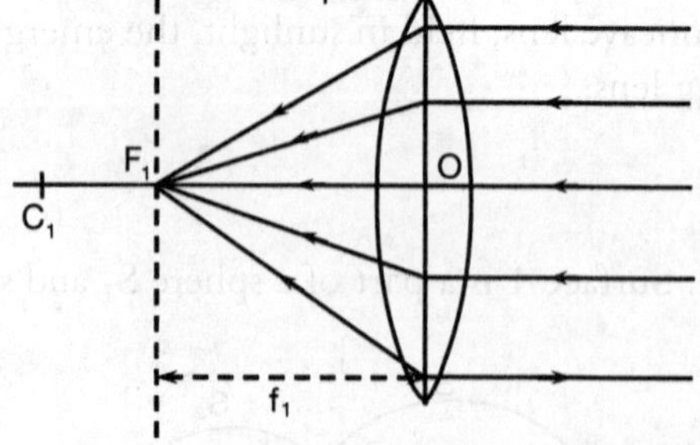

Figure 8.41 Incident rays emerging from focus of a convex lens

Focal Plane

It is a vertical plane passing through the focal point.

Rules for Construction of Images Formed by Thin Lenses

To find out the images formed by the lens by considering convenient rays.

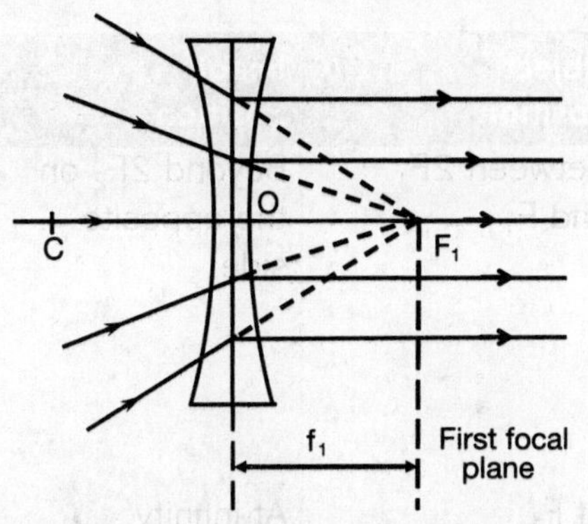

Figure 8.42 Incident rays coming from infinity on a concave lens

1. The rays parallel and close to the principal axis after refraction pass through the principal focus in a convex lens or appear to diverge from the principal focus in case of a concave lens.
2. Any ray of light which is directed through the principal focus or appearing to meet at it (concave lens), after refraction, always emerges parallel to the principal axis.
3. Any ray of light which passes through the optical centre of a lens emerges without deviation.

The above stated rules are used to obtain the position of the image. The point where the rays intersect or appear to intersect gives the image position.

Formation of Images by Convex Lens

Table 8.3 Image formation by Convex lens

S. No.	Diagram	Object Position	Image Position	Nature	Uses
1	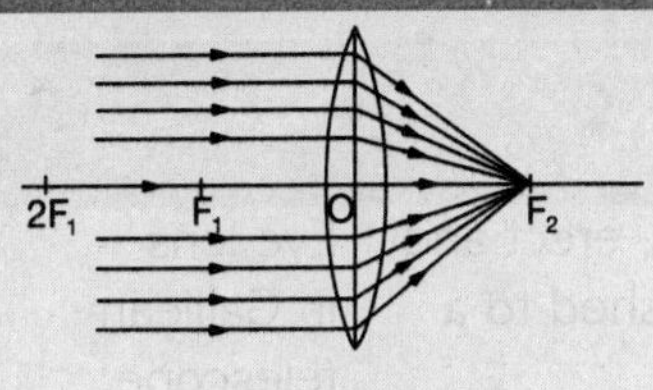	Infinity, rays are parallel to the principal axis	Formed at principal focus on the other side	Real, inverted and highly diminished	Burning glass or magnifying glass
2	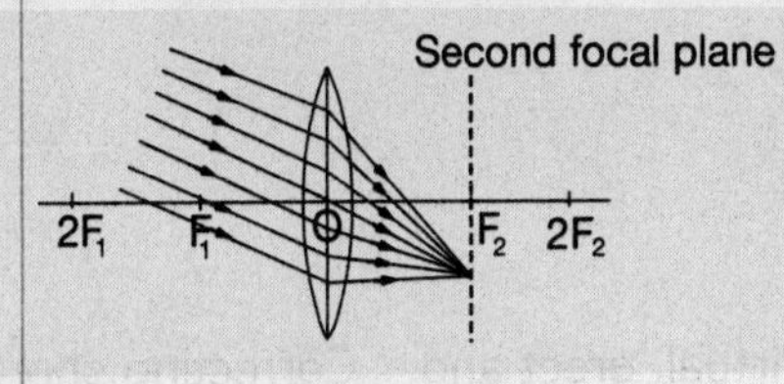	Infinity, rays are not parallel to the principal axis	In the focal plane on the other side.	Real, inverted and highly diminished	Objective of astronomical telescope
3	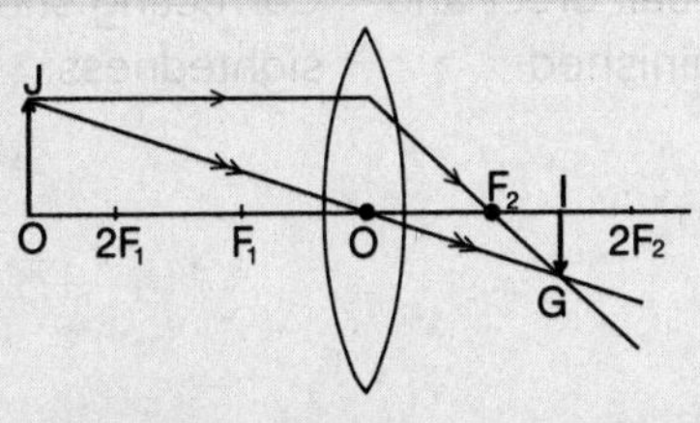	Beyond $2F_1$	On the opposite side, between F_2 and $2F_2$	Real, inverted and diminished	Photographic camera
4	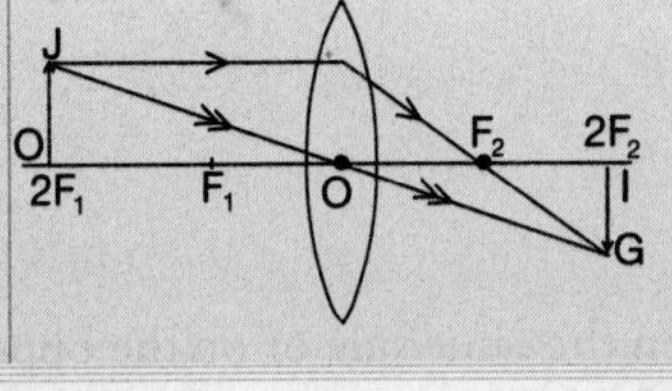	At $2F_1$	At $2F_2$ on the opposite side	Real, inverted, and same size	Terrestrial telescope

(Continued)

S. No.	Diagram	Object Position	Image Position	Nature	Uses
5	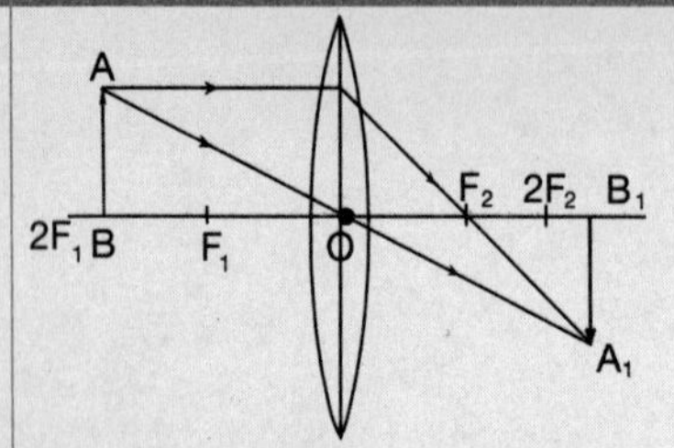	Between $2F_1$ and F_1	Beyond $2F_2$ on the opposite side	Real, inverted and enlarged	Cine projection
6	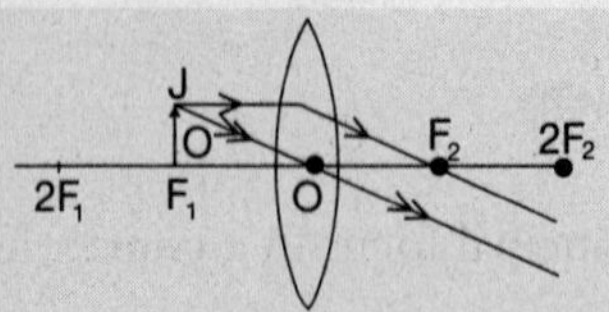	At F_1	At infinity	Real, inverted and enlarged	Search lights and spot lights
7	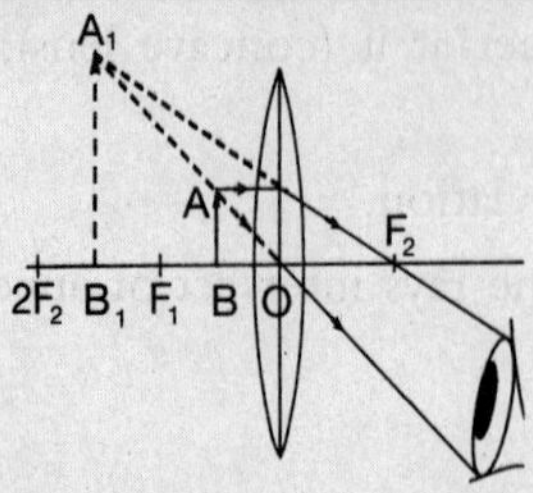	Between F and the optical centre	On the same side	Virtual, erect and enlarged	Simple microscope, reading finger prints, to observe biological specimen and weaving patterns

Formation of Images by Concave Lens

Table 8.4 Image formation by Concave lens

S. No.	Diagram	Object Position	Image Position	Nature	Uses
1	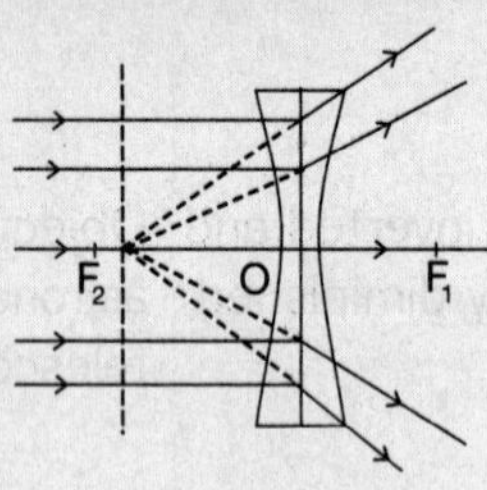	Infinity	At F_2 on the same side	Virtual, erect and diminished to a point	Eye lens in Galilean telescope
2	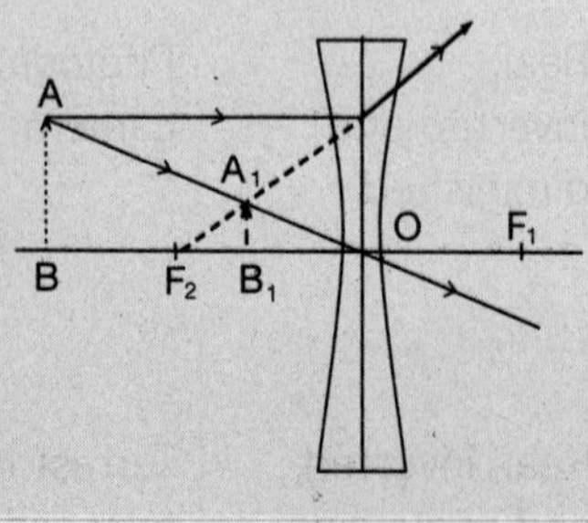	At any distance	On the same side between optical centre and F_2	Virtual, erect and diminished	Correcting short sightedness.

Cartesian Sign Convention

Depending on the distance of the object from the lens, the image formed on the lens is on the same side or on the opposite side. Therefore, it is necessary to use sign convention. The sign convention rules are as follows.

1. All distances are measured from optical centre.
2. Distance measured in the direction of incident light is positive and distance measured against incident light is negative.
3. Distances measured above the principal axis are positive and distances measured below the principal axis are negative.
4. According to sign convention, focal length of a convex lens is positive and that of the concave lens is negative.

Lens Formula

AB is an extended object placed at a distance '*u*' from the optical centre O. A^1B^1 is the image at a distance '*v*' from O.

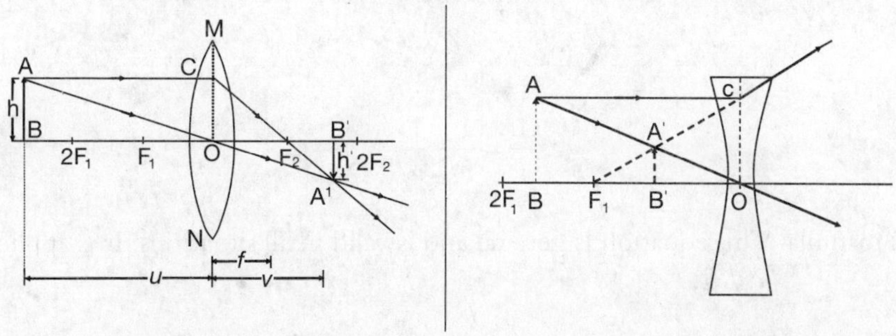

Figure 8.43 Image formation by convex and concave lens

Convex Lens

Using Cartesian sign
Object distance $OB = -u$
Image distance $OB^1 = v$
Focal length of a convex lens $= f$
From similar triangles AOB and A^1OB^1

$$\frac{A^1B^1}{AB} = \frac{OB^1}{OB} = \frac{v}{-u} \quad (1)$$

From similar triangles OCF_2 and $A^1B^1F_2$

$$\frac{A^1B^1}{OC} = \frac{B^1F_1}{OF_1} \quad (2)$$

$$\frac{B^1F_1}{OF_1} = \frac{OF_1 - OB^1}{OF_1}$$

$$\frac{B^1F_1}{OF_1} = \frac{OF_1 - OB^1}{OF_1} = \frac{v - f}{f}$$

∴ (2) can be written as

$$\frac{A^1B^1}{OC} = \frac{v - f}{f} \text{ but OC = AB}$$

$$\frac{A^1B^1}{OC} = \frac{v - f}{f} \quad (3)$$

Comparing (1) and (3),

$$\frac{v}{-u} = \frac{v - f}{f}$$

$$vf = -uv + uf \quad (4)$$

Concave Lens

Using Cartesian sign
Object distance $= -u$
Image distance $= -v$
Focal length of concave lens $= -f$
From similar triangles A^1B^1O and ABO

$$\frac{A^1B^1}{AB} = \frac{OB^1}{OB} = \frac{-v}{-u} = \frac{v}{u} \quad (1)$$

From similar triangles OCF_1 and $A^1B^1F_1$

$$\frac{A^1B^1}{OC} = \frac{B^1F_1}{OF_1} \quad (2)$$

$$\frac{B^1F_1}{OF_1} = \frac{OF_1\text{-}OB^1}{OF^1} = \frac{-f - (-v)}{-f}$$

$$\therefore \frac{B^1F_1}{OF_1} = \frac{-f + v}{-f}$$

∴ Eqn (2) can be written as

$$\frac{A^1B^1}{OC} = \frac{-f + v}{-f} \text{ but OC = AB}$$

$$\frac{A^1B^1}{OC} = \frac{-f + v}{-f} \quad (3)$$

Comparing (1) and (3),

$$\frac{v}{u} = \frac{-f + v}{-f}$$

$$-vf = -uf + uv \quad (4)$$

(Continued)

Dividing (4) by *uvf*	Dividing (4) by *uvf*
$\frac{1}{u}=\frac{-1}{f}+\frac{1}{v}$	$\frac{-1}{u}=\frac{-1}{v}+\frac{1}{f}$
or	or
$\frac{1}{f}=\frac{1}{v}-\frac{1}{u}$	$\frac{1}{f}=\frac{1}{v}-\frac{1}{u}$

$$\therefore \frac{1}{f}=\frac{1}{v}-\frac{1}{u} \qquad (5)$$

Equation (5) is called lens formula. This equation is general and is valid in all situations. It is applicable to the both convex and concave lenses.

Linear Magnification

It is the ratio of size of the image to the size of the object. Magnification is denoted by '*m*'.

$$m=\frac{\text{Height of the image }(A^1B^1)}{\text{Height of the object }(AB)}$$

$m=\frac{A^1B^1}{AB}$ From equation (1) of the previous page.

$$\frac{A^1B^1}{AB}=\frac{v}{u}$$

$$\therefore m=\frac{v}{u}$$

Thus, magnification $m=\frac{h_i}{h_0}=\frac{v}{u}$

where, h_i is the height of the image and h_0 is the height of the object.

Magnification is positive for a convex lens forming a virtual image and magnification is negative if the image formed by the convex lens is real. Image formed by concave lens is always virtual, hence, magnification for concave lens is always positive.

Power of a Lens

Nature and size of the image depends on the focal length of the lens. A lens of short focal length bends the light to a large extent. Thus, the image formed by lens of short focal length will be closer to the optical centre. Power of the lens is the measure of degree of convergence or divergence of the lens. Power of the lens is defined as reciprocal of focal length in meter and is denoted by *P*.

$$P=\frac{1}{f}$$

Unit of power is dioptres, denoted by 'D', when f is in metre.

$$\therefore 1\text{D} = \frac{1}{1\text{m}}$$

Thus, 1 dioptre is the convergence or divergence produced by a lens of 1metre focal length.

Combination of thin Lenses

If two or more thin lenses are kept in contact, then their equivalent focal length

$$\frac{1}{f} = \frac{1}{f_1} + \frac{1}{f_2} + \frac{1}{f_3}$$

where, f_1, f_2, f_3 .... are focal lengths of the lenses then the power of the combination of the lenses.

$$P = P_1 + P_2 + P_3..........$$

where, $P_1 = \frac{1}{f_1}; P_2 = \frac{1}{f_2}$ ....

EXAMPLE 8.10 An object 5 cm high is placed at a distance of 10 cm from a convex lens of focal length 15 cm. Find the nature, position, size and magnification of the image.

SOLUTION

Using Cartesian sign convention

Object distance = −10 cm

Focal length of a convex lens = 15 cm

Height of the object = h_O = 5 cm

Using lens formula

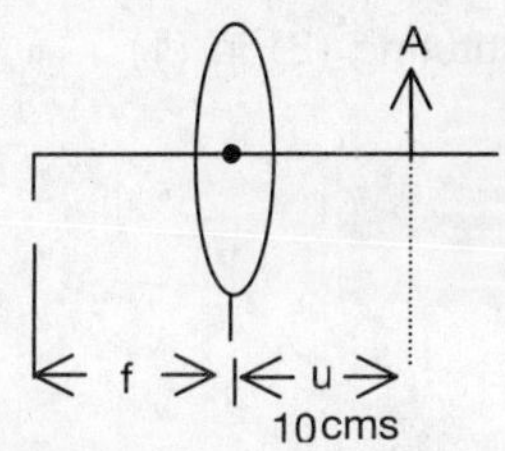

Figure 8.44 Formation of image by a convex lens

$$\frac{1}{f} = \frac{1}{v} - \frac{1}{u}$$

$$\frac{1}{15} = \frac{1}{v} = \frac{1}{-10}$$

$$\frac{1}{15} = \frac{1}{v} + \frac{1}{10} \Rightarrow \frac{1}{v} = \frac{10-15}{15\times10}$$

$$v = -\frac{150}{5} \Rightarrow -30\,\text{cm}$$

Negative sign indicates that it is a virtual image.

$$m = \frac{v}{u}$$

$$m = \frac{-30}{-10} = 3$$

Positive sign indicates that the image is erect.

$$m = \frac{h_i}{h_o} \Rightarrow 3 = \frac{h_i}{5}$$

∴ Height of image = 5 × 3 = 15 cm.

EXAMPLE 8.11 A convex lens throws on a screen 12 m from the lens a magnified image of the object. If the magnification is 15, find the focal length of the lens.

SOLUTION

Magnification $m = 15$

Image distance = v

Magnification = $+\dfrac{v}{u}$ (1)

From lens formula,

$$\frac{1}{f} = \frac{1}{v} - \frac{1}{u}$$

Using Cartesian sign,

$$\frac{1}{f} = \frac{1}{v} - \frac{1}{-u}$$

$$\frac{1}{f} = \frac{1}{v} + \frac{1}{u}$$

$$\therefore \frac{1}{u} = \frac{1}{f} - \frac{1}{v}$$

$$\frac{1}{u} = \frac{v-f}{vf}$$

$$u = \frac{vf}{v-f} \quad (2)$$

Substituting (2) in (1),

$$m = \frac{v(v-f)}{vf}$$

$$\therefore 15 = \frac{12-f}{f}$$

$$15f = 12 - f$$

$$16f = 12$$

$$f = \frac{12}{16} = 0.75\text{m}$$

EXAMPLE 8.12 Two convex lenses A and B of focal lengths 0.3 m and 0.2 m respectively, are placed in contact. Calculate the effective focal length and the power of the combination. If B is a concave lens, what is the effective focal length and the power?

SOLUTION

Reciprocal of effective focal length of the combination of the lens

$$\frac{1}{f} = \frac{1}{f_1} + \frac{1}{f_2}$$

$$\frac{1}{f} = \frac{1}{0.3} + \frac{1}{0.2}$$

$$\frac{1}{f} = \frac{0.2+0.3}{0.06}$$

$$f = \frac{0.006}{0.5} = 0.12 \text{ cm}$$

Power of the combination,

$$P = \frac{1}{f} = \frac{0.5}{0.06} = 8.33D$$

Thus, the combination behaves like a convex lens of focal length 0.12 m.

If lens B is a concave, then the effective focal length is

$$\frac{1}{f} = \frac{1}{f_1} + \frac{1}{f_2}$$

$$\frac{1}{f} = \frac{1}{0.2} + \frac{1}{-0.2}$$

$$\frac{1}{f} = \frac{0.2 - 0.3}{0.006}$$

$$\frac{1}{f} = \frac{-0.5}{0.06}$$

$$f = \frac{-0.05}{0.1} = -0.6m$$

Power of the combination,

$$P = \frac{1}{f} = \frac{1}{-0.6} = -1.67D$$

The combination behaves like a power −1.67D concave lens of focal length 0.6 m.

EXAMPLE 8.13 A convex lens of focal length 0.12 m produces an image which is thrice the size of the object. Find the distance between the object and the lens.

SOLUTION

Focal length of the lens = 0.12 m

$$\text{Magnification, } m = \frac{h_1}{h_O} = \frac{v}{u}$$

$$h_i = 3h_O$$

$$\therefore m = 3$$

$$m = \frac{v}{u}$$

$$3 = \frac{v}{u}$$

$$v = 3u$$

From lens formula,

$$\frac{1}{f} = \frac{1}{v} - \frac{1}{u}$$

Object distance for convex lens = $-u$ (v for a real image, = + $3u$)

$$\frac{1}{0.12} = \frac{1}{3u} - \frac{1}{-u}$$

$$\frac{1}{0.12} = \frac{1}{3u} + \frac{1}{u}$$

$$\frac{1}{0.12} = \frac{4}{3u}$$

$$u = \frac{4 \times 0.12}{3} = 0.16m$$

To obtain real image $u = 0.16$ m

To obtain virtual image v is $-ve$

$$\therefore v = -3u$$

$$\frac{1}{0.12} = \frac{-1}{3u} + \frac{1}{u}$$

$$\frac{1}{0.12} = \frac{-u + 3u}{3u^2}$$

$$\frac{1}{0.12} = \frac{2u}{3u^2}$$

$$u = \frac{2 \times 0.12}{3} = 0.08\text{m}$$

To obtain virtual image, object distance = 0.08 m.

Experiment to Determine Focal Length of a Convex Lens

By Distant Method

1. Mount the lens on a lens stand.
2. Direct the lens towards a distant object such as a tree, etc.

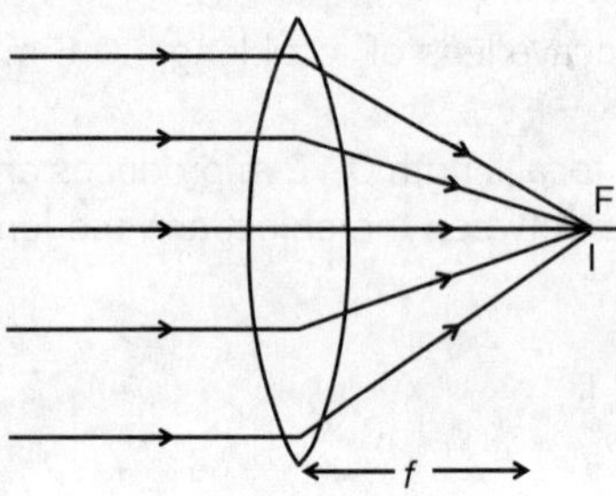

Figure 8.45 Focal length of a convex lens by distant object method

3. Place the screen behind the lens.
4. Adjust the distance between the screen and the lens until a clear and sharp image of the object is obtained.
5. Measure the distance between the screen and the lens. This distance gives the approximate focal length.

By Plane Mirror Method

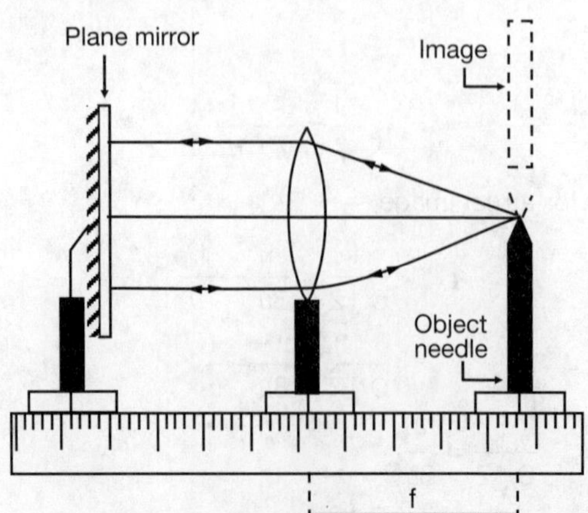

Figure 8.46 Formation of image by convex lens by plane mirror method

1. Mount the convex lens on the lens stand.
2. Place a needle in front of the lens and a plane mirror on the other side of the lens so that the plane of the mirror is vertical and perpendicular to the axis of the lens.
3. Adjust the distance of the lens or the object (needle) until a real and inverted image is formed just above the object.
4. If the tip of the image coincides with the tip of the object, then the distance between the needle and the lens gives the focal length.

Focal Length by u – v Method

1. Mount a convex lens on a lens stand
2. Place an illuminated object in front of it and a screen behind the lens.
3. Adjust the distance between the screen and the lens until a clear and sharp image is obtained on the screen.

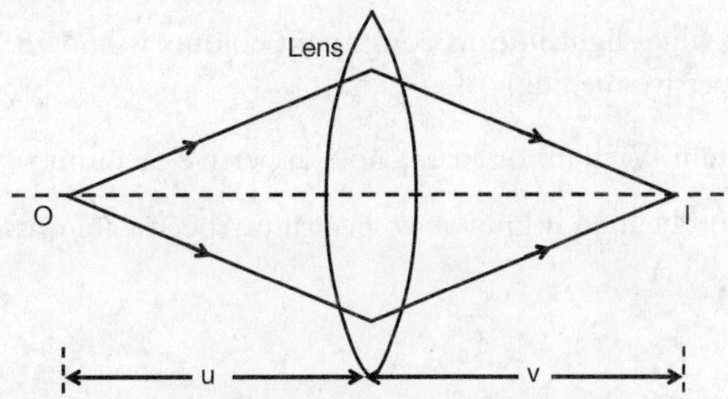

Figure 8.47 u–v method

4. Measure the distance between object and the lens. This gives object distance (u).
5. Distance between the screen and the lens gives the image distance v.
6. Focal length is calculated using the formula $f = uv/(u - v)$ (after appropriate sign convention).

Observation no.	u cm	v cm	$f = \frac{uv}{u-v}$

Application of Lens

1. Lenses are used in optical instruments like telescope, microscope, camera and spectrometer.
2. Lens are used to rectify eyesight of a person having defective eyesight.

Dispersion of Light

Early Discovery of Newton

When Newton was observing stars using astronomical telescope, he found that the stars were coloured near the fringes. He concluded that the colours observed were due to the nature of light but not due to the defect in lens. To prove this, he placed an equilateral prism in a path of narrow beam of light entering through a small aperture of a window in a dark room. Emergent light from the prism was received in the screen. He found that emergent rays were spread out in bands of seven colours with red at one end merging gradually with orange, yellow, green, blue, indigo and violet.

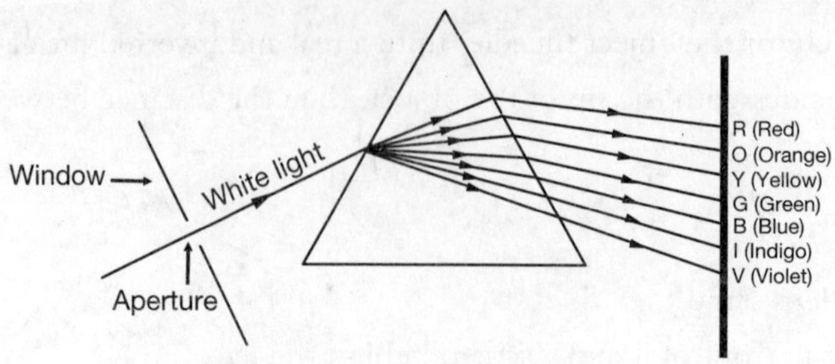

Figure 8.48 Dispersion by a prism

The phenomenon of splitting of white light into its constituent colours is known as dispersion. The medium which brings about dispersion is called dispersive medium.

Example: Prism is a dispersive medium. Vacuum or air is a non-dispersive medium.

The band of colours (wavelength) obtained is known as spectrum. Spectra are classified as pure spectrum and impure spectrum.

Pure Spectrum

It is the spectrum in which the constituent colours occupy their respective position (VIBGYOR) and are distinct. For example, spectrum obtained from prism and spectroscope arrangement.

Impure Spectrum

It is a spectrum in which the bands of colours overlap. There are no well defined boundaries between the bands of colours.

Example: Rainbow

Rainbow Cause for Dispersion

Dispersion occurs because different colours (wavelengths) are refracted or deviated to different extents because speed of different colours of light is different in a given medium.

$$\mu = \frac{\text{Velocity of the light in air or vacuum}}{\text{Velocity of light in air given medium}}$$

The refractive index of violet colour in glass is greater than the refractive index of red, or in other words, speed of violet is least in glass and the speed of red is the maximum.

Refrangibility

It is the ability of light to get refracted when passing from one medium to another. It depends on the refractive index of the medium for a given wavelength of light. In the visible light, the refrangibility for violet is maximum and that of red is least. ($\delta_{\text{violet}} > \delta_{\text{red}}$).

EXPERIMENT II

Experiment to show how white light splits into its constituent colours and it is not the prism which colours white light.

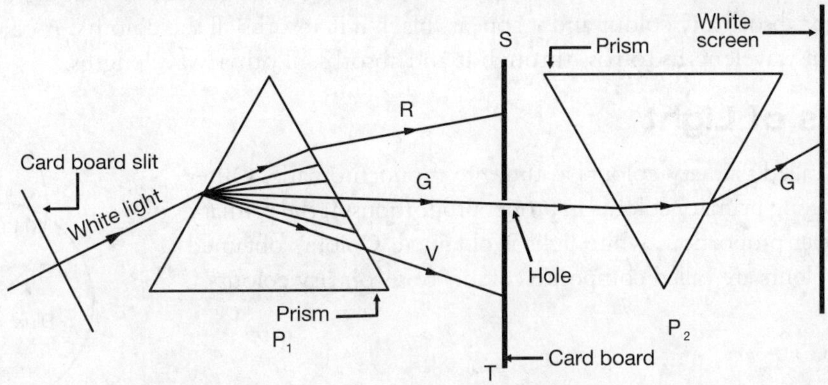

Figure 8.49 Refrangibility of white light through prisms

White light from a slit is made to pass through an equilateral prism placed in a dark room. Dispersed light from this prism is obtained on the white screen having a small hole. The coloured light passing through this hole is made to fall on a second prism P_2, which is placed in an inverted position. The light passing through the second prism gets refracted but does not undergo dispersion.

EXPERIMENT III

Newton's experiment on recombination of white light: Newton took two identical prisms P_1 and P_2. P_2 was placed inverted with respect to P_1. White light emerging out of the slit was made to fall on P_1. The spectrum produced by P_1 was interrupted by the prism P_2. He found that white light was emerged out of P_2. Thus, the spectrum produced by P_1 is recombined in the prism P_2.

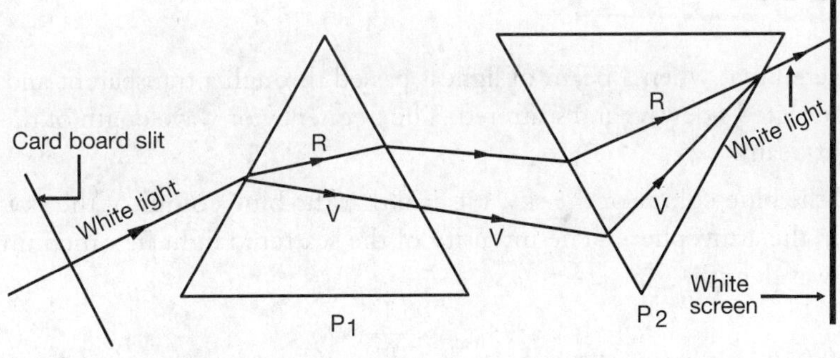

Figure 8.50 Recombination of dispersed light

Second prism P_2 bends the dispersed colours, towards its base through different angles such that the rays emerging out from the prism P_2 are incident at the same point. Thus, P_1 is a dispersing prism and P_2 is a recombining prism.

Colour of the Objects and Pigments

From the above facts, it is seen that white light consists of seven colours.

Colours It is the sensation produced in the brain, when a certain wavelength in the visible region strikes the retina.

Pigments It is an optically active substance which absorbs most of the wavelengths in the visible regions and reflects selective wavelengths. For example, leaf appears green in colour due to the presence of chlorophyll pigment. Pigments are colourless and get activated when white light is incident on them.

When white light is incident on the object, it absorbs some of the colours and reflects certain colours, so, the colour of an object is determined by the wavelength it reflects.

Sunflowers appear yellow because of the pigment present in them which absorbs all colours except yellow. An object appears white if it does not absorb any colour and it appears black if it absorbs all the colours. A colour filter is a transparent body which allows certain wavelengths to pass through it and absorbs all other wavelengths.

Primary Colours of Light

Red, blue and green are called primary colours as they are monochromatic. Other colours are obtained by mixing primary colours in proper proportions. If the primary colours are mixed in proper proportion, white light is obtained. Colours obtained by mixing two primary colours are called composite colours or secondary colours.

Example:

Red + Blue = Magenta

Red + Green = Yellow

Blue + Green = Cyan

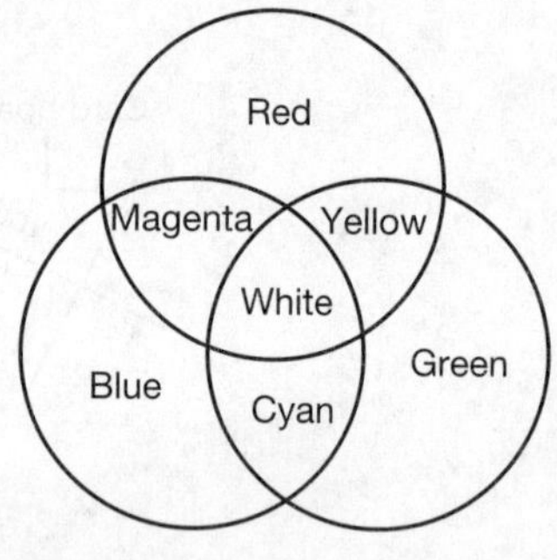

Figure 8.51 Primary colours and their derivative colours

Complimentary Pair of Colours

A pair of colours, in which one is a primary colour and the other is a secondary colour, which on mixing in proper proportion gives white light.

Example: Yellow + Blue = White

Colour on the vertex of the triangle represents a primary colour. Colours at the mid points represent composite colours. Colours at the line joining the vertex and midpoint of the side opposite to it represent complimentary colours.

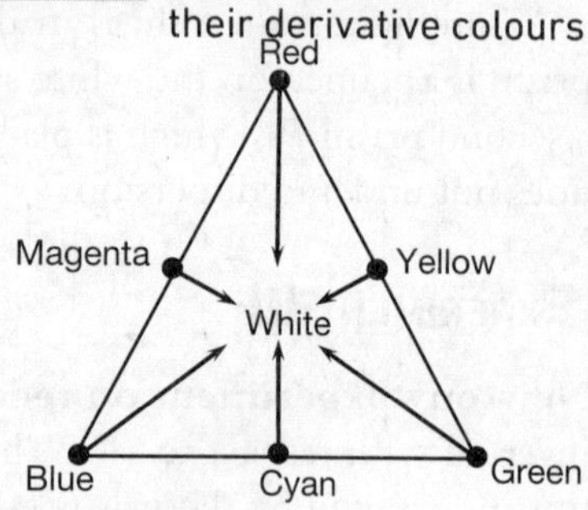

Figure 8.52 Colour triangle

Raman Effect

Tyndall and Rayleigh discovered that when a beam of light is passed through a transparent and homogeneous medium, a part of the incident light is deflected sideways and scattered. The frequency or wavelength of the scattered beam was found to be same as that of incident beam.

Lord Rayleigh explained the blue colour of the sky. He said that the blue colour of the sky is due to the scattering of light by molecules present in the atmosphere. The intensity of the scattered light in a medium is inversely proportional to the fourth power of the wavelength.

$$I_{max} \propto \frac{1}{\lambda^4}$$

I_{max} is the maximum intensity, λ is the wavelength of light. Thus, the wavelength of blue light is minimum and it is scattered most. Rayleigh scattering is also called coherent scattering. Coherent scattering is a scattering in which there is no change in the wavelength of light, i.e., scattered light has the same wavelength as that of the incident light.

At sunrise and sunset, Sun appears red in colour. This is due to Rayleigh scattering, At sunset and sunrise, light from the Sun travels maximum distance. As a result, most of the blue light is scattered and the light reaching the Earth's surface lacks blue colour. It is red colour which reaches the Earth's surface, since it is least scattered.

When Sir C.V. Raman was experimenting the scattering of light by liquids, he discovered that when a monochromatic light is passed through organic liquid like benzene, toluene, etc., it results in the formation of the scattered light which consists of wavelengths of frequencies higher and lower that of the incident light in addition to that of the incident light. This is known as Raman effect. Raman's scattering is an incoherent scattering. Incoherent scattering is a type of scattering in which the scattered light consists of frequencies other than those of the incident light. Raman effect is used to study the structure of molecules.

Spectroscope

Spectroscope is an instrument used to obtain pure spectrum. Spectroscope consists of collimator, prism table and a telescope.

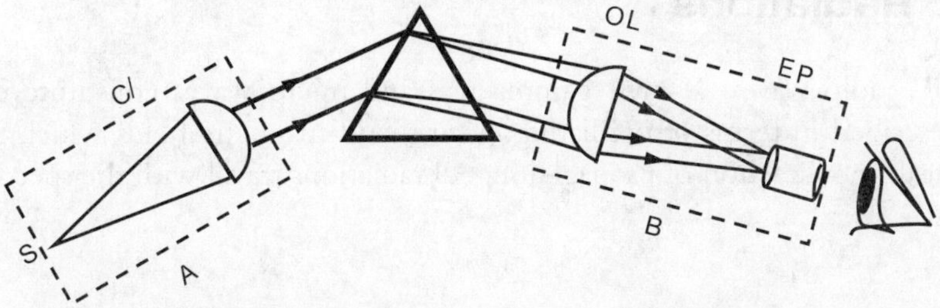

Figure 8.53 Spectroscope

Collimator consists of a slit from which light rays are rendered parallel by the lens. This light is made to fall on a prism placed on the prism table which is in line with the collimator. The rays get dispersed by the prism and the spectrum is observed through a telescope.

Uses of a Spectroscope

Spectrometer helps us to observe spectra. By studying and analysing spectra, information about the sources of light can be obtained. Special spectrometer is required to study Raman lines.

Emission Spectra

Light from a candle or an incandescent bulb consists of all wavelengths present in the visible region. This spectrum is known as continuous emission spectra.

When gases and vapours are made to emit light, the spectrum consists of a number of bright lines against a dark back ground. These spectrum is known as line emission spectrum.

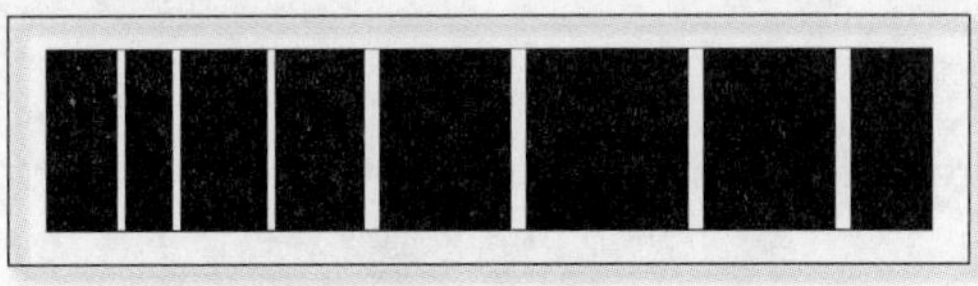

Figure 8.54 Emission spectra

Line emission spectra is a characteristic of an element, i.e., different elements give rise to different line spectra. By studying line spectra, elements present in the gas or molecules can be discovered.

By measuring intensities of the line spectra, an approximate amount of each element present can be found out. This technique is called spectro-chemical analysis. This is used in medicine and crime detection.

Absorption Spectra

When white light is passed through gases or vapour at a low temperature, some of the wavelengths are absorbed. Then spectrum formed is known as absorption spectrum.

Example: When a light from carbon arc is passed through sodium vapour, two lines are blotted out in the yellow region (D_1 and D_2) of the spectrum.

When a solar spectrum is observed by picturing a powerful telescope, the spectrum consists of a number of dark lines. These lines are called Fraunhofer lines, named after Fraunhofer who first studied these lines.

By analysing Fraunhofer lines, elements present in the Sun can be found out. Helium was discovered by studying Fraunhofer lines.

Electromagnetic Radiations

Radiations, IR, visible, UV, radio waves, X-rays, gamma rays and micro waves constitute electromagnetic spectrum. These radiations can be described in terms of oscillating electric and magnetic fields which are at right angles to each other and are perpendicular to the direction of propagation. All radiations travel with the speed of light but differ in their wavelengths or frequencies.

$$c = \nu\lambda$$

where, c is the speed of light, λ is the wavelength and ν is the frequency.

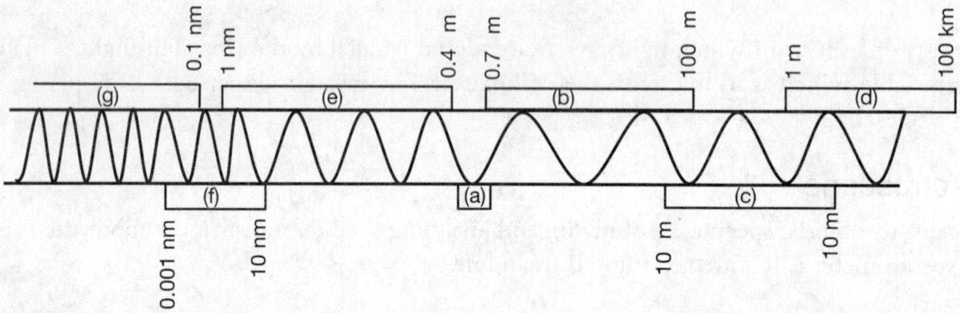

Figure 8.55 Various regions of electromagnetic spectrum and their wavelength ranges

(a) Visible spectrum (b) IR spectrum (c) Microwaves (Radio waves)
(e) UV spectrum (f) X-rays (g) γ-rays

Differences in the properties of different electromagentic radiations are due to the difference in their frequencies.

Visible Spectrum

The wavelength of visible light ranges from 400 nm to 750 nm (4000 A° to 7500 A°). The spectrum within this range is called visible spectrum (VIBGYOR).

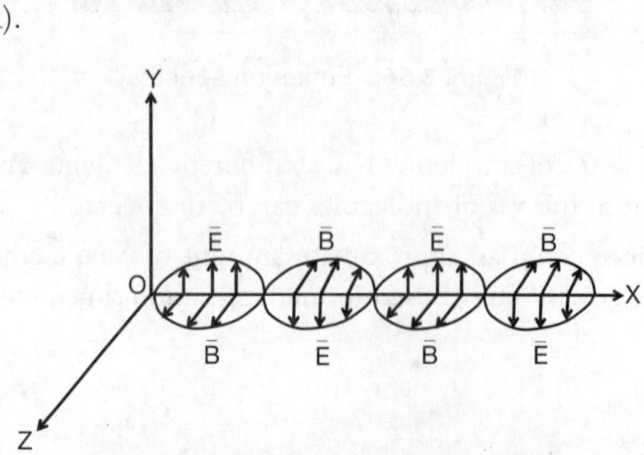

Figure 8.56 Electromagnetic wave

Invisible Spectrum

It is the region of spectrum which does not strike the retina.

Radio Waves

The wavelength of radio waves ranges from 1 m to 100 km. They are produced by electromagnetic oscillators of low frequencies. Radio waves are received from extra-terrestial sources known as radio astronomy. Radio waves of short wavelengths are used in communication which includes satellites, Radars and TV. Longer wavelengths are used in radio broadcasting.

Microwaves

The wavelength of microwave ranges from 10 μm to 10 m. These waves are produced by electromagnetic oscillators of high frequency in an electric circuit. They are used in radio detection and ranging, microwave ovens, telemetry and satellite communications.

Infrared Spectrum

It is an electromagnetic radiation beyond the red region. Its wavelength varies from about 8000×10^{-10} m to $4,00,000 \times 10^{-10}$ m.

Infrared rays were discovered by William Herschel. He obtained a spectrum by passing sunlight through a glass prism. He observed a rise in temperature when he moved a thermometer with a blackened bulb from violet region to red region and there was a sudden increase in temperature beyond the red region. Infrared rays produce heating effect but not the visible effect.

Sources of Infrared Rays

Sun, lamp, burning gases are some of the sources of infrared rays. Any substance which radiates heat is a source of infrared rays. All living beings emit IR rays.

Properties of IR Rays

1. They are electromagnetic radiations which are not affected by electric and magnetic field.
2. They travel with the speed of light.
3. They do not affect photographic plates.
4. They are least scattered by fog and mist because of their long wavelengths.
5. They can be detected by thermopile or thermometer with blackened bulb.
6. They obey the laws of reflection and refraction. Hence, they can be focused by parabolic mirrors or lenses.
7. Infrared rays having wavelength beyond $20,000 \times 10^{-10}$ m can be absorbed by glass.
8. They can penetrate rock salt.

Uses

1. Since they produce heating effect, they are used to relieve pains from muscles and swollen joints.
2. Because of their long wavelength they can travel long distances in fog without much scattering and are used in infrared photography.
3. They are used in surface to air missiles.
   A missile is fired in the direction of an enemy plane. Sensor of infrared radiation present in the missile detects the heat trail left by the enemy plane and sends the message to computer. The computer guides the missile towards the target.
4. They are used to detect diseases in crops. Any change in the heat radiation of crops is due to some kind of disease. Heat radiation is measured through satellites.
5. Night vision devices are used to see objects in dark. These devices can detect infrared radiation emitted by hot objects.

Ultraviolet Spectrum

The region of spectrum beyond violet region is called ultraviolet spectrum.

This spectrum was discovered by J. Ritter. Ritter discovered that when a silver chloride paper was placed beyond violet region, it first turned to violet, then brown and black. Thus, the ray which produced strong chemical effect in silver chloride paper was named as chemical ray or actinic ray. Later on the rays were named as ultraviolet rays. Glass absorbs UV rays but quartz does not absorb these rays.

Sources

1. Any source of light at temperature greater than 2500°C is a good source of UV rays.
2. Sunlight, mercury vapour lamps.

Properties

1. They are electromagnetic waves having wavelength between 4000 A° to 100 A° (1 A° = 10^{-10} m)
2. They are not affected by electric or magnetic fields.
3. They obey the laws of reflection and refraction.
4. They produce fluorescence when incident on substances like zinc sulphide, quinine sulphate solution.

   Fluorescence is a phenomenon in which a substance absorbs light of shorter wavelength and reflects a light of longer wavelength.
5. They produce chemical effects.
6. They travel with the velocity of light.
7. They are absorbed by stratosphere and convert ozone to oxygen.

Uses

1. Ultraviolet rays when absorbed by a human body produce vitamin D which helps in growth of strong bones and teeth but causes blindness when seen directly.
2. Ultraviolet rays are used to detect original gems from fake ones.
3. Ultraviolet rays are used to detect forgery. The document to be checked is placed under ultraviolet rays and any alterations can be easily detected.
4. The UV rays kill germs and microorganisms. Hence, they are used to sterilize surgical instrument and drinking water.

X-rays

They have wavelength ranging from 0.01 Å to 10 nm (100 Å). X-rays are produced when a high speed electron is stopped by a target. X-rays of shorter wavelength are used to study structure of materials because the spacing between the atoms in a solid ranges from 0.1 Å to 10 Å. These X-rays are called hard X-rays. X-rays of longer wavelength called soft X-rays can penetrate flesh but they are stopped by bones and are used in radiography.

Gamma Rays

Gamma rays have wavelength ranging from 0.0001 nm to 0.1 m. Gamma rays are produced by radioactive elements. Gamma rays have the highest penetrating power. Gamma rays are used in treatment of cancer. They are used as γ ray microscope and are used to produce photoelectric effect.

Photoelectric Effect

Max Planck proposed quantum theory in order to explain black body radiation. According to quantum theory, radiation consists of tiny packets of energy called quanta or photon. The energy of each quantum is given by, $E = h\nu$, where, h is Planck's constant whose value is 6.63×10^{-34} J s and ν is the frequency of radiation. These quanta travel with the velocity of light. According to quantum theory, radiation cannot be emitted or absorbed continuously. It can be done in integral multiples of $h\nu$. When light of suitable frequency falls on a metals, electrons are emitted out from the metal surface. This phenomenon is known as photoelectric effect. Electrons emitted are known as photoelectrons. UV rays, X-rays and γ-rays can cause photoelectric effect on certain metals.

The minimum frequency required for the incident light to eject electrons from the metal surface is known as threshold frequency. If the frequency of incident light is less than its threshold frequency, electrons are not emitted from the metal surface. If the frequency of incident light is greater than the threshold frequency, electrons are ejected with kinetic energy or in other words velocity of photoelectrons increases with frequency. Threshold frequency is different for different metals.

Number of photoelectrons depends only on intensity of incident light and the photoelectrons increase with increase in intensity of incident light.

Einstein Explanation of Photoelectric Effect

Einstein made use of Planck's quantum theory in order to explain photoelectric effect. Einstein assumed that tiny packets of energy called photons propagate through space and interact with matter. When a photon of energy $h\nu$ is incident on a metal, it interacts with an electron and transfers the whole of its energy to a single electron. The electrons are bound to the material, and hence, a certain amount of work has to be done to release the electron from the metal surface. If the frequency of incident radiation is lesser than the threshold frequency, electrons cannot be emitted and there is no photoelectric effect. If the frequency of the incident radiation is greater than the threshold frequency, part of the energy is used to release the electron and the remaining part is given as kinetic energy to an electron.

Application of Photoelectric Effect

1. Used to reproduce sound in cinematography
2. Used in burglar alarms
3. Used in automatic opening and closing of doors
4. Used in automatic control of traffic signals
5. Used in exposure meter
6. Used in automatic switching on and off street lights

Theories of Light (a Historical Review)

First century A.D. The Greek scientists Euclid and Hero suggested that light travelled in straight lines and that light originated at the eye and travelled towards the object of vision.

~ 1000 A.D. The Arab scientist Alhazen proposed that light radiating from a luminous source gets reflected from the objects to the eyes allowing them to be seen.

16th century The English thinker Francis Bacon interpreted light as a disturbance that could be detected by the eye and that this disturbance gets 'stained' when they get reflected from an object causing the colours.

Early 17th century Galileo and Kepler succeeded in the construction of a refracting telescope proving the laws of refraction and Snell refined these laws.

17th century Sir Isaac Newton and his contemporary Christian Huygens, a Dutch scientist, came up with contradictory theories on light stirring a debate over the truth in their proposals. While Huygen proposed his wave theory Newton came up with the corpuscular theory. Newton's theory was more readily accepted and prevailed for almost a century.

Newton's Corpuscular Theory

Based on his experiments in 1666 and the laws of mechanics, Newton proposed his corpuscular theory on the following assumptions.

1. Light is made up of point-like particles called corpuscles having negligible mass.
2. These particles are perfectly elastic and travel in straight lines.
3. Based on the laws of motion interfaces of different optical media exert forces of attraction and repulsion leading to the phenomena of reflection and refraction.
4. Speed of light is greater in a denser medium.
5. The different sizes of the corpuscles account for the different colours.

He went on to explain that just as a perfectly elastic collision takes place when a ball hits or strikes a rigid surface, reflection of light takes place when corpuscles strike a reflecting surface.

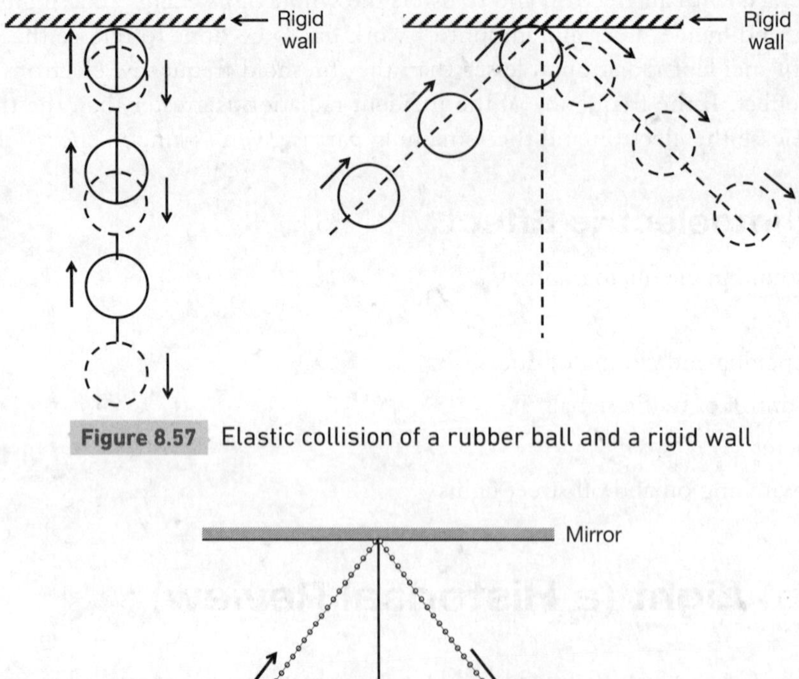

Figure 8.57 Elastic collision of a rubber ball and a rigid wall

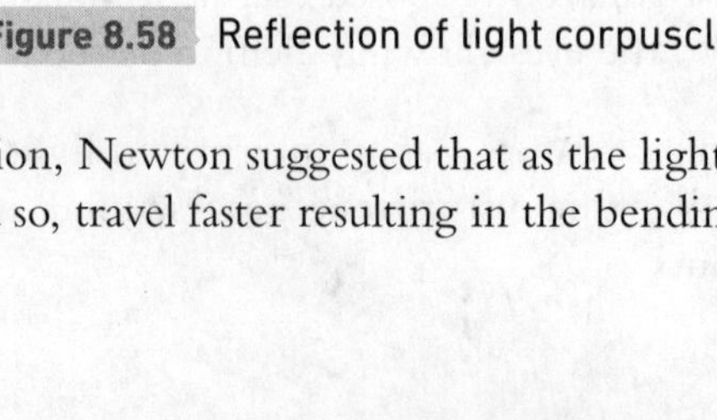

Figure 8.58 Reflection of light corpuscles

To explain the phenomenon of refraction, Newton suggested that as the light particles enter a denser medium they are attracted by particles of the medium, and so, travel faster resulting in the bending of the path traced.

Drawbacks of Newton's Corpuscular Theory

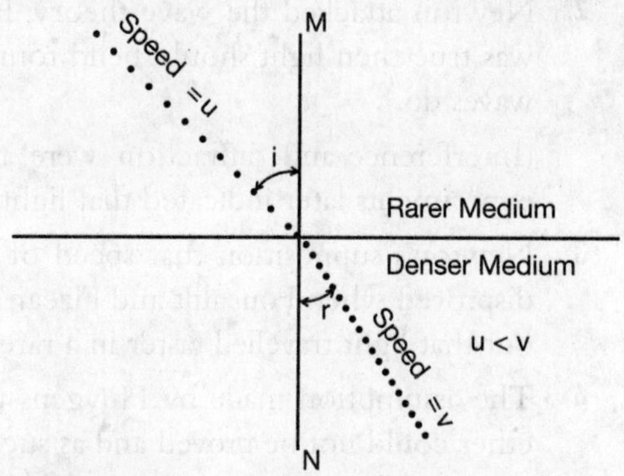

Figure 8.59 Motion of particles during refraction

1. Newton proposed that velocity of light in a denser medium is greater than its velocity in a rarer medium but it was found that velocity of light in the rarer medium is greater than its velocity in the denser medium.
2. There was no justification for the assumption that different colours were due to different sizes of the corpuscles.
3. Newton's theory could not explain phenomenon like interference, diffraction and polarization.

Huygen's Wave Theory

A group of scientists led by the Dutch physicist Christian Huygens challenged Newton's corpuscular theory by claiming that the wave theory gave a better explanation of reflection and refraction. They put forth the following proposals to explain the behaviour of light.

1. All space is filled with an invisible substance called ether and light travels in the form of longitudinal mechanical waves.
2. Every luminous body which is a source of light, either point or extended (a line) would be at the geometrical centre of the propagation of wave and is called primary source.
3. Any point in the medium which would act as a source of light for further propagation is referred to as a secondary source.
4. All points in the medium which receive the light from the source, either primary or secondary, at the same time would lie along a curved surface called wavelet.
5. The envelope of all wavelets in the same phase–receiving light at the same time–would form a wave front.
6. The 'ray of light' would be along the normal, drawn at a point.
7. At large distances from the primary source, (luminous body) the radius of curvature of a wave front would be large such that small protions of the wave front may be approximated to a plane.

On the basis of the above hypotheses, spherical, cylindrical or plane wave fronts may be constructed.

Newton–Huygen Debate

1. Huygen reiterated that reflection and refraction as well as dispersion of light could be convincingly explained with the help of wave theory.

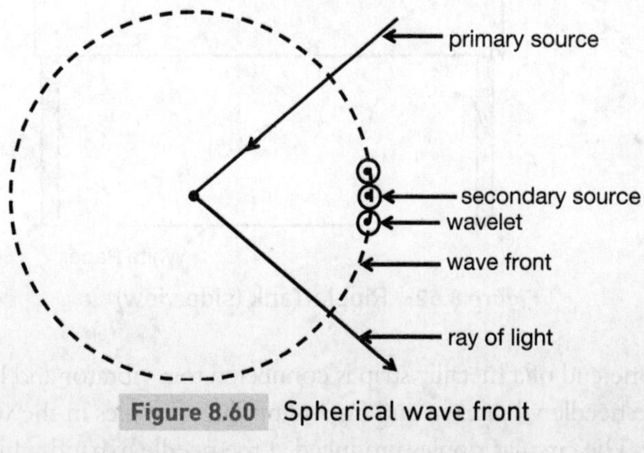

Figure 8.60 Spherical wave front

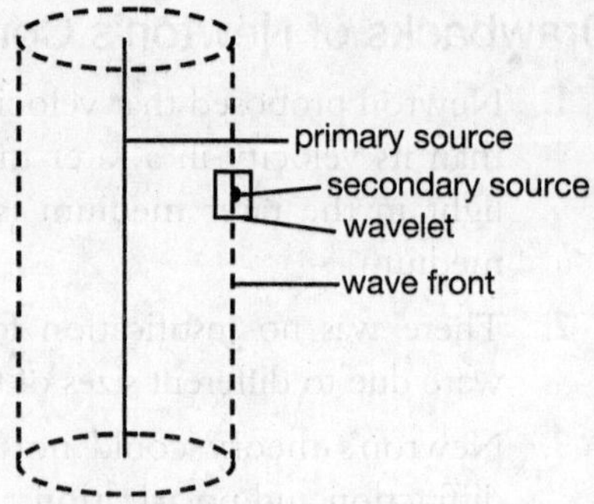

Figure 8.61 Cylindrical wave front

2. Newton attacked the wave theory. He pointed out that if the wave theory was true then light should bend round the corners, just as sound and water waves do.

   (Interference and diffraction were not known until Fransesco Grimaldi's experiments later indicated that light does bend at corners).

3. Newton's supposition that speed of light increased in denser medium was disproved when Foucault and Fizean's experiments on speed of light pointed out that light travelled faster in a rarer medium.

4. The assumption made by Huygens that space was filled with matter called ether could not be proved and as such did not gain much support.

5. Newton's theory suffered a major setback when first Thomas Young (1801) and later Fresnel, Malus and Fraunhofer discovered interference and diffraction, which could not be explained by the corpuscular theory, thus, giving strength to the wave theory of Huygens.

6. Huygen's postulate that light travelled as mechanical waves was disproved when in 1872 James Maxwell discovered the existence of electromagnetic waves; and Heinrich Hertz showed that these electromagnetic waves displayed all the phenomena of light, suggesting that light is also an electromagnetic wave, which is fundamentally a transverse wave.

Light was first believed to be possessing a particle nature giving rise to the particle theory of light. But then it was found that, while some observations could be explained using this theory there were observations which could not be explained. This led to the profounding of new theory put forward by Huygen called 'wave theory of light'. But then certain observations explained by the particle theory of light could not be explained about the wave theory. To resolve this problem certain scientists came up with the idea that light behaves both as a particle and a wave leading to a new consolidated idea of 'dual nature of light'.

Ripple Tank Experiment

Certain phenomena like polarization of light confirmed the transverse wave nature of light. Even waves produced on the surface of water, also called ripples are also transverse waves. Hence, certain phenomena of light which can be explained by its wave nature can be easily understood by taking an anology between water waves, i.e., ripples and light waves. For this purpose, we consider a water tank made of glass or perspex (a transparent material) mounted on four legs kept as supports, at a height. The side view of the tank is shown in the Fig. 8.62.

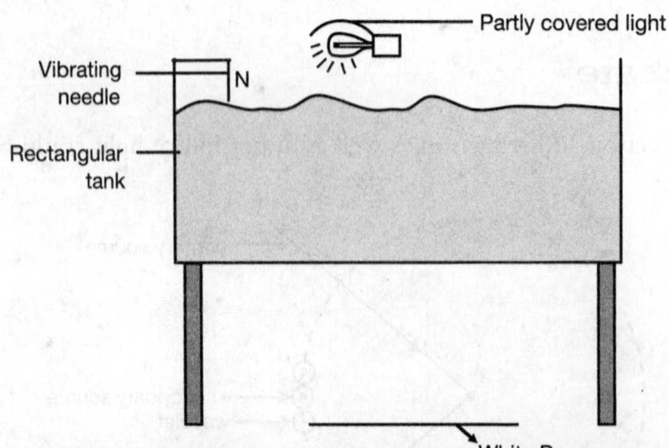

Figure 8.62 Ripple Tank (side view)

A small needle, which is fixed to one end of a metallic strip is connected to a vibrator and held above the water surface so that when the vibrator is switched on, the needle vibrates to and fro and produces ripples in the water. These ripples consist of crests and troughs and are circular in shape. The circular ripples produced at the needle expand while the wave moves in all directions.

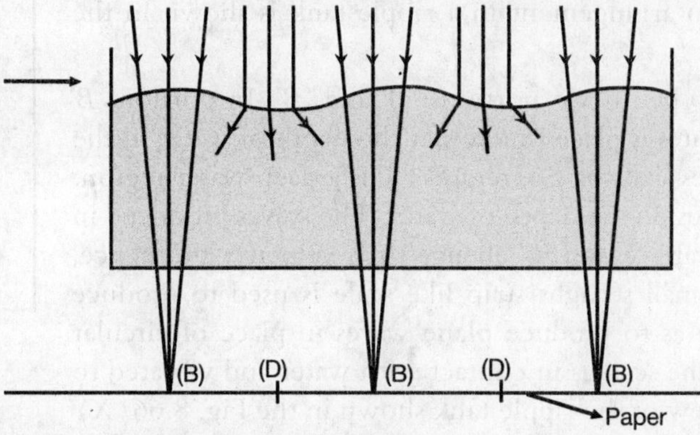

Figure 8.63 Formation of bright (B) and dark (D) bands on paper placed below the ripple tank

A white paper is placed below the tank on the ground surface. A bulb is held horizontally above the water surface. The light from the bulb passes through the water towards the paper kept below the ripple tank. The crest portion of the waves acts as a convex lens, and thus, forms a bright band of light on the paper placed below the tank. Similarly, the trough portion of the waves acts as a concave lens, and thus, forms a dark band of light on the paper placed below the tank. Thus, the motion of ripples in the tank can be understood by the motion of dark and bright bands of light on the paper.

Reflection of Waves in a Ripple Tank

Consider a ripple tank as described earlier, with a pin arrangement which vibrates and produces ripples in the tank. The circular ripples produced will be reflected by a hard surface like the wall of the tank. The top view of the ripple tank where the circular ripples are produced at source '*O*' and reflected at the wall of the tank '*AB*' is shown in the Fig. 8.64.

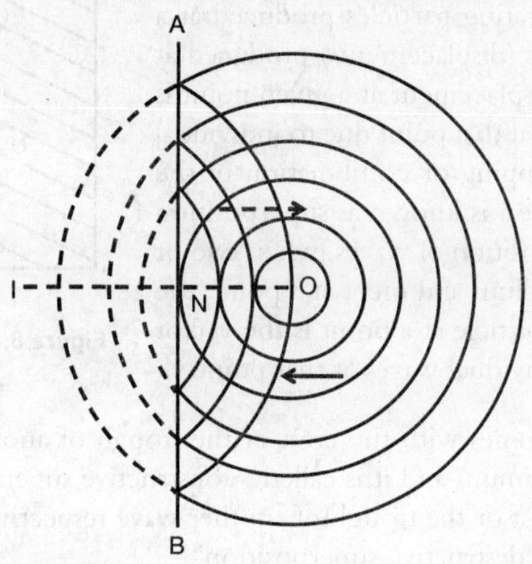

Figure 8.64 Reflection of waves in a ripple tank

The ripples would reflect at *AB* such that the centre of the reflected ripples would be at '*I*'. Thus, '*I*' is the image of '*O*' and the distance *ON* = *IN*, which implies that the object distance is equal to image distance, considering *AB* as the reflecting surface.

The phenomenon of reflection can be studied by observing the movement of bright and dark bands of light on the white paper placed below the ripple tank.

Refraction of Waves in a Ripple Tank

For refraction to take place we require two media with different densities such that waves from one medium travel to another medium. In a ripple tank this is possible by introducing a pile of plates at the bottom portion covering half the area. The side view of such an arrangement in a ripple tank is shown in the Fig. 8.65.

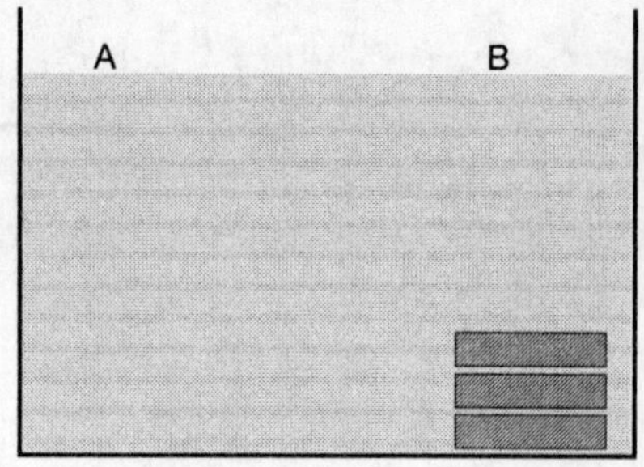

Figure 8.65 Ripple tank

The ripple tank is considered to be of two portions '*A*' and '*B*'. In portion '*B*' at the bottom of water a pile of plates is placed such that the depth of water in the region '*B*' is decreased and becomes shallow. So, region '*A*' is a deep water region. The velocity of water waves depends on the depth of water. The waves produced in the region '*A*' while travelling toward region '*B*' change their velocity; and hence, their wavelength. In this case, a small straight strip like scale is used to produce waves instead of a small needle so as to produce plane waves in place of circular waves. The horizontal portion of the scale is in contact with water and vibrated to produce plane waves. In the top view of the ripple tank shown in the Fig. 8.66, *XY* is an imaginary line which acts as a boundary between shallow region '*B*' and deeper region '*A*'. The waves produced in region '*A*' travel towards '*B*' and in this process their velocity is decreased. Hence, the wavelength of the waves is also decreased. This can be understood by observing the distance between two bright bands of light formed on the white paper below the tank in both the regions '*B*' and '*A*'. The bold lines in the Fig. 8.66 indicate the plane wave fronts and the lines with arrows which are normal to the waves indicate the direction of rays. It can be understood that the rays while travelling from rarer to denser medium bend towards the normal. A similar effect takes place in light.

Superposition of Waves

Consider two vibrating pins placed at different locations in a ripple tank. The waves produced from these two pins propagate in all possible directions and they meet in a common region. When the waves meet, the net effect (displacement) of the vibrating particles produced at a point is the sum of the individual effects (displacements) produced at the point by the two waves. The total displacement at a given point is equal to the vector sum of displacements at that point due to individual waves. This is caused due to the overlapping or combination of the two waves at the point. This phenomenon is known as superposition and according to the principle of superposition of waves, when two or more waves travel through the same medium and meet at a point, the resultant displacement of the vibrating particle at a point is the vector sum of the displacements due to the individual waves at that point.

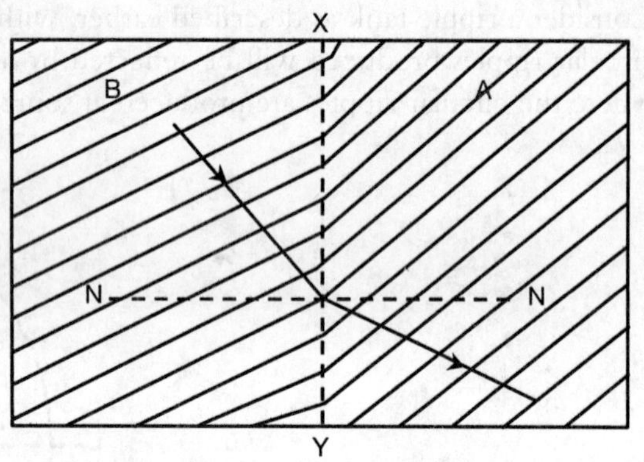

Figure 8.66 Refraction of waves in a ripple tank

If a crest or trough of one wave combines with the crest or the trough of another wave respectively at a given point, the net displacement at the point is maximum and it is called 'constructive superposition'. Similarly when the trough or crest of one wave combines with the crest or the trough of another wave respectively at a given point, a net displacement at the point is minimum and it is called 'destructive superposition'.

Interference of Waves

During the superposition of waves, if the waves produced from two sources have the same frequency and amplitude and travel in the same direction, the superposition of such waves produce well defined constructive and destructive superposition in space and this phenomenon is called 'Interference'.

In interference, when constructive superposition takes place it is called 'constructive interference' and similarly when destructive superposition takes place it is called 'destructive interference'. To obtain a sustained interference pattern, i.e., a regular arrangement of maxima and minima, the following conditions are essential.

1. The waves that take part in interference must be in phase or have a constant phase difference between them. Such waves which have a constant phase difference between them are called coherent waves and the corresponding sources are called coherent sources.
2. The frequency or wavelength of the two waves must be equal.
3. To get a maximum at a point in interference, the phase difference between the two waves must be $2n\pi$, where, $n = 0, 1, 2$, etc.
4. To get a minimum at a point in interference, the phase difference between the two waves must be $(2n - 1)\pi$, where, $n = 1, 2, 3$, etc.

Konnect

Interference is the reason you can hear both constructive and destructive sound when tuning a musical instrument.

Interference of Water Waves in a Ripple Tank

Consider two pins, N_1 and N_2 arranged in a ripple tank instead of a single pin. These are used to produce ripples in the tank. Let these two pins vibrate simultaneously with the same frequency such that circular ripples are produced at the two locations 'N_1' and 'N_2'and travel in all possible directions.

The top view of the ripple tank with the above described arrangement is shown in the Fig. 8.67.

When the distance between the two sources (N_1 and N_2) of the waves is lesser compared to their distance from screen PQ, an interference pattern is observed. The positions where two crests or two troughs of waves from two sources 'N_1' and 'N_2' combine and produce constructive interference are marked with dots and the positions where a crest from one wave combines with a trough of another wave and produces destructive interference are shown by circles. Thus, on the screen 'PQ' we observe the interference pattern, with maximum displacement of the water particles at some points and minimum displacement of the water particles at some points. The points of maximum displacement fall on the antinodal line and the points of minimum displacement fall on the nodal line. We also observe that these nodal and antinodal lines are distributed uniformly on the screen.

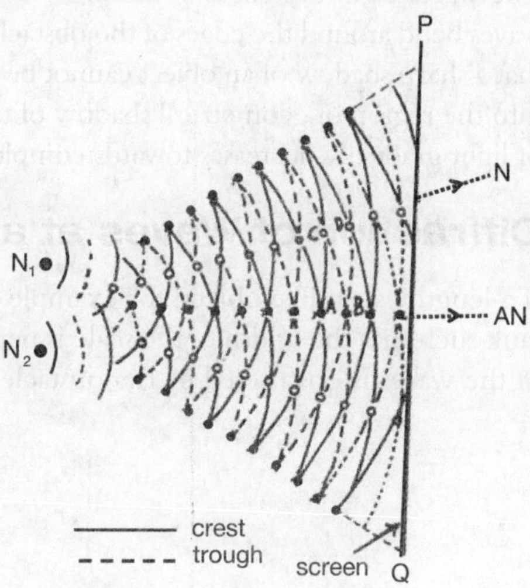

Figure 8.67 Interference of water waves in a ripple tank

Similar to the interference of water waves taking place in a ripple tank, interference also takes place in light and on the screen where we observe interference pattern, the brightness of the light varies from maximum to minimum at equidistant locations forming bands of light called 'fringes'. The band of light where brightness is maximum is called bright band and is caused by constructive interference of light. Similarly, the band of light where brightness is minimum is called dark band and is caused by destructive interference of light.

Diffraction of Waves

Consider a ripple tank where a single pin is placed for producing ripples. The ripples produced are circular in shape. As the wave formed moves away from the source, the circular wavefronts are formed.

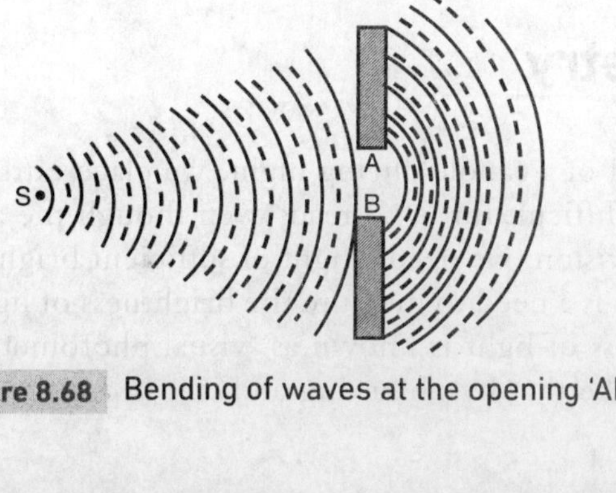

Figure 8.68 Bending of waves at the opening 'AB'

In such a situation, when an obstacle is placed such as a wooden plank with a wide hole '*AB*' called 'aperture' (only cross section of the plank is shown in the Fig. 8.68) as shown in the Fig. 8.68, the part of the wave striking the opening '*AB*' will pass through it. But the hole *AB* itself becomes a 'secondary source' and waves travel in all directions beyond the hole on the other side of the plank. In the Fig. 8.69, the top view of the ripple tank with waves that are passing through the opening '*AB*' is shown.

This bending and travelling of the waves as they pass through the edge of an obstacle is known as diffraction. The bold lines in the Fig. 8.68 indicate the crests of wave fronts while the dotted lines indicate the troughs. If the diameter of the opening, i.e., the hole decreases one can observe that the ripples which pass through the opening are likely to be more circular and this opening will act as another source that produces waves.

The hole itself acts as an obstacle and when the size (i.e., diameter) of the hole decreases to such an extent that the diameter of the hole is comparable with the wavelength of waves, the diffraction pattern is more prominent.

Diffraction of Light

The wavelength of light is of the order of angstroms. So, when light waves encounter obstacles of very small sizes, the light waves bend around the edges of the obstacle and travel. This is known as diffraction of light. It is due to the diffraction of light that a sharp shadow of an object cannot be obtained on any screen placed behind it. Due to diffraction, light bends and travels into the region of geometrical shadow of the object, and thus, complete darkness is not found in the shadow. The brightness of light gradually decreases towards complete darkness as we go gradually into the geometrical shadow of the obstacle.

Diffraction of Waves at a Straight Edge

If a lengthy strip like object, for example a half meter scale (*AB*), is held perpendicular to the motion of waves in a ripple tank such that the width of the scale is perpendicular to the surface of water as shown in the Fig. 8.69, the bottom portion of the waves is obstructed by the obstacle '*AB*' and the upper portion of the waves advances further.

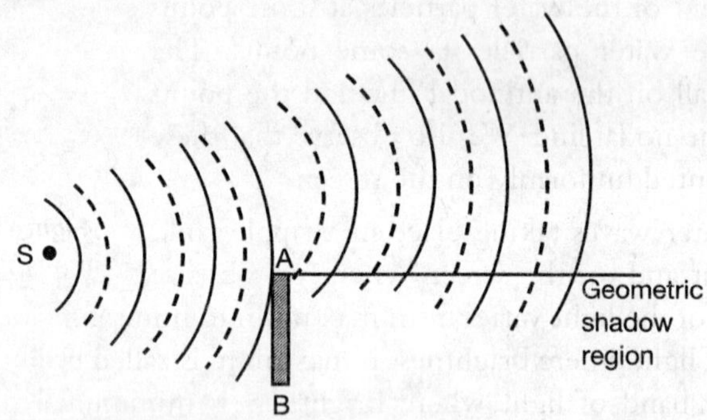

Figure 8.69 Diffraction of waves at a straight edge

But the waves moving beyond '*AB*' bend and travel into the geometric shadow region of the obstacle. This is the diffraction of waves observed due to a straight edge. Similar diffraction is observed when light is diffracted at a straight edge and the light after diffraction encroaches into the geometric shadow of the straight edge where one can observe a gradual decrease in brightness of light in the shadow.

Visual Photometry

When we tend to study in the light of a candle during night, we place ourselves near the candle. When we move away from the candle, it becomes difficult for us to read; even though the amount of light emitted by the candle does not change. Hence, for clear vision, we need a light of sufficient brightness. Our eyes cannot bear too much of brightness of light also. So, there is a need to measure the brightness of light. The branch of physics which deals with the measurement of brightness of light is known as 'visual photometry'. Brightness of light from different sources cannot be compared just like that by observing and if it is done that way, it is not authentic. So, certain standards and techniques are used to measure the brightness of light from a source. The branch of physics which deals with measurement of brightness of light emitted by different sources using certain standards and some special techniques is known as visual photometry. The following are some of the basic terms that are used in visual photometry.

1. Luminous flux or light flux (φ): A source of light emits radiations depending on its temperature and the surface of the body. But eye is sensitive only to the amount of visible energy emitted by it. Luminous flux is the amount of radiant visible (luminous) energy emitted per second from the source. It is denoted by φ and is measured in Lumen.

2. **Solid Angle:** Consider a small portion of an area on the surface of a sphere as shown in the Fig. 8.70. From the centre of the sphere, draw the normal lines on to the boundary of the area considered on the surface of the sphere. These lines form a cone.

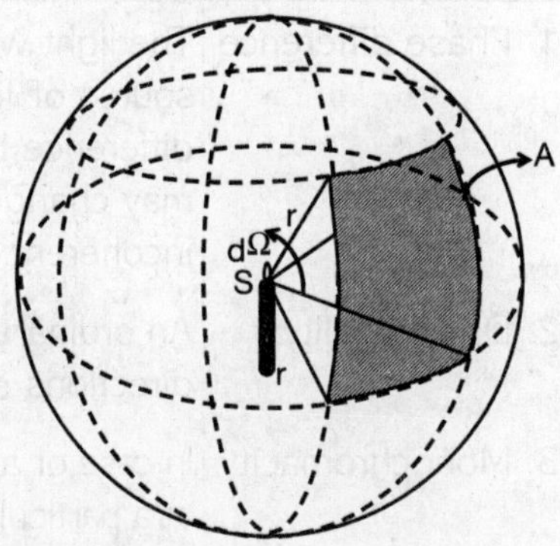

Figure 8.70 Concept of solid angle

The angle enclosed by the conical surface is known as solid angle. It is equal to the ratio of the area of the portion on the surface of the sphere to the square of the radius of the sphere.

If the area of the portion on the spherical surface is 'A' and the radius of the sphere is 'r', then the solid angle is given by, $\Omega = (A/r^2)$, and is measured in steradians (sr).

3. **Luminous Intensity**: A light source emits light in all directions. The luminous flux emitted by a light source per unit solid angle in a particular direction is called luminous intensity. It is denoted by I.

   So, $$I = \frac{\varphi}{\Omega}.$$

   Luminous intensity is measured in units of candela (cd).

> **Info Bytes!**
>
> The total surface area of a sphere is $4\pi r^2$ where 'r' is its radius.
>
> ∴ Solid angle in a sphere $= \frac{4\pi r^2}{r^2}$
>
> $= 4\pi$ sr.

4. **Candela (cd):** Luminous intensity of a point source is said to be 1 candela if one lumen of luminous flux is emitted per unit solid angle.

   $$1 \text{ cd} = 1 \text{ lm sr}^{-1}$$

5. **Lumen (lm):** Lumen is the unit of luminous flux. One lumen is defined as the amount of luminous energy emitted per second by a uniform source of light of luminous intensity one candela within a cone of unit solid angle.

   1 lm = 1 cd sr

   $1 \text{ lm} = \frac{1}{683}$ W at 555 nm of wavelength.

6. **Candle Power:** Candles emit different intensities of light in different directions. The luminous intensity of the light source in a particular direction is known as candle power. It is expressed in candela (cd).

Laser

It is the acronym of light amplification by stimulated emission of radiation. Amplification is the process of increasing the energy and that is done in the light by stimulated emission of radiation, and so, it is called laser. Lasers can be identified by their characteristic properties and because of them they differ from ordinary light.

Let us have a comparative study of ordinary light and a laser.

Table 8.5 Properties of Ordinary light and laser

Property	Ordinary light	Laser
1. Phase difference	The light waves emitted from an ordinary source of light do not have a constant phase difference between them. The phase difference may change with time. Thus, ordinary light is incoherent.	The light waves emitted from a laser source have a constant phase relationship between them which does not change with time. This is called temporal coherence.
2. Directionality	An ordinary light source emits light in all directions due to divergence.	Laser emits light only in one particular direction, and hence, has high directionality.
3. Monochromacity	In case of an ordinary light, intensity is maximum at a particular wavelength. But the intensity of light is not zero in the neighbourhood wavelengths of that particular wavelength. So, it has a bandwidth and it is of the order of 1000 A°.	For a laser, the intensity of light is maximum at a particular wavelength and in the neighbourhood of that wavelength, the intensity of light is zero. So, the bandwidth of laser is very less and it is of the order of 10 A°
4. Intensity	The light energy received per second per unit area is intensity. It is less in the case of ordinary light as an ordinary source spreads light uniformly in all directions.	The light from a laser source is limited to a small region and it is not spread out like an ordinary light. So, intensity of light is high in laser light.

The above differences between ordinary light and laser light help in the study of characteristics of laser light which makes it different from an ordinary light.

Characteristics of Laser Light

1. Generally light is emitted from a source by transition of electrons in atoms from an excited state to ground state. When transitions take place in a random manner, there is no phase relationship between light waves emitted during the transitions of electrons. But in the case of a laser source, this transition of electrons from an excited state to ground state takes place in a regular order. Due to this, there exists a definite phase relationship between light waves emitted during the transition, which does not change with time. Thus, we say that these waves are coherent and the phenomenon relating to the constancy of this phase relationship is known as 'temporal coherence'. This is an important property of laser light.
2. We know that the light from a normal source is divergent and moves in all possible directions, distributing the light energy over a large area. But the light from a laser source is spread over very small area when compared to ordinary light. Thus, we can say that laser light is more limited to a particular direction and this property is known as 'directionality'.
3. The energy received per unit time per unit area is known as intensity. Since the laser light is not spread over a large area and is limited to a smaller one, all the light is incident on a small portion. So, the intensity of laser light is many times more than that of an ordinary light.
4. It is observed that the intensity of light varies with its wavelength. As the wavelength of light increases, its intensity increases and at a particular value of wavelength, it is maximum. Further, as the value of the wavelength becomes higher the intensity gradually decreases. So, the wavelength of a light is specified as the wavelength at which its intensity is maximum. The intensity of light does not abruptly become zero for certain wavelength range on either sides of the wavelength corresponding to maximum intensity. This range of wavelength, about a wavelength corresponding to maximum intensity is called 'bandwidth' and this bandwidth is very less for laser light when compared to that of ordinary light. Hence, we can specifically assign a single value of wavelength to a laser light than to mention the bandwidth of wavelength. This property of laser light is known as 'monochromacity', as 'chromacity' refers to colour which is a characteristic of wavelength of light.

Working of Lasers—The Process

The processes involved in working of lasers are:

1. absorption,
2. spontaneous emission,
3. pumping and population inversion, and
4. stimulated emission of electromagnetic radiation.

Light is emitted from a source when electrons have a transition from higher energy level to a lower energy level. So, for a transition to take place, electrons are initially excited from the ground state to a higher state (energy level).

Absorption

Consider two energy levels E_1 and E_2. When a photon of energy hν (ν is the frequency of radiation) is incident on an atom, the electron absorbs this energy, and if this energy $h\nu = E_2 - E_1$, the electrons jumps from the ground state E_1 to the excited state E_2. In cases of gases or solid, a large number of atoms participate in the absorption of electromagnetic energy from an external source.

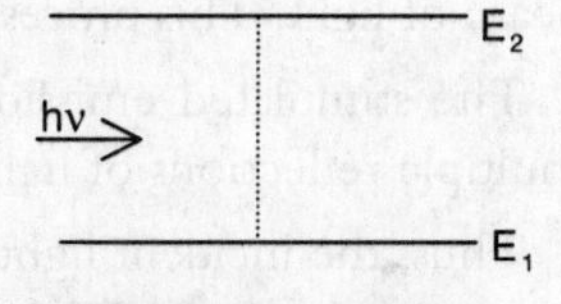

Figure 8.71 Absorption of energy by an atom

Spontaneous Emission

Electrons absorb energy from an external source like ordinary light. Once energy is absorbed from an external source, the electrons move from ground state to an excited state. But the electrons in the excited state cannot be maintained there for a long time and tend to come back to the ground state, on their own. Thus, electrons from excited state are transmitted to the ground state spontaneously and the resultant emission of light due to that spontaneous transition is known as spontaneous emission. But these spontaneous transitions of electrons take place at random, and hence, the light energy in spontaneous emission lacks coherence.

Population Inversion

To have a coherent radiation, a special system called 'active system' is introduced whose energy level lies between the ground state and the excited state of electrons and the electrons transited to this active level (active state) from excited state remain in the state for longer period than their stay in the excited state. The radiation which is emitted when electron transitions take place from excited state to the active state, is very less and is completely absorbed by the active medium as thermal energy. Hence, this radiation is 'invisible radiation'. The stability of the electrons in the active state is more and is called 'meta stable state'. As the transition of electrons from excited state to active state continues, a stage may be reached where the number of electrons in the active state may be more than that in the ground state. Thus, the number of electrons in the active medium in the meta stable state is more than that in the ground state and this stage of increasing electrons in the meta stable state (i.e., active medium) is called 'population inversion'.

This achievement of population inversion can be done by inducing radiation to the active state from an external source. The process of achieving population inversion by inducing radiation from an external source is called pumping.

Consider three states of energy level E_1, E_2 and E_3.

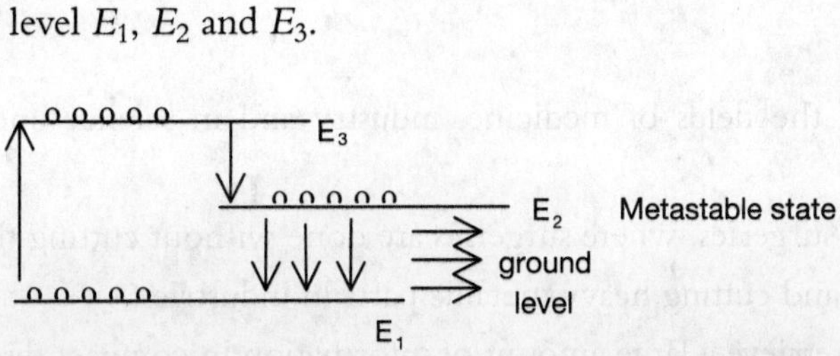

Figure 8.72 Active system for population inversion

When a photon of energy $h\nu = E_3 - E_1$ is incident, the electrons from the ground state are excited to energy level E_3. But the lifetime of the electrons in the excited state is very short (10^{-8} s). As a result, electrons return to the ground state by spontaneous emission but some electrons jump to energy level E_2 emitting a small amount of energy equal to $E_3 - E_2$. This energy is absorbed as thermal energy by the medium. This is known as non-radiative transition.

Electrons in the energy level E_2 have comparatively longer lifetime (milli seconds). This energy level is called meta stable state. At some instant the number of electrons in the meta stable state is greater than the number of electrons in the ground state. This is known as population inversion.

Stimulated or Induced Emission

The induced radiation (whose energy is equal to the energy difference of active and ground levels) stimulates the electrons in the active state, and so, is also called stimulated radiation. When a large number of electrons in the active state are stimulated, they are transited from the active state to the ground state simultaneously which gives rise to a temporal coherent beam of light. This process is called 'stimulated emission' which increases the intensity of light.

The stimulated emission can be made dominant by placing the active medium discussed above in a cavity so that multiple reflections of light take place before the beam comes out, thereby, amplifying the light energy.

Thus, the incident light is amplified by stimulated emission of radiation, and hence, LASER.

Actual Laser and Its Working

Actual laser consists of an active medium in a resonator, two mirrors, one perfectly reflecting and the other partially reflecting are fixed, one at each ends of the resonator. The mirrors are parallel to each other. Energy is supplied by a flash of light from an external source for optical pumping which results in population inversion.

During stimulated emission, light or photon travels to and fro (perpendicular to mirror surface) after being reflected by the mirrors. Intensity of light increases due to multiple reflection. This amplified light escapes through a partially reflecting mirror as a narrow beam of monochromatic light.

Types of Lasers

Different types of lasers that are available are, solid state lasers like ruby laser, liquid and dye lasers and gaseous lasers like helium neon (He-Ne) lasers.

In lasers, solid, liquid or gas is used. Thus, laser can be broadly classified as:

1. solid laser
2. liquid and dye laser
3. gaseous lasers

Ruby laser is a solid laser and the active system used is ruby (Al_2O_3, Cr^{3+}). Xenon discharge tube provides flash light required for optical pumping. Wavelength of ruby laser is 6943 A°. Helium – Neon laser is a gas laser. Neon acts as the active system. Radio frequency is used for optical pumping. Wavelength of He-Ne laser is 6328 A°.

Uses of Lasers

Lasers have many applications in the fields of medicine, industry and in science and technology. Some of them are mentioned below.

1. These are used in bloodless surgeries, where surgeries are done without cutting the body parts with knife.
2. Lasers are used for welding and cutting heavy metallic parts in industries.
3. They are used to store and retrieve a large amount of information in compact discs.
4. They are used to destroy inter continental ballistic missiles in air itself without the help of any other missile.
5. They are used in three dimensional photography called holography.

6. They are used in the field of communication through fibre optics.
7. Lasers are used to study Raman scattering to analyse the molecular structure of a material.
8. Lasers are used to separate isotopes.

Optical Instruments

Instruments like mirrors, lenses, etc., which deal with light are called optical instruments.

The human eye is a sense organ which causes the sensation of vision, and this helps us to 'see' the objects and also perceive their colours. But the human eye has certain limitations. Some of the limitations are listed below.

1. Defects of vision, like short sight, long sight, colour blindness, etc.
2. Range of visibility.
3. Inability to see very small objects like cells, etc.
4. Make visual recording for posterity.

To overcome these limitations, man has invented optical instruments like spectacles, microscopes, telescopes, etc. To record visual observations for further reference, photographic camera, video camera, etc., were invented.

There has been a continuous effort to make these instruments more sophisticated and effective with the advances made in science and technology.

The Human Eye

The eye is a spherical ball having a diameter of about 2.5 cm, with a slight bulge in the front portion. The posterior part of the eyeball is filled with a fluid called vitreous humour which helps in preventing the eyeball from collapsing. The exterior part of the eyeball is covered by a thick fibrous tissue called sclerotic which gives a definite shape to the eyeball and protects the interior parts.

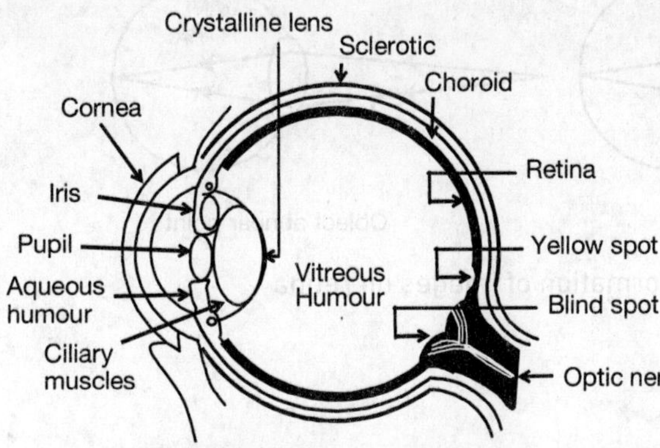

Figure 8.73 The human eye

A crystalline lens is located in the front part of the eye. The focal length of the lens is varied with the help of ciliary muscles along the periphery such that the image of the object viewed falls on the retina, which forms the screen. This process of altering the focal length of the lens is known as accommodation of the eye. Several thousand nerves coming from the brain enter the eye from the rear and terminate along the retina in the form of light sensitive cells. These cells are of two types—rods and cones, and they help us to perceive the brightness and colour of the objects viewed.

The choroid between the sclerotic and the retina is a dull grey membrane preventing internal reflections, and thus, keeping the interior of the eyeball dark.

The slight bulge in the front is due to the presence of a fluid called aqueous humour in front of the crystalline lens. This fluid forms a primary lens of almost a fixed focal length. It prevents collapsing of eye due to changes in atmospheric pressure.

Light enters the aqueous humour through the cornea which is a thin membrane holding the aqueous humour in place.

Behind the cornea is the iris which is an opaque muscular diaphragm having a small aperture or an adjustable opening called pupil. This controls the light entering the retina. When the muscles contract, the size of the pupil increases allowing more light to enter and vice versa.

The light passing through the pupil falls on the eye lens which is held in position by ciliary muscles. These rays after passing through the eye lens are focused on retina. Real and inverted image is informed on the retina. Any image formed on the retina is converted into optical impulses which are sent to the brain through the optic nerve.

Yellow spot is situated at the centre of the retina and is the most sensitive part of the retina that helps us to view objects closely. The blind spot refers to the portion of the retina where there are no light sensitive cells.

Two eye-balls are present in the front part of the head to estimate the distances of objects and their relative visual depth. The human brain cannot perceive more than two images formed on the retina within an interval of 1/16th second. This is called persistence of vision.

Formation of Images on Retina

The images formed on the retina are always real, inverted and highly diminished. While viewing distant objects (at infinity), the ciliary muscles relax and this leads to an increase in the focal length of the lens. In this case, the image is focused on the retina. While viewing nearer objects, the ciliary muscles contract. This leads to a decrease in the focal length of the lens and the focus is formed in front of the retina such that the image would form on the retina, i.e., between f and $2f$.

Least distance of distinct vision: It is the minimum distance at which objects can be seen more distinctly without strain. It is also called near point of the eye. It is denoted by D. For a normal person least distance of distinct vision is 25 cm. Infinity is referred to as far point.

Info Bytes!

- The human eye can distinguish approximately 10 million different colors.
- The images formed on your retina are actually upside down; your brain flips them right side up.

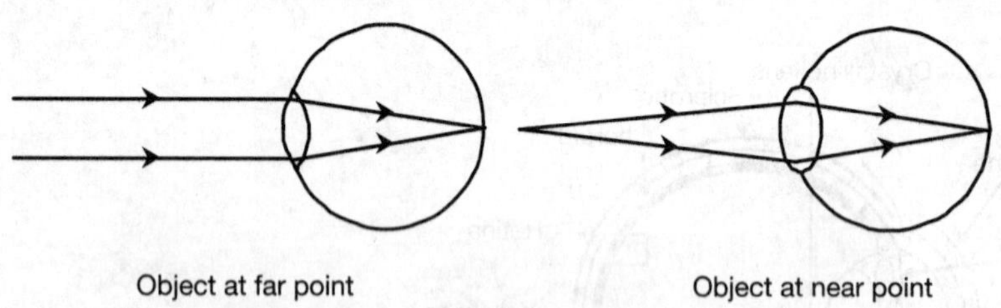

Figure 8.74 Formation of images on retina

Perception of Colours

The rod shaped cells on the retina respond only to the intensity of the incident light, but cannot perceive colours. The cone shaped cells are sensitive to colours. There are three types of cones responding to each of the three primary colours—red, green and blue, helping us perceiving and distinguishing between different colours. Absence of certain cone cells sensitive to specific colours would lead to a defect known as colour blindness in some people.

Defects of Vision and Rectification

1. **Myopia or Short Sightedness:** It is the ability to see near objects and inability to see distant objects. This defect occurs due to slight elongation of the eyeball. As a result, the distance between eye lens and retina is greater and the image is formed in front of the retina and not on the retina.

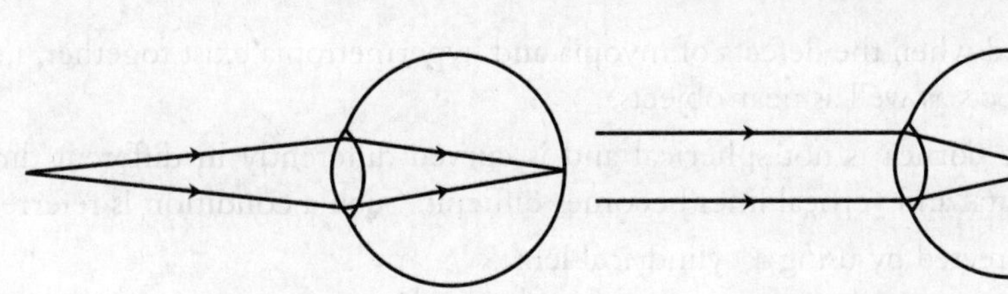

Figure 8.75 Myopic eye

Correction

Myopia can be corrected by using a concave lens of suitable focal length to have the apparent position of the far point at near point.

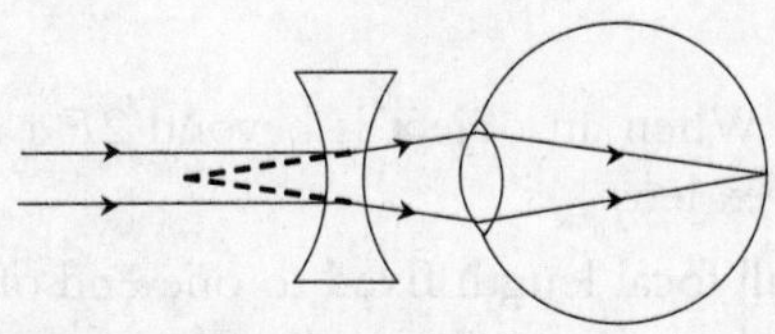

Figure 8.76 Use of concave lens for myopic eye

2. **Hypermetropia or Long-sightedness**: Ability to clearly and comfortably see objects at a distance and inability to see clearly objects that are nearby is referred to as hypermetropia, more commonly known as long-sightedness.

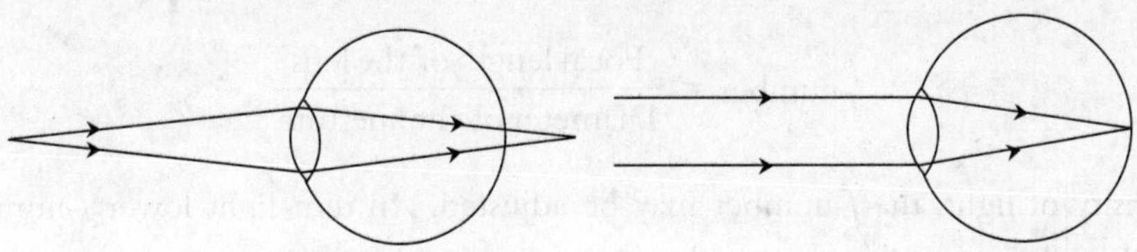

Figure 8.77 Hypermetropic eye

This defect is caused by slight flattering of the eyeball. The distance between the eye lens and the retina is less than in case of a normal eye. As a result, the image formed by nearby objects is behind the retina.

Correction

Hypermetropia can be corrected by using a convex lens of suitable focal length to make the image form on the retina, i.e., by decreasing the combined focal length or by increasing the power of the combination.

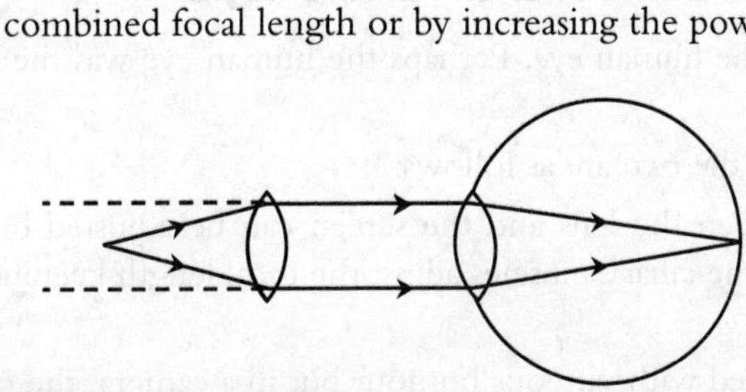

Figure 8.78 Use of convex lens for hypermetropic eye

3. **Presbyopia:** Inability to see clearly objects that are near due to the ageing of the ciliary muscles is referred to as presbyopia. Thus, presbyopia is the condition of hypermetropia due to ageing.

   Presbyopia can be corrected by using a 'reading glass', i.e., a suitable convex lens—a magnifying glass.

A bi-focal lens is often used when the defects of myopia and hypermetropia exist together, i.e., the person is unable to see both far distant objects as well as near objects.

4. **Astigmatism:** When the cornea is not spherical and is curved differently in different directions, then focusing simultaneously on horizontal and vertical lines becomes difficult. Such a condition is referred to as astigmatism.

   Astigmatism can be corrected by using a cylindrical lens.

5. **Cataract:** Due to ageing, a thin membrane forms over the crystalline lens making it hazy. This leads to decrease in the brightness of objects and may also lead to blindness. This condition is called cataract and can be corrected by suitable surgery.

   Bees have some retinal cones which are sensitive to ultraviolet light. Humans retina are not sensitive to ultraviolet light, and hence, we cannot see objects in the ultraviolet light. Cones of chicks are sensitive to bright light only, and hence, chicks wake up with sunrise and sleep in the dusk.

Camera

Camera is used to record image on a film. When an object is beyond $2F$ a real, diminished, inverted image is formed between F and $2F$ on the other side of convex lens.

A camera consists of a convex lens of small focal length fixed to one end of a box. To the other end is a light sensitive film. The inner sides of the box are blackened to prevent internal reflection. Distance between the screen and the lens can be adjusted by the knob. A circular plate having an aperture in it is placed behind the lens and it is called diaphragm. The diameter of the aperture can be varied and the aperture controls the amount of light falling on the film. The size of the aperture is expressed as *f*-numbers.

f-number is defined as the ratio of the focal length of the lens to the diameter of the aperture.

$$\therefore f\text{-number} = \frac{\text{Focal length of the lens}}{\text{Diameter of the aperture}}$$

According to the intensity of light, the *f*-number may be adjusted. In dim-light lower *f*-number is used and higher *f*-number is used in bright light.

To control the exposure time of the film, a shutter is provided, whose speed can be controlled.

To take a photograph of an object the distance between the lens and the film is adjusted, so as to get a clear image in the view finder. Then *f*-number and shutter speed are adjusted depending upon the intensity of light. When the button is pressed, the film gets exposed to the light entering through the lens. The film is then treated chemically, a process known as 'development' and then prints of the film are taken on a photographic paper.

Comparison between a Camera and the Eye

A camera in many ways is similar to the human eye. Perhaps the human eye was the source of inspiration for the design of a camera.

The important differences between the two are as follows:

1. In a camera, the distance between the lens and the screen can be adjusted but not the focal length of the lens, whereas, in the case of the eye, the ciliary muscles adjust the focal length keeping the distance between the lens and the retina constant.
2. The interior of the eyeball is filled with vitreous humour but in a camera, the chamber is hollow and empty.
3. The image formed on the retina is temporary and its impression is recorded in the brain as memory. The image formed on the film is a permanent record.
4. Distance between crystalline lens and retina remains the same but in camera distance between the lens and the film can be changed.

5. Retina converts light signals to electrical impulses which are transmitted to brain whereas in camera film gets exposed when light is incident on it, due to chemical reactions.
6. Eye is subjected to a number of defects whereas in camera there are no such defects.

Simple Microscope

A convex lens of short focal length which is used to observe small objects clearly is known as a simple microscope. It is also called magnifying glass. To construct a simple microscope, a convex lens of short focal length is fixed in a circular metallic frame provided with a handle to hold.

Working

The size of the image of an object formed on our retina increases if the distance of the object from our eyes decreases. This happens due to the fact that as the object comes closer to our eyes, the angle subtended by the object at our eyes increases, and so, the size of the image of the object on the retina also increases. This is known as 'angular magnification'.

If an object of size '*h*' is placed at the least distance of distinct vision (D) from the eye, the angle which it subtends at the eye can be given by, $\alpha_0 = \frac{h}{D}$.

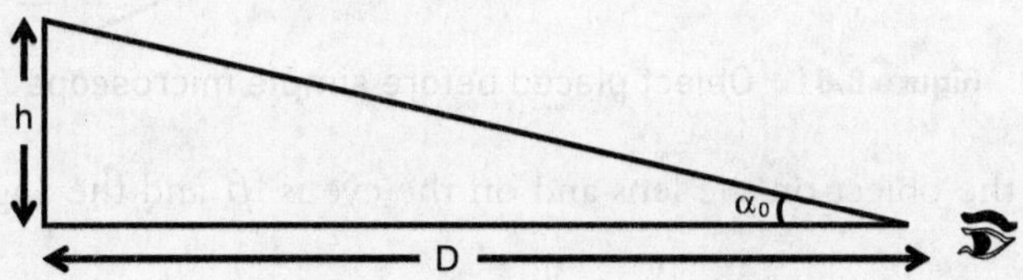

Figure 8.79 An object placed at the least distance of vision from eye

If this angle is increased, the size of the image of the object increases and this can be done by placing a convex lens of short focal length between the eye and the object such that the distance between the lens and the object is equal to the focal length of the convex lens. Then the image of the object is formed at an infinite distance. In this situation, the image can be observed with the least strain to eye. This adjustment is called normal adjustment.

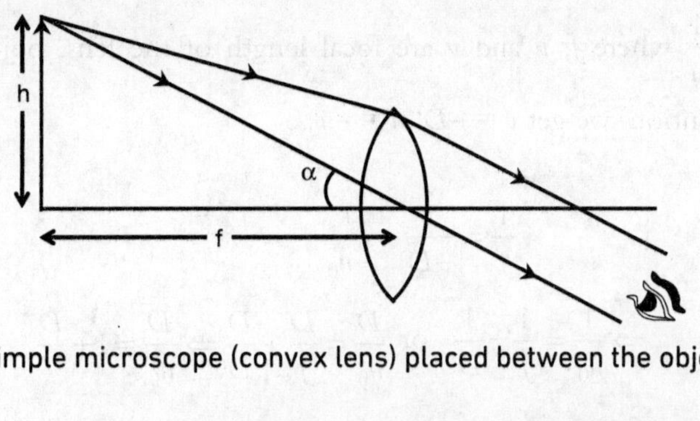

Figure 8.80 Simple microscope (convex lens) placed between the object and the eye

Here, the angle subtended by the object at the eye is equal to the angle subtended by the object at the optic centre of the lens (α) and it is greater than the angle subtended by the object, when it is placed at '*D*' from the eye. So, the image of the object is magnified.

Here, $$\alpha = \frac{h}{f}$$

Magnification in Normal Adjustment

Magnifying power of the image of the object is the ratio of the angle subtended by the object at the eye in the normal adjustment situation to the angle subtended by it at the eye when it was at the least distance of distinct vision (*D*).

$$\therefore \text{ Magnification, } M = \frac{\alpha}{\alpha_0} = \frac{h/f}{h/D} = \frac{D}{f}$$

Magnification When The Object is Placed between the Focus and Optical Centre of the Lens

If the object is placed before the lens at a distance less than its focal length, a virtual, erect and a magnified image is formed on the same side of the lens to which the object is placed. The distance of the object from the lens can be adjusted so that the image is formed at a distance from the lens which is equal to '*D*' from the lens.

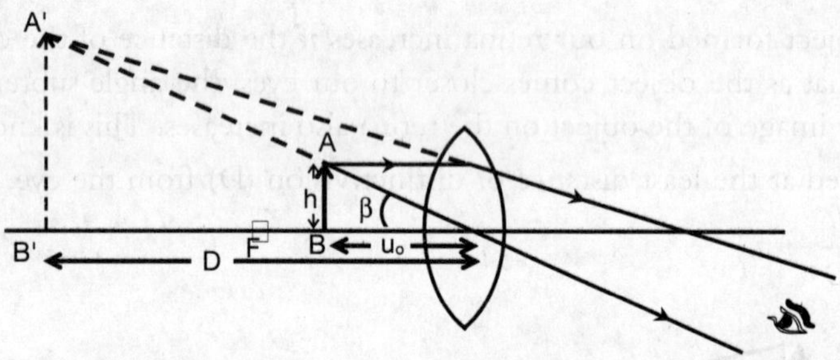

Figure 8.81 Object placed before simple microscope

Now, the angle subtended by the object on the lens and on the eye is 'β' and the angular magnification now is given by $m, = \dfrac{\beta}{\alpha_0}$.

But $$\beta = \frac{h}{u_0} \text{ and } \alpha_0 = \frac{h}{D}.$$

$$\therefore m = \frac{h/u_0}{h/D} = \frac{D}{u_0}$$

The lens formula is $\dfrac{1}{f} = \dfrac{1}{v} - \dfrac{1}{u}$ where *f*, *u* and *v* are focal length of the lens, object distance and image distance, respectively. Using the sign convention, we get $v = -D$, $u = -u_0$.

So, $$\frac{1}{f} = \frac{1}{-D} - \frac{1}{-u_0}$$

$$\Rightarrow \frac{1}{u_0} = \frac{1}{f} + \frac{1}{D} \text{ or } \frac{D}{u_0} = \frac{D}{f} + \frac{D}{D} \Rightarrow \frac{D}{u_0} = 1 + \frac{D}{f}$$

As $\dfrac{D}{u_0} = m$, the magnification $m = 1 + \dfrac{D}{f}$.

Uses

1. Used as reading glass.
2. To observe weaving patterns and to read vernier scale.

Compound Microscope

A simple microscope can produce images having magnification up to a certain limit. It is not possible for a simple microscope to produce images of greater magnification. When images of greater magnification are required, we use another convex lens in combination with the one used in a simple microscope. The combination of these two lenses which is used to obtain images of greater magnification is called 'compound microscope'.

Construction and Working

The two lenses that are used in a compound microscope are each fixed to the outer ends of two hollow tubes one tube can slide one over the other such that their principal axes of two lenses coincide. The lens that faces the object is called an 'objective' and is of smaller focal length when compared to the focal length of the other lens which faces the eye and is called 'eye piece'.

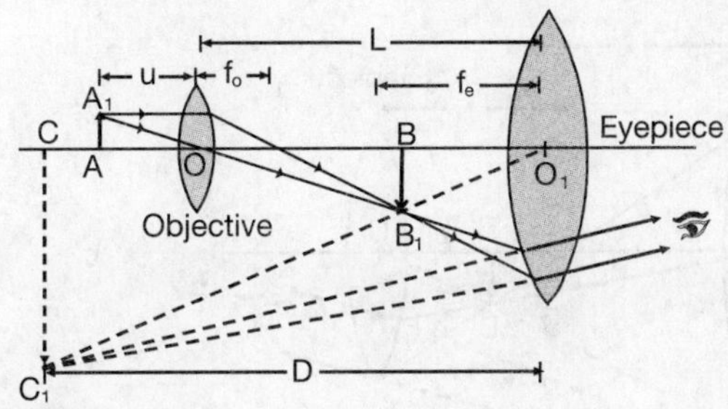

Figure 8.82 Formation of image by a compound microscope

A screw is provided so that on rotating, the distance between the objective and the eye piece can be adjusted.

An object AA_1 is placed beyond the principal focus of the objective and its image BB_1 is formed between the objective and the eye-piece. This image (BB_1) is inverted, real and magnified with respect to the object. This first image acts as an object to the second convex lens, i.e., eye piece. The distance of the first image 'BB_1' from the eye piece is less than the focal length of the eye piece. So, it is further magnified and a second and final image 'CC_1' is formed beyond 'BB_1'. The final image is inverted with respect to the object but virtual with respect to the first image. It is highly magnified when compared to the first image.

Magnification

The magnification of the compound microscope is the ratio of the size of the final image to the size of the object.

$$m = \frac{CC_1}{AA} = \frac{CC_1}{BB_1} \times \frac{BB_1}{AA_1} = m_e \times m_o$$

Where, m_o = magnification produced by the objective.

m_e = magnification produced by the eye piece.

When the final image is formed at infinity

$\therefore m = m_o \times m_e = L/f_o \times D/f_e$

Where, L = length of the tube = distance between the lenses

D = least distance of distinct vision

f_o = focal length of the objective

f_e = focal length of the eye piece

Telescopes

When an object is very far from the eye, the angle it subtends at the eye is very small, and so, it appears to be small. To make the object appear nearer to the eye, the angle it subtends at the eye should be increased. To make the distant objects appear nearer, the optical instrument used is called telescope.

There are two types of telescopes, viz., the astronomical telescopes and the terrestrial telescopes. The astronomical telescopes are used to observe the celestial bodies and the terrestrial telescopes are used to observe distant objects on the Earth's surface.

Astronomical Telescope

An astronomical telescope has the same construction as that of a compound microscope, but the focal length of the objective is larger when compared to the focal length of the eye piece.

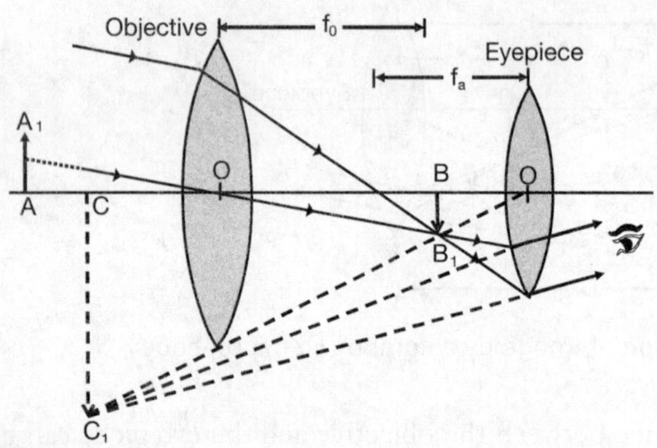

Figure 8.83 Formation of image by astronomical telescope

Info Bytes!

The Hubble Space Telescope can look back in time over 13 billion years, almost to the birth of the Universe.

Working

A parallel beam of light rays from a distant object (AA_1) almost parallel to the principal axis of the objective are incident on the objective and an image (BB_1) of the object is formed between the objective and the eye piece. This first image which is diminished, inverted and real acts as an object for the eye piece. The distance between the first image and the eye-piece is less than the focal length of the eye piece. So, a magnified and a virtual image (CC_1) is formed on the same side of the eye piece to which the first image lies. The final image is erect with respect to the first image but is inverted with respect to the object. The angle subtended by the final image at the eye piece, and so, at the eye is larger than that of the angle subtended by the object at the eye. So, the final image is magnified and appears to be having larger size than that of the object.

If the first image formed by the objective (i.e., BB_1) is formed at the principal focus of the eye piece, the final image is formed at infinity. This situation is called 'normal adjustment'. In the normal adjustment position, the length of the telescope (L) (which is the distance between objective and eye piece) is equal to the sum of the focal lengths of the objective and the eye piece ($L = f_o + f_e$). In the normal adjustment position, the magnification obtained by the telescope is given by $m = \dfrac{f_o}{f_e}$

Terrestrial Telescope

In an astronomical telescope, the final image obtained or formed is inverted with respect to the object. Due to this reason, it cannot be used to view distant objects on the Earth's surface. Thus, the astronomical telescope is modified by adding one more lens between the objective and the eye piece. The purpose of this lens is to make the image erect with respect to the object, and so, it is called image erecting lens (EL) or simply erecting lens.

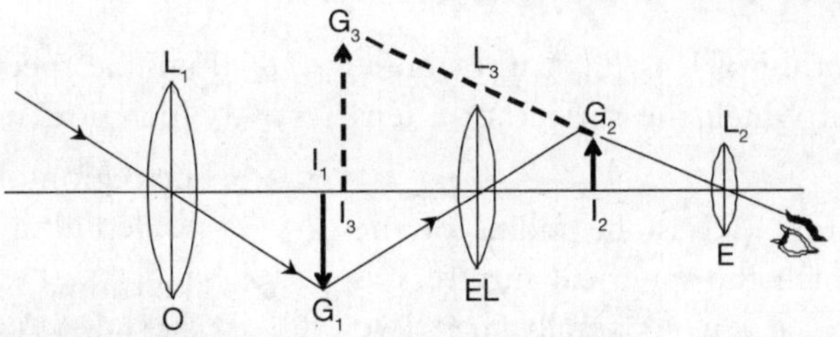

Figure 8.84 Formation of image by a terrestrial telescope

The first image (I_1G_1) formed by the objective is real, inverted and diminished and is formed at the centre of curvature of the erecting lens. This image (I_1G_1) acts as an object for the erecting lens and a second image (I_2G_2) is formed at the centre of curvature of the erecting lens between the erecting lens and the eye piece. The size of the second image (I_2G_2) is equal to that of I_1G_1. It is erect with respect to the original object and inverted with respect to I_1G_1. I_2G_2 acts as an object for the eye piece. The distance between I_2G_2 and eye piece is less than the focal length of the eye piece, and so, a third and final image I_3G_3 is formed. This image is erect with respect to I_2G_2. So, the final image is erect with respect to the object.

POINTS TO REMEMBER

- ✔ When light is incident on a surface, separating two media, a part of the light is bounced back to the first medium. This is known as reflection.
- ✔ Linear magnification is the ratio of image height to the object height.
- ✔ When light passes from one medium to another medium, there is a change in the path of light in the second medium. This is known as refraction.
- ✔ Refractive index of a medium is the ratio of velocity of light in air or vacuum to its velocity in a given medium. This is known as the absolute refractive index.
- ✔ The medium of lower refractive index is called rarer medium.
- ✔ The medium of higher refractive index is called denser medium.
- ✔ If a ray of light travels from medium 1 to medium 2 along a certain path, it retraces the path when it travels from medium 2 to medium 1. Thus, the path of light is reversible. This property is called principle of reversibility of path.
- ✔ Lateral displacement is the perpendicular distance between the emergent ray and the incident ray produced.
- ✔ The angle of incidence in the denser medium at which angle of refraction is 90° is called critical angle.
- ✔ When angle of incidence in the denser medium is greater than the critical angle, the light reflected back into same medium. This phenomenon is called total internal reflection.
- ✔ Appearance of water without its actually presence is called mirage.
- ✔ Total reflecting prisms are right angled isosceles prisms. They are based on the principle of total internal reflection.
- ✔ Optical fibres are devices used to transmit light in any desired path. It works on the principle of total internal reflection.
- ✔ Prism is a transparent medium. It is bounded by two triangular surfaces and three rectangular surfaces.
- ✔ A lens is a transparent material which is bounded by two spherical surfaces or one spherical surface and one plane surface.

- ✔ Centre of curvature of lens (C) is the centre of the sphere of which the surface of a lens form S a part.
- ✔ Radii of curvature (R) is the radius of the sphere from which the spherical surface was obtained. Since a lens generally has two curved surfaces, it has two radii of curvature.
- ✔ Principal axisis a straight line joining the centre of curvatures of the two spherical surfaces of the lens.
- ✔ Linear Magnification is the ratio of size of the image to the size of the object. Magnification is denoted by 'm'.
- ✔ Power of the lens is defined as reciprocal of focal length in meter and is denoted by P.
- ✔ Pure spectrum is the spectrum in which the constituent colours occupy their respective position (VIBGYOR) and are distinct.
- ✔ Impure spectrum in which the bands of colours overlap. There are no well defined boundaries between the bands of colours.
- ✔ Refrangibilty is the ability of light to get refracted when passing from one medium to another.
- ✔ Red, blue and green are called primary colours as they are monochromatic. Other colours are obtained by mixing primary colours in proper proportions.
- ✔ A pair of colours, in which one is a primary colour and the other is a secondary colour, which on mixing in proper proportion gives white light.
- ✔ Spectroscope is an instrument used to obtain pure spectrum.
- ✔ When white light is passed through gases or vapour at a low temperature, some of the wavelengths are absorbed. Then spectrum formed is known as absorption spectrum.
- ✔ Radiations, IR, visible, UV, radio waves, X-rays, gamma rays and micro waves constitute electromagnetic spectrum.
- ✔ The wavelength of visible light ranges from 400 nm to 750 nm (4000 A° to 7500 A°).
- ✔ Invisible spectrum is the region of spectrum which does not strike the retina.
- ✔ The region of spectrum beyond violet region is called ultraviolet spectrum.
- ✔ The minimum frequency required for the incident light to eject electrons from the metal surface is known as threshold frequency.
- ✔ If a crest or trough of one wave combines with the crest or the trough of another wave respectively at a given point, the net displacement at the point is maximum and it is called 'constructive superposition'.
- ✔ During the superposition of waves, if the waves produced from two sources have the same frequency and amplitude and travel in the same direction, the superposition of such waves produce well defined constructive and destructive superposition in space and this phenomenon is called 'Interference'.
- ✔ Amplification is the process of increasing the energy and that is done in the light by stimulated emission of radiation, and so, it is called laser.
- ✔ Instruments like mirrors, lenses, etc., which deal with light are called optical instruments.
- ✔ The images formed on the retina are always real, inverted and highly diminished.
- ✔ Myopia or Short Sightedness: It is the ability to see near objects and inability to see distant objects. This defect occurs due to slight elongation of the eyeball.
- ✔ Hypermetropia or Long-sightedness: Ability to clearly and comfortably see objects at a distance and inability to see clearly objects that are nearby is referred to as hypermetropia, more commonly known as long-sightedness.
- ✔ A convex lens of short focal length which is used to observe small objects clearly is known as a simple microscope. It is also called magnifying glass.
- ✔ The magnification of the compound microscope is the ratio of the size of the final image to the size of the object.
- ✔ To make the distant objects appear nearer, the optical instrument used is called telescope.

PRACTICE QUESTIONS CLASSROOM WING

Very Short Answer Type Questions

1. What does a combination of a convex lens of power +2 D and a concave lens of power −1 D behave as?
2. What does a combination of a convex lens of power +3 D and a concave lens of power −2 D behaves as?
3. What is luminous flux?
4. What is magnification?
5. What is spontaneous emission?
6. What is the condition required for constructive interference to take place?
7. Which spherical mirror is used as rear view mirror?
8. Which type of lens is used to correct hypermetropia?
9. What is the principle of superposition?
10. What is refraction?
11. What is presbyopia?
12. Why do different electromagnetic radiation have different properties?
13. When is the angle of incidence greater than the angle of refraction?
14. What is meant by refrangibility?
15. Define refractive index.
16. Define candela.
17. How does lateral displacement vary with wavelength?
18. What is coherent scattering?
19. What are the factors on which angle of deviation depends?
20. What are composite colours?

Short Answer Type Questions

21. A light ray is incident on a surface with a glancing angle of reflection of 30°. Find the angle of deviation.
22. Derive the expression for the magnification of an astronomical telescope in normal adjustment.
23. What is the frequency that corresponds to a light ray of wavelength 450 nm, when travelling through a glass of refractive index 3/2?
24. State the condition for total internal reflection.
25. An object is placed in front of a plane mirror. Determine the shift in position of the image if the object and the mirror are moved 5 cm each towards each other.
26. What is photoelectric effect?
27. What is astigmatism? Explain how it can be corrected.
28. What are total reflecting prisms?
29. A tree of height 10 m is viewed by a diver under water at a certain distance from the surface. Determine the apparent height $\left[\mu_w = \frac{4}{3}\right]$ of the tree.
30. What are the postulates of Newton's corpuscular theory?
31. What are infrared rays? Name the source of IR rays and write their uses.
32. What is a refracting periscope?
33. Explain the construction of wavefronts using Huygen's principle.
34. A person is unable to view the objects placed beyond 3 m. What is the power (in D) of the lens required to correct the defect?
35. What are optical fibres?

Essay Answer Type Questions

36. An object is placed in front of a concave and convex mirror as shown below. Determine the value of 'x' if the virtual images are formed on the same plane.

The focal length of the concave and convex mirrors are 40 cm and 6.5 cm, respectively.

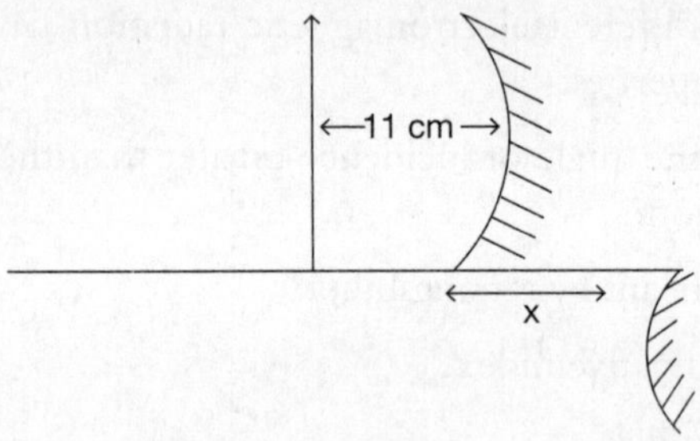

37. Explain the construction and working of a compound microscope with a ray diagram. Derive the expression for magnification when image is formed at infinity.

38. State the new cartesian sign convention used in reflection by spherical mirrors

39. The critical angle of a medium A with respect to medium B is 60°. Determine the velocity of light in B if the velocity of light in A is 2×10^8 m s^{-1}.

40. The refractive index of glass is $\sqrt{3}$. Determine the angle of minimum deviation of an equilateral prism made of the glass.

PRACTICE QUESTIONS COMPETITION WING

Level 1: Apply Your Concepts

Direction for questions from 1 to 17:
Fill in the blanks.

1. ______ lens produces real image.
2. A green-coloured dress appears ______ when viewed in red light.
3. The power of an eye lens used by a person is +2D. The person suffering from ______ defect.
4. When an ink spot which is at the bottom of a glass $\left(\mu = \frac{3}{2}\right)$ slab of thickness 9 cm is viewed from top, the image of the ink spot appears to be raised by ______ cm.
5. ______ mirror does not form a real image?
6. A blue-coloured object appears blue when viewed in some light. Then it is __________ light.
7. The power of a lens used by a person is –0.5 D. The person suffering from __________ defect.
8. For an object placed at a certain distance in front of a convex mirror the magnification is 0.8. If the focal length of the convex mirror is 40 cm, then the distance of the object from the mirror is ______ cm.
9. The angle of incidence of a ray of light passing through the centre of curvature of a concave mirror is ______.
10. Both particle and wave nature are attributed to light according to ______ theory and ______theory, respectively.
11. A yellow coloured dress would appear to be ________ when viewed through a green filter.
12. Due to ________ of laser, large energy can be concentrated into an extremely small bandwidth.
13. The combination of a convex lens of power + 2 D and a concave lens of power –2 D, acts as a ________
14. The minimum length of a plane mirror required to view the full image of a person 6 feet tall is ______.
15. A bird is flying 12 m above the surface of a pond. The apparent position of the bird as viewed by a fish 1m below the surface is ________. $\left({}_a\mu_w = \frac{4}{3}\right)$
16. An object is placed on the principal axis of a concave mirror at a distance of 60 cm. If the focal length of the concave mirror is 40 cm, then the magnification obtained is equal to ________.
17. The power of a biconcave lens having focal length 25 cm is ______.

Direction for questions from 18 to 24:
State whether the following statements are true or false.

18. Interference takes place whenever two or more wave motions combine in space.
19. In the minimum deviation position of a prism, the refracted ray is always parallel to its base.
20. A person suffering from myopia cannot see distant objects clearly.
21. The focal length of a given lens depends on the surrounding medium.
22. Prismatic periscopes use the principle of total internal reflection.
23. A dentist uses a convex mirror to view the inner parts of a patient's mouth.
24. The solar spectrum in general is an absorption spectrum.
25. Match the statements of Column A with those of Column B.

Column A	Column B
A. Real image	a. Convex mirror
B. Diminished virtual image	b. Plane mirror
C. Virtual image with magnification one	c. Concave mirror
	d. Concave lens
	e. Convex lens

Direction for questions 26 to 69:
For each of the questions, four choices have been provided. Select the correct alternative.

26. When a light ray is passed through a prism, three different colours are seen on the screen as shown below. If the λ_1, λ_2 and λ_3 are their wavelengths, μ_1, μ_2 and μ_3 are their refractive indices, arrange the following steps to compare the wave lengths and refractive indices of these colours.

(A) Use the fact-more the angle of deviation, more is the refractive index.

(B) Compare the angle of deviation.

(C) Use the relation between refractive index and velocity of light.

(D) Compare the wavelength of light and velocity.

(E) Use the relation, $V = n\lambda$

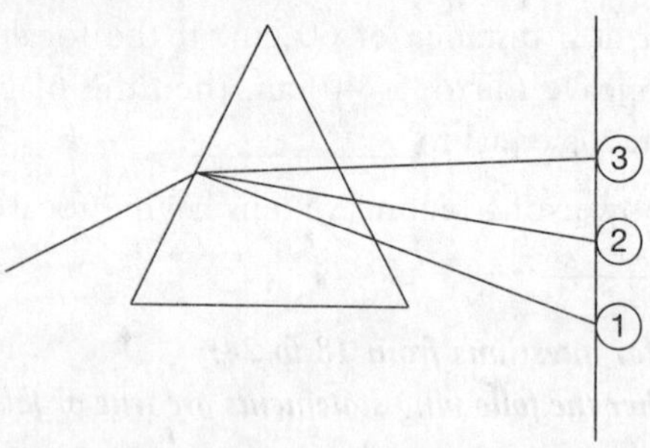

(a) A C B D E (b) E D B A C

(c) B A C E D (d) B A D C E

27. Raman effect is an example of ______.

(a) coherent scattering of light.

(b) incoherent scattering of light

(c) coherent interference of light

(d) incoherent interference of light

28. The optical phenomenon which Newton's theory of light failed to explain is ______.

(a) interference

(b) polarization

(c) diffraction

(d) All the above three

29. An observer moves towards a stationary plane mirror at a speed of 4 m s^{-1}. The speed of image with respect to mirror is ______.

(a) 4 m s^{-1} towards the mirror

(b) 8 m s^{-1} towards the mirror

(c) 4 m s^{-1} away from the mirror

(d) 8 m s^{-1} away from the mirror

30. The process in which the electrons in the excited atoms are released on their own from their higher energy state to the ground state is called ______.

(a) forced emission

(b) population inversion

(c) spontaneous emission

(d) None of these

31. The refractive index of diamond is 2.4. If the velocity of light in air or vacuum is 3×10^8 m s^{-1}, then the velocity of light in diamond is ______ $\times 10^8$ m s^{-1}.

(a) 1.25 (b) 12.5

(c) 0.8 (d) 125

32. A convex mirror is used

(a) by a dentist.

(b) for shaving.

(c) as a rear view mirror in vehicles.

(d) as a light reflector for obtaining a parallel beam of light.

33. When an equilateral glass prism is in minimum deviation position

(A) the refracted ray is parallel to the base of the prism.

(B) the angle of incidence is equal to the angle of emergence.

(a) Only A is true.

(b) Only B is true.

(c) Both A and B are true.

(d) Both A and B are false.

34. The colour of a green leaf, when white light passing through a yellow filter is incident on it, is ______.

(a) black (b) yellow

(c) red (d) green

35. Spectrometer is used to measure ______.

(a) angle of prism

(b) refractive index of material of a prism

(c) the dispersion

(d) All the above

36. The expression for the magnification of a spherical mirror in terms of focal length (f) and the distance of the object from mirror (u) is

(a) $\frac{-f}{u-f}$ (b) $\frac{f}{u+f}$

(c) $\frac{-f}{u+f}$ (d) $\frac{f}{u-f}$

37. According to Newton, different colours of light are due to the difference in ______ of the corpuscles.

(a) mass (b) nature

(c) shape (d) size

38. If the speed of light in medium – 1 and medium – 2 are 2.5×10^8 m s^{-1} and 2×10^8 m s^{-1}, respectively, then the refractive index of medium – 1 with respect to medium – 2 is ________.

(a) $\frac{3}{2.5}$ (b) $\frac{2}{2.5}$

(c) $\frac{2.5}{3}$ (d) $\frac{2.5}{2}$

39. A coin is placed at the bottom of a swimming pool. To obtain a vertical shift of 20 cm of the image of the coin, the required height of the water column is ______ $\left(\mu_{water} = \frac{4}{3}\right)$.

(a) 20 cm (b) 2 m

(c) 80 m (d) 80 cm

40. The apparent vertical shift of the image of a coin placed at the bottom of a water tank having constant depth of water is proportional to ________.

(a) μ (b) $\frac{1}{\mu}$

(c) $\mu - 1$ (d) $\mu + 1$

41. The final image formed by the refracting periscope is ________ and ________ than the reflecting periscope.

(a) bright (b) sharp

(c) dimmer (d) Both (a) and (b)

42. Light is made to travel from medium 1 to medium 3 through medium 2 as shown in figure. If μ_1 , μ_2 and μ_3 a are the refractive indices of first, second and third media and $i_2 > i_1$, then

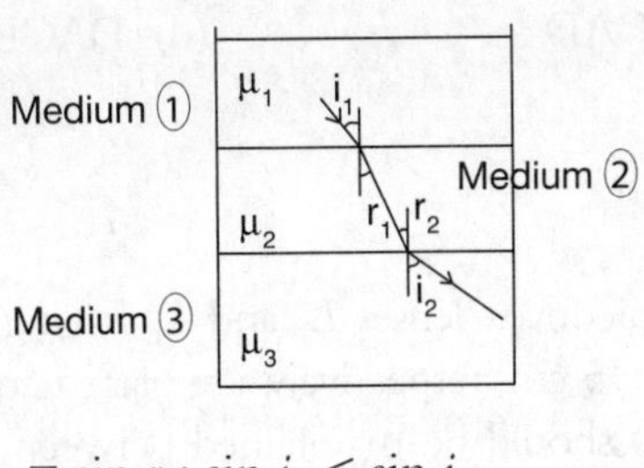

(a) $\sin r_1 = \sin r_2$; $\sin i_1 < \sin i_2$.

(b) ${}^1\mu_2 > {}^2\mu_1$; ${}^2\mu_3 < {}^3\mu_2$

(c) ${}^1\mu_3 < {}^3\mu_1$

(d) All the above.

43. What are the factors that determine the angle of deviation in a prism?

(a) Angle of incidence (b) Wavelength

(c) Angle of the prism (d) All the above

44. Astigmatism can be rectified by a suitable .... lens.

(a) concave (b) convex

(c) cylindrical (d) None of the above

45. Human eye has maximum luminous efficiency to .... light.

(a) yellow (b) red

(c) violet (d) green

46. Arrange the proper sequence of the steps to determine the refractive index of a prism by using angle of minimum deviation method.

(A) Fix a white sheet of paper on a drawing board.

(B) Draw the outer line of the prism by placing its triangular cross-section (*ABC*) on the paper,

(C) Draw a line which makes a certain angle with the normal. This is the incident ray.

(D) Mark a point on one of the sides and draw a normal at that point.

(E) Fix two pins *P* and *Q* on this line.

(F) Place the prism inside its outer line and observe the pins *P* and *Q* from the other side of the prism.

(G) Fix two more pins *R* and *S* on the other sides such that the images of the pins P and Q, *R* and *S* are in a straight line.

(H) Join the points *R* and *S* and the line segments *PQ* and *RS*.

(I) Remove the pins and the prism from the paper.

(J) Draw a normal *XY* where the line segment *RS* meets the side *BC*.

(K) Draw a graph by taking the angle of incidence and angle of deviation along the *X* and *Y* axes, respectively.

(L) Extend line segments *PQ* and *RS* and determine the angle between them. This is known as the angle of deviation.

(M) Determine refractive index as μ

$$= \frac{\sin\left(\frac{A+D_m}{2}\right)}{\sin\left(\frac{A}{2}\right)}$$

(N) Repeat the experiment for different angles of incidence and in each case, determine the angle of deviation.

(O) Determine angle (*A*) between the refracting surfaces of the prism (*P*). Determine the minimum value of angle of deviation (D_m).

(a) ABCEDFGIHJKLMONP

(b) ABDCEFGHIJLKONPM
(c) BACDEJKHIJMLNOP
(d) ABDCEFGLHKMIPOJ

47. Find out the correct option from the following.
(A) The magnification is positive for all virtual images and is negative for all real images.
(B) The magnification of concave lens and convex mirror is always positive where as the magnification of convex lens and concave mirror can be positive or negative depending on the position of the object before the lens.
(a) Only *A* is true.
(b) Only *B* is true.
(c) Both *A* and *B* are true.
(d) Both *A* and *B* are false.

48. Find the incorrect statements related to the rainbow.
(a) The rainbow is formed in the same direction to the position of the Sun.
(b) When the light rays undergo dispersion and total internal reflection, the water droplets present in the atmosphere forms rainbow.
(c) A rainbow is formed in the shape of circle.
(d) When light rays undergo one internal reflection and two refractions produce primary rainbow whereas two internal reflections and two refractions produces secondary rainbow.

49. Choose the incorrect option from the following options:
(a) When a monochromatic light is passed through organic liquid like benzene, toluene, etc., it results in the formation of the scattered light. Which consists of wavelengths of frequencies higher and lower that of incident monochromatic light also that of the incident light.
(b) Incident scattering is a type of scattering in which the scattered light consists of frequencies other than those of the incident light.
(c) The intensity of the scattered light in a medium is inversely proportional to the fourth power of the wavelength.
(d) Rayleigh scattering is called incoherent scattering and Raman scattering is coherent scattering.

50. When a light ray is passed through a prism, two different colours are seen on a screen as shown below. If μ_1, μ_2 and V_1, V_2 are the refractive indices and velocities of these colours (1) and (2), respectively, arrange the following steps to compare their refractive indices and velocity of light in the prism.
(A) Use the relation between refractive index and velocity of light.
(B) Use the fact that higher the angle of deviation, higher is the refractive index.
(C) Compare the angle of deviation of the two colours.
(D) Compare the velocity of light.

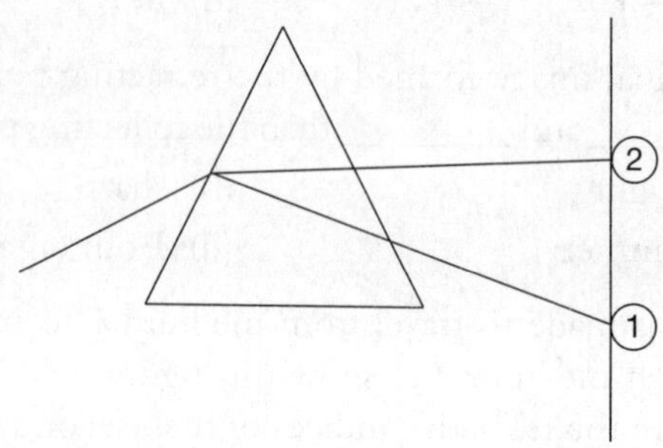

(a) CABD
(b) ACBD
(c) BCAD
(d) DACB

Level 2: Review Your Concepts

51. The angle of deviation of a light ray when it is reflected from a surface is 120°. What will be the angle of incidence?

52. A light ray of frequency 5×10^{14} Hz is travelling through water. If the refractive index of water is 4/3, then determine the wavelength?

53. An object is placed in front of a plane mirror at a distance *x* cm. Determine the shift in position of the mirror required to shift the image through 20 cm towards the mirror.

54. Two thin biconvex lenses L_1 and L_2 having focal lengths 10 cm and 15 cm, respectively, are placed coaxially. What distance (d) should be maintained between them so that a parallel beam of light parallel to their axis, incident on the lens L_1 emerges from L_2 undeviated? If the distance between them is increased by '*d*', at what distance from L_1, on the axis, does the emergent beam converge?

55. An ant moves with a uniform speed along a straight line path from *P* to Q, 60 cm apart, in front of a mirror and takes two minutes to cover this distance. The line segment *PQ* is inclined to the mirror MM' at an angle of 30°. What is the rate at which the distance between the ant and its image changes?

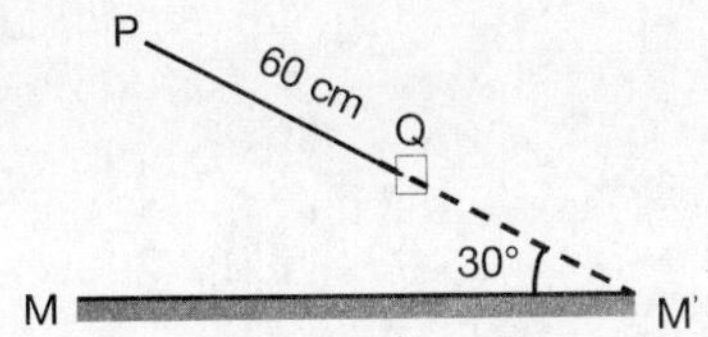

56. *ABCD* represents a glass slab and *PQRS* indicates the path of a light ray passing through the slab. If the refractive index of the glass is $\sqrt{3}$, find '*x*'. (See figure below)

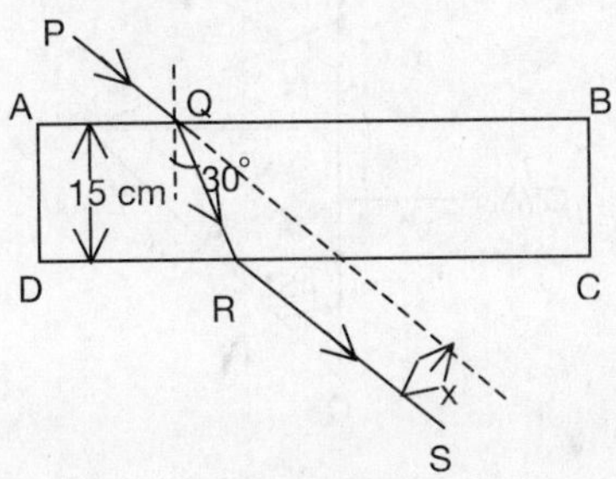

57. A person on the top of a coconut tree of height 10 m looks at the bottom of a swimming pool of depth 2 m. Determine the apparent position of the bottom of the pool viewed by the person (Refractive index of water $= \frac{4}{3}$).

58. A lens of focal length 20 cm produces a real image of a stationary object having magnification 2. Find the distance by which the lens should be moved so that it produces a virtual image of the same magnification.

59. An object A is placed on the principal axis of a convex mirror at a distance of 60 cm in front of it. A plane mirror is inserted between the object and the convex mirror at a distance of 40 cm from the object with the reflecting surface of the plane mirror facing the object. If the images formed by the two mirrors coincide, find the focal length of the convex mirror.

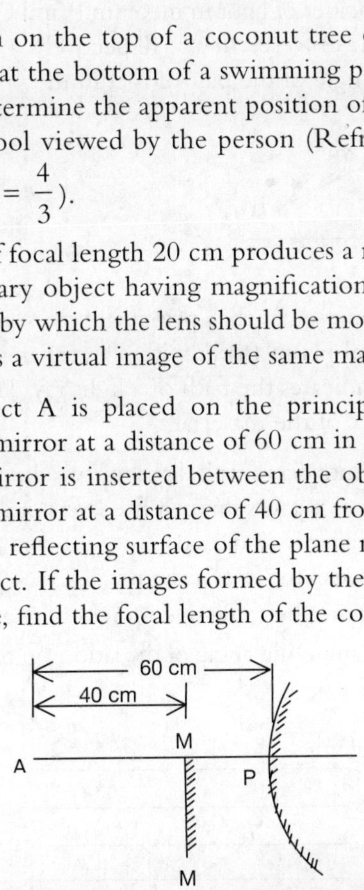

60. If an object is placed at a distance of 20 cm from the pole of a concave mirror, the magnification of its real image is 3. If the object is moved away from the mirror by 10 cm, find the decrease in its image magnification.

61. Why are red coloured lights are used in traffic signals to stop the vehicles?

62. A convex lens forms a real image on a screen when an object is placed at 10 cm from the screen. On shifting the lens by 2 cm, a real image is again formed on the screen. Find the focal length of the lens.

63. A bird flying above a pond starts moving vertically down towards the water below at a speed of v m s^{-1}. Find its apparent velocity as viewed by a fish located at a depth of d *m* below the surface of water.

64. An object (*O*) and a plane mirror (*M*) are placed in the positions as shown in the figure. If the object and the mirror move simultaneously towards right in a straight path at uniform speeds of 2 cm s^{-1} and 5 cm s^{-1}, respectively, find the shift in the image of the object at the end of 10 seconds.

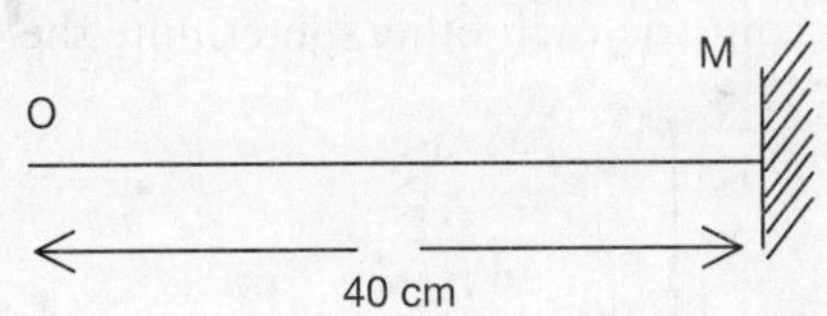

65. An object and its image are as shown in the diagram below.

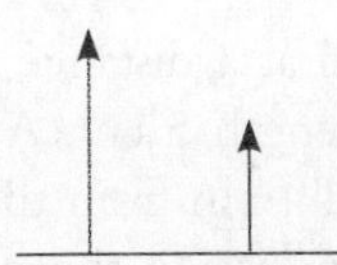

If the object image distance is 4 cm and the magnification is 3, find the ratio *u*: *v* : *f*. What is the type of the lens used? Draw the ray diagram to show the position of the lens and the principal focii.

66. An object is placed on the principal axis of a concave mirror at a distance of 60 cm. If the focal length of the concave mirror is 40 cm, then determine the magnification of the obtained image.

67. A person is unable to view the objects placed closer than 50 cm. What will be the power of the lens required to correct the defect?

68. Three filters, one of cyan (C), one of magenta (M) and the last, yellow (Y) are placed in front of a 100% transparent equilateral glass prism as shown in the figure. A

screen (S) is placed on the other side of the prism. When a white light ray is allowed to pass through the filters as shown in the figure and incident on the prism, what colours are obtained on the screen?

69. The angle of minimum deviation of a prism of refracting angle 60° is 30°. Determine its refractive index.

Level 3: Assess Your Concepts

70. An object is placed in front of a convex and concave lens as shown below. What will be the image distances (in cm) on the convex and concave lens? The focal length of both the lenses are 30 cm.

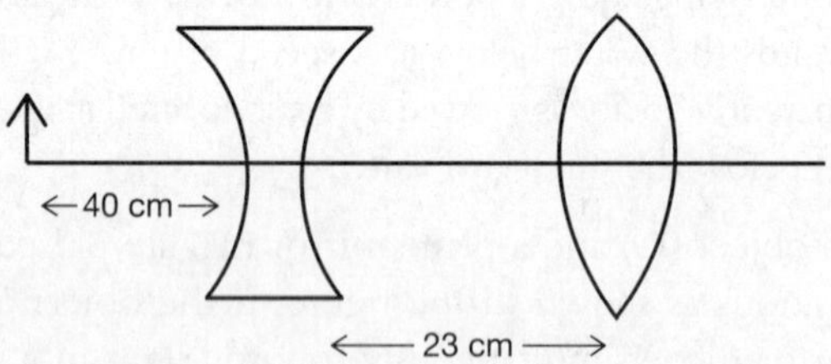

71. An object is placed infront of a concave and plane mirror as shown in the figure given below. If the focal length of the concave mirror is 25 cm and the virtual images coincide each other, determine the value of x.

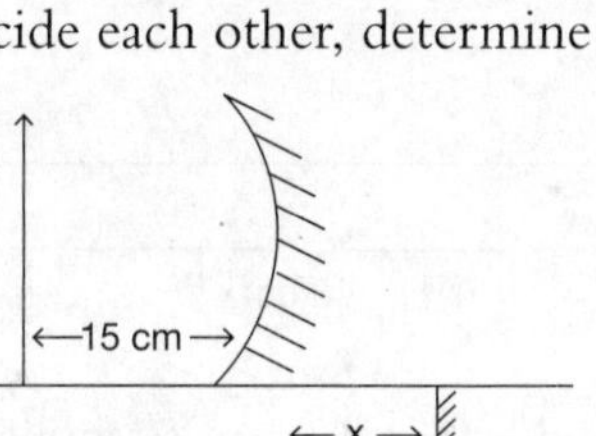

72. A point object is placed at a distance of 10 cm from a convex lens of focal length 5 cm. A convex mirror is placed at a distance of 4 cm from the lens on other the side of the lens opposite to the object such that the centre of curvature of the convex mirror coincides with the image formed by the convex lens. Show the position of the final image with the help of a ray diagram. Find the focal length of the convex mirror.

73. The figure shows an arrangement of two transparent slabs A and B with their respective thickness and refractive indices as shown. Find the vertical shift of the image of a point object placed at the bottom of A due to both the slabs. Also find the effective refractive index of the compound slab.

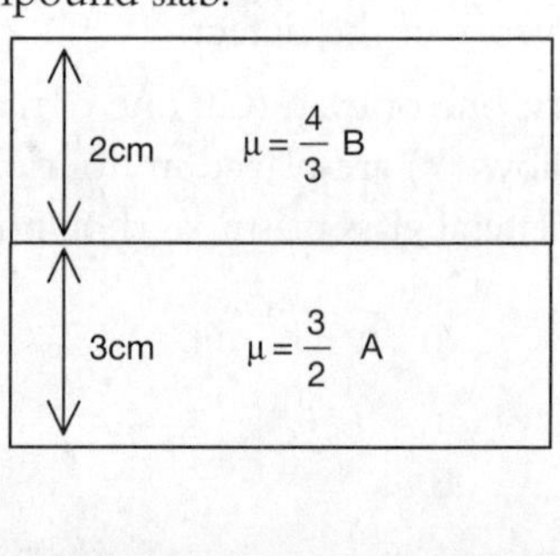

74. The refractive index of the glass prism shown in the figure is 2 for green light. A ray of cyan colour light is incident at P on the face BC of the prism. From which side would the light emerge? Given the critical angle for blue colour is greater than 15°.

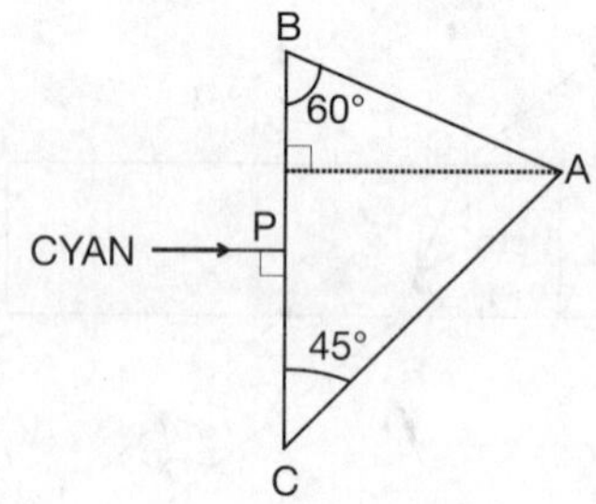

75. The velocities of light in medium P and Q are 2.5×10^8 m s^{-1} and 2×10^8 m s^{-1}, respectively. Determine the critical angle of the pair of medium.

76.

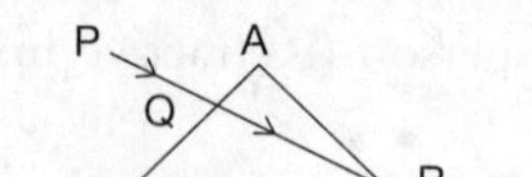

ABC represents the principal cross-section of an equilateral prism made with a transparent material. If $PQRS$ indicates the path of a light ray, find the refractive index of the material.

77. A ray of monochromatic light follows the path shown in the figure as it passes through five layers of different optical media of refractive indices μ_0, μ_1, μ_2, μ_3 and μ_4. If the angle of incidence in the first medium is 30°,

(i) compare the refractive indices of the media.

(ii) determine the angle of deviation on the whole.

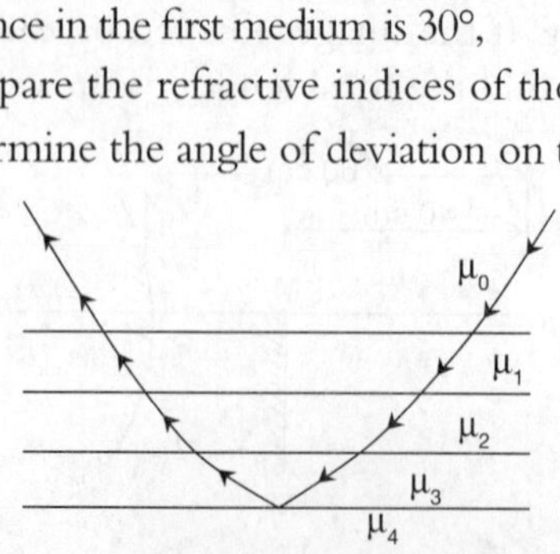

78. The critical angle for a medium X is 60° and for another medium Y is 45°. Calculate the ratio of velocity of light in the medium X to that in medium Y.

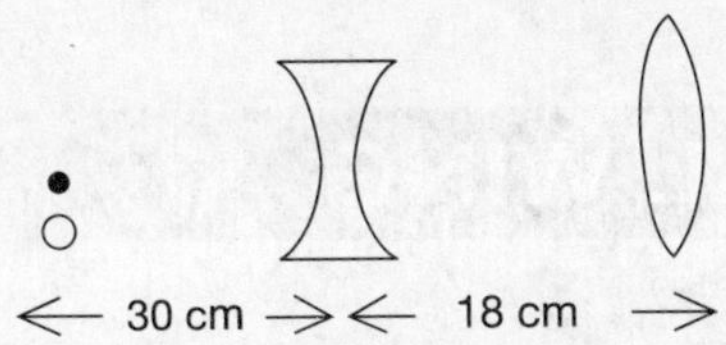

79. An object is placed in front of a convex lens of focal length 50 cm and concave lens as shown below. Find the focal length of concave lens if the image on the convex lens is formed at 80 cm from it.

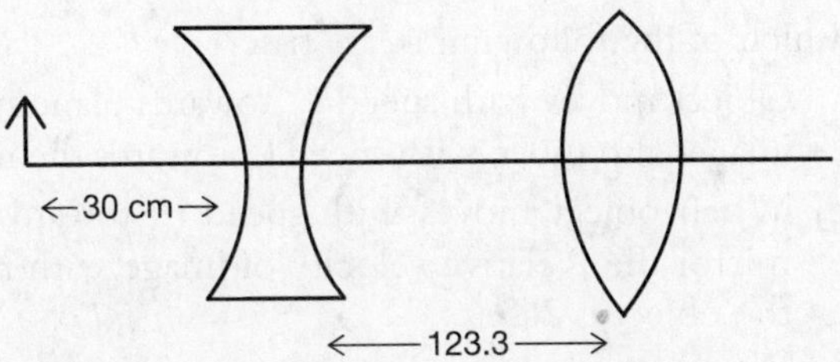

80. A concave mirror of radius of curvature 36 cm is fixed to a stand and placed it on a table. How far is an object from the mirror if an image is formed that is real and $\frac{1}{6}$ times the size of the object?

81. The apparent depth of a black dot on the surface of a transparent sphere of total surface area 16 π cm^2 is 2 cm, when it is seen from diametrically opposite side. Find the refractive index of the material sphere.

82. A double convex lens is placed in front of a linear object which is normal to the principal axis of the lens at 30 cm from the object. The image of the object is observed on a screen placed on the other side of the lens as that of the object, which is at 90 cm from the object. What is the focal length of the lens?

83. A glass prism of refracting angle 30° is kept on a prism table. A ray of light incidents at an angle of 60° at the first surface, emerges out by making an angle of 30° with the incident ray. Find the angle of emergence.

84. A convex lens throws on a screen 12 m from the lens a magnified image of the object. If the magnification is 15, find the focal length of the lens.

AT

PRACTICE QUESTIONS JEE-NEET SPECIAL WING

Multiple-Answer Type Questions

Directions for questions 1 to 10: **Select one or more correct alternative(*s*) from the given choices.**

1. We have concave mirror of focal length of 10 cm and object in placed at 20cm from pole of the mirror. Which of the following is/are true?

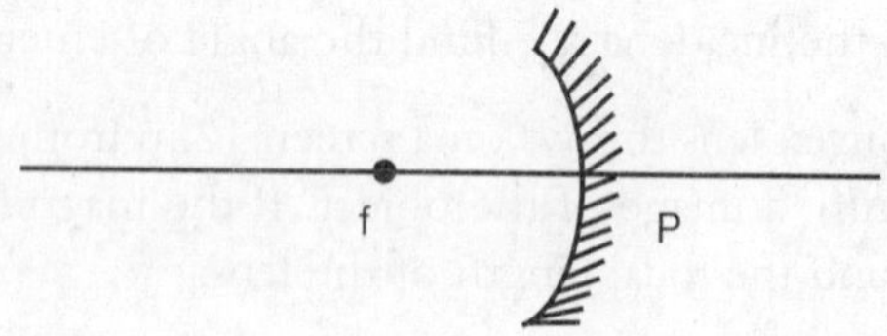

(a) $R = -20$ cm (b) $v = -20$ cm
(c) $|m|=1$ (d) $R = 15$ cm

2. For which of the pairs of u and f for a concave mirror image a smaller in size?
(a) $u = 15$ cm, $f = 5$ cm
(b) $u = 10$ cm, $f = 5$ cm
(c) $u = 20$ cm, $f = 5$ cm
(d) $u = 15$ cm, $f = 10$ cm

3. An object placed at depth 30 cm in a liquid of $\mu = \frac{5}{3}$. Which of the following is/are true?
(a) Apparent depth = 12 cm.
(b) Apparent depth = 18 cm.
(c) Normal shift = 18 cm.
(d) Norma shift = 12 cm.

4. Which of the following is/are true?
(a) Focal length of concave mirror is positive.
(b) Focal length of convex mirror is positive.
(c) Plane mirror forms virtual image.
(d) Magnification of plane mirror is one.

5. When light travels from denser medium to rarer medium. Which of the following is/are true?
(a) Speed of the light decreases.
(b) Speed of the light increases.
(c) No change in frequency of light.
(d) Wavelength of light also increases.

6. Which of the following is/are true?
(a) Object moves with speed V_0 towards plane mirror, images also move with speed V_0 towards the mirror.
(b) When object moves with speed V_0 towards fixed mirror the Relative velocity of image with respect the object is $2V_0$.
(c) When mirror moves with speed V_m towards fixed object speed of the images is $2V_m$.
(d) For plane mirror object distance and image distance always same.

7. Light travelling from denser medium to rarer medium, μ_D is refractive index of denser medium, μ_r is refractive index of rarer medium θ_c is critical angle. Which of the following is/are true?
(a) $\mu_D = \sqrt{2}$, $\mu_r = 1$, $\theta_c = 45°$
(b) $\mu_D = 2$, $\mu_r = 1$, $\theta_c = 60°$
(c) $\mu_D = 4$, $\mu_r = 2$, $\theta_c = 30°$
(d) $\mu_D = \frac{3}{2}$, $\mu_r = \frac{4}{3}$, $\theta_c = \sin^{-1}\left[\frac{8}{9}\right]$

8. For an equiconvex lens of refractive index $\frac{3}{2}$ and with radius of curvature 30 cm, which of the following is/are true?
(a) Focal length = 15 cm.
(b) Focal length = 30 cm.
(c) If the object distance is 20 cm, then $v = -60$ cm.
(d) If the object distance is 40 cm, then $v = 120$ cm.

9. Light incident on the first refracting surface of a prism at an angle of incidence 60° such that it undergoes minimum deviation. Angle of the prism is 60°. Which of the following is/are true?
(a) Minimum deviation is 60°.
(b) Minimum deviation is 30°.

(c) If refractive index of prism is $\sqrt{3}$, angle of refraction at first surface is 30°.

(d) If refraction index of prism is $\sqrt{3}$, angle of refraction at first surface is 45°.

10. Which of the following is/are true?

(a) Focal length pf convex lens is positive.

(b) Focal length of concave mirror is negative.

(c) Radius of curvature of a concave mirror is double its focal length.

(d) Speed of light is more in rarer medium than that in denser medium.

Comprehension-Based Questions

Directions for Questions 11 to 15:

When light travels from one medium to another medium, its speed and wavelength changes but frequency remains the same. Bending of a light ray when it travels from one medium to other medium is called refraction. When light travels from denser medium (whose refractive index is more) to rarer medium (whose refractive index is less), its speed increases and bends away from the normal. When light travels from rarer medium to denser medium, its speed decreases and bends towards the normal.

11. Ray of light enters medium of refractive index μ_2 from medium of refractive index μ_1 as shown in figure. Then angle of refraction is ________

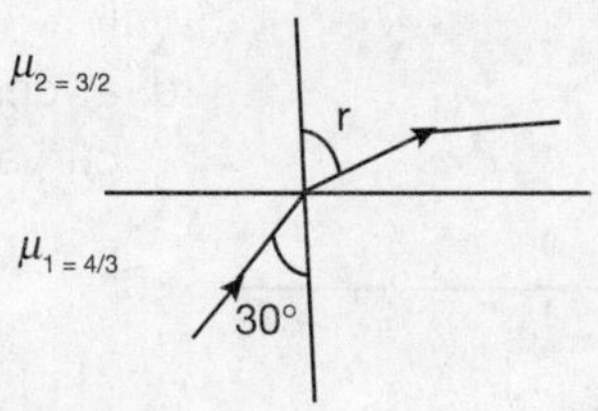

(a) $r = \sin^{-1}[9/4]$

(b) $r = \sin^{-1}[4/9]$

(c) $r = \sin^{-1}[9/8]$

(d) $r = \sin^{-1}[8/9]$

12. Ray of light enters a medium of refractive index $\sqrt{2}$ from another medium of refractive index 1 at angle of incidence 45°. The angle of refraction is

(a) 30° (b) 60°

(c) 45° (d) 15°

13. In above question, the angle of deviation is

(a) 45° (b) 30°

(c) 60° (d) 15°

14. As per given data, the ratio of apparent depths in two cases.

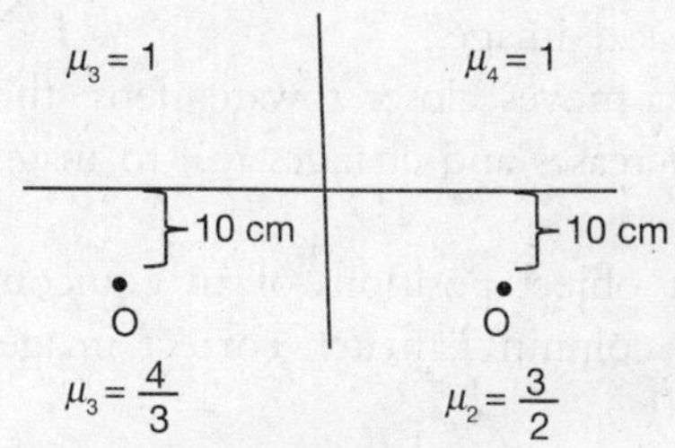

(a) $\frac{3}{4}$ (b) $\frac{4}{3}$

(c) $\frac{9}{8}$ (d) $\frac{1}{2}$

15. A ray of light incident at an angle of 45° as shown in the figure.

The refractive index of medium three is ________

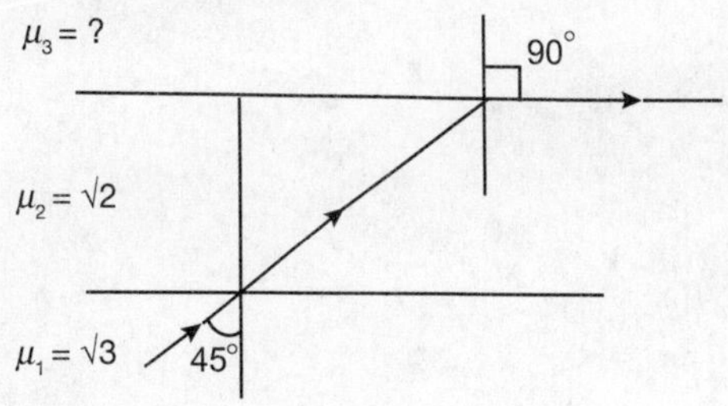

(a) $\frac{\sqrt{3}}{2}$ (b) $\sqrt{\frac{3}{2}}$

(c) $\sqrt{\frac{2}{3}}$ (d) $\frac{2}{\sqrt{3}}$

Match the Column

Directions for question 16: **Using the information given in the below paragraph and match the following:**

16. The lens which is thicker at the middle than the end is called a convex lens. It is also called a converging lens as it converges the parallel beam of light into a point.
When an object is placed at Infinity, it forms a real, inverted and diminished image at focus.
When an object is placed behind the centre of curvature (C), it forms a real and inverted image between F and $2F$.
When object is placed on C, it forms real, inverted and the same size image.
As object moves closer towards lens, the size of the image increases and changes real to magnified virtual Image.
Different object positions of an equiconvex lens are given in column I, match correct image position in column II.

Object position	Image position
A. 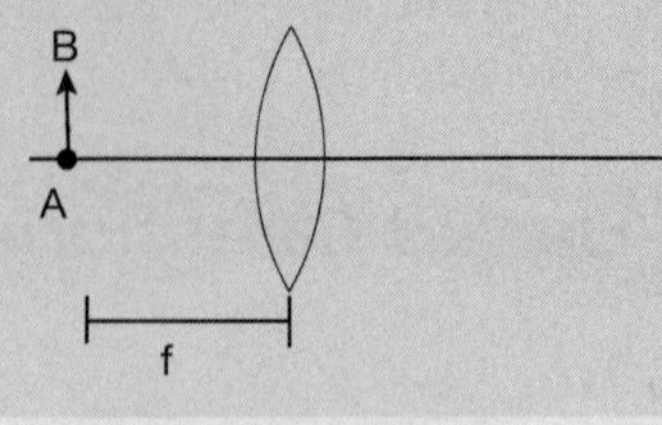	a. at focus
B. 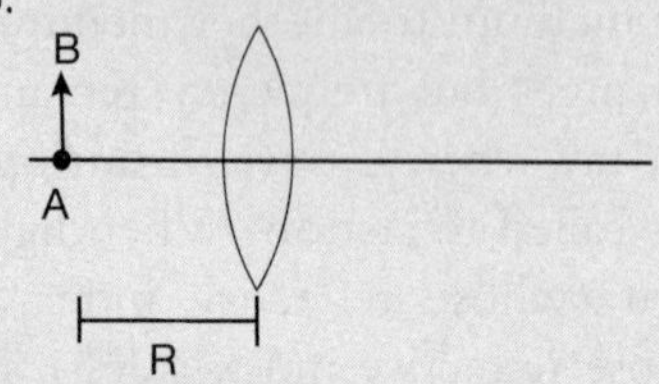	b. greater than 'R'
C. 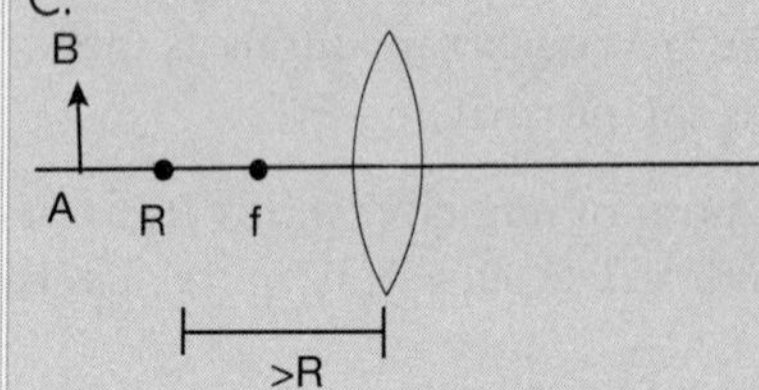	c. between 'f' and 'R'
D. 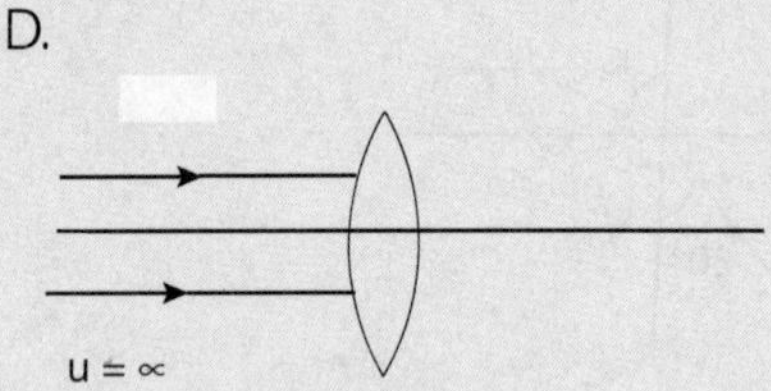	d. at centre of curvature
E. 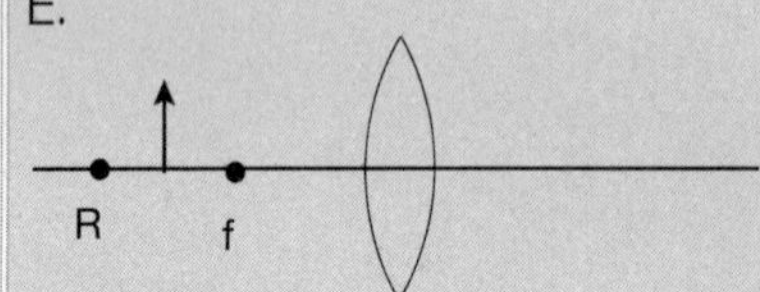	e. at infinity

ANSWER KEYS

Crossword

Across

3. Converging mirror
9. Shimmering effect
10. Negative

Down

1. Lateral displacement
2. Diopters
4. Astigmatism
5. Real image
6. Optic centre
7. Mirage
8. Rainbow

Classroom Wing

Very Short Answer Type Questions

1. Convex lens of power +1 D.
2. A convex lens of power + 1D.
6. Phase difference is 0 or $2n\pi$
7. Convex
8. Convex lens (converging)
11. Hypermetropia due to ageing
12. Difference in λ and ν
15. Ratio of sin i to sin r
17. Inversely
18. Rayleigh scattering

Competition Wing

Level 1: Apply Your Concepts

1. Concave
2. Black.
3. Hypermetropia
4. 3
5. Plane
6. Blue or white
7. Myopia
8. 10
9. 0°
10. quantum, electromagnetic
11. black
12. high monochromatic nature
13. glass slab
14. 3 feet
15. 15 m
16. 2
17. Myopia
18. False
19. False
20. True
21. True
22. True
23. False
24. True
25. A : c, e; B : b; C : a, d
26. (c)
27. (b)
28. (d)
29. (a)
30. (c)
31. (a)
32. (c)
33. (c)
34. (d)
35. (d)
36. (d)
37. (d)
38. (b)
39. (d)
40. (b)
41. (d)
42. (d)
43. (d)
44. (c)
45. (d)
46. (b)
47. (c)
48. (a)
49. (d)
50. (a)

JEE-NEET SPECIAL WING

Multiple-Answer Type Questions

1. (a, c)
2. (a, c)
3. (b, d)
4. (b, c, d)
5. (b, c, d)
6. (a, c, d)
7. (a, c, d)
8. (b, c, d)
9. (a, c)
10. (a, b, c, d)

Comprehension-Based Questions

11. (b)
12. (a)
13. (d)
14. (c)
15. (b)

Match the Column

16. A-e, B-d, C-c, D-a, E-b

For answer key of Classroom wing and Competition wing, refer to Hints and Solutions

Hints and Explanations

CLASSROOM WING

Very Short Answer Type Questions

1. Convex lens of power +1 D.
2. A convex lens of power + 1D.
3. Amount of radiant visible energy emitted per seconds
4. Ratio of image distance to object distance
5. The returning of excited electrons back to their normal states.
6. Phase difference is 0 or $2n\pi$
7. Convex
8. Convex lens (converging)
9. Overlapping of two waves when they meet in same part of medium
10. Bending of light when passed from rarer to denser medium
11. Hypermetropia due to ageing.
12. Difference in λ and ν
13. When light enters from rarer to denser medium.
14. Ability of light to get retracted when passed from one medium to another.
15. Ratio of sin i to sin r
16. One lumen of luminous flux emitted for one second
17. Inversely
18. Rayleigh scattering
19. Angle of prism, angle of incidence, μ, colour of light
20. Colours obtained by mixing primary colours

Short Answer Type Questions

Note: This is how you should frame your answer covering.

21.

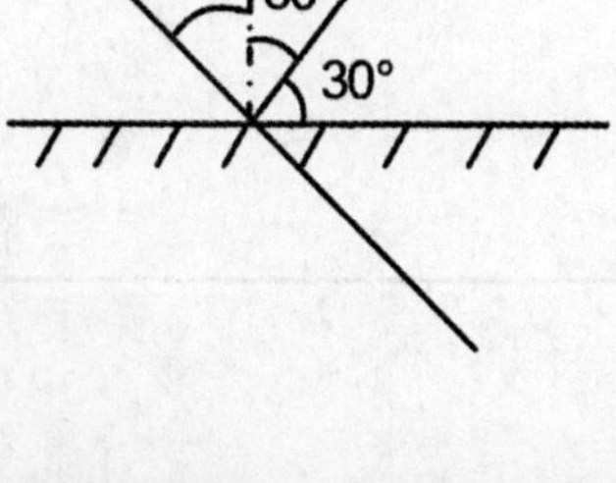

$d = 180 - 2r = (180 - 2 \times 60)$

$= 180 - 120$

$= 60°.$

22. $m = \dfrac{f_0}{f_e}$

23. $\lambda = 450 \text{ nm} = 450 \times 10^{-9}$ m

$\mu = \dfrac{c}{v}$

$V = \dfrac{c}{\mu} = \dfrac{3 \times 10}{\frac{3}{2}}$

$= 2 \times 10^8 \text{ m s}^{-1}$

$V = n\lambda$

$f = \dfrac{V}{\lambda} = \dfrac{2 \times 10^8}{450 \times 10^{-9}} = \dfrac{2}{450} \times 10^{17}$

$= 4.4 \times 10^{14}$ Hz.

24. (i) Definition of critical angle.

(ii) i > C

25.

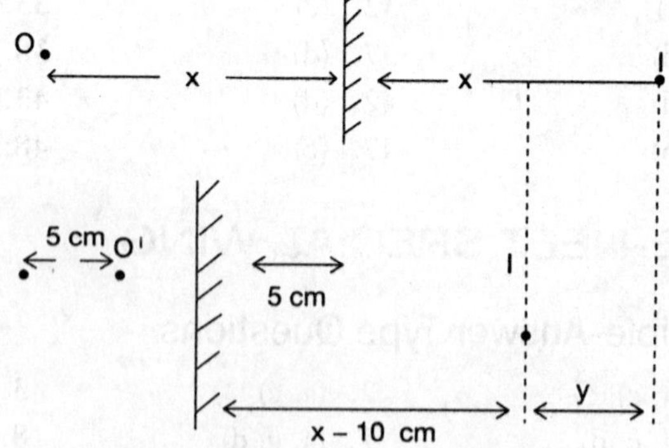

$u^1 = x - 10$ cm

$v^1 = (x - 10 \text{ cm})$

∴ Shift in position of the image $y = x + 5 - (x - 10)$

$= x + 5 - x + 10$

$= 15$ cm.

26. When light of suitable frequency falls on a metal surface, electrons are emitted from it, this phenomenon of emission of photo-electrons is known as photoelectric effect.

27. Defect in cornea, no proper focussing, cylindrical lens

28. Right angled isosceles prism

29. $\mu_w = \frac{3}{4}$

$$\mu_w = \frac{\text{Real depth}}{\text{Apparent depth}}$$

$$= \frac{3}{4} = \frac{10}{x}$$

$$x = \frac{40}{3}\text{ m}$$

30. Particle nature (light corpuscles)

Reflection, Refraction different sizes of the corpusescles.

31. Invisible radiation, more wavelength, produces heat, Sun. Missile system infrared photography, etc.

32. Refracting periscope consists of two right angled isosceles prisms. The light rays entering the periscope are rotated through 180° by the total reflecting prisms which make the image of a distant object visible.

33. Wave nature

- Longitudinal mechanical waves
- Primary source, secondary source
- Wave fronts (spherical, cylindrical)
- Reflection, refraction, dispersion

34. When the object is at infinity the light rays should appear to come from 3 m.

$\therefore u = \infty, v = -3$ m

$$\frac{1}{f} = \frac{1}{v} - \frac{1}{u}$$

$$= \left(\frac{1}{-3}\right) + 0$$

$$P = \frac{-1}{3} D = -0.33\ D$$

35. (i) Thin glass fibre

(ii) Works on principle of total internal reflection.

Essay Answer Type Questions

Note: This is how you should frame your answer covering.

36.

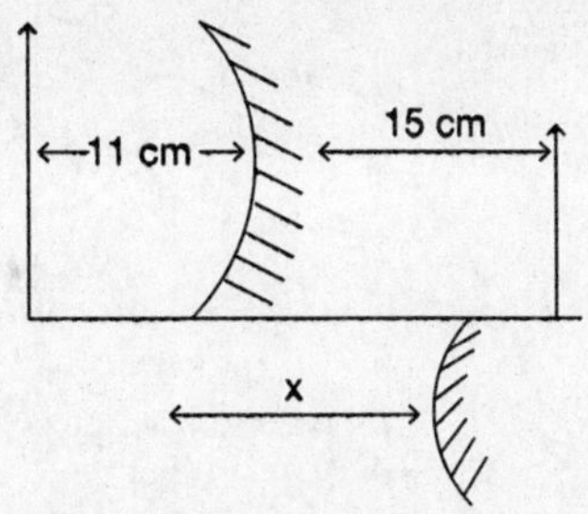

For concave mirror $u = -11$ cm, $f = -40$ cm, $v = ?$

$$\frac{1}{f} = \frac{1}{u} + \frac{1}{u}$$

$$\frac{1}{-40} = \frac{1}{-11} + \frac{1}{v}$$

$$\frac{1}{v} = \frac{-1}{40} + \frac{1}{11} = \frac{-11+40}{440}$$

$$v = \frac{440}{29} = 15\text{ cm}$$

For convex mirror

$u = x + 11$ cm, $f = 6.5$ cm

$v = (15 - x)$

$$\frac{1}{f} = \frac{1}{u} + \frac{1}{v}$$

$$\frac{1}{6.5} = \left(\frac{1}{-x-11}\right) + \frac{1}{(15-x)} \Rightarrow x = 10\text{ cm.}$$

37. Objective, eye piece

m = m_o × me = L/fo × D/fe

Ray diagram, find the values of L, fo, fe and obtain magnification (m).

38. (i) Obtain ray diagram.

(ii) Find relation between f, u and v.

39. ${}^{B}C_{A} = 60°$

$${}^{r}\mu_{d} = \frac{1}{\sin^{r} C_{d}}$$

$${}^{B}\mu_{A} = \frac{1}{\sin^{B} C_{A}}$$

$${}^{B}\mu_{A} = \frac{V_B}{V_A} = \frac{2}{\sqrt{3}}$$

$$\frac{V_B}{2\times10^8}=\frac{2}{\sqrt{3}}$$

$$V_B=\frac{4\times10^8}{\sqrt{3}}\ \text{m s}^{-1}.$$

40.

$$\mu=\frac{\sin\left(\frac{A+D}{2}\right)}{\sin\left(\frac{A}{2}\right)}$$

$$\sqrt{3}=\frac{\sin\left(\frac{60+D}{2}\right)}{\sin 30}$$

$$\sqrt{3}=\frac{\sin\left(\frac{60+D}{2}\right)}{\frac{1}{2}}$$

$$\sin\left(\frac{60+D}{2}\right)=\left(\frac{\sqrt{3}}{2}\right)$$

$$\frac{60+D}{2}=60$$

$$60+D=120$$

$$D=60°.$$

Competition Wing

Level 1: Apply Your Concepts

1. Virtual images are formed by refraction, reflection and convex mirror. Concave lens can produce real image.

2. Red light is absorbed by green object.

$\therefore$ Black.

5. Real images are formed by refraction, reflection, concave mirror and convex lens. Plane mirror does not form a real image.

26. $\mu_1 > \mu_2 > \mu_3$ and $\lambda_1 < \lambda_2 < \lambda_3$.

Hence, the correct option is (c).

Explanation for questions from 41 to 50:

41. Final image formed by the refracting periscope is bright and sharp then reflecting periscope since no rays of light are absorbed.

The quality of the image is affected by the presence of dust and moisture in case of reflecting periscope but least in case of refracting periscope.

42.

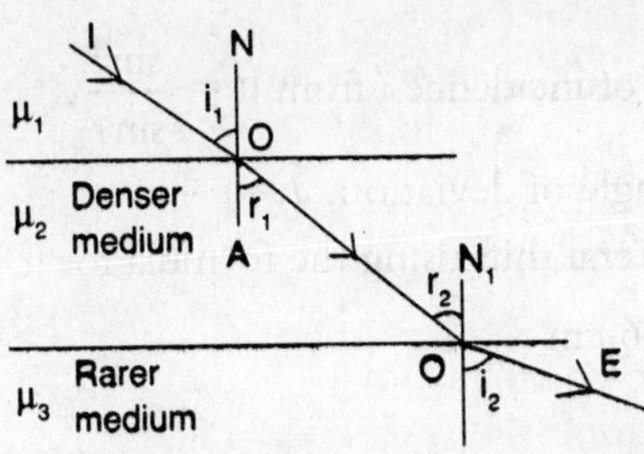

Given, $i_2 > i_1$

From figure $r_1 = r_2$

Because $\angle AOO^1 = \angle OO^1N_1$ are alternate angles,

$\Rightarrow \sin r_2 = \sin r_2$ and $\sin i_2 > \sin i_1$, let $r_1 = r_2 = r$

$$\text{Here, } {}^1\mu_2 = \frac{\mu_2}{\mu_1} = \frac{\sin i_1}{\sin r_1} = \frac{\sin i_1}{\sin r}$$

$${}^2\mu_1 = \frac{\mu_1}{\mu_2} = \frac{\sin r_1}{\sin i_1} = \frac{\sin r}{\sin i_1}$$

$${}^2\mu_3 = \frac{\mu_3}{\mu_2} = \frac{\sin r_2}{\sin i_2} = \frac{\sin r}{\sin i_2}$$

$${}^3\mu_2 = \frac{\mu_2}{\mu_3} = \frac{\sin i_2}{\sin r_2} = \frac{\sin i_2}{\sin r}$$

Since $\sin i_1 > \sin r$,

$$\Rightarrow \frac{\sin i_1}{\sin r} > \frac{\sin r}{\sin i_1} \Rightarrow {}^1\mu_2 > {}^2\mu_1$$

Since $\sin i_2 > \sin r$,

$$\Rightarrow \frac{\sin i_2}{\sin r} > \frac{\sin r}{\sin i_2} \Rightarrow {}^2\mu_3 > {}^3\mu_2$$

Since $\sin i_1 > \sin r$,

$$\Rightarrow \frac{\sin i_1}{\sin i_2} < \frac{\sin i_2}{\sin i_1}$$

43. The angle of deviation depends on the angle of incidence and wavelength of the incident light, angle of prism and refractive index of the prism.

44. A suitable cylindrical lens rectifies astigmatism.

45. Human eye has its maximum sensitivity around 555 nm which belongs to green region.

46. Initially the white paper is fixed on the drawing board and the prism is placed on the paper. The out line of the prism is drawn on the paper and a point is marked on one of the sides. A normal is drawn at that point and a line which makes a certain angle with the normal is drawn on the paper. Two pins P and Q are fi xed on the line and the prism is placed in its initial position. The images of the pins P and Q are viewed from the other side of the prism. Two more pins R and S are fixed such that R and S are on the same line with the images of P and Q. Remove the pins and join the line segment RS with the side of the prism. Join the line segments PQ and RS. Extend the lines PQ and RS. Determine the angle between PQ and RS. This is known as the angle of deviation. Repeat the experiment for different angles of incidence and determine the angle of deviation in each case. Plot a graph by taking the angle of incidence along the X-axis and angle of deviation along the Y-axis. Determine the angle of minimum deviation and determine the refractive index

$$\mu = \frac{\sin\left(\frac{A + D_m}{2}\right)}{\sin\left(\frac{A}{2}\right)}$$

47. The magnification is positive for virtual images and is negative for real images. The concave lens and convex mirror from virtual images and its magnification is positive where as convex lens and concave mirror can produce both real and virtual images, hence, their magnification is negative and positive, respectively.

48. The rainbow is always formed in a opposite direction of the position of the Sun.

49. Rayleigh scattering is called incoherent scattering where as Raman scattering is an coherent scattering.

50. (a)

$C \rightarrow A \rightarrow B \rightarrow D$

$\mu_1 > \mu_2$ and $V_1 < V_2$.

Level 2: Review Your Concepts

Note: This is how you should frame your answer covering.

51. $d = 120°$

$d = 180 - 2i$

$$i = \frac{180 - 120}{2} = 30°.$$

52. $$V = \frac{C}{\mu} = \frac{3\times10^8}{\frac{4}{3}} = \frac{9}{4}\times10^8 \text{ m s}^{-1}$$

$V = n\lambda$

$$\frac{9}{4}\times10^8 = 5\times10^{14}\lambda$$

$$\lambda = \frac{9}{20}\times10^{-6}$$

$= 0.45 \times 10^{-6}$ m

$\lambda = 450 \times 10^{-9}$ m.

53.

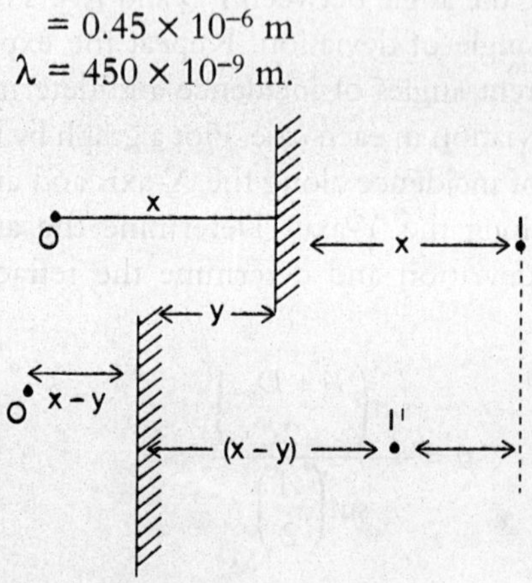

From the diagram $y + x = (x - y) + 20$

$2y = 20$

$y = 10$ cm.

54. (i) Is the emergent beam a parallel beam parallel to the axis?
(ii) What should be the position of the object to get the image at infinity?
(iii) Does the first image formed serve as an object to the lens L_2?
(iv) 25 cm, 74 cm

55. (i) Find the value of uniform speed of the ant. Shift the mirror horizontally and coincide it with the point Q.
Apply the trigonometric formula.
Find the distance of the ant from the mirror.
The object distance is equal to the image distance.
Then find the distance between the ant and its image, when ant is at *P* and Q.
Find the difference between the distance of the ant and the image, when present at *P* and Q.
Divide the obtained distance by the time taken.
Then, from this find the rate at which the distance between the ant and its image changes.
(ii) 0.5 cm s^{-1}

56. (i) Find angle of incidence *i* from $\mu = \frac{\sin i}{\sin r}$.
(ii) Find the angle of deviation, $d = i - r$.
(iii) Find the lateral shift using the formula for it.
(iv) $5\sqrt{3}$ or 8.66 cm

57. $$\frac{4}{3} = \frac{2}{x}$$

$$x = \frac{3}{2}$$

$$\text{Apparent position} = 10 + \frac{3}{2} = \frac{23}{2} \text{ m}.$$

58. (i) Find the nature of the lens with the help of given information.
(ii) Use lens formula.
(iii) Find the object distance in the two cases and then find the distance moved by the lens.
(iv) 20 cm

59. (i) Find the object-distance with respect to the convex mirror.
Is the object-distance and the image-distance equal in the case of a plane mirror?

Find the distance between the plane mirror and the convex mirror.
Find the distance between the convex mirror and the image formed in the plane mirror.
Determine the image-distance for the convex mirror.
Find the focal length of the convex mirror by using the mirror formula $\left(\frac{1}{f}=\frac{1}{v}+\frac{1}{v}\right)$.

(ii) 30 cm

60. (i) Using mirror formula, express magnification 'm' in terms of focal length 'f' and object distance 'u'.
(ii) Use the expression to find the magnification in both the cases.
(iii) Find the new object distance and then find the magnification.
(iv) Difference in magnification gives the answer.
(v) 2

61. What is Reyleigh's scattering principle?
In all the seven colours, which colour deviates the least?
Which colour has more wavelength?
From Rayleigh's scattering formula, $I_{max} = \frac{1}{\lambda^4}$, find whether red colour scatters more or less.
Can a least scattering colour be used as danger sign in traffic signals?

62. (i) **Case 1:**
Take the object distance from convex lens as 'x' cm.
Then, the image distance will be $(10 - x)$ cm.
Substitute the values in lens formula $\frac{1}{f}=\frac{1}{v}-\frac{1}{u}$ and find the value of focal length (f) of the lens in terms of 'x'. (1)
Case 2:
When the lens is shifted by 2 cm, take the object distance from convex lens as $(x + 2)$ cm.
Find the image distance from the lens. $(10 - x - 2)$
Substitute the values in lens formula $\frac{1}{f}=\frac{1}{v}-\frac{1}{u}$ to find the focal length (f) of the lens in terms of 'x' (2).
(use sign convention)
Is the focal length of a lens constant for a given medium?
Compare (1) and (2), and find x. Then, find the value of 'f'.
(ii) 2.4 cm

63. (i) Which is the observer - bird or fish?
Which is the object?
What is the speed of the bird?
What is the distance travelled by the bird in one second?
If the real distance of the bird is RD_1 $(x + d)$ and after one second the real distance of the bird becomes RD_2 from the free surface of the water, where $RD_2 = (x - v + d)$, then find the relation between RD_2 and RD_1.
What is the relation between real depth, apparent depth and refractive index?
What is the apparent depth of the bird as viewed by the fish?
Apparent velocity is equal to the rate of change in apparent depth.
Then find the value of apparent velocity of the bird as viewed by the fish.
(ii) μv

64. (i) Represent the positions of the object, mirror and the image along X- axis.
(ii) Difference in the final and initial positions of the image.
(iii) 80 cm

65. (i) From the given problem, the distance between the object and image is 4 cm.
The distance between object and image = x = 4 cm.
Find the image distance, v.
$$v = u + x. \quad (1)$$
What is the formula for magnification?
$$\left(m=\frac{u}{v}\right) \quad (2)$$
Find value of u, v from (1) and (2).
Find the focal length (f) of the lens by using lens formula,
$$\left(\frac{1}{f}=\frac{1}{v}-\frac{1}{u}\right).$$
To find the type of lens used, draw a straight line passing through the two arrow tips and draw another straight horizontal line from tip of arrow of the smaller line.

Draw the refracted ray and produce backward.
In the ray diagram, locate the lens, object and image.

(ii) $u : v : f = 2 : 6 : 3$

66. $u = -60$ cm; $f = -40$ cm, $v = ?$

$$\frac{1}{f} = \frac{1}{u} + \frac{1}{v}; \Rightarrow \frac{1}{40} = -\frac{1}{60} + \frac{1}{v} \Rightarrow \frac{1}{v.} = \frac{1}{60} - \frac{1}{40}$$

$$\frac{1}{v} = \frac{2-3}{120} = \frac{-1}{120} \Rightarrow v = -120\,\text{cm}$$

$$m = \frac{-v}{u} = \frac{+120}{60} = -2$$

67. $u = -25$ cm $= \frac{-1}{4}$ m (least distance of distinct vision)

$v = -50$ cm $= \frac{-1}{2}$ m

$$\frac{1}{f} = \frac{1}{v} - \frac{1}{u}$$

$$\frac{1}{f} = \frac{1}{-50} + \frac{1}{25} = \frac{1}{50}\ \text{cm}^{-1}$$

$P = +2$ D

68. White light, while passing through the cyan filter, emerges as cyan light.
Cyan, being a combination of blue and green, renders the emergent white light passing through the magenta filter, blue.
As magenta is a combination of blue and red, green colour of cyan is absorbed by the filter and only blue is transmitted.
The third filter is yellow, which is a combination of red and green.
Thus, the yellow filter completely absorbs the blue light incident on it and transmits none. Thus, no light is incident on the prism and no colours are observed on the screen.

69.

$$\mu = \frac{\sin\left(\frac{A+D}{2}\right)}{\sin\frac{A}{2}} = \frac{\sin\left(\frac{60+30}{2}\right)}{\sin\left(\frac{60}{2}\right)}$$

$$= \frac{\sin 45}{\sin 30} = \frac{\frac{1}{\sqrt{2}}}{\frac{1}{2}} = \sqrt{2}.$$

Level 3: Assess Your Concepts

Note: This is how you should frame your answer covering.

70.

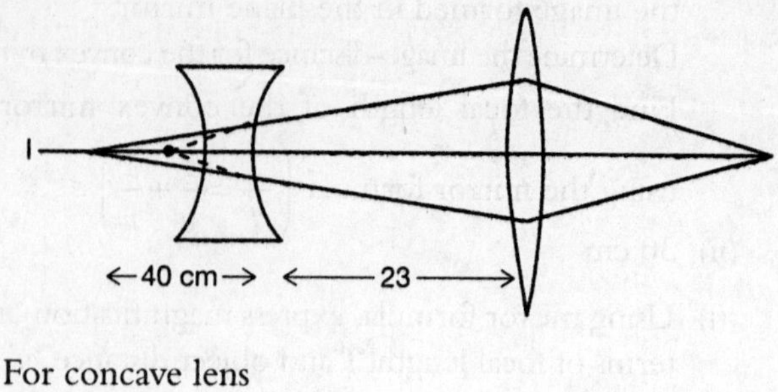

For concave lens

$$\frac{1}{f} = \frac{1}{v} - \frac{1}{u}$$

$$\Rightarrow \frac{1}{-30} = \frac{1}{v} + \frac{1}{40}$$

$$\frac{1}{v} = \frac{-1}{30} - \frac{1}{40} = \frac{-40-30}{1200}$$

$$v = \frac{1200}{-70} = -17\ \text{cm}$$

For convex lens

$u = -(17 + 23) = -40$ cm

$f = 30$ m

$$\therefore \frac{1}{30} = \frac{1}{v} + \frac{1}{40}$$

$$\frac{1}{v} = \frac{1}{30} - \frac{1}{40} = \frac{40-30}{1200}$$

$$v = \frac{1200}{10} = 120\ \text{m.}$$

71. For concave mirror, $f = -25$ cm

$u = 15$ cm

$$\frac{1}{f} = \frac{1}{u} + \frac{1}{v}; \frac{1}{-25} = \frac{-1}{15} + \frac{1}{v}$$

$$\frac{1}{v} = \frac{-1}{25} + \frac{1}{15}$$

$$\frac{1}{v} = \frac{-15+25}{25 \times 15}$$

$$v = \frac{25 \times 15}{10} = \frac{75}{2} = 37.5\ \text{cm}$$

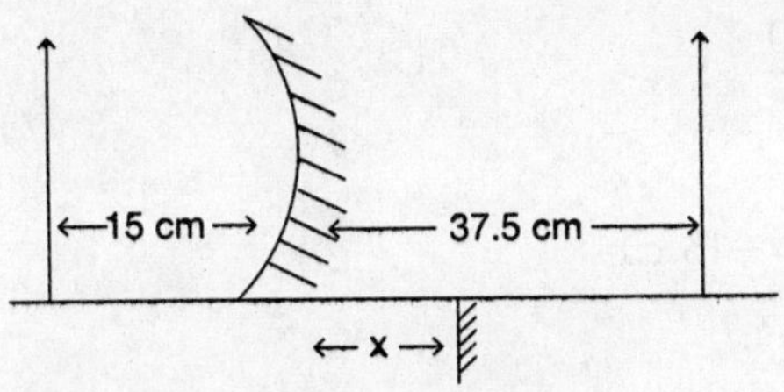

The distance between the object and plane mirror is

$\therefore (x + 15) = 37.5 - x$

$2x = 37.5 - 15$

$x = \dfrac{22.5}{2}$

$= 11.25$ cm

72. (i) What is the value of 'u' and 'f' for convex lens? (Follow sign convention.)
What is the distance between convex lens and convex mirror?
Find the value of the image distance, 'v' for convex lens by using the lens formula, $\dfrac{1}{f} = \dfrac{1}{v} - \dfrac{1}{u}$.
Here, $v = 4 + 2f$ (where f = focal length of convex mirror).
Find the value of 'f'.
(ii) 3 cm

73. (i) $\Delta h = \Delta h_1 + \Delta h_2$.
(ii) $\Delta h = h\left(1 - \dfrac{1}{\mu}\right)$.
(iii) 1.5 cm

74. Find the refractive index of the glass prism for green light from the given information.
What colours are present in cyan?
Find the critical angle for green colour light, using the formula $\mu = \dfrac{1}{\sin C}$.
Bending power of blue colour light is more than that for green colour. Then will the critical angle for blue be less or more?
At point P, find the angles of incidence and refraction.
Find the angle of incidence of the light rays on the face AC with the help of a ray diagram.
Find whether it undergoes total internal reflection.
Then, will the light ray incident on the face AB?
Find the angle of incidence on the face BC.
Is this angle equal to the critical angle for green colour?
Then, find whether green colour grazes out from the face AB.
From geometry, show that blue colour emerges from the face AC.

75. $V_p = 2.5 \times 10^8$ m s^{-1}

$V_Q = 2 \times 10^8$ m s^{-1}

$${}^P\mu_Q \frac{1}{\sin C} = \frac{V_P}{V_Q} = \frac{2.5\times10^8}{2\times10^8}$$

$$\frac{1}{\sin C} = \frac{5}{4}$$

$$\sin C = \left(\frac{4}{5}\right)$$

$$C = \sin^{-1}\left(\frac{4}{5}\right).$$

76.

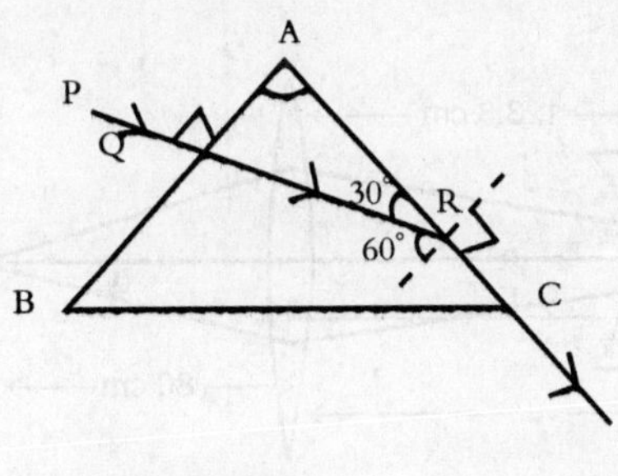

From the figure, it is clear that the angle of incidence of the light may be on the face AC of the prism inside; it is 60°.

As the emergent ray grazed the face AC, the critical angle of the material of the prism is 60°.

Hence, $\mu = \dfrac{1}{\sin 60°} \Rightarrow \dfrac{2}{\sqrt{3}}$

77. At each interface, the rays deviate away from the normal. Therefore, $\mu_0 < \mu_1 < \mu_2 < \mu_3 < \mu_4$. At the interface of medium 3 and medium 4, total internal reflection takes place.
Angle of devitation in the cases of reflection
$= 180° - 2i$
$= 180° - 60° = 120°$

78. Critical angle of medium X is $C_X = 60°$.
Critical angle of medium Y is $C_Y = 45°$.
Let C_1 and C_2 are velocities of light in X and Y, respectively.
Let μ_1 and μ_2 are the refractive indices of X and Y, respectively.

Then $\mu_1 = \dfrac{1}{\sin C_x} = \dfrac{1}{\sin 60°} = \dfrac{1}{\left(\sqrt{3}/2\right)} = \dfrac{2}{\sqrt{3}}$

And $\mu_2 = \dfrac{1}{\sin C_y} = \dfrac{1}{45°} = \left(\dfrac{1}{1/\sqrt{2}}\right) = \sqrt{2}$

Let 'C' be velocity of light in air then μ_1

$$= \frac{C}{C_1} \text{ and } \mu_2 = \frac{C}{C_2} \therefore \frac{C}{C_1} = \frac{2}{\sqrt{3}} \quad (1) \text{ and}$$

$$\frac{C}{C_2} = \sqrt{2} \quad (2)$$

Dividing equation (1) with equation (2), we get

$$\frac{\left(\frac{C}{C_1}\right)}{\left(\frac{C}{C_2}\right)} = \frac{\left(\frac{2}{\sqrt{3}}\right)}{(\sqrt{2})} \text{ or } \frac{C_2}{C_1} = \frac{\sqrt{2}}{\sqrt{3}} \text{ or } \frac{C_1}{C_2} = \frac{\sqrt{3}}{\sqrt{2}} = \sqrt{\frac{3}{2}}$$

79.

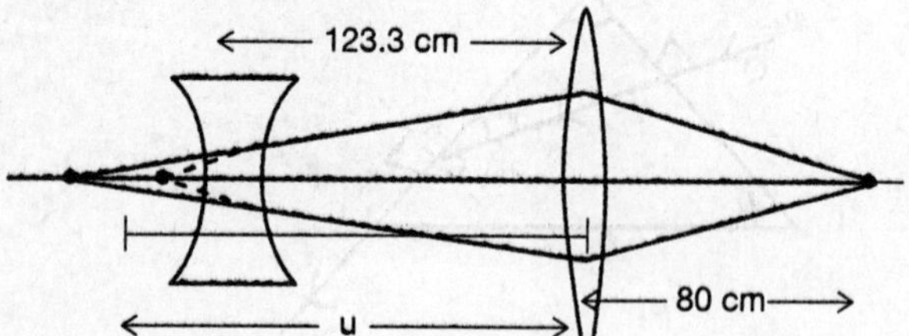

For convex lens

$$\frac{1}{f} = \frac{1}{v} - \frac{1}{u}$$

$$\frac{1}{50} = \frac{1}{80} - \frac{1}{u}$$

$$\frac{1}{u} = \frac{1}{80} - \frac{1}{50} = \frac{50-80}{80 \times 50} \Rightarrow u = -133.3 \text{ cm}$$

$\therefore$ For concave lens

$v = 133.3 - 123.3$

$= 10$ cm

$u = 30$ cm

$$\frac{1}{f} = \frac{1}{v} - \frac{1}{u}$$

$$= \frac{1}{-10} + \frac{1}{30}$$

$$= \frac{30-10}{-300}$$

$$f = \frac{-300}{20} = -15 \text{ cm}$$

80. Given, radius of curvature, R = 36 cm
Then the focal length, f = R/2 = 36/2 = 18 cm
Magnification is negative for real images and positive for virtual images.

For real images formed by a concave mirror, u, v, and f are negative.
From the mirror formula $\dfrac{1}{f} = \dfrac{1}{v} + \dfrac{1}{u}$, we have

$$\frac{1}{u} = \frac{1}{f} - \frac{1}{v} \Rightarrow \frac{u}{u} = \frac{u}{f} - \frac{u}{v} \Rightarrow 1 = \frac{u}{f} - \frac{1}{-m} = \frac{u}{f} + \frac{1}{m}$$

$$\therefore \frac{u}{f} = 1 - \frac{1}{m} = \frac{m-1}{m} u = \frac{(m-1)f}{m}$$

Magnification, m = $\dfrac{1}{6}$ and real image

$$\therefore u = \frac{\left(\frac{1}{6}-1\right)(-18)}{-\frac{1}{6}} = \frac{\left(\frac{7}{6}\right)(-18)}{-\frac{1}{6}} = 7 \times (-18) = -126$$

$\therefore$ Object distance = 126 cm

81. $4\pi r^2 = 16\pi \Rightarrow r = 2$

$\Rightarrow$ diameter is = 4 cm

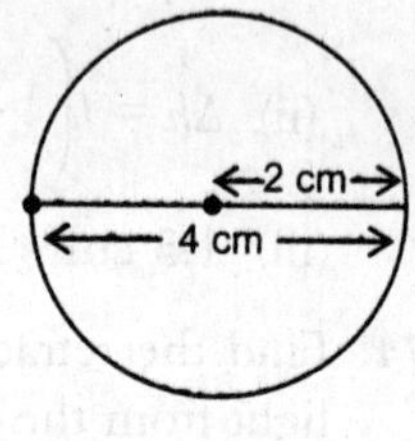

$$\mu_m = \frac{\text{Real depth}}{\text{Apparent depth}} = \frac{4}{2} = 2$$

$\mu_m = 2$

82. Given, u = –30 cm, v = +(90 – 30) cm = 60 cm
Let f be the focal length of the given convex lens.

We know

$$\frac{1}{f} = \frac{1}{v} - \frac{1}{u}$$

$$\Rightarrow \frac{1}{f} = \frac{1}{60} - \left(\frac{1}{-30}\right) = \frac{1}{60} + \frac{1}{30} = \frac{1}{60} + \frac{2}{60} = \frac{3}{60} = \frac{1}{20}$$

$\Rightarrow f = 20cm$

83. Given, Angle of prism, A = 30°
Angle of incidence, i = 60°

Angle of deviation, d = 30°

Angle of emergence, e =?

We have, angle of deviation (d) = i + e − A

$30° = 60° + e - 30°$

$\Rightarrow 30° = 30° + e$

$\Rightarrow e = 0°$

Therefore, the ray emerges normally from the second surface.

84. Magnification m = 15

Image distance = v

Magnification $= +\frac{v}{u}$ (1)

From lens formula

$\frac{1}{f} = \frac{1}{v} - \frac{1}{u}$ using Cartesian sign convention

$\frac{1}{f} = \frac{1}{v} - \frac{1}{-u} \Rightarrow \frac{1}{f} = \frac{1}{v} + \frac{1}{u} \therefore \frac{1}{u} = \frac{1}{f} - \frac{1}{v} \Rightarrow \frac{1}{u} = \frac{v-f}{vf}$

$$u = \frac{vf}{v-f} \quad (2)$$

substituting (2) in (1)

$m = \frac{v(V-f)}{vf} \Rightarrow m = \frac{V-f}{f} \therefore 15 = \frac{12-f}{f}$

$\Rightarrow 15f = 12 - f \Rightarrow 16f = 12 \Rightarrow f = 12/16 = 0.75\,m$

JEE-NEET SPECIAL WING

Multiple-Answer Type Questions

1. $R = 2f$

$R = 2(10) = 20$ cm

$\frac{1}{f} = \frac{1}{v} + \frac{1}{u}$

$\frac{1}{-10} = \frac{1}{v} \frac{1}{20}$

$\frac{1}{v} = \frac{1}{20}\frac{1}{10} = \frac{1-2}{20} = -\frac{1}{20}$

$v = -20$

$|m| = \left|\frac{v}{u}\right| = \left|\frac{20}{20}\right| = 1.$

Hence, the correct option is (a, c)

2. u = Object distance and f = focal length.

We have $u > 2f$.

The image is smaller than the object.

Hence, the correct option is (a, c)

3. $d_a = \frac{d}{\mu}$

$d_a = \frac{30}{5/3} = \frac{30 \times 3}{5}$

$d_a = 18$ cm

Normal shift $= d - d_a = 30 - 18 = 12$ cm.

Hence, the correct option is (b, d)

4. The options *b*, *c*, and *d* follow.

Hence, the correct option is (b, c, d)

5. Frequency of light will not change when it travels from any medium to any medium

$v = f\lambda;\ v \propto \lambda$

Hence, the correct option is (b, c, d)

6. The options a, *c*, and *d* follow.

Hence, the correct option is (a, c, d)

7. $\mu_D \sin\theta_c = \mu_r \sin 90°$

$\sin\theta_c = \frac{\mu_r}{\mu_D}$

(a) $\sin\theta_c = \frac{1}{\sqrt{2}};\ \theta_c = 45°$

(b) $\sin\theta_c = \frac{1}{2};\ \theta_c = 30°$

(c) $\sin\theta_c = \frac{2}{4}$

$\sin\theta_c = \frac{1}{2};\ \theta_c = 30°$

(d) $\sin\theta_c = \frac{4/3}{3/2} = \frac{8}{9}$

$\theta_c = \sin^{-1}\left[\frac{8}{9}\right]$

Hence, the correct option is (a, c, d)

8. (a and b):

$\frac{1}{f} = \left(\frac{\mu_g}{\mu_a} - 1\right)\left(\frac{1}{R_1} - \frac{1}{R_2}\right)$

$\frac{1}{f} = (\mu_g - 1)\left(\frac{2}{R}\right)$ (Since, $R_1 = R$, $R_2 = -R$ and $\mu_a = 1$)

$\frac{1}{f} = \left(\frac{3}{2} - 1\right)\left(\frac{2}{30}\right)$

$\frac{1}{f} = \frac{1}{2} \times \frac{2}{30}$

$f = 30$ cm.

(c) Given that u = -20.

$\frac{1}{f} = \frac{1}{v} - \frac{1}{u}$

$\frac{1}{30} = \frac{1}{v} + \frac{1}{20}$

$\frac{1}{v} = \frac{1}{30} - \frac{1}{20} = \frac{23}{60}$

$V = -60$ cm

(d) Given that u = - 40.

$\frac{1}{f} = \frac{1}{v} - \frac{1}{u}$

$\frac{1}{30} = \frac{1}{v} + \frac{1}{40}$

$\frac{1}{v} = \frac{1}{30} - \frac{1}{40}$

$\frac{1}{v} = \frac{4-3}{120}$

$v = 120$ cm

Hence, the correct option is (b, c, d)

9. (a and b): $d = 2i - A$

$d = 2(60°) - 60°$

$d = 60°$

(c and d): $\mu_{air} \sin I = \mu_p \sin r$

(1). $\sin 60° = \sqrt{3}. \sin r$

$\frac{\sqrt{3}}{2} = \sqrt{3} \sin r$

$\sin r = \frac{1}{2}$

$r = 30°$

Hence, the correct option is (a, c)

10. The options a, b, c, and d follow.
Hence, the correct option is (a, b, c, d)

Comprehension-Based Questions

11. $\mu_1 \sin i = \mu_2 \sin r$

$\frac{4}{3} \sin 30° = \frac{3}{2} \sin r$

$\frac{4}{3} \cdot \left(\frac{1}{2}\right) = \frac{3}{2} \sin r \Rightarrow \sin r = \frac{4}{9}.$

$r = \sin^{-1}[4/9]$

Hence, the correct option is (b)

12. $\mu_1 \sin 45° = \mu_2 \sin r$

$(1)\frac{1}{\sqrt{2}} = \sqrt{2} \sin r$

$\text{Sin } r = \frac{1}{2};$

$r = 30°$

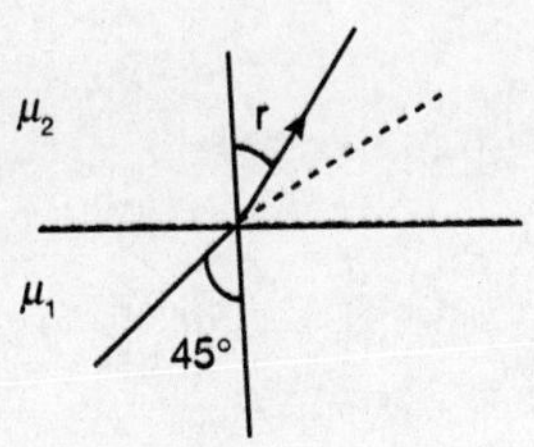

Hence, the correct option is (a)

13. $d = \angle i - \angle r$

$= 45° - 30° = 15°.$

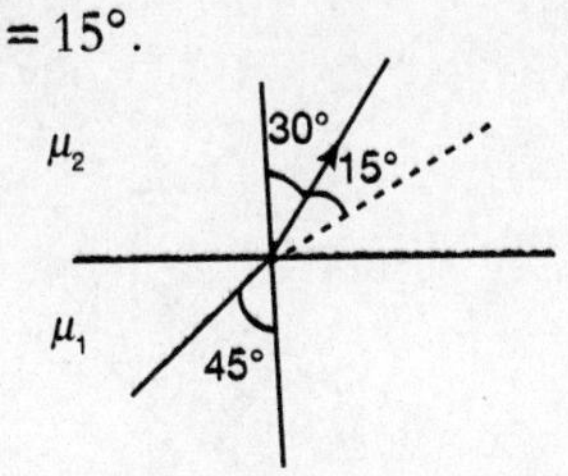

Hence, the correct option is (d)

14. Apparent depth $= \frac{R.d}{\mu}$

$\frac{(d_a)_1}{(d_a)_2} = \frac{\mu_2}{\mu_1}$

$= \frac{\frac{3}{2}}{\frac{4}{3}} = \frac{9}{8}$

Hence, the correct option is (c)

15. $\mu_1 \sin 45° = \mu_2 \sin \theta_2$

$\sqrt{3}\frac{1}{\sqrt{2}} = \sqrt{2} \sin \theta_2$

$\sin \theta_2 = \frac{\sqrt{3}}{2} \Rightarrow \theta_2 = 60°$

$\mu_2 \sin 60° = \mu_3 \sin 90°$

$\sqrt{2}\frac{\sqrt{3}}{2} = \mu_3 (1)$

$\mu_3 = \frac{\sqrt{3}}{\sqrt{2}} = \sqrt{\frac{3}{2}}$

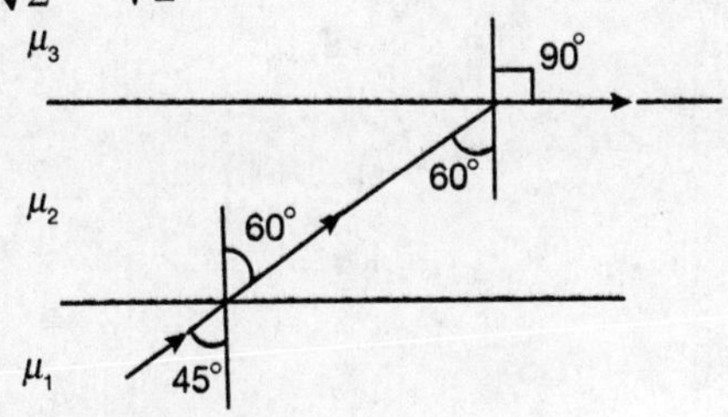

Hence, the correct option is (b)

Match the Column

16.

A ↔ e
B ↔ d
C ↔ c
D ↔ a
E ↔ b

Unit VII

Modern Physics

In this Unit

CHAPTER
9

Modern Physics

Remember

Before beginning this chapter, you should be able to:

- Explain the atomic structure.
- Study about discharge of electricity through gases by different experiments.
- Define the term radioactivity and types of radiations.

Key Ideas

After completing this chapter, you should be able to:

- Learn about the discovery of different subatomic particles.
- Discuss the concepts of radioactivity and types of radiations.
- Study radioactive series and its properties.
- Discuss the different nuclear reactions and the changes that happen inside the nucleus during these nuclear reactions.

Scientific Crypt

A Tribute to Madame Curie (1867 - 1934)

Madame Curie born on November 7th, 1867 in Warsaw, Poland was one of the first women scientists of the 20th century. She went to Paris for higher studies. She married Pierre Currie a professor in the school of physics in 1895.

Madame Curie along with her husband studied on Radioactivity and discovered that radioactivity was not a result of chemical reaction. She discovered radium and both of them received a Nobel Prize in 1903, for the studies they had done on radium. For her work on radioactivity she was awarded the Nobel Prize for chemistry once again in 1911.

In 1910, Madame Curie competed for a membership in a science academy in France. The male society of the academy tried to stop her advancement in Science. During her research she was exposed to an incredible level of radiations and died on July 4, 1934 in France.

FUN TIME

CROSSWORD

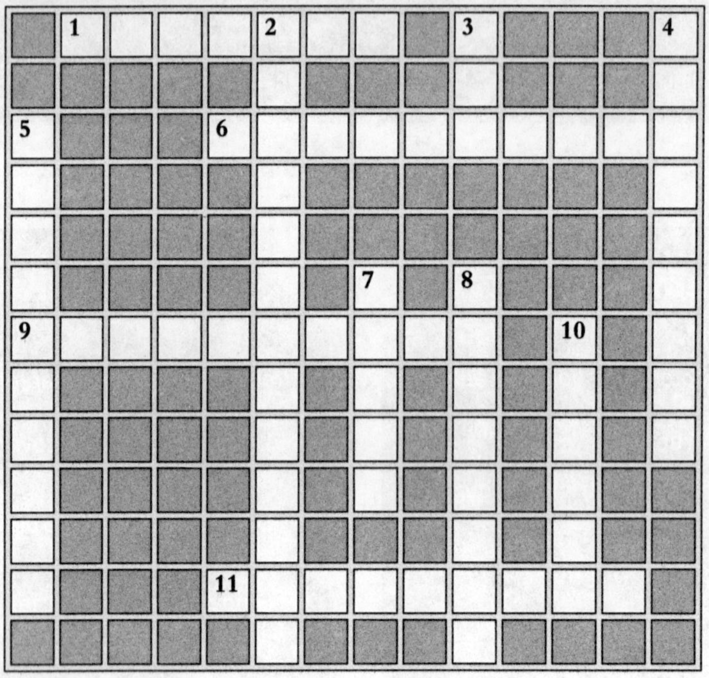

Across

1. $_6C^{13}$ and $_7N^{13}$ are examples of______.
6. The reproduction factor k is equal to one for a ______ reaction.
9. The positively charged radioactive radiation is______. (2 words)
11. The phenomenon of radioactivity was first discovered by ______.

Down

2. The number of protons present in a nucleus of an atom is equal to its_______. (2 words)
3. A radioactive substance reduced from 10 g to 2.5 g in 4 days. The half life period of the radioactive substance is ______ days.
4. ______ is used to slow down the neutrons in a nuclear reactor.
5. The radioactive radiation which is not deflected by electric and magnetic field is ______. (2 words)
7. The inert gas present in the radioactive series is ___.
8. $_{14}Si^{31}$ and $_{15}P^{32}$ are examples of_______.
10. Cathode rays ____ the gas through which they pass.

INTRODUCTION

Just as the universe at the macro-level has intrigued the human mind and intellect for ages, so at the micro level, man has been continuously in search of the smallest particle and has discovered a fathomless new world of sub-atomic particles. In the process of all the research having been done in this direction, a whole new branch of physics unfolded leading to the revolutionary discoveries and inventions—radio, transistor, X-ray, photoelectric effect, computers, etc., being only a part of the endless list which opened the doors to a new modern world. This branch of physics came to be referred to as modern physics. Nuclear physics, electronics, etc., are all off-shoots of the developments in modern physics.

Cathode Rays

Gases do not conduct electricity at ordinary pressures. However, if very high potential difference (more than 30 kV) is applied between the two electrodes in the presence of air, then electric charges pass through air. As electricity passes, intense light in the form of spark is produced. The flash of lightning during rainy days is an example of conduction of electricity through gases at normal atmospheric pressure.

When the gas pressure is lowered, it is found that gases conduct electricity at sufficiently high potential which is less than the potential required at ordinary pressure. The conduction of electricity through gases is also called discharge of electricity or simply electric discharge. During electric discharge, different gases emit light of different colours. To study the electric discharge phenomenon at low pressures, a given gas is enclosed in a hard glass tube called discharge tube; as shown in the Fig. (9.1).

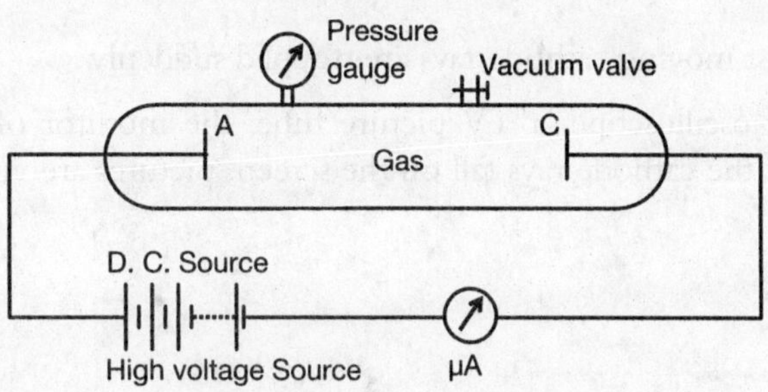

Figure 9.1 Discharge tube

Usually, the discharge tube is from 30 cm to 40 cm long and 2 cm to 3 cm in diameter. Two aluminium dishes, called electrodes are sealed in the tube on its ends. A high potential difference can be applied across the two electrodes. The electrode connected to positive terminal (high potential) of the DC source is called anode (A) and the one connected to negative terminal (low potential) is called cathode (C). To reduce the pressure inside the discharge tube, it is provided with a side tube which is connected to the vacuum pump.

To study the electric discharge, the pressure of the gas inside the tube is gradually reduced. The electric discharge passes through various stages, as the gas pressure is gradually reduced. Finally, at a pressure of about 0.01 mm of Hg, the tube becomes dark. The wall of the tube opposite to the cathode glows with greenish fluorescence which is due to the invisible radiation given out from the cathode surface called cathode rays.

Properties of Cathode Rays

1. Cathode rays are always emitted along the normal to the surface of cathode, irrespective of the position of the anode.
2. Cathode rays travel in a straight line path.

3. Cathode rays exert mechanical force on the objects placed in their path.
4. They are deflected in electric and magnetic fields.
5. They ionize the gas through which they pass.
6. Cathode rays produce fluorescence in many substances, like Zinc Sulphide, etc.
7. They can pass through thin metal foils.
8. They affect photographic plates.
9. When cathode rays are stopped by certain objects like metals, X-rays are produced.

Info Bytes!

The discovery of the electron came from studies on cathode rays, leading to a revolution in our understanding of atomic structure.

Nature of Cathode Rays

Cathode rays are deflected in electric and magnetic fields. This shows that they consist of charged particles. From the direction of deflection in electric and magnetic field, it is concluded that they are negatively-charged particles. In 1897, J. J. Thomson measured electron-mass ratio of those particles and proved that they are the common constituents of all matter. G. J. Stoney named these particles as electrons.

John Dalton in 1808, in his atomic theory had proposed that 'the atom is the smallest indivisible particle of matter.' However, discovery of electrons proved that atom itself is made up of still smaller particles and that the atom is divisible.

After the determination of e/m of electrons, the charge on it was found to be -1.6×10^{-19} C. Using $\frac{e}{m}$ ratio and charge, the mass of an electron is found to be 9.11×10^{-31} kg.

–by Amrican Professor, R.A. Millton

Uses of Cathode Rays

1. X-rays are produced when fast moving cathode rays are stopped suddenly.
2. The screen of a cathode ray oscilloscope, a TV picture tube, the monitor of a computer, etc. are coated with fluorescent substances. When the cathode rays fall on the screen, pictures are visible on the screen.

X-rays

X rays were discovered in the year 1895 by Wilhelm Röntgen of Germany. While studying electric discharge phenomena, he noticed that a screen (coated with barium salt) placed near a cathode ray tube was glowing whenever the tube was working. He further observed that the screen glowed even after the tube was covered with a black paper. On further investigation, he found that the photographic plates wrapped in a black paper were fogged when kept near the tube. When he placed his hand between the tube and photographic plate, he obtained a photograph of the bones. Roentgen concluded that some unknown, highly penetrating radiations were responsible for his observations. He named these unknown radiations as X-rays.

Production of X-rays

X-rays are produced when fast moving cathode rays are stopped by a block of a metal called target. The modern device used in the production of X-ray is called Coolidge tube, named after Dr Coolidge who designed it in the year 1913. It consists of a highly evacuated glass bulb as shown in the Fig. (9.2).

A filament F emits electrons when it is heated by passing a low current through it. It also acts as a cathode. It is surrounded by a molybdenum cylinder M. The cylinder M focusses the electrons as a fine beam. The target is tungsten which is embedded in a copper anode A. The anode A is inclined at 45° to the horizontal. It is cooled by circulating water around it. To produce X rays, high speed electrons are required. For this, the electrons emitted from the filament are accelerated by applying a high potential difference between the anode and the cathode. The fast moving electrons produce X-rays when they strike the target.

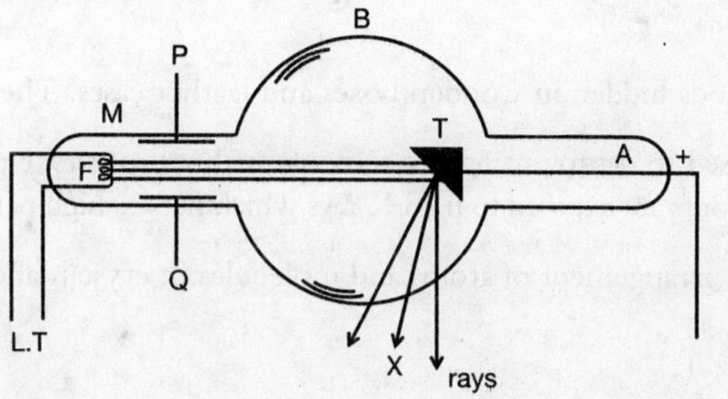

Figure 9.2 Coolidge tube

Properties of X-rays

1. X-rays are electromagnetic radiations. Their wavelength are very small, of the order of 1 A°. They are invisible.
2. X-rays, being electromagnetic radiations, travel in a straight line with a velocity of light (3×10^8 m/s^{-1}).
3. They affect photographic plates.

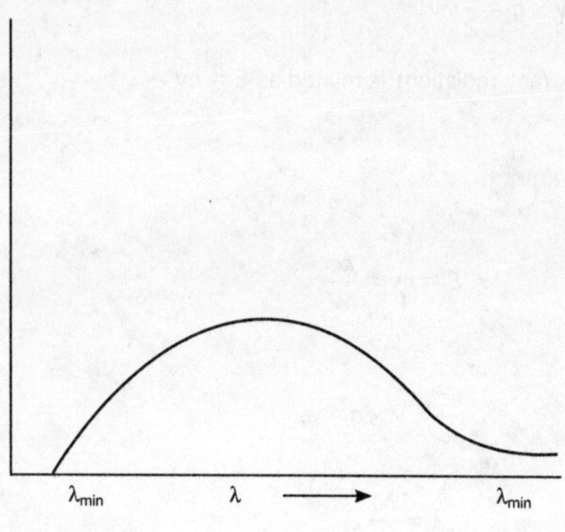

4. They produce fluorescence in certain materials.
5. They are not affected by electric and magnetic fields.
6. X-rays have a high penetrating power. However, they are stopped by bones, dead cells, etc.
7. They ionize the gases through which they pass.
8. They bring about chemical and biological changes in the substances and living beings through which they pass.
9. They are diffracted by crystals.

Uses of X-rays

X-rays are used extensively in different fields.

1. **Medicine:** In medicine, X-rays are employed to detect fracture and dislocation of the bones, presence of foreign bodies and early detection of certain diseases like tuberculosis.
2. **Industry and Engineering:** X-rays are used to detect flaws in machinery parts, metal castings, metal structures, etc.
3. X-rays are used to detect goods hidden in wooden boxes and leather cases. They are also used in testing.
4. **Radiotherapy:** X-rays are used to destroy malignant tumours without surgery, especially when malignant tumours are situated deep inside. The tumours are exposed to hard X-rays which possess high penetrating power.
5. X-rays are used to study the arrangement of atoms and molecules in crystals and other matter.

EXAMPLE 9.1

In a Coolidge tube, cathode rays emitted from the cathode are accelerated through a potential difference of 20 kV. Find the minimum wavelength of the X–rays produced.

(Take Planck's constant h = 6.6×10^{-34} J s)

SOLUTION

When cathode rays fall through a potential difference, the work done on them equals change in their kinetic energy. When cathode rays are stopped, they lose kinetic energy which is then converted into X-rays.

Thus,

Work done on cathode rays (W) $= V \times q = \frac{1}{2}mv^2$ (1)

The energy and frequency of X-rays (any radiation) is related as $E = h\nu$

where, 'h' is Planck's constant.

But $\nu = \frac{c}{\lambda}$

$$\therefore E = h\nu = \frac{hc}{\lambda} \qquad (2)$$

Equating (1) and (2) and solving λ.

$$\frac{hc}{\lambda} = V \times q$$

$$\lambda = \frac{hc}{Vq}$$

Substituting $h = 6.6 \times 10^{-34}$ J s, we have

$$c = 3 \times 10^8 \text{ m s}^{-1}$$

$$V = 20 \times 10^3\ V,\ q = 1.6 \times 10^{-19}\text{ C}$$

$$\lambda = \frac{6.6 \times 10^{-34} \times 3 \times 10^8}{20 \times 10^3 \times 1.6 \times 10^{-19}} = 0.625 \text{ Å (approximately)}$$

Radioactivity

Radioactivity is the phenomenon of self-disintegration and spontaneous emission of radiation by some unstable nuclei with atomic number greater than 82.

Natural Radioactivity

The phenomenon of radioactivity was first discovered by A.H. Becquerel and further investigations were made by Madame Marie Curie and Prof. Pierre Curie.

In 1896 Henri Becquerel, the French scientist, quite accidentally discovered radioactivity while studying the phenomenon of fluorescence. He found that the photographic plates get fogged when placed near pitchblende, an ore of uranium. It was discovered that certain substances like, uranium radium, etc., emit some rays which were initially referred to as 'Becquerel rays'. Research work carried out by the Curies led to the discovery that these rays are emitted due to a phenomenon called radioactivity which is a nuclear phenomenon of self-disintegration.

This type of spontaneous radiation is referred to as 'natural radioactivity'. Substances which give such spontaneous emission of radiations are known as radioactive substances.

α, β and γ- Radiations

The radiations emitted by radioactive substances were found to consist of three distinct constituents. They were called alpha, beta and gamma radiations. When the radiations were allowed to pass through an electric field, the constituent which deflected towards the negative plate was called α-rays. The constituent which got deflected towards the positively-charged plate was called β- rays. The constituent which emerged undeflected was called γ-radiations.

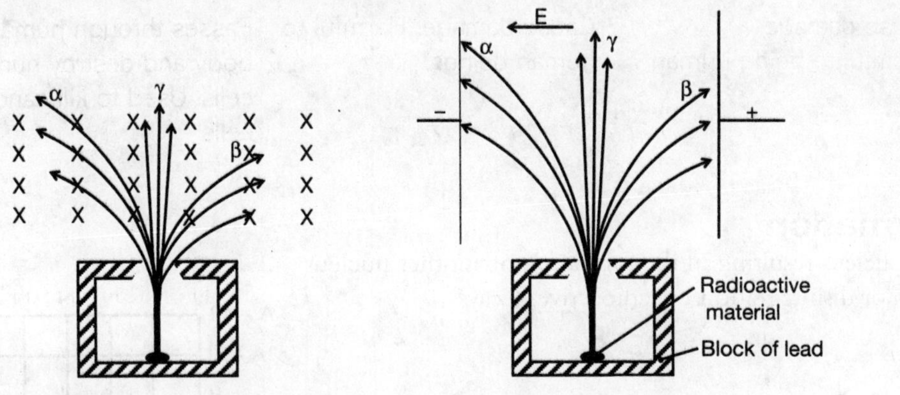

Deflection in a magnetic field

Deflection in an electric field

Figure 9.3 Deflection of alpha, beta and gamma particle in magnetic and electric field

Info Bytes!

- Some fruits like bananas are naturally radioactive due to the presence of potassium-40.
- Alpha particles can be stopped by a sheet of paper, while gamma rays require lead or several inches of concrete for shielding.

Properties of α, β and γ Radiations

Table 9.1 Different properties of radiations

Property	α-rays	β-rays	γ-rays
1. Nature	Positively charged	Negatively charged	Electrically neutral
2. Constituents	He^{++} (2 protons and 2 neutrons)	High energy electrons	Electromagnetic radiations
3. Speed	Nearly 10^7 m s^{-1}	About 2.7×10^8 m s^{-1}	3×10^8 m s^{-1}
4. Rest mass	4 times the mass of a proton, i.e., 6.64 z $\times 10^{-27}$ kg	Equal to the mass of an electron, i.e., 9.1 $\times 10^{-31}$ kg	No mass

(Continued)

Property	α-rays	β-rays	γ-rays
5. Charge	Positive charge = +3.2 × 10^{-19}C	Negative charge = −1.6 × 10^{-19}C	No charge
6. Specific charge (q/m)	4.83 × 10^7 C kg^{-1}	1.76 × 10^{11}C kg^{-1}	–
7. Wavelength	–	–	10^{-13}m (less than the wavelength of X-rays)
8. Effect of electric field	Deflects towards the negative plate	Deflects towards the positive plate, deflection more than that for α rays	No effect
9. Effect of magnetic field	Less deflected.	More deflected, direction opposite to that of α-rays	No effect
10. Ionizing power	Intense ionization (10000 times that of γ-rays)	High ionization power (100 times that of γ rays)	Little
11. Penetrating power	Small (3-8 cm in air)	Large (up to few metres in air)	Very large (up to a few hundred metres in air)
12. Stopping substance	Thin paper, human skin	About 1 mm of lead or about 3 mm of aluminium	About 30 cm of iron or few metres of concrete
13. Effect on photographic plate. Effect on a fluorescant screen.	They affect photographic plates and cause scintillations on afluorescent screen	Affect photographic plates and cause scintillations on a fluorescent screen	Affect photographic plates and cause scintillations on a fluorescent screen
14. Biological damage	Cause damage. Harmful to being human	Cause damage. Harmful to human beings.	Passes through human body and destroy human cells. Used to kill cancer cells

Radioactive Transformation

The disintegration of an unstable nucleus resulting in the formation of another nucleus is called radioactive transformation or disintegration or radioactive decay.

Types of Transformation

1. **α-Decay or α-Emission:** When an α-particle is emitted from a radioactive nucleus, the atomic number (Z) decreases by 2 and the mass number (A) decreases by 4.

$$_ZP^A \rightarrow {}_{Z-2}D^{A-4} + {}_2H_e^4 (\alpha - \text{Particle})$$

'P' is called parent nucleus.

'D' is called daughter nucleus.

Example: $_{92}U^{238} \rightarrow {}_{90}Th^{234} + {}_2He^4$

Here, uranium is the parent nucleus and thorium is the daughter nucleus.

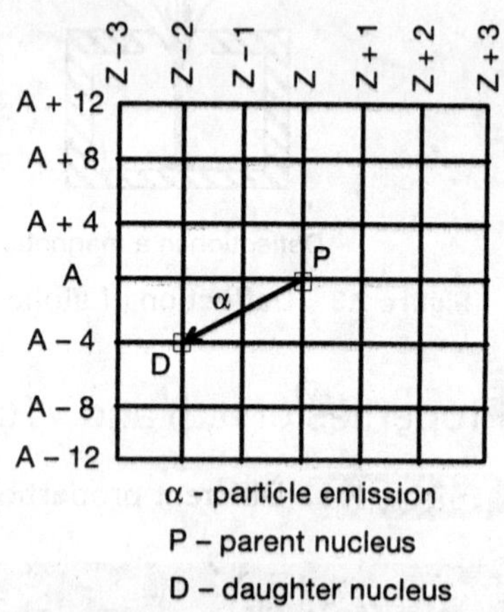

Figure 9.4 Graph between atomic number and mass number for an alpha particle

This is summarized as Rutherford and Soddy's law of α-emission, which states that 'whenever an α- particle is emitted from a radioactive nucleus, the atomic number decreases by 2, the mass number decreases by 4 and the position of the element shifts by two places to the left in the periodic table'.

2. **β-Decay or β-Emission:** The presence of excess neutrons in an unstable nucleus lead to a neutron changing into a proton by emitting an electron (for charge conservation).

$$_0n^1 \rightarrow {_1H^1} + {_{-1}e^0} + \upsilon$$

(neutron) (proton) (β-particle) (υ-electron-anti-neutrine)

In general, $_ZP^A \rightarrow {_{Z+1}D^A} + {_{-1}\beta^0}$

(parent nucleus) (daughter nucleus) (β-particle)

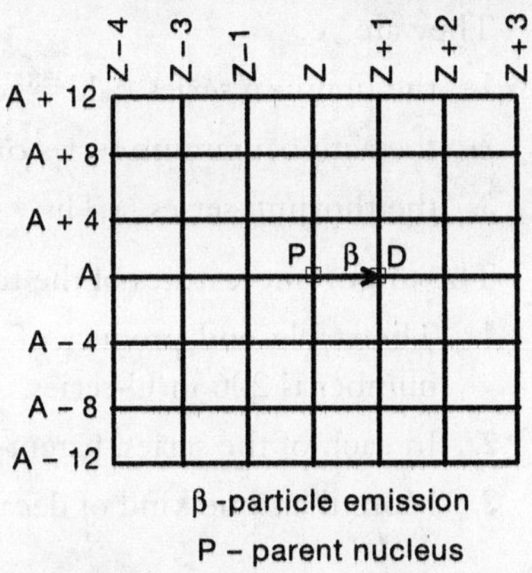

Figure 9.5 Graph between atomic number and mass number for a beta particle

Example:

$$_{90}Th^{234} \rightarrow {_{91}Pa^{234}} + {_{-1}\beta^0}$$

(thorium) (protactinium) (β-particle)

Rutherford and Soddy's law of β-decay summarizes the above as 'Whenever a β-particle is emitted from a radioactive nucleus, the atomic number increases by 1 whereas the mass number remains the same and the position of the element shifts one place to the right in the periodic table'.

3. **γ-Decay** or **γ-Emission:** There is no change in the atomic number (Z) or in the mass number (A) of the atom which undergoes gamma decay. However, the emission of γ-rays results in a change in the energy state of the nucleus.

In a single radioactive decay, both α-decay and β-decay never take place together. There will be either an α-decay or a β-decay, which may be accompanied by a γ-emission.

Radioactive Series

An unstable parent nucleus undergoes disintegration several times producing daughter nuclei, which would also be unstable. The radioactive daughter nucleus would undergo further disintegration giving rise to a new daughter nucleus. This sequential decay of a given radioactive nucleus resulting in the production of new nuclei at each stage and giving rise to a series of elements is called radioactive decay series.

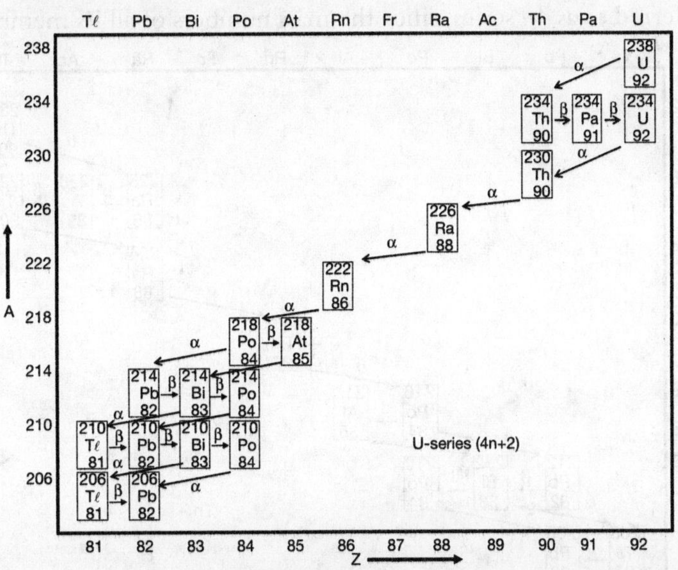

Figure 9.6 Uranium series

There are three radioactive series depending on the starting element naturally available on the Earth.

They are:

1. the uranium series ($_{92}U^{238}$ series),
2. the actino-uranium series or Actinium series (Ac-U series) and
3. the thorium series ($_{90}Th^{232}$ series).

The important features of the radioactive series are as follows:

1. The stable end-product of all the three series is an isotope of lead having an atomic number 82, but the mass number is 206 in U-series, 207 in Ac U-series and 208 in Th-series.
2. In each of the series, parent–daughter sequences exist.
3. More than one kind of decay is possible for an intermediate radioactive species.

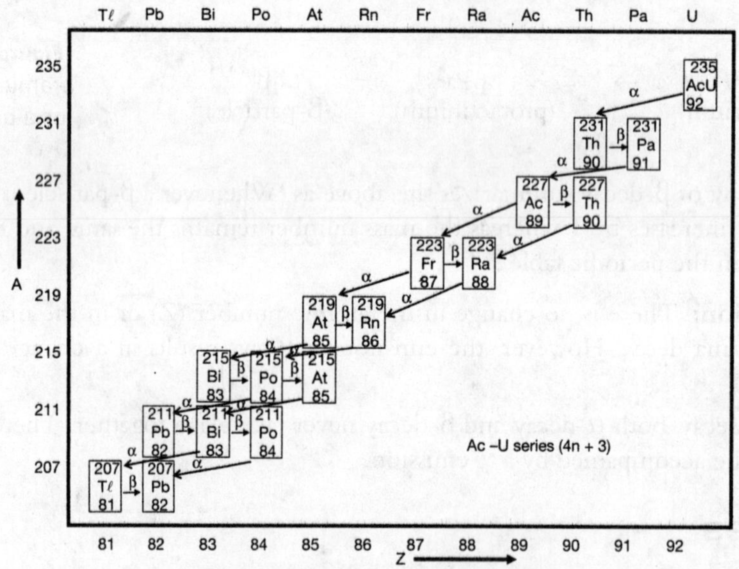

Figure 9.7 Actino–uranium series

4. In each of the three series, the element Radon (Rn) with atomic number 86 is present.
5. In all the three series, a change in the mass number A, [if any (due to α-decay)] is always equal to 4.
6. The thorium series is referred to as 4*n* series, since the mass numbers of all its members are multiples of 4.

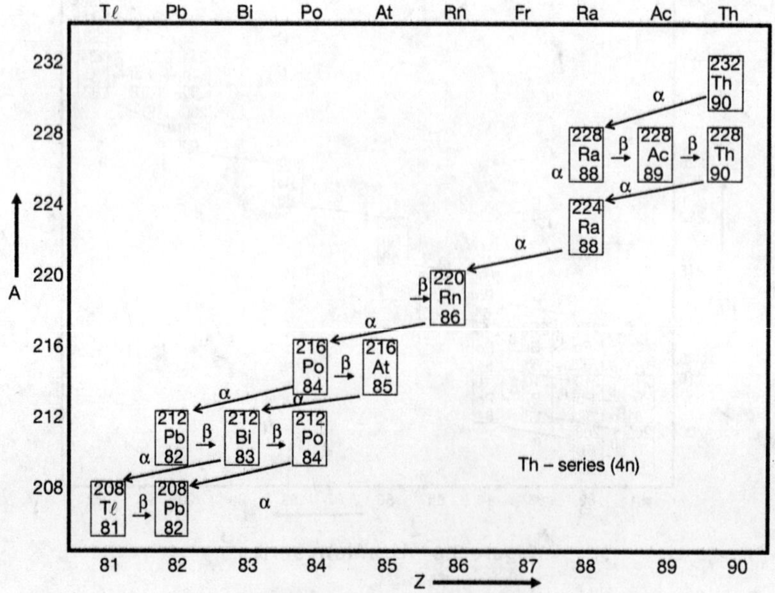

Figure 9.8 Thorium series

7. The uranium series is referred to as $(4n+2)$ series, since (A–2) is always a multiple of 4 for each one of the elements of the series. (A is mass number of elements.)
8. The actinium series is identified as $(4n+3)$ series, since (A – 3) is always a multiple of 4 for each one of the elements of the series. (A is mass number of elements.)
9. The neptunium series ($_{93}NP^{237}$series) is obtained from artificially produced radioactive material. This series is also known as $(4n + 1)$ series.

It is found that during radioactive transformation due to either α-emission or β-emission, not all the nuclei undergo disintegration simultaneously. Also the rate at which the decay takes place depends on the number of parent atoms available at a given instant.

This is summarized in the law of radioactive disintegration.

Law of Radioactive Disintegration

The law of radioactive disintegration states that 'in any radioactive substance, the number of nuclei disintegrating per second is directly proportional to the number of nuclei present'.

$$\frac{\Delta N}{\Delta t} \alpha N$$

$$\frac{\Delta N}{\Delta t} = -\lambda N$$

where, λ, the proportionality constant, is called decay constant. The negative sign indicates that the number of nuclei decreases with time.

Using calculus, we can show that $N = N_0 e^{-\lambda t}$ where, N_o and N are the number of nuclei of the substance at instants when time is zero and 't' s, respectively and 'e' is an irrational number.

The Half-Life Period

The half-life period (T) of a radioactive substance is defined as the time during which half the amount of the substance disintegrates.

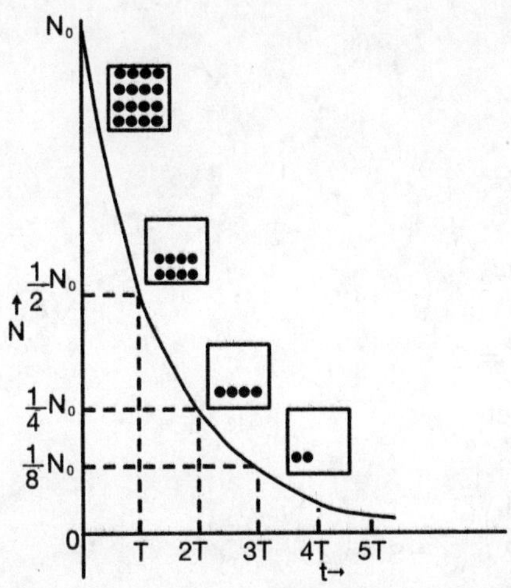

Info Bytes!

Technetium-99m, used in medical imaging, has a half-life of only 6 hours, making it ideal for quick studies without long-term radiation exposure.

Figure 9.9 Graph to show a half-life period of a radioactive substance

For example, if there are 4 atoms with a half-life period of 2 seconds, it mean that after 2 seconds exactly 2 atoms will disintegrate. In fact, it is just the probability of half of the atoms disintegrate (approximately).

The half-life period (T) is different for different substances. It is impossible to say exactly when a particular atom of a radioactive element would disintegrate. The fraction of the substance decaying during a given period will be the same as that during any other equal period. Smaller value of T (half-life period) indicates faster decay. Decay constant (λ) of a radioactive substance is defined as $\lambda = (0.693/T)$.

The higher value of λ indicates faster decay. Thus, the decay constant is a characteristic property of a radioactive element.

EXAMPLE 9.2 If (7/8) th of the initial mass of the radioactive substance decays in 15 days, then what is the half-life period of the radioactive substance?

(Take Planck's constant h = 6.6×10^{-34} J s)

SOLUTION

Let the initial number of radioactive nuclei be N_0.

Then, after a half-life period, the number of nuclei present would be $N_0 \times \frac{1}{2}$ (1)

After two half-lives, the number of nuclei present would be

$$\frac{1}{2} \times \left(N_0 \times \left(\frac{1}{2}\right)\right) = N_0\left(\frac{1}{2}\right)^2.$$

After 'n' half-lives, the number of nuclei present would be $N = N_0\left(\frac{1}{2}\right)^n$

If 't' is the given time period and T is the half-life period of the radioactive substance, then,

$$n = \frac{t}{T} \tag{2}$$

Also, if 'm_o' is the initial mass and 'm' the mass of undecayed nuclei of the substance, then,

$$\frac{N}{N_0} = \frac{m}{m_0} \tag{3}$$

∴ Equation (1) can be written as

$$m = m_0\left(\frac{1}{2}\right)^n \tag{4}$$

In the given problem, undecayed mass $m = m_0 - \frac{7}{8}m_0 = \frac{1}{8}m_0$

$$t = 15 \text{ days}, T = ?$$

Substituting the values of 'm' and 'm_0' in equation (4), we get

$$\frac{1}{8}m_0 = m_0\left(\frac{1}{2}\right)^{\frac{15}{T}} \Rightarrow \frac{1}{8} = \left(\frac{1}{2}\right)^{\frac{15}{T}}$$

$$\Rightarrow \frac{1}{8} = \left(\frac{1}{2}\right)^{\frac{15}{T}} \Rightarrow \frac{15}{T} = 3$$

$$T = \frac{15}{3} \text{ days} = 5 \text{ days}$$

EXAMPLE 9.3 A 100g sample of a radioactive substance decays to 50g in 3 days. How much of the substance will remain undecayed after 12 days?

SOLUTION

Given that 100g decays to 50g in 3 days, the half-life period, T, must be 3 days. Using the formula:

$$m = m_0 \times \left(\frac{1}{2}\right)^n$$

$m_0 = 100\ g$

$$\text{No. of half-lives } (n) \text{ in 12 days} = \frac{12 \text{ days}}{3 \text{ days/half-life}} = 4 \text{ half-lives}$$

Substituting the values, we have

$$m = 100g \times \left(\frac{1}{2}\right)^4 = 100g \times \left(\frac{1}{16}\right) = 6.25g$$

So, after 12 days, 6.25g of the radioactive substance will remain undecayed.

Isotopes, Isobars and Isotones

The atoms of some elements exist in different forms depending on the variations in their atomic numbers and mass numbers but have same common factor and are referred to as isotopes, isobars or isotones.

Isotopes

Isotopes are the atoms of the same element having the same atomic number, but different mass number due to difference in the number of neutrons in their nuclei.

Examples of isotopes

1. $_1H^1$, $_1H^2$, $_1H^3$ isotopes of hydrogen
2. $_{17}Cl^{35}$, $_{17}Cl^{37}$ isotopes of chlorine
3. $_8O^{16}$, $_8O^{17}$, $_8O^{18}$ isotopes of oxygen
4. $_{92}U^{235}$, $_{92}U^{238}$ isotopes of uranium
5. $_{19}K^{39}$, $_{19}K^{40}$ isotopes of potassium

Isobars

Atoms of different elements, having the same mass number but different atomic number are called isobars.

Examples of isobars

1. $_6C^{13}$, $_7N^{13}$
2. $_{19}K^{40}$, $_{20}Ca^{40}$
3. $_{18}Ar^{40}$, $_{20}Ca^{40}$
4. $_{12}Mg^{24}$, $_{11}Na^{24}$

Isotones

Atoms with their nuclei having the same number of neutrons but different number of protons are called isotones.

Examples of isotones: The atomic number and the mass number of $_{14}Si^{31}$ are 14 and 31, respectively, which give the number of neutrons as 31 – 14 = 17. The atomic number and the mass number of $_{15}P^{32}$ are 15 and 32, respectively, which give the number of neutrons as 32 – 15 = 17. Thus, $_{14}Si^{31}$ and $_{15}P^{32}$ are isotones.

Artificial Transmutation

Unstability in the nucleus leads to a natural and spontaneous radioactive disintegration only in certain heavy elements. However, in 1919, Rutherford succeeded in producing nuclei of lighter elements which exhibit the property of radioactivity.

Definition

Artificial transmutation is the process of transformation of one element into another by artificial disintegration means of bombarding it with high energy particles.

$_2He^4$	+	$_7N^{14}$	$\rightarrow$	$_8O^{17}$	+	$_1H^1$
Incident α-particle		nitrogen (target)		oxygen		proton

Such artificial transmutation can be achieved by employing α-particles, protons, deuterons, neutrons or small nuclei as the bombarding particles. These particles, which are used for the bombardment of target nuclei, are referred to as 'projectiles'.

Artificial Transmutation by α-Particles

Artificial transmutation of fluorine and aluminum is possible by using the α-particles as projectiles.

$$_2He^4 + {}_9F^{19} \rightarrow {}_{10}Ne^{22} + {}_1H^1$$

$$_2He^4 + {}_{13}Al^{27} \rightarrow {}_{14}Si^{30} + {}_1H^1$$

Artificial Transmutation by Protons

$$_1H^1 + {}_3Li^7 \rightarrow {}_2He^4 + {}_2He^4$$

$$_1H^1 + {}_{11}Na^{23} \rightarrow {}_{10}Ne^{20} + {}_2He^4$$

In these transmutations, a proton (nucleus of hydrogen atom) is used as a projectile to transmute the lighter elements lithium and sodium. In this type of artificial transmutation which was conducted by Cockroft and Walton in 1932, the α-particles are obtained as one of the products.

In some of the artificial transmutations, the product nucleus is found to be radioactive. It undergoes further disintegration by emitting particles like neutrons and protons. It was first discovered in 1934 by Madam Irene Curie Joliot and M. Frederic Joliot. This phenomenon came to be referred to as 'artificial radioactivity'.

Artificial or induced radioactivity is a nuclear process in which a stable element, which is not radioactive, is converted into another element, which is radioactive in nature.

The Curies found that when the atoms of stable aluminium were bombarded by α-particles, an unstable isotope of phosphorous, $_{15}P^{30}$was produced which, being radioactive, disintegrated producing stable silicon ($_{14}Si^{30}$) and a particle whose mass was the same as that of an electron, but with a positive charge. This particle was referred to as a 'positron', discovered by Carl Anderson.

$$_{13}Al^{27} + {}_2He^4 \longrightarrow {}_{15}P^{30} + {}_0n^1 + \text{energy}$$

$$_{15}P^{30} \longrightarrow {}_{14}Si^{30} + {}_1e^0 + \text{(positron)}$$

Thus, we see that while β-particles are emitted in natural radioactivity, positrons are emitted in the artificial radioactivity.

Instead of α-particles, energized protons, neutrons, etc., can also be used to induce radioactivity in stable atoms. These isotopes of elements which are obtained in artificial transmutation and are radioactive in nature are called 'radioisotopes'. About 500 radioactive isotopes have been artificially produced by the bombardment of stable elements with α-particles.

Uses of Radioisotopes

Some of the applications of radioisotopes are as follows:

1. Sodium - 24 isotope is used to detect a clot in the blood in the human body.
2. Cobalt - 60 isotope is used to kill cancer cells since it is an intense source of γ-radiations.
3. Iodine - 131 isotope is used to test the functioning of the thyroid gland.
4. Radioisotopes like $_{27}Co^{60}$ are used to detect the internal flaws in a cast-material.
5. Which are also used in agriculture in the selection of fertilizers.
6. Unnecessary mutations of plants can be prevented by irradiating seeds using radioisotopes.
7. Perishable food items can be kept fresh for longer periods by exposing them to mild γ radiations from a radioisotope.
8. Radioactive gases are injected into the atmosphere and by suitable detectors, the course of monsoon winds and the changes they undergo can be studied.

Carbon Dating or Radioactive Dating

Carbon in the atmosphere is found to exist as three isotopes $_6C^{12}$, $_6C^{13}$ and $_6C^{14}$. $_6C^{14}$ (or C-14) is an unstable isotope with half-life period of 5730 years, and is continuously produced in the atmosphere by the action of cosmic rays on atmospheric nitrogen.

$$\underset{\text{Atmospheric nitrogen}}{_7N^{14}} + \underset{\text{Neutron of cosmic radiation}}{_0n^1} \rightarrow \underset{\text{Radioactive carbon}}{_6C^{14}} + \underset{\text{Proton}}{_1H^1}$$

This C-14 is continuously absorbed by the cells of living beings. In living beings, the ratio C-14:C-12 is constant. In dead plants or animals, C-14 undergoes radioactive decay without replenishment. By determining the ratio C–14/C-12 in fossils, their age is determined. This process of estimating the age by measuring the disintegration of C-14 is known as 'Carbon dating'.

For estimating the age of Earth or rocks, U-235 isotope is used. This is done by determining the present ratio of U-235 to stable lead isotope.

Effects of Radioactive Radiations

The α, β and γ rays emitted during radioactive disintegration of an unstable substance cause several biological effects (kill the living cells and cause radiation burns) on human beings.

The biological effects are of the following types:

1. Short-term recoverable effects
2. Long-term irrecoverable effects
3. Genetic effects

The first two types are limited to the affected person, whereas the third type affects the later generations.

Safety precautions for the people regularly working with radioactive substances:

1. Special lead-lined aprons, gloves, etc., should be worn and long tongs made of lead should be used while handling radioactive substances.
2. Special film badges should be worn to determine periodically the amount of radiation to which a person is exposed, and to ascertain whether any particular person is exposed to more than the permissible levels.
3. The radioactive substances should be handled with the utmost care and stored in lead containers with narrow openings to stop radiations in all directions.

Background Radiations

Background radiations are those radioactive radiations that everyone is exposed to due to the presence of natural radioactive substances on the Earth as well as the cosmic radiations, and also the radioactive substances present in the body.

Internal background radiations are from the radioactive substances K-40, and C-14 present in the entire body and radium present in the bones. External background radiations are from the cosmic rays and radiations from the radioactive rocks on the Earth.

Geiger Counter

Geiger counter is an instrument used for recording the rate of emission from a radioactive substance.

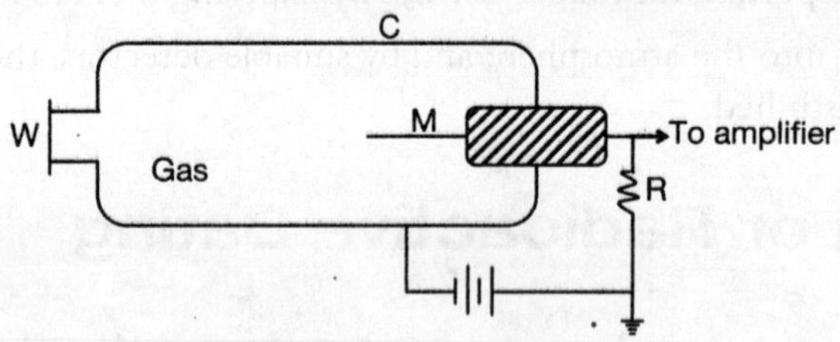

Figure 9.10 Geiger counter

It consists of a metallic cylinder '*C*' and a metallic wire 'M' fixed along the axis of a metallic cylinder. The cylinder is filled with argon gas with traces of chlorine and the pressure inside it is maintained between 50 mm of Hg and 100 mm of Hg. A potential difference that is slightly less than the necessary potential to produce discharge in the gas is maintained between the wire and the cylinder. α-particles from a given source enter the cylinder through the thin mica window '*W*' and ionize the gas molecules in the cylinder. This leads to a rapid build-up of current and a momentary change of potential across 'R'. This electric surge is amplified and given to an electronic counter.

Nuclear Energy

The experiments and the studies conducted by Rutherford in the early twentieth century, in understanding the atomic structure led to further research and the discovery of the process of artificial transmutation. This along with the discovery of neutron in 1932 by Chadwick gave a new direction to the research being carried out by the physicists in Europe. In 1939, the German scientists Otto Hahn and Fritz Strassmann conducted several experiments and showed that heavy uranium atoms could be split into lighter atoms of smaller atomic number. But what excited the scientists most was the discovery that these reactions resulted in a substantial difference in the masses of the products and reactants. And when Einstein proposed the mass-energy equivalence with his famous $E = mc^2$ equation, the foundation for the fission and fusion reactions was laid down, shifting the focus to the (nuclear) energy released in these nuclear reactions.

Before we venture into the study of these nuclear reactions in detail, we need to understand some basic concepts like mass defect, binding energy, etc.

Atomic Mass

The mass of an atom is measured in units called unified 'atomic mass unit'(*u*); defined as 1/12th of the mass of a neutral carbon atom $_6C^{12}$ (Carbon – 12 atom).

$$1 \text{ u} = 1.6605402 \times 10^{-27} \text{ kg.}$$

Thus, the mass of a carbon atom is 12 *u*.

Example: Estimation of mass of helium nucleus.

Consider a helium atom $_2He^4$.

It has 2 electrons, 2 protons and 2 neutrons.

The mass of a proton = 1.0078 u

The mass of a neutron = 1.0087 u

$\therefore$ The total expected mass of the nucleus = 2 × 1.0078 + 2 × 1.0087
= 4.0330 u

But the actual mass of a helium nucleus determined experimentally is 4.0026 u. Then, what happened to the remaining mass of 0.0304 u?

Mass Defect

The difference between the sum of the individual masses of constituents in a nucleus and the mass of the nucleus itself is called 'mass defect'. In the above example, the mass defect is found to be 0.0304 *u*.

Einstein's Mass Energy Equivalence

According to Einstein, mass and energy are not independent, but are mutually convertible. Any body which changes its energy content '*E*' undergoes a change in its mass, 'Δm' so that the ratio $\frac{E}{\Delta m}$ is always constant, i.e., if the energy of a particle is increased, its mass also increases.

Thus, if m_0 is the 'rest mass' (mass of the particle at rest), then the 'moving mass' *m* of the particle having velocity '*v*' is given by,

$$m = \frac{m_0}{\sqrt{1-\frac{V^2}{c^2}}}$$

Einstein's mass-energy equivalence is given as $E = (\Delta m)c^2$, where, c is the velocity of light in vacuum. Thus, the mass of 1 u = 931.5 × 10^6 eV = 931.5 MeV. 1 kg of mass, if completely changed into energy, would be equivalent to 9 × 10^{10} MJ. (Electron volt ($\overline{ev}$) is unit of energy and 1 eV = 1.6 × 10^{-19}J)

What had puzzled the scientists the most was how the protons having positive charge are packed together within a distance of less than 10^{-15} m without being repelled due to the electrostatic forces. Since the gravitational force of attraction between the protons is far less than the electrostatic force of repulsion between them, there must be some other stronger force binding the protons staying together. This force is called nuclear force.

Similarly, the role of the neutrons was also puzzling. It was thought that a neutron is formed when the electron of a hydrogen atom collapses into the nucleus under high and extreme pressure, bringing the electron very close to the proton and holding it there, by some form of nuclear energy. Thus, a neutron (a collapsed hydrogen atom) is electrically neutral.

It must be noted that these nuclear forces are much stronger than the electrostatic or electromagnetic forces. Thus, the nucleons – protons and neutrons are bound together by the nuclear energy arising out of the mass defect and the mass-energy equivalence.

Thus, here we define two quantities, binding energy and binding energy per nucleon, which play an important role in the stability of a nucleus.

Binding Energy

The nucleons of a nucleus are bound together by the energy that results from the loss in the total mass of the nucleons when they are held in the nucleus, i.e., the mass defect; this energy is called binding energy and is measured in MeV.

Binding energy of a nucleus = $\Delta m \times 931.5$ MeV,

where, Δm is the mass defect of the nucleus in atomic mass units '*u*'.

Thus, for the nucleus of a helium atom, the binding energy = $0.0304\ u \times 931.5$ MeV = 28.32 MeV

Binding Energy Per Nucleon

It is the average energy required to extract one nucleon from the nucleus.

$$\text{Binding energy per nucleon} = \frac{\text{Binding energy}}{\text{A}}$$

Binding energy per nucleon is the measure of the stability of the atom. The higher is the binding energy per nucleon, the greater is the stability of the atom.

EXAMPLE 9.4 If a nuclear reaction results in a decrease of mass by 0.5 unified atomic mass units, how much energy is released in the process?

SOLUTION

$\Delta m = -0.5\mu$ (The negative sign indicates a decrease in mass)

Using the equation, $E = mc^2$

We have, m = change in mass = –0.5u; c = speed of light ≈ 3×10^8 m/s

$E = \Delta m \times c^2 = -0.5\mu \times c^2 = -0.5 \times 931.5\text{Mev} = -465.75\text{MeV}$

(To convert this energy to MeV, we use the equivalence of 1u being approximately 931.5 MeV/c^2)

The negative sign indicates that the energy is released. So, the nuclear reaction releases 465.75 MeV of energy due to a decrease in mass by 0.5u.

EXAMPLE 9.5 Calculate the mass defect and binding energy for $^{60}Ni_{28}$ which has a nucleus of mass 59.930*u*. Given that the mass of a proton m_p is 1.0078*u* and the mass of a neutron m_n is 1.0087*u*.

SOLUTION

For $^{60}Ni_{28}$,

Number of protons (Z) = 28; and, Number of neutrons (N) = (60 – 28) = 32

Total mass of protons = $Z \times m_p$ = (28 × 1.0078*u*) = 28.218*u*

Total mass of neutrons = $N \times m_n$ = 32 × 1.0087*u* = 32.2784*u*

Total mass if separate = (28.2184*u* + 32.2784*u*) = 60.4968*u*

Now, mass defect Δm = (60.4968*u* – 59.930*u*) = 0.5668*u*

Binding energy = (Δm × 931.5MeV) = (0.5668*u* × 931.5MeV) = 528.3422MeV

Thus, for $^{60}Ni_{28}$, the mass defect is 0.5668*u* and its binding energy is 528.3422MeV.

Nuclear Reactions

Any reaction that tends to change the configuration of the nucleus of an atom can be termed as a nuclear reaction.

There are two types of nuclear reactions. They are:

1. Nuclear fission reactions
2. Nuclear fusion reactions

In electron volt MeV the energy released in a nuclear reaction is generally expressed.

$$1 \text{ eV} = 1.602 \times 10^{-19} \text{ J.}$$

Fission Reactions

As already studied in natural radioactivity, U^{235} and U^{238} are highly unstable and emit powerful radiations. In this process, uranium isotope ultimately ends up as 'stable lead', releasing energy of 1 MeV to 5 MeV. Thus, if it is possible to break an unstable nucleus into two or more smaller ones, this would lead to the release of a great amount of energy. This is the principle of a nuclear fission reaction.

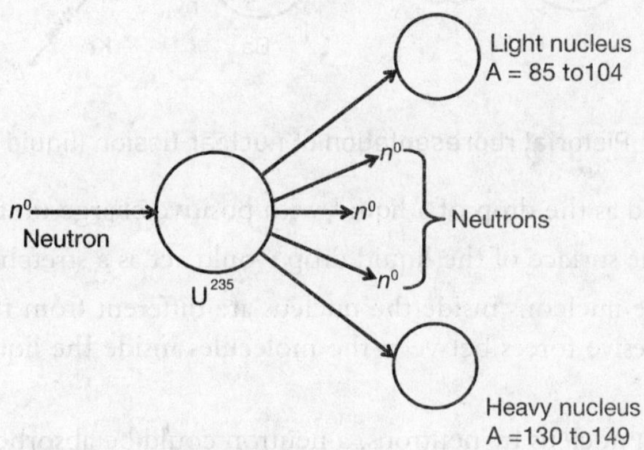

Figure 9.11 Fission reaction

Nuclear fission is a process in which the heavy nucleus of a radioactive substance like uranium is split into lighter nuclei by the bombardment of a low energy (slow moving) neutron, the reaction being accompanied by the release of energy and two or three or more neutrons.

The low energy neutrons used for the bombardment of the nuclei of heavier atoms of uranium are called 'thermal neutrons'. They have a kinetic energy of less than 1eV.

The salient features of a fission reaction are as follows:

1. A fission reaction takes place when the nucleus of a heavy atom such as U-235 is bombarded with a slow moving, low energy thermal neutron.
2. Fast moving neutrons cannot produce a fission.
3. The products of a fission reaction are generally a light nucleus, a heavy nucleus and 2 or 3 neutrons. The atomic mass number of the lighter nucleus is in the range of 85 to 104, whereas the atomic mass number of the heavier nucleus is between 130 and 149.
4. On an average, about 2.5 neutrons are produced in one fission reaction.
5. There are three types of fission reactions–spontaneous, prompt and delayed reactions. In spontaneous fission reactions, fission takes place continuously and spontaneously in certain (radioactive) substances without bombardment by any projectile. In a prompt reaction, fission takes place as soon as the heavy nucleus is bombarded with a neutron, whereas in a delayed fission, the neutron enters a heavy nucleus causing instability and eventually leading to the fission.

6. Every fission reaction is accompanied by the release of enormous energy in the form of light and heat. This is due to the mass defect, i.e., the difference in the masses of the reactants and the products.
7. Another by-product of a fission reaction is γ-radiations. These radiations of very short wavelength have harmful effects on living organisms.

Liquid Drop Model

After Otto Hahn and Fritz Strassmann discovered the fission reaction in 1939, Niels Bohr, Frenkel and Wheeler suggested the liquid drop model to explain the nuclear fission. According to this model, the various stages of a nuclear fission are as follows.

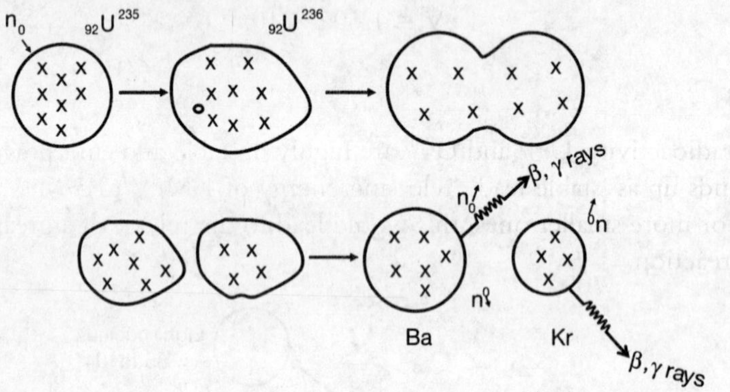

Figure 9.12 Pictorial representation of nuclear fission (liquid drop model)

1. A heavy nucleus can be treated as the drop of a liquid with positive charge uniformly distributed.
2. Due to the surface tension, the surface of the liquid drop would act as a stretched rubber membrane.
3. The forces acting between the nucleons inside the nucleus are different from those acting between nucleons close to the surface, just as the cohesive forces between the molecules inside the liquid are different as compared to the adhesive forces at the surface.
4. During the bombardment of a nucleus by neutrous, a neutron could be absorbed by the 'drop-like' nucleus leading to the disturbance of the internal forces and setting up oscillations.
5. These oscillations lead to the development of a thick neck forming two parts, giving the nucleus an elongated shape.
6. From this stage the repulsive forces take over causing the fission (breaking up) of the nucleus.

Determination of Energy Liberated in a Nuclear Reaction

In the fission of $_{92}U^{235}$, the energy liberated can be calculated as follows:

$$_{92}U^{235} + {_0n^1} \longrightarrow {_{36}Kr^{92}} + {_{56}Ba^{141}} + 3\,{_0n^1} + \text{energy}$$

The mass of $_{92}U^{235}$ = 235.124 u

The mass of $_{36}Kr^{92}$ = 91.944 u

The mass of $_{56}Ba^{141}$ = 140.948 u

The mass of a neutron = 1.009 u

∴ The total mass of reactants = 235.124 u + 1.009 u = 236.133 u

∴ The total mass of products = 91.944 u + 140.948 u + 3 (1.009 u)

= 235.919 u

The mass defect = 236.133 u – 235. 919 u = 0.214 u

The mass of the products is less than that of the reactants. This loss in mass can be accounted for by the liberation of heat.

1 u = 931.5 MeV

∴0.214 u = 931.5 × 0.214 MeV = 199.3 MeV

≈ 200 MeV

$= 200 \times 1.6 \times 10^{-13}$ J $= 3.2 \times 10^{-11}$ J per fission

Considering the fact that 235 g of uranium contains 6.023×10^{23} atoms of uranium, if all the atoms in 1 kg of U-235 undergo fission, it would liberate energy equal to 8.2×10^{13} J.

Taking 30% efficiency in conversion from nuclear energy to electrical energy, 2.46×10^{13} J of electrical energy can be generated if 1 kg of U-235 undergoes fission. If coal were to be used for the generation of this amount of energy, 2500 kg of coal would be required. Similarly, the energy liberated by 1 atom of U^{235} is two million times the energy obtained in the combustion of one molecule of methane.

Thus, harnessing nuclear energy for the generation of electrical energy has become important. Bhabha Atomic Research Centre (BARC) in Mumbai is a major research centre in India working on the atomic research. The major research reactors employed in India are APSARA (1 MW), Cirus (100 MW), Dhruva (100 MW), Purnima (zero energy fast breeder) and Zerlina (zero energy experiment research reactor).

The four nuclear power plants in India used for the generation of electricity are Tarapur Atomic Power Plant (420 MW), Rajasthan Atomic Power Plant (440 MW), Narora Atomic Power Plant (470 MW) and Chennai Power Plant (IGCAR) (470 MW). These power plants have been set up by Nuclear Power Corporation.

EXAMPLE 9.6 Consider the following nuclear fusion reaction:

$${}_2D^1 + {}_2D^1 \longrightarrow {}_3T^1 + {}_1H^1 + \text{energy}$$

Given the following atomic masses:

Mass of ${}_2D^1$ (Deuterium) $= 2.0141u$

Mass of ${}_3T^1$ (Tritium) $= 3.0160u$

Mass of ${}_1H^1$ (Proton) $= 1.0078u$

SOLUTION:

Total mass of reactants $= 2 \times$ mass of ${}_2D^1 = 2 \times 2.0141u = 4.0282u$

Total mass of products $=$ mass of ${}_3T^1 \times$ mass of ${}_1H^1 = 3.0160u + 1.0078u = 4.0238u$

Mass defect, $\Delta m = (4.0282u - 4.0239u) = 0.0044u$

Energy released

$= \Delta m \times 931.5\text{MeV/u}$

$= 0.0044u \times 931.5 \approx 4.0986\text{MeV}$

So, the energy released during the reaction is approximately 4.0986MeV

Kinds of Nuclear Fission Reactions

There are two kinds of nuclear fission reactions. They are uncontrolled fission reactions and controlled fission reactions.

The main difference between these reactions is that in the former, the amount of energy released is enormous in a short span of time and causes explosion, whereas in the latter case, there is a slow and controlled release of energy, which can be effectively utilized without causing any destructive explosion.

Uncontrolled Fission Reaction or Chain Reaction or Explosive Fission Reaction

When uranium (U-235) is bombarded by neutrons, each uranium nucleus is broken into two nearly equal fragments and along with it, huge energy is released and two or three fresh neutrons are liberated.

Under favourable conditions, these neutrons cause fission reaction in other uranium nuclei and the process continues till a stable product is obtained. However, a minimum mass of U^{235} is required to start a chain reaction. This minimum mass is known as critical mass. The probability of fission is high in U-235 isotope.

The composition of U-235 isotope in natural uranium is only ~ 0.7%. The other isotopes are U-234 and U-238. The concentration of U-235 in natural uranium is increased by a process called 'enrichment' and the uranium thus produced is referred to as 'enriched uranium'.

Chain Reaction

'A chain reaction is a series of nuclear fissions whereby the neutrons produced in each fission cause additional fissions, releasing enormous amount of energy'.

It is estimated that in one minute 10^{23} uranium atoms undergo fission in an uncontrolled chain reaction and as a consequence, tremendous amount of energy is released in a very short time causing destructive explosion. The atom bombs dropped on Hiroshima and Nagasaki by the Americans in 1945 resulting in the death of about 1.5 lakh people within minutes are examples of this type of fission reaction.

Pictorial Representation of Chain Reaction Controlled Chain Reaction or Critical Fission Reaction

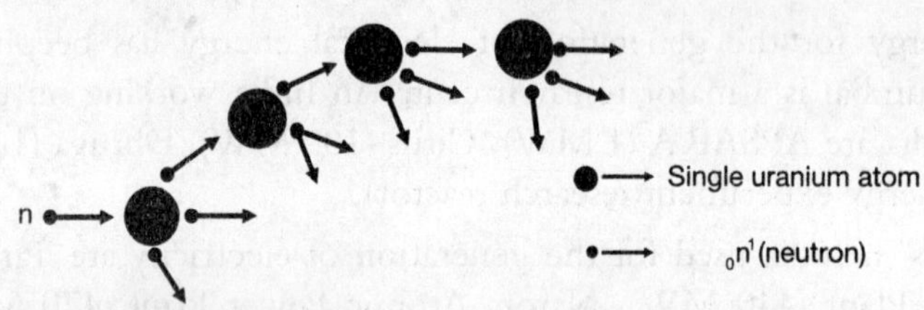

Figure 9.13 Critical fission reaction

The energy released in chain reaction is enormous and if this reaction is controlled, the energy can be used effectively.

The control and harnessing of the nuclear energy becomes possible if the number of neutrons in the immediate environment of uranium nuclei is limited by some means.

Thus, a fission reaction in which the number of neutrons participating in the fission in unit time is controlled by some means is referred to as 'controlled fission reaction'. In such a reaction, the rate of release of nuclear energy is also controlled.

A fission reaction can be controlled if

1. the neutron absorbed by a nucleus of uranium atom does not cause fission,
2. the released neutrons are stopped from being captured by other uranium nuclei, or
3. the neutrons released in a fission reaction escape from the system.

Nuclear Reactor

A nuclear reactor, is a device in which a self sustaining controlled chain reaction is produced in a fissionable material. It is, thus, a source of controlled energy which is utilized for many useful purposes. The first nuclear reactor was constructed by Fermi in 1942. It used U^{235} as fuel.

Generation of Electricity

A nuclear reactor used for the generation of electricity has five fundamental parts.

1. **Nuclear Fuel**: It is the most important part of the reactor and is the substance used for fission. The fissionable materials like U-235 and P*u*–239 used for the generation of heat energy in a nuclear reactor are called 'nuclear fuels'. Enriched uranium containing about 2% to 3% of U-235 is often used as nuclear fuel.

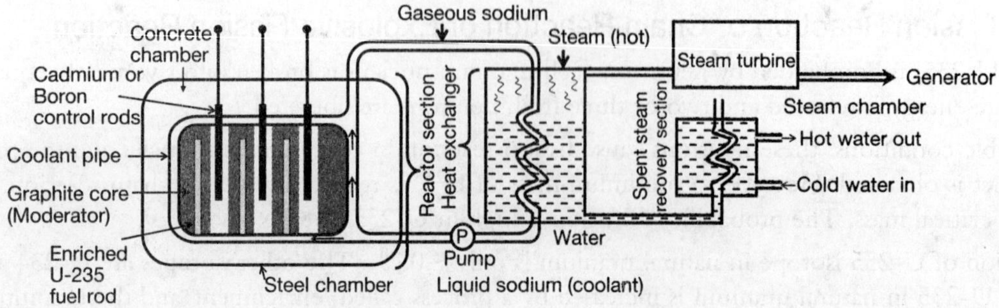

Figure 9.14 Nuclear Power Plant

2. **Moderator**: It is used to slow down the fast moving neutrons. Heavy water, graphite or beryllium oxide is used for this purpose. Heavy water is the best moderator available.

   The neutrons produced in a fission reaction have high energy (1 MeV) and the probability of these neutrons producing fission is 500 times less than that of slow moving thermal neutrons. Thus, the moderator converts fast neutrons to thermal neutrons.

3. **Coolant**: The energy released inside the reactor in the form of heat is removed by a coolant. For this purpose, molten sodium, ice cold water or CO_2 is used in the reactor. This heat removed from the reactor is utilized for producing steam which is, then, used to drive turbines for generating electricity.

   Molten sodium is the most efficient and commonly used coolant.

4. **Shield**: Various types of harmful intense rays are emitted from the reactor during fission reactions. To protect the people from these rays, the reactor is surrounded by 7 to 8 feet thick concrete and lead walls forming a shield.

5. **Control Rods**:For controlled fission reaction to take place, only one of the three neutrons produced in a fission reaction should be allowed to participate in the next fission, the other two being absorbed by some other material. These materials are called 'control rods'. Cadmium rods are used to control the rate of fission in the reactor. These rods are fixed in the walls of the reactor.

During the operation of a nuclear reaction, two stages occur: shut down position and critical stage. In the shut down position, the control rods are completely inserted into the reactor so that all the neutrons emitted are absorbed, and no further fission reactions take place.

In the critical stage, the control rods are drawn out of the reactor appropriately such that the right number of neutrons is available to sustain the controlled fission reaction at the required rate.

Nuclear Power Plant

A nuclear power plant essentially consists of four units:

1. Nuclear reactor
2. Heat exchanger
3. Steam turbine
4. Electric generator or dynamo

Info Bytes!

The sun generates energy through nuclear fusion, combining hydrogen atoms to form helium.

Working

1. In order to start the nuclear reactor, the control rods are slowly lifted till the reactor goes critical.
2. The heat energy produced in a reactor vaporizes the molten sodium. The vapors of sodium pass on the heat to the water in the heat exchanger, converting water to steam.
3. The steam turns the turbine converting heat energy into mechanical energy.
4. The turbine is coupled to a generator, which, in turn, converts mechanical energy into electric energy.
5. The condensed steam in the turbine and liquefied sodium in the heat exchanger are circulated through pumps.

Nuclear Fusion

Fusion means joining together or combining together. 'A nuclear reaction in which nuclei of lighter atoms combined fuse together to form heavier nuclei resulting in the release of tremendous amount of energy is called nuclear fusion reaction'.

It is found that this heavier nucleus has a mass less than that of the sum of the masses of the reacting nuclei. Thus, such a process results in the conversion of mass into energy.

Nuclear fusion reactions were discovered in the 1930s. In 1939, Hans Bethe suggested that the enormous amount of heat energy produced in Sun and other stars are due to such fusion reactions taking place in their core. These fusion reactions which take place at high temperatures are referred to as thermo-nuclear reactions. The main advantage of a fusion reaction is that they are not accompanied by the release of harmful radiations.

Fusion Theory

In a typical nuclear fusion reaction, four protons (nucleus of hydrogen) combine forming a helium nucleus. The other products are two positrons and two neutrinos (neutral particles of negligible mass) and the reaction is accompanied by the release of about 27.6 MeV energy. This reaction takes place in three stages.

I Stage reaction

$$\underset{\text{(Proton)}}{{}_1H^1} + \underset{\text{(Proton)}}{{}_1H^1} \longrightarrow \underset{\text{(deuteron)}}{{}_1H^2} + \underset{\text{(positron)}}{{}_{+1}e^0} + \underset{\text{(neutrino)}}{{}_0\upsilon^0}$$

II Stage reaction

$$\underset{\text{(deuteron)}}{{}_1H^2} + \underset{\text{(Proton)}}{{}_1H^1} \longrightarrow \underset{\text{(Helium isotope)}}{{}_2He^3}$$

III Stage reaction

$$\underset{\text{(Helium isotope)}}{2\ {}_2He^3} \longrightarrow \underset{\text{(helium)}}{{}_2He^4} + \underset{\text{(proton)}}{2\ {}_1H^1}$$

Combining the three equations, we have

$$\underset{\text{(Proton)}}{4\ {}_1H^1} \longrightarrow \underset{\text{(helium)}}{{}_2He^4} + \underset{\text{(Positrons)}}{2\ {}_{+1}e^0} + \underset{\text{(neutrino)}}{2\ {}_0\nu^0} + \underset{\text{(energy)}}{Q}$$

This group of reactions of the three stages are called proton–proton cycle since two protons are released in the III stage reaction.

The mass–energy equivalence in a fusion reaction:

The mass of proton = 1.0078 u

The mass of helium nucleus = 4.001506 u

The masses of positrons and neutrinos being negligible, we have

The mass of reactants = 4 × 1.0078 u = 4.0312 u

The mass of products = 4.001506 u

∴ The mass defect = 4.0312 u – 4.001506 u = 0.0297 u

The equivalent energy = 0.0297 u × 931 MeV/u = 27.67 MeV

All this energy is converted into heat.

A fusion reaction can be initiated when a high energy proton (KE = 0.01 MeV) accelerated in a particle accelerator, is made to strike on a target and fuse with the nuclei of the target. The target consists of nuclei of low atomic number.

Alternately, the kinetic energy of the light nuclei (protons) can be increased by raising the temperature to as high as 4×10^6 K in an enclosure. At these high temperatures, the atoms are completely ionised and the electrons move at high speeds. Matter in such a state is called plasma in which the fusing nuclei easily overcome the electrostatic repulsion between them.

Hydrogen Bomb

Hydrogen bomb, like atom bomb, is a weapon of mass destruction, employing the thermo-nuclear reactions, which can release enormous energy within a few minutes. The high temperature required for the uncontrolled fusion reaction in a hydrogen bomb is produced by a fission bomb containing uranium (U^{235}) or plutonium (Pu^{239}). Thus, the hydrogen bomb is a fission-fusion bomb.

Nuclear Fusion Reactor

The energy released in a fusion reaction is much higher than the energy released in a fission reaction. Thus, there is a considerable interest in harnessing this energy for useful applications such as generation of electricity. However, fusion reactors could not be built so far for the following reasons.

1. Unlike fission reactions, fusion reactions are not chain reactions.
2. The order of the magnitude of temperature enabling a fusion reaction to take place is 10^6 K. Producing such high temperature is very difficult. Even if the temperature is produced using a fissi on bomb, there is no material which can withstand such a high temperature.
3. It is difficult to harness and convert the high amount of heat energy produced in a fusion reaction into mechanical energy.

Nuclear Hazards and Safety Measures

Nuclear radiations affect all living beings as well as materials including buildings. The effects due to nuclear radiations given out during the explosion of a nuclear bomb cause death of lakhs of people, plants and animals. The materials and buildings are damaged extensively. In humans, exposure to nuclear radiations causes somatic and genetic effects. Due to somatic disorders, deadly diseases like cancer develop whereas genetic effects are observed generation after generation. In genetic effect, nuclear radiations change the genes of the exposed person for the worst and pass them on to the next generation. The offsprings born to such persons have deformities. Nuclear reactors are another source of nuclear radiations. Continuous nuclear reactions in them produce a large quantity of radioactive materials. The fuel rods, after use, become highly radioactive and contain toxic elements like plutonium. The spent nuclear fuel rods should be handled carefully so that humans are not exposed to the radiations given out by them. For this, they are first stored under water in a nuclear plant and then sent to a processing plant so as to retrieve usable materials. After that, they are stored in safe places like unused deep mines. Care should be taken to ensure that there is no leakage present in moderators and cooling water used in a nuclear plant. Such a leakage, if present, can cause contamination of water bodies and soil.

Nuclear Research in India

In 1945, under the leadership of Dr Homi Jehangir Bhabha, the atomic research in India started. The atomic energy commission is established and Dr Bhabha was made its first Chairman.

Under his leadership, atomic reactors such as Apsara, Cirus, Zerlina and a plant to enrich Uranium were started. Indian scientists have developed the capability to prepare nuclear fuel, design and fabrication of nuclear reactors and also explosive devices like atom bomb and hydrogen bomb.

The major centre of nuclear related research and development is Bhabha Atomic Research Centre (BARC) situated at Bombay in Maharashtra. The major research nuclear reactors are Apsara, Cirus, Dhruva, Purnima and Zerlina. The nuclear power station are Tarapur atomic power station (Maharashtra), Rajasthan atomic power Station, Narora atomic power Station (Uttar Pradesh), and Chennai Power Station (Tamil-Nadu). In India, Uranium occurs at Jaduguda in Jharkhand. The natural ore is processed and enriched at Nuclear Fuel Complex in Andhra Pradesh.

Info Bytes!

India is one of the few countries that have developed fast-breeder reactors, which can produce more fissile material than they consume.

EXAMPLE 9.7

In a given radioactive sample, there are 10^{24} nuclei present. If its half-life period is 20 years, how many nuclei will be present after 10 years?

$$\left(\text{Take } = \frac{1}{\sqrt{2}} = 0.707\right)$$

SOLUTION

The number of nuclei (N) present after '*n*' half lives is given by,

$$N = N_0\left(\frac{1}{2}\right)^n \quad (1)$$

$$\text{Where } n = \left(\frac{t}{T}\right)$$

In the question, we are given that $N_o = 10^{24}$

$$n = \frac{10}{12} = \frac{1}{2} \quad N = ?$$

Substituting the above values in equation (1), we get

$$N = 10^{24}\left(\frac{1}{2}\right)^{\frac{1}{2}}$$

$$= 10^{24} \times 0.707$$

$$= 7.07 \times 10^{23}$$

EXAMPLE 9.8

Calculate the binding energy per nucleon for Beryllium ^9_4Be, its mass being 9.012 u. The masses of proton and neutron are 1.008 u and 1.009 u.

(Take 1 u = 931.5 MeV)

SOLUTION

First, let us find the mass defect. The Beryllium nucleus contains 4 protons and 5 neutrons.

Mass of 4 protons = 4 × 1.008 = 4.032 u

Mass of 5 neutrons = 5 × 1.009 u = 5.045 u

Total mass of protons (4) and neutrons (5) = 4.032 + 5.045 = 9.077 u

Mass defect = 9.077 – 9.012 = 0.065 u

The mass defect converted into equivalent energy gives binding energy.

1 u = 931.5 Me V

∴ 0.065 u = 0.065 × 931.5 MeV = 60.5475 MeV

Binding energy per nucleon

$$= \frac{\text{Binding energy}}{\text{No. of nucleons}} = \frac{60.5475}{9} = 6.7275 \text{ MeV}$$

EXAMPLE 9.9 Assuming 200 MeV energy is released per fission of $^{235}_{92}\text{U}$, calculate the energy released when 1 kg of $^{235}_{92}\text{U}$ undergoes complete fission. What percentage of mass of $^{235}_{92}\text{U}$ gets converted into energy?

SOLUTION

235 g of $^{235}_{92}\text{U}$ contains Avogadro number (6.023 × 10^{23}) of atoms.

No. of atoms of $^{235}_{92}\text{U}$ in 1 kg of uranium

$$= 1000 \times \frac{60.023 \times 10_{23}}{235} = 2.563 \times 10^{24}$$

Energy released = No. of atoms × Energy released per fission.

$$= 2.563 \times 10^{24} \times 200 \text{ MeV}$$

$$= 5.126 \times 10^{26} \text{ MeV}$$

The mass that liberates the above energy can be calculated using $E = mc^2$ (2)

where, E = $5.126 \times 10^{26} \times 1.6 \times 10^{-13}$ J

$$= 8.2 \times 10^{13} \text{ J}$$

$$c = 3 \times 10^{8} \text{ m s}^{-1}$$

Substituting in (2), we get

$$m = \frac{E}{c^2} = \frac{8.2 \times 10^{13}}{9 \times 10^{16}} = 9.11 \times 10^{-4} \text{ kg}$$

$$\% \text{ of mass} = \frac{9.11 \times 10^{-4}}{1} \times 100 = 0.0911\%$$

$$= 0.1\% \text{ approximately}$$

EXAMPLE 9.10 Two protons and two neutrons combine to form a nucleus of $^{4}_{2}\text{He}$. Find the energy released during the process. What type of nuclear reaction is it? Take masses of proton, neutron and helium as 1.007 u, 1.009 u, 4.002 u, respectively.

SOLUTION

The nuclear reaction is $2^1_1\text{P} + 2^1_0 n \rightarrow ^4_2 \text{He}$

First, let us find mass defect and then energy.

The mass of $2p$ and $2n$ is (2 × 1.007 + 2 × 1.009) = 2 × 2.016 = 4.032 u.

The mass of helium is = 4.002 u.

The mass defect = 4.032 – 4.002 = 0.030 u.

1 u liberates 931.5 MeV of energy. The energy equivalent to 0.030 u = 0.03 × 931.5

$$= 27.94 \text{ MeV.}$$

The above nuclear reaction is called fusion as lighter nuclei combine together to form a single nucleus.

EXAMPLE 9.11 The binding energy of $^{7}_{3}Li$ and $^{4}_{2}He$ are 39.2 MeV and 28.24 MeV, respectively. Which one of the two nuclei is more stable?

SOLUTION

The nucleons present in $^{7}_{3}Li$ is 7.

The binding energy per nucleon for lithium is $= \frac{39.2}{7} = 5.6$ MeV.

The binding per nucleon for helium is $\frac{28.24}{4} = 7.06$ MeV.

The binding energy per nucleon is the measure of stability of the nucleus. Therefore, helium is more stable than lithium.

EXAMPLE 9.12 A nuclear reactor generates 500 MW of electrical energy using the fission of $^{235}_{92}U$. Find the mass of $^{235}_{92}U$ required to produce electricity for 30 days. (0.1% of the mass of $^{235}_{92}U$ gets converted into energy).

SOLUTION

The electrical energy produced in one second is 500 MJ. The electrical energy generated in 30 days is

$$E = 500 \times 10^6 \times 60 \times 60 \times 24 \times 30$$

$$= 1.3 \times 10^{15} \text{ J. (approximately)}$$

To generate above energy, the mass required can be found using the formula

$$E = mc^2$$

$$\text{or } m = \frac{E}{c^2} = \frac{1.3\times10^{15}}{(3\times10^8)^2} = 0.144\times10^{-1}\text{kg} = 1.44\times10^{-2}\text{kg}.$$

Let M be the mass of uranium required to generate energy E. Then 'm' is 0.1% of M.

i.e.,
$$m = \frac{0.1}{100}\times M$$

$$\Rightarrow M = 1000\, m = 1000 \times 1.44 \times 10^{-2} = 14.4 \text{ kg}.$$

POINTS TO REMEMBER

- ✔ Cathode rays are deflected in electric and magnetic fields. This shows that they consist of charged particles.
- ✔ X-rays are electromagnetic radiations. Their wavelength is very small, of the order of 1 A°.
- ✔ Radioactivity is the phenomenon of self-disintegration and spontaneous emission of radiation by some unstable nuclei with atomic number greater than 82.
- ✔ The radiations emitted by radioactive substances were found to consist of three distinct constituents. They were called alpha, beta and gamma radiations.
- ✔ The disintegration of an unstable nucleus resulting in the formation of another nucleus is called radioactive transformation or disintegration or radioactive decay.

- ✔ When an α-particle is emitted from a radioactive nucleus, the atomic number (Z) decreases by 2 and the mass number (A) decreases by 4.
- ✔ The presence of excess neutrons in an unstable nucleus lead to a neutron changing into a proton by emitting an electron (for charge conservation).
- ✔ There is no change in the atomic number (Z) or in the mass number (A) of the atom which undergoes gamma decay.
- ✔ The sequential decay of a given radioactive nucleus resulting in the production of new nuclei at each stage and giving rise to a series of elements is called radioactive decay series.
- ✔ The law of radioactive disintegration states that 'in any radioactive substance, the number of nuclei disintegrating per second is directly proportional to the number of nuclei present'.
- ✔ The half-life period (T) of a radioactive substance is defined as the time during which half the amount of the substance disintegrates.
- ✔ Isotopes are the atoms of the same element having the same atomic number, but different mass number due to difference in the number of neutrons in their nuclei.
- ✔ Atoms of different elements, having the same mass number but different atomic number are called isobars.
- ✔ Atoms with their nuclei having the same number of neutrons but different number of protons are called isotones.
- ✔ Atoms with their nuclei having the same number of neutrons but different number of protons are called isotones.
- ✔ Artificial transmutation is the process of transformation of one element into another by artificial disintegration means of bombarding it with high energy particles.
- ✔ The process of estimating the age by measuring the disintegration of C-14 is known as 'Carbon dating'.
- ✔ The α, β and γ rays emitted during radioactive disintegration of an unstable substance cause several biological effects (kill the living cells and cause radiation burns) on human beings.
- ✔ Background radiations are those radioactive radiations that everyone is exposed to due to the presence of natural radioactive substances on the Earth as well as the cosmic radiations, and also the radioactive substances present in the body.
- ✔ Geiger counter is an instrument used for recording the rate of emission from a radioactive substance.
- ✔ The mass of an atom is measured in units called unified 'atomic mass unit'(u); defined as 1/12th of the mass of a neutral carbon atom 6C12 (Carbon – 12 atom).
- ✔ The difference between the sum of the individual masses of constituents in a nucleus and the mass of the nucleus itself is called 'mass defect'.
- ✔ Binding energy per nucleon is the average energy required to extract one nucleon from the nucleus.
- ✔ Any reaction that tends to change the configuration of the nucleus of an atom can be termed as a nuclear reaction.
- ✔ Nuclear fission is a process in which the heavy nucleus of a radioactive substance like uranium is split into lighter nuclei by the bombardment of a low energy (slow moving) neutron, the reaction being accompanied by the release of energy and two or three or more neutrons.
- ✔ 'A chain reaction is a series of nuclear fissions whereby the neutrons produced in each fission cause additional fissions, releasing enormous amount of energy'.
- ✔ A nuclear reactor, is a device in which a self sustaining controlled chain reaction is produced in a fissionable material.
- ✔ 'A nuclear reaction in which nuclei of lighter atoms combined fuse together to form heavier nuclei resulting in the release of tremendous amount of energy is called nuclear fusion reaction'.

PRACTICE QUESTIONS CLASSROOM WING

Very Short Answer Type Questions

Directions for questions 1 to 21:
Answer the following questions.

1. For which of the following is specific charge maximum for?
2. What are $_7N^{14}$, $_7N^{15}$ called as?
3. What is the use of heavy water in a nuclear reactor?
4. If the half-life period of a radioactive substance is 0.693 years, what is its decay constant?
5. What happens when cathode rays are suddenly stopped?
6. In a nuclear reactor, what is the function of heat exchanger?
7. What is the measure of the stability of the atom?
8. How can you say that cathode rays are negatively-charged particles?
9. Define nuclear binding energy.
10. Is the following statement true about nuclear fission?

    Products formed are radioactive and are not harmful.
11. What is the function of cadmium rod in a nuclear reactor?
12. What forces are responsible for keeping the nucleons together in a nucleus?
13. Why are nuclear fusion reactions also known as thermo-nuclear reactions?
14. Which rays among α, β and γ are deflected most in a magnetic field? Which rays remain undeflected?
15. What is a moderator? Give one example.
16. What is radioactive transformation or radioactive decay?
17. What is the use of control rods?
18. What is the use of Geiger counter?
19. In all radioactive series, what is the end element formed?
20. Name the three radioactive series. Which series is referred to as 4*n* Series?
21. Define isotopes, isobars and isotones.

Short Answer Type Questions

22. State the laws of emissions.
23. Find the binding energy per nucleon for a lithium nucleus $_3Li^7$. Take mass of $_3Li^7 = 7u$, mass of proton 1.007825 u and mass of neutron = 1.008665 u. Take 1 u = 931.5 MeV.
24. Explain how the age of fossils is determined.
25. What are prompt fission and delayed fission reactions?
26. What is nuclear fusion? How many?
27. Explain nuclear chain reactions.
28. Explain why the energy released during fusion cannot be used to produce electricity.
29. Mention the properties of X-rays.
30. What is a nuclear reactor? Name its different parts.
31. Give any three uses of radioisotopes.
32. Explain nuclear fission by giving an example.
33. Match the statements of Column A with those of Column B.

	Column A		Column B
A.	Binding energy per nucleon	a.	Controlled chain reaction
B.	Reproduction factor $K = 1$	b.	Can determine the age of rocks
C.	Uranium dating	c.	Positrons are emitted
D.	Artificial radioactivity	d.	Stability of nucleus

34. Using $E = mc^2$, find out the energy released, when 1 u of mass disappears.
Take 1 $u = 1.66 \times 10^{-27}$ kg.

35. Match the statements of Column A with those of Column B.

Column A	Column B
A. $_{11}Na^{24}$	a. Checks the function of thyroid gland
B. D_2O	b. Detects blood clot
C. $_{53}I^{131}$	c. Hard X – rays
D. Radio therapy	d. Moderator

Essay Answer Type Questions

36. What is a Liquid Drop Model? How does it help in the understanding of fission reaction?

37. Explain in detail the nuclear hazards and the safety precautions to be taken while?

38. Radius of the nucleus is given as 1.3×10^{-15} m. If the mass number of the nucleus is increased to 8 times, then determine the volume of the new nucleus.

39. The masses of the proton and the neutron are 1.0078 u and 1.0087 u, respectively. Mass of $_4Be^9$ is 9.012 u. Determine binding energy of its nucleus.

PRACTICE QUESTIONS COMPETITION WING

Level 1: Apply Your Concepts

Directions for questions from 1 to 16:
Fill in the blanks.

1. Energy released in a nuclear reaction is given by ______.
2. _____ are used to absorb the neutrons in a nuclear reactor.
3. Thorium series is also called ______.
4. The first radioactive element discovered is _____.
5. $_1H^3 +$ _____ $\rightarrow {}_2He^4 + {}_0n^1$ + Energy
6. Radioactive isotope of carbon is _____.
7. In artificial transmutation, the bombarding particles are called ______.
8. The radioactive isotope used in the treatment of cancer is a good source of _____ radiations.
9. 4 n + 2 series is called _______ series.
10. If the binding energy per nucleon for 3Li7 is 5.6 MeV, the total binding energy of a lithium nucleus is ____ MeV.
11. The conversion of 1 u of mass results in _______eV of energy.
12. The common product formed in the artificial transmutation by a proton is _____.
13. In plants and animals, the ratio of C^{14} to C^{12} is ______.
14. The radioactive radiation which can be stopped easily is _____.
15. When an α-particle is ejected, the atomic number of the atom decreases by _______.
16. The cathode rays emitted from a concave cathode meet at _____.

Direction for questions from 17 to 23:
State whether the following statements are true or false.

17. Moderator is used to control the reaction.
18. The positron has charge equal to that of proton.
19. Nuclear force is always attractive and dependent of charge.
20. $_{14}Si^{31}$, $_{15}P^{31}$ are isobars.
21. X–rays have higher penetrating power as they travel with very high velocity.
22. Higher the mass defect, higher will be the stability of the nucleus.
23. The e/m ratio of Cathode rays is constant irrespective of the gas filled inside the discharge tube.

Direction for question 24:
Match the entries in Column A with appropriate ones from column B.

24.

	Column A		Column B
A.	Coolidge tube	a.	present in all natural radioactive series
B.	α decay	b.	isobars
C.	Radon	c.	isotones
D.	$_{14}Si^{31}$, $_{15}P^{32}$	d.	stability of a nucleus
E.	β-decay	e.	to slow down neutrons
F.	Binding energy per nucleon	f.	decrease in atomic number by two
G.	Moderator	g.	X-rays
H.	Thermonuclear reaction	h.	$E = mc^2$
I.	Mass energy equivalence	i.	clot of blood in human body
J.	Sodium - 24	j.	nuclear fusion

Direction for questions from 25 to 43:
For each of the questions, four choices have been provided. Select the correct alternative.

25. **Assertion:** Nucleus with more mass defect is more stable than that with less mass defect.

 Reason: More the mass defect more is binding energy and that implies more stability

(a) A and R are true and R is the correct explanation of A.
(b) A and R are true, but R is not the correct explanation of A.
(c) A is true but R is false.
(d) Both A and R are false.

26. **Assertion:** It is easy to separate the constituents of a nucleus with high binding energy.
Reason: More the binding energy of a nucleus, the lesser is its stability
(a) A and R are true and R is the correct explanation of A.
(b) A and R are true, but R is not the correct explanation of A.
(c) A is true but R is false.
(d) Both A and R are false.

27. The mass number of an element in a radioactive series is 223. Then the radioactive series is ______.
(a) $4n$ (b) $4n + 3$
(c) $4n + 2$ (d) $4n + 1$

28. Carbon dating is used to
(a) assess the age of fossils.
(b) assess the amount of radioactivity.
(c) assess the rate of radioactivity.
(d) none of the above.

29. The kinds of force(s) that are present between two protons in a nucleus is/are ______.
(a) electrostatic force (b) nuclear force
(c) magnetic force (d) Both (a) and (b)

30. ${}_{Z}X^{A}$ and ${}_{Z+1}Y^{A}$ are two radioactive elements. X emits one α particle whereas Y emits one β particle. The daughter nuclei formed are ______.
(a) isotopes (b) isobars
(c) isotones (d) isomorphic

31. The e/m of three singly ionized atoms A, B and C are x, y, z, respectively. If $x > y > z$ and m_A, m_B, and m_C are their atomic weights, the correct relation among the following is ______.
(a) $m_A > m_B > m_C$ (b) $m_c > m_B > m_A$
(c) $m_A = m_B = m_C$ (d) $m_A > m_B = m_C$

32. A radioactive substance was reduced to $\frac{1}{4}$ of the total amount in 8 days. The time taken by this radioactive substance to get reduced to $\frac{1}{8}$th of the remaining amount is ______.
(a) 12 days (b) 16 days
(c) 20 days (d) 8 days

33. ${}_{1}H^{1} + {}_{3}Li^{7} \rightarrow$ ______ $+ {}_{2}He^{4}$
(a) ${}_{2}He^{4}$ (b) ${}_{6}C^{12}$
(c) ${}_{4}Be^{9}$ (d) ${}_{4}Be^{8}$

34. The property of cathode rays used in a monitor of a computer is ______.
(a) high velocity
(b) high ionization power
(c) cause fluorescence of phosphors
(d) rectilinear propagation

35. If the radiations from a radioactive substance, in the presence of an electric field, deflect towards the anode, the rays are
(a) α-rays (b) β-rays
(c) γ-rays (d) X-rays

36. A radioactive isotope of radium placed in the second group in the periodic table emits one α-particle and one β-particle. The new element formed is in the ______ group.
(a) first (b) second
(c) third (d) fourth

37. Which among the following statements is incorrect about visible light and X-rays?
(a) They have same velocity in vacuum or air.
(b) They are electromagnetic radiations.
(c) They have same wavelength in a given medium.
(d) They are not affected by electric field.

38. Cathode rays exert ______ force on the object place in their path.
(a) mechanical (b) electrical
(c) magnetic (d) electromagnetic

39. Which among the following has the lowest speed when travelling through a given medium?
(a) γ-rays (b) α-rays
(c) β-rays (d) Cathode rays

40. Write the following steps in sequential order to calculate the binding energy per nucleon of an element ${}_{z}X^{A}$, given the actual mass of ${}_{z}X^{A}$, mass of proton (m_p) and mass of neutron (m_n) (All the values are given in atomic mass units.)
(A) Note the actual mass of the nucleus (M), number of nucleons in ${}_{z}A^{X}$, m_p and m_n.
(B) Calculate the mass defect of the given nucleus.
(C) Find the number of protons and number of neutrons in the nucleus.
(D) Determine the sum of the individual masses of constituents in ${}_{z}A^{X}$.
(E) Calculate the binding energy (B.E) of the nucleus.

(F) Divide it with the number of nucleons present in the element to get binding energy per nucleon.

(a) AEDCBF (b) ACDBEF
(c) ACBDEF (d) ADCBEF

41. The process of increasing the percentage of fissionable U-235 in naturally occurring uranium is called _______

(a) controlled fission.
(b) artificial transmutation.
(c) chemical process.
(d) enrichment.

42. _______ reaction takes place in the Sun.

(a) Nuclear fission (b) Nuclear fusion
(c) Chemical (d) Both (a) and (b)

43. Write the following steps of the liquid drop model in sequential order to show the various stages of a nuclear fission reaction.

(A) During the bombardment of a nucleus by neutrons, a neutron could be absorbed by the drop like the nucleus.
(B) A heavy nucleus is treated as the drop of a liquid with the positive charge uniformly distributed.
(C) This leads to the disturbance of the internal forces and sets up oscillations.
(D) From this stage the repulsive forces take over causing the fission of the nucleus.
(E) These oscillations lead to the development of a thick neck forming two parts, giving the nucleus an elongated shape.

(a) BCEAD (b) ACEDB
(c) ADCEB (d) BACED

Level 2: Review Your Concepts

44. The binding energy per nucleon for deuterium and helium are 1.1 MeV and 7 MeV, respectively. Find how much energy is released by the fusion of 1 g of deuterium?

45. Write the following steps in sequential order to calculate the binding energy of helium nucleus. Given the actual mass of helium is (*M*).

(A) Determine the sum of the individual masses of constituents in $_2He^4$
(B) Note the actual mass of the nucleus (*M*), number of nucleons in helium is 4, M_p and M_n. Find the number of protons and number of neutrons in the nucleus.
(C) Calculate the binding energy of the nucleus from the formula, binding energy = $931.5 \times \Delta m$
(D) Calculate the mass defect of the given nucleus (Δm).

46. Show that iron $_{26}Fe^{56}$ is more stable than carbon $_6C^{12}$, given binding energy of $_{26}Fe^{56}$ is 492.35 MeV and that of $_6C^{12}$ is 89.14 MeV.

47. How many electrons, protons and neutrons are there in 12 g of $_6C^{12}$?

48. In Ac-U series, the decay of the parent nucleus starts with an α-particle. The decay is continued such that an α-and β-particles are emitted alternately until an unstable nucleus radium is formed. Identify the isotopes, isobars, isotones formed and the change in the number of neutrons and protons of parent and daughter nuclei.

49. How many grams of U^{235} is required to produce 8×10^{11} J of energy if 200 MeV of energy is released when one U^{235} atom undergoes fission?

50. $\frac{15}{16}$th of a radioactive substance disintegrates in 12 days. What is the half-life period of the radioactive substance? How much more time will it take for the remaining amount of radioactive substance to reduce to $\frac{1}{32}$ of the reduced amount?

51. The half-life period of C^{14} is 5670 years. If 56 *g* of C^{14} was present initially, how many atoms of C^{14} is left after 22,680 years?

52. Is there any force of attraction between two neutrons in a nucleus? Explain.

53. The total binding energies of $_1H^2$, $_2He^4$, $_{26}Fe^{56}$ and $_{92}U^{235}$ are 2.22 MeV, 28.3 MeV, 492 MeV and 1786 MeV, respectively. Which among the above four is the most stable nucleus? Why?

54. Complete the following nuclear reactions.

(1) $_{92}U^{238} +$ _______ $\rightarrow\ _{99}E^{247} + 5\,_0n^1$
(2) $_{96}Cm^{244} + {}_2He^4 \rightarrow$ _______ $+ {}_{97}Bk^{245} + {}_1H^1$
(3) $_{94}Pu^{292} +$ …… $\rightarrow\ _{104}Ku^{260} + 4\,_0n^1$

55. What percentage of initial amount of radioactive substance is approximately left, after 10 half lives?

56. Write down the sequence of radiations emitted in the following radioactive processes.

(1) $_ZP^A \rightarrow {}_{Z-1}Q^A \rightarrow {}_ZR^A$

(2) $_ZK^A \rightarrow {}_{Z-2}L^{A-4} \rightarrow {}_{Z-1}M^{A-4}$

57. How many nuclei of $_{92}U^{235}$ should undergo fission per second to produce a power of 10MW if 200 MeV of energy is released per fission of $_{92}U^{235}$?

58. Which radiation of a radioactive substance is electrically neutral?

59. What is the use of control rods?

60. Sikar read that when $_{92}U^{235}$ undergoes fission, approximately 0.1% of its original mass changes into energy. With this information, calculate the amount of energy released when 1 kg of $_{92}U^{235}$ undergoes fission.

61. The mass number of an element in a radioactive series is 223. Which radioactive series is this?

62. If the binding energy per nucleon for $_3Li^7$ is 5.6 MeV, determine the total binding energy of a lithium nucleus.

63. A radioactive substance was reduced to 1/4 of the total amount in 8 days. Determine the further time taken by this radioactive substance to get reduced to 1/4th of the remaining amount.

Level 3: Assess Your Concepts

64. Explain how a radioactive nucleus can emit negatively-charged β-particles, even though the nucleus itself is positively charged.

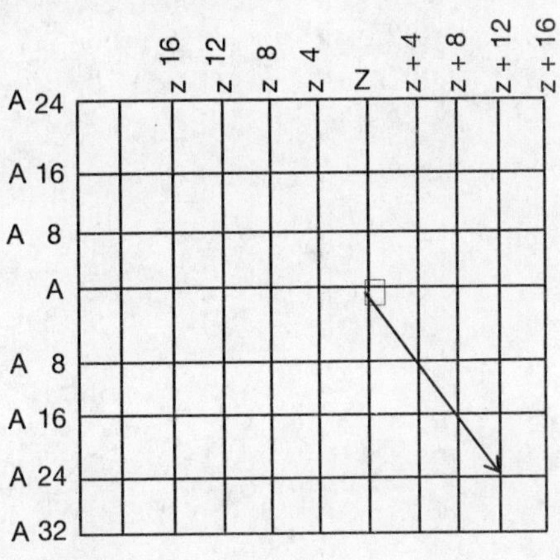

65. $_{60}Nd^{144} \rightarrow {}_{58}Ce^{140} + {}_2He^4 + 1.77$ MeV. In the above nuclear reaction if the parent nucleus is at rest, determine the velocity of α-particle.

66. The masses of proton and neutron are 1.0078 u and 1.0087 u, respectively. Actual mass of the $_2He^4$ is 4.0026 u, determine the mass defect (in kg). (where $1\ u = 1.66 \times 10^{-27}$ kg)

67. When the nuclear reaction started in a nuclear reactor, the amount of $_{92}U^{235}$ and $_{36}Kr^{92}$ present after 2000 s is found to be 10 g and 23 g, respectively. Determine the output power of the nuclear reactor if its efficiency is 70%. Fission of one nucleus of U–235 releases 200 MeV of energy.

68. How many α and β particles are emitted when uranium $_{92}U^{238}$ disintegrates to form lead $_{82}Pb^{206}$?

69. An α particle is emitted from a heavy radioactive nucleus. Compare the momenta of the α particle and the daughter nucleus.

70. Determine the energy released during the fusion of $_1H^1$ to form a $_2He^4$ nucleus if the total mass of the products is 4.001506 u, mass of proton is 1.0078u and mass of neutron is 1.0087u.

71. Mass of $_{92}U^{235}$ required to produce electrical energy in a nuclear reactor for 30 days is 23.5 kg. If 40% of the energy released by the fission is converted into electrical energy, determine the power of the nuclear reactor. (Assume that 200 MeV energy is released per fission of $_{92}U^{235}$.)

72. Write down the sequence of radiations emitted in the following radioactive processes.

(a) $_zX^A \longrightarrow {}_{z+1}P^A \longrightarrow {}_{z-1}Y^{A-4} \longrightarrow {}_{z-1}Y^{A-4}$

(b) $_{z+1}X^A \longrightarrow {}_{z-1}Y^{A-4} \longrightarrow {}_{z-1}Y^{A-4} \longrightarrow {}_zK^{A-4}$

73. How much energy is released when the mass of $_8O^{16}$ nucleus is completely converted into energy? The binding energy per nucleon of $_8O^{16}$ is 7.97 MeV and $m_p = 1.0078\ u$ and $m_n = 1.0087\ u$.

74. Assuming 200 MeV energy is released per fission of $_{92}U^{235}$, calculate the energy released when 1 kg of $_{92}U^{235}$ undergoes complete fission.

75. The binding energy of $_3Li^7$ and $_2He^4$ are 39.2 MeV and 28.24 MeV respectively. Which one of the two nuclei is more stable?

76. What is the mass defect and binding energy of $_{27}Co^{59}$ which has a nucleus of mass of 58.933 u? (m_p = 1.0078 u, m_n = 1.0087 u)

77. In a given radio-active sample, there are 10^{24} nuclei present. If its half-life period is 20 years, how many nuclei will be present after 10 years?

78. Calculate the binding energy per nucleon for Beryllium $_4Be^9$, its mass being 9.012 u. The masses of proton and neutron are 1.008 u and 1.009 u. (Take 1 u = 931.5 MeV)

AT

PRACTICE QUESTIONS JEE-NEET SPECIAL WING

Multiple-Answer Type Questions

Directions for questions 1 to 5: **Select one or more correct alternative(*s*) from the given choices.**

1. Referring to the cathode rays, identify the correct statement(*s*) from the following.
   (a) They are electromagnetic radiations.
   (b) they are affected by the electric and magnetic fields.
   (c) they ionise the gases through which they pass.
   (d) they are used to detect flaws in cast materials.

2. Cut off wavelength of *X* rays produced by the electrons accelerated by a potential difference of 230 volts is
   (a) 54 Å (b) 540 nm
   (c) 540 Å (d) 5.4 nm

3. In the following nuclear reaction, the values of *X* and *Y* are
   $_{92}U^{x} + {}_{0}n^{1} \rightarrow {}_{36}Kr^{92} + {}_{y}Ba^{141} + 3{}_{0}n^{1}$ + Energy
   (a) X = 233 (b) X = 235
   (c) Y = 54 (d) Y = 56

4. A radioactive sample of half-life period 30 minute has 800 atoms at the beginning. Then, the atoms disintegrated in 2.5 hour will be
   (a) 25 (b) 775
   (c) 96.875% (d) 3.125%

5. Binding energy of helium nucleus is 28.4 MeV. The binding energy per nucleon of helium is
   (a) 11.36×10^{-13} J (b) 7100 keV
   (c) 7.1 MeV (d) 11.36×10^{-19} *J*

Comprehension-Based Questions

Directions for questions 6 to 10: **Read the paragraph given below and answer the questions**

Protons and neutrons present in the nucleus of an atom are known as nucleons. Despite the electrostatic repulsion amongst the protons, these nucleons are held together within a small region by strong nuclear forces. The energy required to bind the nucleons is called binding energy and is obtained by an atom from its own mass. According to Einstein, mass and energy are interconvertible. At the atomic level, masses are expressed in atomic mass unit (*u*) and the mass of one *u* is equivalent to 931.5 MeV energy. Mass of an atom, as a whole, is less than the sum of the masses of its constituents. The difference in the masses (mass defect) is converted into the energy according to Einstein's mass energy equivalence $E = mc^2$. The average binding energy spent on a single nucleon is called binding energy per nucleon and it is the measure of the stability of the nucleus. The more the binding energy per nucleon, the more is the stability of the nucleus.

6. Neutrons are electrically
   (a) Positive
   (b) negative
   (c) neutral
   (d) may be positive or negative

7. Binding energy per nucleon of O^{16} is 7.97 MeV. The total binding energy of the oxygen nucleus is
   (a) 127.52 MeV .
   (b) 2.04×10^{-11} J.
   (c) Both (a) & (b)
   (d) None of these

8. The number of neutrons present in the nucleus of a normal hydrogen atom is
   (a) 0 (b) 1
   (c) 2 (d) 3

9. The mass defect corresponding to an energy of 2 nJ is
   (a) 7.68 amu (b) 26.84 amu
   (c) 1 amu (d) 13.42 amu

10. Binding energy per nucleon of a nucleus stands for its
    (a) Density (b) Size
    (c) Stability (d) Shape

Directions for questions 11 to 16: **Read the paragraph given below and answer the questions.**

Unstable nuclei with atomic number more than 82 emit invisible radiations like alpha, beta and gamma rays spontaneously and this process is called radioactivity. An alpha particle is a collection of two protons and two neutrons, and a beta particle is an electron which is emitted when a neutron in the nucleus gets converted into a proton. Emission of a gamma particle results in the decrease of energy of the parent nucleus as it is a chargeless and massless particle.

A radioactive substance by emitting alpha or beta particle gets transformed into another substance which would also be radioactive. Thus, this process of disintegration leads to a series of new substances which finally end up with stable lead isotope. The disintegration process results in atoms of the same element with different mass numbers, and atoms of different elements with the same mass number that are respectively called isotopes and isobars. There can be atoms of different elements with the same number of neutrons in their nuclei, which are called isotones.

As a result of this disintegration process, the amount of the original substance gradually decreases. The time taken for half of the amount to disintegrate is called its half-life period(*T*). The law of radioactive disintegration states that "the number of nuclei disintegrating per unit time is directly proportional to the number of nuclei present."

Decay constant (λ) of a radioactive substance is defined as $\lambda = (0.693/T)$. A higher value of λ indicates faster decay. Thus, the decay constant is a characteristic property of a radioactive element. The rate at which the decay takes place varies from element to element. Thus, different elements have different half-life periods and different disintegration constants.

11. The radiations that do not respond to the electric and magnetic fields are

(a) Alpha rays (b) beta rays
(c) gamma rays (d) all of them

12. $\frac{15^{th}}{16}$ of a substance gets disintegrated in ______ half-life periods.

(a) 2 (b) 4
(c) 5 (d) 8

13. Complete the following nuclear reaction

$_{92}U^{235} \rightarrow$ ------ + α - particle

(a) $_{90}Th^{235}$ (b) $_{90}Th^{233}$
(c) $_{90}Th^{237}$ (d) $_{90}Th^{231}$

14. When a beta particle is emitted, the atomic number of the element

(a) Increases by one unit.
(b) decreases by 2 units.
(c) decreases by 4 units.
(d) remains the same.

15. The half-life period of a sample whose decay constant is 9.9 per second is

(a) 7 s (b) 700 *s*
(c) 70 ms (d) 7 ms

16. Using the data given in the paragraph, match the entries in column A with those in column B

Column – A	Column – B
A. $_6C^{14}$, $_8O^{16}$	a. Isotopes
B. $_6C^{12}$, $_6C^{14}$	b. Isobars
C. $_6C^{14}$, $_7N^{14}$	c. Isotones
D. $_ZP^A$ ----> $_ZD^A$	d. Beta decay
E. $_0n^1$ ----> $_1H^1$	e. Gamma decay

ANSWER KEYS

Crossword

Across

1. Isobars 6. Controlled 9. Alpha rays 11. Becquerel

Down

2. Atomic number 3. Two 4. Moderator 5. Gamma rays
7. Radon 8. Isotones 10. Ionize

Classroom Wing

Very Short Answer Type Questions

1. X-rays 2. Isotopes 3. Heavy water is used to slow down the neutrons
10. No

Competition Wing

Level 1: Apply Your Concepts

1. $E = mc^2$ 2. cadmium rods 3. 4n series 4. uranium 5. $_1H^2$
6. C^{14} 7. projectiles 8. γ rays 9. Uranium series 10. 39.2
11. 931.5×10^6 12. helium 13. $1:1.35 \times 10^{-12}$ 14. α - rays 15. 2
16. centre of curvature 17. False 18. True 19. False 20. True
21. False 22. False 23. False
24. A : g, B : f, C : a, D : c, E : b, F : d, G : e, H : j, I : h, J : i
25. (a) 26. (d) 27. (b) 28. (a) 29. (d)
30. (c) 31. (b) 32. (c) 33. (a) 34. (c)
35. (b) 36. (a) 37. (b) 38. (a) 39. (b)
40. (b) 41. (d) 42. (b) 43. (d) 45. BADC

JEE-NEET SPECIAL WING

Multiple-Answer Type Questions

1. (b, c) 2. (a, d) 3. (b, d) 4. (b, c) 5. (a, b, c)

Comprehension-Based Questions

6. (c) 7. (c) 8. (a) 9. (d) 10. (c)
11. (c) 12. (b) 13. (d) 14. (a) 15. (c)
16. A-c, B-a, C-b, D-e, E-d

For answer key of Classroom wing and Competition wing, refer to Hints and Solutions

Hints and Explanations

CLASSROOM WING

Very Short Answer Type Questions

1. The specific charge is maximum for X-rays.
2. Isotopes
3. Heavy water is used to slow down the neutrons
4. $\lambda = \frac{0.693}{T}$
5. X-rays are produced.
6. To convert water into stream.
7. Binding energy per nucleon.
8. Direction of deflection in electric and magnetic fields.
9. Energy that results from the loss of mass when nucleus is formed.
10. No, the products of nuclear fission are harmful.
11. Cadmium rod is used to control the reactions.
12. Nuclear forces are responsible.
13. Take place at very high temperatures.
14. (i) β-rays
    (ii) γ - rays
15. Used to slow down neutrons. Heavy water.
16. Disintegration of an unstable nucleus resulting in the formation of another nucleus.
17. For controlling the fission reaction.
18. True. A positron is a positive electron with positive charge and mass equal to the mass of the electron.
19. lead
20. (i) Uranium series, actino-uranium series and thorium series.
    (ii) Thorium series.
21. (i) Atoms of same element with same atomic number but different mass number-Isotopes.
    (ii) Atoms of different elements, with same mass number but different atomic number-Isobars.
    (iii) Atoms with their nuclei, with same number of neutrons but different number of protons Isotones.

Short Answer Type Questions

Note: This is how you should frame your answer covering.

22. It states that in any radioactive sustance, the number of nuclei disintegrating per second is directly proportional to the original number of nuclei present.
23. (i) Mass defect = $[3 \times m_p + 4 \times m_n] - 7u$
    (ii) Binding energy = Mass defect × 931.5 MeV
    (iii) Binding energy per nucleon
    $= \frac{\text{Binding energy}}{7}$
24. By determining the ratio of C-14 and C-12 in fossils.
25. (i) Fission takes place as soon as the heavy nucleus is bombarded with a neutron.
    (ii) Neutron enters a heavy nucleus causing instability and eventually leading to the fission.
26. (i) Two or more lighter nuclei combine to give a heavy nucleus.
    (ii) These fusion reactions which take place at very high temperatures are referred to as thermo-nuclear reactions.
27. (i) A series of nuclear fissions where by the neutrons produced in each fission cause additional fissions, releasing enormous amount of energy.
    (ii) Pictorial representation of nuclear chain reaction.
28. (i) Fusion reactions are not chain reactions – Not possible to sustain the reaction.
    (ii) Requires a high temperature for nuclear reaction to take place.
    (iii) Difficult to harness and convert the heat energy produced into mechanical energy.
29. (i) Electromagnetic radiations.
    (ii) Wavelength is of the order of 1Å.
    (iii) Affect photographic plates.

(iv) Travel with velocity of light in straight line.

(v) Produce fluorescence in certain materials.

(vi) Not affected by electric and magnetic fields.

30. (i) A device, in which a self-sustaining controlled chain reaction is produced in a fissionable material.

(ii) Nuclear fuel, moderator, coolant, shield, control rods.

31. (i) Sodium-24 – To detect a clot in the blood in the human body.

(ii) Cobalt-60– To kill cancer cells.

(iii) Iodine-131 – To test the functioning of the thyroid gland.

32. (i) A process in which a heavy nucleus of a radioactive substance like uranium is split into lighter nuclei by the bombardment of low energy neutrons.

(ii) ${}_{92}U^{235} + {}_{0}n^{1} \longrightarrow {}_{36}Kr^{92} + {}_{56}B^{141} + 3\ {}_{0}n^{1} +$ energy

33. A → d → Binding energy per nucleon shows the stability of nucleus.

B → a → For a controlled chain reaction, reproduction factor $K = 1$.

C → b → Uranium dating can determine the age of rocks.

D → c → In artificial positrons are emitted.

34. $E = \Delta mc^2$

35. A → b → ${}_{11}Na^{24}$ isotope detects the blood clot.

B → d → D_2O is a moderator.

C → a → ${}_{53}I^{131}$ checks the function of thyroid gland.

D → c → In radiotherapy, hard X – rays are used.

Essay Answer Type Questions

Note: This is how you should frame your answer covering.

36. Refer to 'Liquid Drop Model' in notes section.

37. Refer to 'Nuclear Hazards and Safety Measures' in notes section.

38. $r_1 = 1.3 \times 10^{-15}$ m

$A_2 = 8A1$

$r_2 = ?$

$V_2 = ?$

$V \langle A$

$r_1^3 \langle A_1$

$r_2^3 \langle A_2$

$r_2 = 2r_1$

$V_2 = 73.58 \times 10^{-45}\ m^3$

$= 7.4 \times 10^{-44}\ m^3$

39. $M_p = 1.0078$ u; $m_n = 1.0087$ u

Actual mass of ${}_4Be^9 = 9.012$ u; $n_p = 4$; $n_n = 9 - 4 = 5$

Calculated mass of ${}_4Be^9 = (n_p \times m_p) + (n_n\ m_n)$

$= (4 \times 1.0078) + (5 \times 1.0087)$

$= 4.0312 + 5.0435$

$= 9.0747$ u

Mass defect (Δm) = calculated mass – actual mass

$= 9.0747 - 9.012$

$= 0.0627$ u

Binding energy = → $\Delta m \times 931.5$ MeV

$= 0.0627 \times 931.5 = 58.4$ MeV

Competition Wing

Level 1: Apply Your Concepts

17. False. Moderator is used to slow down the neutron.

18. True. A positron is a positive electron with positive charge and mass equal to the mass of the electron.

19. False. Nuclear force is always attractive and independent of charge.

20. True

25. More mass defect implies more binding energy and more stability.

Hence, the correct option is (a).

26. More binding energy implies more the stability. Hence, it is difficult to separate the constituents of a nucleus with higher binding energy.

Hence, the correct option is (d).

35. Negatively-charged particles deflect towards anode (positive electrode) in an electric field. Among the given options, β-rays are negatively charged, and hence, they deflect towards anode.

36. When an α particle and a β-particle are emitted from a radioactive nucleus, the atomic number decreases by 2 units and increases by one unit, respectively. Hence, the new element formed will be in first group. (2–1 = 1 unit, effectively decreases).

37. X-rays and visible light are electromagnetic radiations and their properties are different only due to the difference in their wavelength or frequency.

38. Cathode rays exert mechanical force on the object place in their path.

39. The velocity of α-rays is less than the other rays.

40. The given values of actual mass of the nucleus (M) number of nucleons, mass of proton (m_p) and mass of neutron (m_n) are noted (a). The number of protons (Z) and neutrons (A – Z) are also noted (c). The sum of the individual masses is determined as ($Z \times m_p + (A - Z)\, m_n$) and the mass defect ($\Delta m$) is calculated (d), (b). When Δm is multiplied by 931.5 MeV, we get binding energy (B.E) (e). Dividing B.E by the number of nucleons, i.e., its mass number (A), gives the binding energy per nucleon (*f*).

41. The process of increasing the percentage of fissionable U-235, in naturally occurring uranium is called enrichment.

42. A nuclear reaction combining nuclei of lighter atoms together to form heavier nuclei resulting in the release of tremendous amount of energy is called nuclear fusion reaction. Nuclear fusion reaction takes place in the Sun.

43. A heavy nucleus can be treated as the drop of a liquid with the positive charge uniformly distributed (b). Due to surface tension, the surface acts as a stretched membrane and different forces act between the nucleons inside the nucleus and between the nucleons close to the surface. During the bombardment of a nucleus by neutrons, a neutron could be absorbed by the drop like nucleus (a). This leads to the disturbance of the internal forces and sets up oscillations (c). These oscillations lead to the development of a thick neck forming two parts, giving the nucleus an elongated shape (e). From this stage, the repulsive forces take over causing the fission of the nucleus (d).

Level 2: Review Your Concepts

Note: This is how you should frame your answer covering.

44. 3.55×10^{24} MeV or 5.68×10^{11} J.

45. b, a, d, c

(B) Note the actual mass of the nucleus (*M*), number of nucleus in helium is 4, M_p and M_n are masses of proton and neutron. Find the number of protons and number of neutrons in the nucleus.

(A) Determine the sum of the individual masses of constituents in ${}_2He^4$.

(D) Calculate the mass defect of the given nucleus (Δm).

(C) Calculate the binding energy of the nucleus with expression, binding energy = $931.5 \times \Delta m$.

46. Stability increases with binding energy per nucleon.

47. (i) 12 g of carbon consists of 6.023×10^{23} atoms.

Number of protons in one carbon atom = its atomic number = number of electrons.

Number of neutrons in one carbon atom = A – Z

(ii) Number of neutrons = number of protons = 3.6138×10^{24}.

48. (i) Isobars are atoms with different atomic number and same mass number.

Isotopes are atoms having same atomic number but different mass number.

Isotones are the atoms with same number of neutrons in their nucleus.

$^{A}P_{Z} \rightarrow {}^{A-4}D_{Z-2}$

$^{A}P_{Z} \rightarrow {}^{A}P_{Z+1}$

(ii) $_{90}Th^{231}$, $_{91}Pa^{231}$

$_{90}Th^{231}$, $_{90}Th^{227}$

4, 8

49. (i) 1 MeV = 1.6×10^{-13}J

200 MeV = $200 \times 1.6 \times 10^{-13}$ J = energy released by one U^{235} atom

235 g of uranium contains 6.023×10^{23} atoms

From the given information, we can determine the number of uranium atoms required to produce 8×10^{11} J of energy and the mass of uranium required.

(ii) 9.8 g

50. (i) The fraction of amount of radioactive substance left = 1 – fraction of radioactive substance disintegrated.

Use the definition of half-life period to determine the time taken to disintegrate to the given amount.

(ii) 15 days

51. (i) Number of half lives = $\dfrac{\text{Total time}}{\text{Half life period}}$

Number of atoms in 14 g of C^{14} = 6.023×10^{23}

Determine the amount of radioactive substance left in given number of half lives.

(ii) 1.50575×10^{23}

52. (i) Nuclear forces are charge independent.

(ii) Nuclear attractive forces are between any two nucleons.

53. (i) Stability ∝ binding energy per nucleon.

(ii) $_{26}Fe^{56}$ is the most stable nucleus as its binding energy per nucleon is the largest among the given four entities.

54. (i) Balance the mass number and atomic number in the reactant side and in the product side.

Find out the difference in atomic and mass number. Identify the missing part with that atomic number and mass number.

(ii) $_{92}U^{238} + {}_{7}N^{14} \rightarrow {}_{99}Es^{247} + 5{}_{0}n^{1}$

(iii) $_{96}Cm^{234} + {}_{2}He^{4} \rightarrow 2{}_{0}n^{1} + {}_{92}Bk^{245} + {}_{1}H^{1}$

(iv) $_{94}Pu^{242} + {}_{10}Ne^{22} \rightarrow {}_{104}Ku^{260} + 4{}_{0}n^{1}$

55. (i) $N\% = \dfrac{1}{2^n} N_o\, 100$, where, n is the number of half lives, N_o is the total number of atompresent initially.

(ii) Approximately 0.1%

56. (i) α decay $_{Z}P^{A} \rightarrow {}_{Z-2}D^{A-4}$

β - decay $_{Z}P^{A} \rightarrow {}_{Z+1}D^{A}$

Emission of positron

$P \rightarrow n$ + positron

(ii) Positron, β-particle

(iii) α-particle, β-particle

57. (i) Power = $\dfrac{\text{Energy}}{\text{Time}}$

Convert 200 MeV into MJ and calculate the number of atoms required to produce 10 MJ of energy in one second = 10 MW.

(ii) 3.125×10^{17}

58. r-rays are electrically neutral.

59. The materials which control the fission reaction by absorbing the two neutrons of the three produced are called control rods.

60. Out of 1 kg of uranium, 0.1%, mass of uranium is converted into energy. Now, 0.1% of 1 kg

$$\frac{0.1}{100} \times 1\text{kg} = \frac{1}{1000}\text{kg} = 10^{-3}\text{ kg}$$

Using the equation,

$E = mc^2 = 10^{-3} \times (3 \times 10^8)^2$

$= 10^{-3} \times 9 \times 10^{16} = 9 \times 10^{16-3}$; $E = 9 \times 10^{13}$J

61. 223 = 220 + 3

= 4 × 55 + 3

Therefore, the mass number of any element can be represented as $4n + 3$.

62. 39.2 MeV

Binding energy = 5.6 × 7 MeV= 39.2 MeV

63. 8 days

The time taken to reduce to $\left(\dfrac{1}{4}\right)^{\text{th}}$ of total amount (t) 8 days.

$$\therefore n = n_o\left(\frac{1}{4}\right)^{\frac{t}{T}};\left(\frac{1}{4}\right)n_0 = n_0\left(\frac{1}{2}\right)^{\frac{8}{T}}$$

$$\left(\frac{1}{2}\right)^2 - \left(\frac{1}{2}\right)^{\frac{8}{T}};\ 2 = \frac{8}{T} = 4 \text{ days} = \text{half-life period}$$

∴ Let 'x' be the remaining amount of substance

$$\frac{x}{4} = \left(\frac{1}{2}\right)^n$$

$\therefore n = 2$

Further time = 2 × 4 = 8 days

Level 3: Assess Your Concepts

Note: This is how you should frame your answer covering.

64. How does the neutron form initially?

What is the change in atomic number and mass number during the emission of a 'β' particle?

65. (i) $m_1v_1 = m_2v_2$

Write the velocity of one of the daughter nuclei in terms of the other.

Law of conservation of energy.

$$\frac{1}{2}m_1v_1^2 + \frac{1}{2}m_2v_2^2 = \text{Q value}.$$

(ii) 0.92×10^7 m s^{-1}

66. $M_p = 1.0078$ υ

$M_n = 1.0087$ υ

$_2{}^4He \rightarrow n_p = 2$

$n_n = 4 - 2 = 2$

Actual mass of the $_2{}^4He = 4.00264$ υ

$\Rightarrow \Delta m$ (mass defect) =

$= (M_p\, n_p + M_n\, n_n) -$ Actual mass

$= (2 \times 1.0078 + 2 \times 1.0087) - 4.00264$

$= (2.0156 + 2.0174) - 4.00264$

$= 4.033 - 4.00264$ a.m.u

$= 0.03036 \times 1.66 \times 10^{-27}$ kg

$= 0.0504 \times 10^{-27}$

$\Rightarrow \Delta m = 5.04 \times 10^{-29}$ kg

67. (i) The amount of uranium disintegrated when 92 g of krypton is formed = 235 g.

Determine the number of uranium atoms disintegrated in a given time.

The energy released per uranium atom = 200 MeV

$$\text{Output power} = \frac{\text{Output energy}}{\text{Time}}$$

(ii) 1687 MW

68. (i) The mass number changes only during the emission of α particles.

Therefore, the number of α particles emitted

$$= \frac{\text{Change in the mass number}}{4}$$

The atomic number of the parent nucleus decreases by two during the emission of an α particle and increases by one during the emission of a 'α' particle.

Therefore, the number of α particles emitted = (Number of α particles × 2) – Change in atomic number.

(ii) 8 α particles and 6 α particles are emitted.

69. A daughter nucleus formed after emitting an α-particle is heavier than the α-particle. When a heavy nucleus emits an α-particle, its momentum before emission of the α-particle is equal to the sum of momenta of the α-particle and the daughter nucleus formed after the emission of the α-particles. If the parent nucleus (the nuclei emitting α particle) is at rest, then the momentum of the parent nucleus is zero. After emitting α-particle, the total momentum of α-particle and the daughter nuclei must be zero. This implies that the momenta of α-particles and daughter nuclei are equal in magnitude but opposite in direction.

70. $4\,{}_1H^1 \rightarrow {}_2He^4 + 2\,{}_1e^0 + Q$

Total mass of reactants = 4 × 1.0078

u = 4.0312 u

Mass of $_2He^4$ is 4.001506 u

Mass defect Δm = 4.0312 u – 4.001506

u = 0.0287u

The energy released = 0.0297 × 931.5 = 27.67 MeV.

71. Mass = 23.5 kg

235g of $_{92}U^{235} = 6.023 \times 10^{23}$ atoms

$$1\text{g of uranium } \frac{6.023\times10^{23}}{235} \text{ atoms}$$

23.5 kg of Uranium

$$\frac{6.023\times10^{23}\times23.5\times1000}{235}\text{ atoms}$$

Energy released

$$\frac{6.023\times10^{23}\times23.5}{235}\times1000\times200\text{MeV}$$

$6.023 \times 10^{25} \times 200 = 12.046 \times 10^{27}$ MeV

$= 12.046 \times 10^{27} \times 1.6 \times 10^{-13}$

$J = 19.28 \times 10^{14}$ J

$$40\% \text{ of Energy} = \frac{19.28\times10^{14}\times40}{100}$$

$$= 77.12\times10^{13}\text{ J}$$

$$\text{Power} = \frac{E}{t} = \frac{77.12\times10^{13}}{30\times24\times60\times60}$$

$$= \frac{77.12\times10^{13}}{2592\times10^{3}} = \frac{77.12\times10^{10}}{2592}\text{ W}$$

$$= 2.97\times10^{8}\text{ W} = 297\text{MW}$$

72. (a) When X changes to P, the atomic number increases by 1 but mass number remains the same. So, the particle emitted must be a β particle. During the change from P to Y, the atomic number decreases by two and mass number by 4. So, the particle emitted must be an α particle.

In the last process, there is no change in the atomic number and atomic mass number. Therefore, the particle emitted must be γ rays. Hence, the sequence is $\beta - \alpha - \gamma$.

(b) In the first process, atomic number decreases by 2 and atomic mass number decreases by 4. So, the particle emitted is an α-particle.

In the second process, there is no change in the atomic number or atomic mass number. So, γ-rays are given out. In the last process, the atomic number increases by one and there is no change in the atomic mass number. The particle emitted must be the β-particle.

So, the sequence in which the particles are emitted is $\alpha - \gamma - \beta$.

73. Mass of 8 protons + 8 neutrons = Mass of ${}_8O^{16}$ + Mass defect

⇒ Energy equivalent of 8 protons + 8 neutrons

= Energy equivalent of ${}_8O^{16}$ + energy equivalent of mass defect (1)

At the time of formation of the nucleus, the mass equivalent to mass defect gets converted into energy.

∴ Energy equivalent of mass defect is binding energy of ${}_8O^{16}$ = 16 × 7.97 MeV = 127.52 MeV (2)

Energy equivalent of 8 proton + 8 neutrons

= 8 $(m_p + m_n)$ × 931.5 MeV.

= 8 (1.0078 + 1.0087) × 931.5

= 8 × 2.0165 × 931.5

= 15026.958 MeV (3)

Substituting the values of (2) and (3) in (1).

The energy equivalent of ${}_8O^{16}$

= 15026.958 – 127.52

= 14899.438 MeV.

74. 235 g of ${}_{92}U^{235}$ contains Avogadro number (6.023×10^{23}) of atoms.

No. of atoms of ${}_{92}U^{235}$ in 1 kg of uranium

$$= 1000 \times \frac{6.023 \times 10^{23}}{235} = 2.563 \times 10^{24}$$

Energy released = No. of atoms × energy released per fission = $2.563 \times 10^{24} \times 200$ MeV

= 5.126×10^{26} MeV

75. The nucleons present in ${}_3Li^7$ is 7.

The binding energy per nucleon for lithium is 39.2 MeV/7 = 5.6 MeV

The binding per nucleon for helium is 28.24 MeV/4 = 7.06 MeV

The binding energy per nucleon is the measure of stability of the nuclei.

Therefore, helium is more stable than lithium.

76. In ${}_{27}Co^{59}$ number of protons = 27.

Number of neutrons = 59 – 27 = 32.

∴ The total mass of the nucleus

= 27 × 1.0078 u + 32 × 1.0087 u

= 27. 2106 u + 32.2784 u = 59.489 u.

Given, The actual mass of the nucleus = 58.933 u.

∴ The mass defect = 59.489 u – 58.933 u = 0.556 u.

∴ The binding energy = $\Delta m \times 931.5$ MeV

= 0.556 u × 931.5 MeV = 517.914 MeV.

77. The number of nuclei (N) present after 'n' half-lives is given by

$$N = N_o\left(\frac{1}{2}\right)^n \quad \text{....(1)}$$

$$\text{Where } n = \frac{t}{T}$$

In the question, we are given that $N_o = 10^{24}$;

n = 10/20 = ½; N = ?

Substituting the above values in equation (1), we get

$$N = 10^{24}\left(\frac{1}{2}\right)^{\frac{1}{2}} = 10^{24} \times 0.707 = 7.07 \times 10^{23}$$

78. First, let us find the mass defect. The Beryllium nucleus contains 4 protons and 5 neutrons.

Mass of 4 protons = 4 × 1.008 = 4.032 u;

Mass of 5 neutrons = 5 × 1.009 u = 5.045 u

Total mass of protons (4) and neutrons (5)

= 4.032 + 5.045 = 9.077 u

Mass defect = 9.077 – 9.012 = 0.065 u

The mass defect converted into equivalent energy gives binding energy.

1 u = 931.5 Me V

∴ 0.065 u = 0.065 × 931.5 MeV = 60.5475 MeV

Binding energy per nucleon

$$= \frac{\text{Binding energy}}{\text{No. of nucleons}} = \frac{60.5475}{9} = 6.7275 \text{ MeV}$$

JEE-NEET SPECIAL WING

Multiple-Answer Type Questions

1. Options (b) and (c) follow.
Hence, the correct option is (b, c)

2. $\lambda_{min} = \frac{hc}{eV} = \frac{6.625\times10^{-34}\times3\times10^{8}}{1.6\times10^{-19}\times230}$
$= 0.054\times10^{-7}\ m$
$= 5.4\times10^{-9}\ m$
$= 5.4\times10^{-9}\ m$
$= 5.4$ nm $= 54$ Å
Hence, the correct option is (a, d)

3. Equating the mass numbers on both the sides we get
$x + 1 = 92 + 141 + 3(1)$
$\Rightarrow x = 235$
Equating the atomic numbers on both sides,
$92 + 0 = 36 + y + 3\ (0)$
$\Rightarrow y = 56$
Hence, the correct option is (b, d)

4. $\frac{N}{N_0} = \left[\frac{1}{2}\right]^{\frac{t}{t_{1/2}}}$
$\frac{N}{800} = \left[\frac{1}{2}\right]^{\frac{150}{30}} = \frac{1}{32}$
$\therefore N = \frac{800}{32} = 25$
$\Rightarrow$ Number of remaining atoms = 25
$\therefore$ Number of atoms disintegrated = 800 – 25 = 775
% of atoms disintegrated $= \frac{775}{800}\times100$
$= 96.875\%$
Hence, the correct option is (b, c)

5. Binding energy per nucleon $= \frac{\text{B.E.}}{\text{A}}$
$= \frac{28.4}{4} = 7.1$ MeV
7.1 MeV $= 7.1\times10^{3}$ keV = 7100 keV
7.1 MeV $= 7.1\times1.6\times10^{-13}\ J$
Hence, the correct option is (a, b, c)

Comprehension-Based Questions

6. Neutral
Hence, the correct option is (c)

7. $\frac{\text{BE}}{\text{A}} = 7.97$ MeV
$\Rightarrow \text{BE} = 7.97\times\text{A}$
$= 7.97\times16 = 127.52$ MeV
$1\text{eV} = 1.6\times10^{-11}$ J
Hence, the correct option is (c)

8. Normal hydrogen is, $_1H^1$
It contains only one proton in its nucleus.
Hence, the correct option is (a)

9. $2\text{nJ} = 2\times10^{-9}\times\frac{1}{1.6\times10^{-13}}$ MeV
$= 1.25\times10^{4}$ MeV
Mass defect, $\Delta m = \frac{1.25\times10^{4}\ \text{MeV}}{931.5\ \text{MeV/amu}} = 13.42$ amu
Hence, the correct option is (d)

10. Stability
Hence, the correct option is (c)

11. Gamma rays as they are massless and chargeless.
Hence, the correct option is (c)

12. $\frac{15}{16}$ is disintegrated $\Rightarrow \frac{1}{16}$ is remaining
$N = N_o\left(\frac{1}{2}\right)^n$
$\frac{N}{N_o} = \left(\frac{1}{2}\right)^n$
$\frac{1}{16} = \left(\frac{1}{2}\right)^n$
$\left(\frac{1}{2}\right)^4 = \left(\frac{1}{2}\right)^n$
$n = 4$
Hence, the correct option is (b)

13. α – particle $\Rightarrow {}_2\text{He}^4$
$\therefore {}_{92}U^{235} \rightarrow {}_{90}\text{Th}^{231} + {}_2\text{He}^4$
Hence, the correct option is (d)

14. β – particle $\Rightarrow {}_{-1}e^0$ or ${}_{-1}\beta^{A}$
$\therefore {}_Z\text{P}^{A} \rightarrow {}_{-1}\beta^0 + {}_{Z+1}D^0$
Hence, the correct option is (a)

15. $\lambda = \frac{0.693}{T}$
$T = \frac{0.693}{\lambda} = \frac{0.693}{9.9}$
$= 0.07s$

$T = 70 \times 10^{-3}\ s = 70$ ms

Hence, the correct option is (c)

16. p.

$\left.\begin{array}{l} 14 - 6 = 8 \\ 16 - 8 = 8 \end{array}\right\}$ Same number of neutrons

⇒ Isotones (c)

A. same atomic number but different mass numbers

⇒ Isotopes (a)

B. Different atomic numbers but same mass numbers

⇒ Isobars (b)

C. No change in atomic number and mass number

⇒ Gamma decay (e)

D. ${}_0n^1 \rightarrow {}_1H^1 + {}_{-1}e^0$

$\Rightarrow \beta$ – decay (d)

A ↔ c

B ↔ a

C ↔ b

D ↔ e

E ↔ d